THE PICTURES IN THE COLLECTION OF
HER MAJESTY THE QUEEN

THE TUDOR · STUART AND
EARLY GEORGIAN PICTURES
BY OLIVER MILLAR
PHAIDON

THE TUDOR · STUART AND EARLY GEORGIAN PICTURES

IN THE COLLECTION OF

HER MAJESTY THE QUEEN

BY

OLIVER MILLAR

TEXT

PHAIDON PUBLISHERS INC
DISTRIBUTED BY
NEW YORK GRAPHIC SOCIETY PUBLISHERS LTD
GREENWICH · CONNECTICUT

The reproduction in this Catalogue of pictures and other works of art in the royal collection,
and the use of material in the Royal Archives,
are by gracious permission of Her Majesty The Queen

MADE IN GREAT BRITAIN
PRINTED BY HUNT BARNARD AND COMPANY LTD
AT THE SIGN OF THE DOLPHIN · AYLESBURY · BUCKINGHAMSHIRE
BOUND AT THE PITMAN PRESS · BATH

CONTENTS

PREFACE

THIS is the first part of a Catalogue Raisonné of the royal collection of pictures which it is hoped to complete in a further five volumes. It will be the first catalogue to contain all the pictures in the collection and to be divided, not according to the palaces in which the pictures hang – a division bound to grow speedily out of date – but into the main schools of painting. This volume contains the pictures painted in England from the late Yorkist or early Tudor age to the eve of the accession of George III, by painters of British birth or by foreign painters working in this country. All the pictures by such foreigners, from Holbein, Van Dyck, Lely and Kneller to very much lesser fry, have been included in this volume because their English works are an indispensable part of the un-rivalled demonstration, provided in the royal collection, of the development of the English portrait. It has also seemed undesirable to split the *œuvre* of an artist and more logical to include pictures painted abroad by such artists as Holbein, Van Dyck, Cornelius Johnson and Hanneman than to postpone treatment of such pictures to later volumes.* This volume also contains the pictures in the collection by a small number of shadowy foreign painters whose only works in the collection are English royal portraits, admittedly painted abroad but important links in the succession of royal portraits. For this reason the portraits by Charles Wautier, Martin Maingaud, Kayser and Klyher have been included. On the other hand more important foreign painters of royal portraits, whose links with the royal families were more tenuous, have been kept back for a later volume. For example, the portraits of James IV and his family by Van der Goes, of Henry VIII by Joos van Cleve or of Mary, Queen of Scots, from the studio of François Clouet, will ultimately be found in the Flemish and French sections of this Catalogue. Amigoni's royal portraits, on the other hand, justify his inclusion in this part.

This Catalogue has been based, as its successors will be, on an examination of the pictures combined with a detailed analysis of the inventories of the royal collections and of other related sources. This analysis has, I believe, been carried out more thoroughly than at any earlier period and has covered much more material than was known to earlier workers on the history of the collection. Although other sources will no doubt be discovered and will reveal fresh information, the sources that have been used for this volume have yielded a mass of information. Often, moreover, the investigation of documentary sources has led to the same conclusions as those based on the examination of the pictures themselves.

The examination of the royal pictures for this Catalogue and its companion volumes involves subjecting them to a closer scrutiny than any undertaken since the monumental survey of the whole collection begun in 1858 and carried out in the main by Richard Redgrave. Every picture in this volume has been carefully inspected and, with the exception of nos. 200, 296, 336, 384, 472, 474, 480 and 597, the back of every picture has been measured and examined. It will at once be apparent that my principal obligation in preparing this volume has been to the Superintendents of the palaces where the pictures hang or are stored: Mr. E. J. Rainbow at Hampton Court, Mr. Stanley Williams at Buckingham Palace and Mr. Stanley Lucking at Windsor Castle. However busy they have been,

---

* It is impossible to be entirely consistent in this. The derivations from Mor's portrait of Mary I, for example, will be found in this volume (nos. 53–5), but his more important pieces in the royal collection would have been out of context here.

3

they have unfailingly made available for me the pictures that were to be looked at and it is no exaggeration to say that without their co-operation this Catalogue could not have been compiled. Of their colleagues who have so cheerfully spared many hours of labour in getting at the pictures, I particularly wish to thank Mr. W. Watson at Hampton Court, Mr. W. J. Beatty, Mr. A. Benstead and Mr. R. Crisp at Windsor, and Mr. W. G. Bannochie and Mr. S. L. Martin at Buckingham Palace. At Holyroodhouse I have received the most valuable assistance from Mr. H. G. White and Mr. W. L. Ross.

The form in which the entries have been set out for items in this Catalogue will be followed throughout the Catalogue Raisonné. Biographies of artists placed before the entries for their works have been kept as short as possible. I have, however, aimed to provide for any artist who worked for the court a short account of his royal service. To such an account I have added references from contemporary or near-contemporary sources to pictures by the artist, painted for the Crown and formerly in the collection. The biographical notices of such painters as Van Somer, Danckerts and Goupy may seem disproportionately long compared with those of Mor and Hogarth, but from these biographies the student should be able to gauge the extent to which an artist worked for the Crown and to collect material for a consecutive account of royal patronage from Henry VIII to Frederick, Prince of Wales. I have tried to provide a backbone for such an account in the Introduction and it will be seen from the List of Contents on p. 47 that the Catalogue has been set out on a chronological basis.

After the title of the painting its present location is given. The pictures in the royal collection are, however, often moved from place to place and this part of the entry may soon become out of date. At Hampton Court and Windsor the series of numbers established in Redgrave's survey is still in force and the relevant number has been placed in brackets in the entries immediately after the location of an item. This series is not, however, still in use at Buckingham Palace and does not seem to have been established for the smaller palaces and houses. But the relevant Redgrave numbers which a picture bore at various dates have been placed at the appropriate points in its history. These numbers are always to be found on the pictures at Hampton Court and Windsor, and more often than not on those that were at Buckingham Palace when the great survey was made; at Hampton Court and Windsor they enable a picture to be instantly found.

After the location of the item comes a note of the material on which it is painted and its size. Every picture in this Catalogue is in oil on canvas unless otherwise described. Measurements are given in inches and centimetres. The sizes of a large number of royal pictures, particularly of those in this volume, have been altered from time to time; they have been cut down or enlarged so that they could be set into particular positions over doors or fireplaces or fitted symmetrically into a scheme of hanging. The measurements given in this Catalogue are of the panel as it is at present composed or of the canvas as it is stretched. The additions are then described and the size of the original picture indicated as far as possible.*

The measurements are followed by the signature, date and inscriptions, where they exist; I have drawn a distinction between contemporary and later inscriptions. Suggested readings for breaks in an inscription have been placed within square brackets. The descriptions of the pictures have been kept as brief as possible, but points of topography, costume (particularly where the sitter is seen in the robes or insignia of an Order of Chivalry or wears or holds an emblem of office) and identity (in, for ex-

---

* Where the later additions to a canvas are particularly distorting, they have been removed from the reproductions, *e.g.* of nos.102, 103, 132, 141, 150, 165, 166.

ample, a group-portrait or conversation piece) have been made. In describing a picture, the terms 'right' and 'left' refer to the spectator's right and left, except when they clearly refer to the stance or actions of a sitter in a portrait: to the gestures, for example, of the sitter's right or left hand.

The description of the picture is followed by an account of its history. This constitutes the basis of the entry for many items in a volume in which so many of the pictures were painted for the Crown and have an unbroken history in the collection. Whenever possible I have stated how a picture came into the collection. For all but the least important pictures I have indicated where they were first placed. In the history of pictures secured for the collection before 1649 I have described their fate at the protracted Sale of many of the royal goods after the death of Charles I and their return at the Restoration in 1660 or later. After recording the earliest stages of a picture's history within the collection I have only given a summary of its later movements. Where the placing of a picture seemed to throw light on a royal patron's tastes or foibles, or where it played a significant part in the decoration of an interior, this has been mentioned, but to give a detailed account of the movement of every picture would burden this volume with a mass of purely domestic detail. I have therefore in principle only listed the houses in which the picture is recorded during its later history.

The references on which the history of a picture is based are given in brackets at the relevant points in this section. The history is followed by the more important literary references to the picture. I have used throughout a fair number of abbreviated references to the most hard-worked sources and an explanatory list of these will be found on pp. 45–46. I have not attempted to include in this Catalogue a complete list of exhibitions at which royal pictures have been shown, but references will be found, in the section dealing with *Literature*, to important exhibitions and to those of which good catalogues were produced.

The main body of the entry follows the literary references, and at the end of an entry for a portrait there will be found a brief biographical notice of the sitter, in which I have stressed, wherever necessary, the sitter's connection with the court. Entries for royal portraits have not been provided with a biography; for royal sitters the reader is referred to the Genealogical Table between pp. 34 and 35, in which the parentage, dates of birth, marriage and death are recorded, where they are required, for all those of royal birth who appear in this volume.

THE catalogue of a great royal collection, built up by a succession of royal patrons and reflecting the claims, tastes, interests and diversions of many characters in more than four centuries of active collecting, inevitably presents certain peculiar problems. The pictures in this volume (many of which are here published for the first time) range in quality from utterly unimportant canvases, deservedly in store, to some of the most celebrated portraits in England; or from pictures which can be dismissed in a few lines to those on which sizeable monographs could easily be written. A catalogue of this kind also demands a knowledge of iconographical, topographical, ornithological, military and sartorial matters which could hardly be found in one compiler. Protracted research into some of the pictures in this volume (many of them among the least distinguished as works of art) would reveal more information for specialists in these fields; but I have aimed only at producing a survey of The Queen's Tudor, Stuart and early Georgian pictures and do not wish to hold it back too long from those specialists who may wish to work over sections of it in detail.

A further problem is presented by the inventories on which so much of this Catalogue is based. Broadly speaking they become from the time of Charles I steadily and inevitably less reliable in their attribution of the earlier royal pictures. By the time of James II and William III, for example, confusions have arisen between Holbein, Dürer and the ubiquitous 'Gennet', and Tudor and Jacobean portraits very seldom appear with the name of an artist attached to them. Compared with the great days of Charles I and Van der Doort, descriptions are extremely brief and no measurements are given in any inventory between the Restoration and the time of George III. In the inventories from the reign of James II onwards, there are many entries for landscapes and for portraits which bear no attributions and cannot therefore safely be worked into the history of a picture still in the collection. The accounts of the provenance of nos. 26, 29 and 31 in this Catalogue perhaps indicate the confusions implicit in the increasing inaccuracies of the writers of many of the late seventeenth- and early eighteenth-century inventories. It is impossible to attach to the right picture many references in the inventories which could be made to apply to a number of different pictures: James I in black, Anne of Denmark, the Duke of York and his Duchess by Lely or a Landscape by Danckerts are the most obvious examples of titles that could be made, in each case, to fit a number of pictures. I hope I have indicated on every occasion where it is doubtful whether a reference in an inventory should be linked to a particular picture, and in principle I have preferred to set out a short and accurate provenance rather than build up anything apparently more complete but in fact speculative. Inevitably many tantalising entries in the early documents continue to go begging; but by working carefully through the inventories and other sources in chronological sequence it has been possible to build up much more accurate histories of the pictures, and thereby to solve more problems of authorship and identifications, than was possible for previous workers in this field. The provenances, identifications and attributions of many pictures in this volume will be found to differ from those suggested by authorities from Vertue and Walpole to Law and Collins Baker. In most instances the reasons for the revised opinions will be obvious, but it is clearly not possible to state at every point where the view of an earlier authority has been proved wrong and I hope the reader will accept many tacit but carefully considered emendations to earlier accounts.

The royal collection contains inevitably many originals and versions of the official portraits of sovereigns and their consorts from the time of James I, and the originals of a number of popular royal portraits and groups, such as Van Dyck's of the children of Charles I. In the entries for these it is of course impossible to provide a complete list of all versions, copies and derivations, especially of those that pass through the sale-rooms. Where the collection holds the original of an oft-repeated portrait I have given in the entry for it as full a list as possible of the derivations from it; where the collection only has a copy, I have said where and what the original is and given a much briefer indication of the extent to which the design was repeated. Likewise I have only recorded the earlier engravings from a given royal portrait and have not attempted to disentangle later derivations from them. In the entries for the principal royal portraits by Van Dyck I have tried to give an impression, from the series of entries as a whole, of the extent to which certain designs had become popular within a comparatively short time of Van Dyck's death. In producing the originals of the official royal portraits, the leading portrait painters in London may have relied on assistance from members of their studio; where opinions on this problem can be given with some degree of assurance I have done so in the entries, but it would be very dangerous to attempt to define in such portraits exactly how much was painted by Seeman or Shackleton – or even by Lely and Kneller or Van Somer and Mytens – and how much by their more capable assistants.

The two sections of the new Catalogue Raisonné which will ultimately contain all the pictures in the Queen's collection defined for this purpose as British, have been divided chronologically at *c.* 1760. This volume includes painters who worked for Frederick, Prince of Wales, and for his widow before the accession of George III. The sequel will contain the painters who worked for the Crown between 1760 and 1837. This has proved a convenient division, except in one small regard: the group of military portraits attributed to David Morier. The personality of this painter is still very shadowy and it is clear that a number of different hands worked on the pictures in the collection that go under his name. Those that fall chronologically within this volume, including the only picture that can be safely attributed to him on documentary grounds (no. 591), have been dealt with here, but the portraits ascribed to Morier of the Duke of Cumberland have been held back for the sequel, where the other pictures relating to Cumberland will be found.

The condition of the pictures in this volume has been described where it affects the problems of authorship. It would have been impossible to provide an accurate scientific report on the state of all the pictures in the volume, but many problems have been investigated, and a number of them solved or clarified, by scientific investigation. I am deeply indebted to Mr. Stephen Rees-Jones of the Courtauld Institute, and to his staff, for carrying out many such investigations. All the technical comments in this Catalogue on the state of pictures have been inspired by Mr. Rees-Jones or by the restorers who have worked on them: the late Mr. Horace Buttery, Mr. Clifford and Mr. Gerald Freeman, Mr. Roy Vallance and Miss Nancy Stocker. I gratefully acknowledge the pleasure and profit I have derived from conversations with them.

I SHOULD like to thank the owners of private collections in whose houses I have seen so much of the comparative material used in this volume and who have answered many tiresome questions. I am particularly grateful to the Duke of Richmond and Gordon, Earl Fitzwilliam, Earl Spencer, Sir Gyles Isham and Lt.-Col. Ririd Myddleton for their help in clearing up a number of problems.

I have received unfailing kindness in the Royal Library: from Sir Owen Morshead, Librarian Emeritus, and his successor in the Library, Mr. Robert Mackworth-Young, and from Miss Scott-Elliot, Keeper of the Prints and Drawings. I owe a special debt to Miss Olwen Hedley, who has placed at my disposal her expert knowledge of the topography of Windsor and its environs and of the *dramatis personae* of the royal households in the past. In dealing with these two subjects her kindness to me has been invaluable.

To Mr. David Piper I owe the comfort of his patience in listening to innumerable theories and answering endless questions. To him and to his colleagues at the National Portrait Gallery, Mr. Kingsley Adams and Mr. John Kerslake, I am grateful for many kindnesses and for access to their records and photographic library. I have benefited greatly from discussions with Mr. Roy Strong on some special sixteenth-century problems.

Mr. F. Grossmann read the entries for Holbein and made a number of points therein; Dr. Sydney Anglo discussed with me the iconography of nos. 24 and 25; Miss Frances Yates and Mrs. Eric Newton generously gave me their opinions on the problems of iconography and costume respectively in no. 87; Dr. R. E. W. Maddison made additions to my notes for no. 332; Mr. I. Galbraith and Mr. R. Goodwin helped me to identify the birds in Bogdani's canvases; and Mr. Ralph Edwards read my entries for nos. 520 and 521. For their guidance on specialised questions I am very grateful to the following: the late Sir James Mann on armour, Mr. Michael Robinson and Mr. E. Archibald on marine painting, Mr. T. Tremlett on heraldry and Mr. Brian Vesey-Fitzgerald on dogs. Mr. R. E. Hutchison has coped with many tiresome questions that can only be answered in Scotland, Dr. Horst Gerson has been equally helpful in Holland and Mr. Povl Eller in Denmark. On topographical problems I have received much help from Dr. Margaret Whinney, Sir John Summerson, Dr. K. Downes and Mr. J. L. Howgego. Among those who have helped on particular points I would like especially to thank Mr. Levi Fox, Mr. J. W. Goodison, Mr. Harold Jennings, Dr. Peter Murray, Mr. Clifford Musgrave, Mr. Robin Price and Mr. Richard Walker. While recording the kindness of my friends, I would not wish to hold them responsible for anything stated in this volume. I should also like to acknowledge the help I have invariably received from the staff of the British Museum (in the Reading Room and in the Departments of Manuscripts and of Prints and Drawings), the Public Record Office, the Duchy of Cornwall Office, the Witt Library and the libraries of the Society of Antiquaries and the Courtauld Institute, and from Messrs. Christie, Manson & Woods. I am very grateful to Messrs. A. C. Cooper Ltd. and to Photo Studios Ltd. for unfailing promptness in the supply of photographs; the excellent colour photographs have been taken by Mr. Percy Hennell.

There are two debts, however, which outweigh all others. Mrs. Gilbert Cousland has typed every word of this Catalogue, but I value even more highly her lively interest in all the problems that it has raised and in the solution of some of them. My wife made an index, which has proved invaluable, of all the documents relating to the royal pictures up to the recovery of them at the Restoration and compiled both the indexes in this volume; and on many excursions to collect the raw material for this Catalogue I have had the help and pleasure of her company.

O. N. M.

1963

INTRODUCTION

I N 1851, on one of his later visits to Windsor, Dr. Waagen noted 'five-and-thirty portraits of distinguished personages, which His Royal Highness has had placed together in a small room.'[1] The Stygian darkness in which Waagen saw the room prevented him from noticing the portraits in detail, and perhaps from realising that in this room, optimistically known as the Holbein Room, the Prince Consort had assembled almost all the little early English, Burgundian, French and Habsburg portraits that had been in the royal collection since the time of Henry VIII and still combine to give an impression of the early Tudor collection. Portraits of allied or related royal sitters, of friendly rulers who had given their portraits to English sovereigns or exchanged portraits with them, still hang near the portraits of the sovereigns themselves. The relentless accumulation of English royal portraits and of portraits of the royal families' friends at home and relations abroad, of hoped-for allies or prospective brides, has formed the backbone of the English royal collection from the Plantagenets to the present day.

The oldest English royal portraits in the collection form a familiar late mediaeval group: Henry V (6), Henry VI (8), Edward IV (10) and Richard III (14).* Of these the portrait of Edward IV is the most distinguished: Flemish in technique, apparently contemporary and perhaps a first-hand record of the King's appearance. The other three could have been painted late in the fifteenth century and in a workshop in which the Flemish element must have been strong. *Henry VI* and *Richard III* were perhaps painted by the same artist and may record fairly accurately some *ad vivum* image of the sitters. The four portraits are in better condition than is usually assumed; and taken as a group they provide the best extant examples, and probably the primary source, of types that were to be reproduced as the standard portraits in the sets of royal portraits that became increasingly popular from the early sixteenth century onwards[2] and were later augmented by portraits stretching back in time to Edward III and down to Mary I.[3]

I. THE TUDORS

B Y 1542, when Henry VIII's inventory was drawn up, additional royal portraits had been acquired or painted for the Crown: of the King's grandmother (see no. 15), of Prince Arthur (see no. 20) and of Elizabeth of York (see no. 17). The heavily overpainted portrait of Elizabeth Woodville (12) is also probably one of the oldest pictures surviving in the royal collection. By the middle of the sixteenth century at least two portraits of Henry VII (see no. 16) were in the collection. In the time of Charles I many of these little royal portraits were hanging together at the upper end of the Privy Gallery at Whitehall,[4] and seem still to have been in the painted and gilded frames which were so integral a part of these little works of art.

* The numbers in brackets refer to entries in the Catalogue.

1. *Treasures of Art in Great Britain* (1854), vol. II, p. 437.

2. Waterhouse, *Painting in Britain*, pp. 2–3.

3. For example, the set acquired by Queen Caroline, for which see below p. 27.

4. *Van der Doort*, pp. 27–31. The first picture recorded in this group (. . . *A younge Kings picture without a beard . . . with a Crown* on his head Saide to be Kinge Edward the third . . . almost Soe bigg as the life without hands. In a goulden habitt*) does not seem to be identifiable. A pair of full-lengths of Henry VII and his Queen, valued at £15 each by the Trustees for Sale at St. James's (L.R. MS., f. 67) and sold to Hunt and Bass on 1 March 1653, can no longer be traced; they were presumably later works based on earlier sources.

9

The portraits of Henry VIII in the first part of his reign may have been conceived *en suite* with these earlier royal portraits. One of the panels in the Privy Gallery was a *picture of King Henrie the 8ᵗʰ in his youth In a guilden dublitt with a glove on his right hand* which could have been the picture (no. 97) in the inventories of 1542 and 1547: *a table with the picture of Kynge Henry the VIII then being yonge.*[5] No. 44 in the same inventories was *a table with two folding leavis with the picture of the King Henry theight being yonge wearing his heare with a flower of silver upon the locke.*

Of the pictures listed in the early Tudor inventories, only one can with certainty be identified with a portrait by Hans Holbein, the famous full-length of Christina of Denmark in the National Gallery. Of the surviving royal portraits by Holbein,[6] not even the little panel in the Thyssen collection (*Fig. IV*) can be shown to have belonged to the King;[7] rather it should perhaps be seen as a splendid but still conventional present to a foreign power, a friend or a potential ally, comparable in scale and intention with a portrait by Sittow or Perréal. On a very different scale, Holbein's great mural, painted in the Privy Chamber at Whitehall in 1537 and recorded in Leemput's little copy (216), contained, in the figure of Henry VIII, the first *ad vivum* life-size full-length English royal portrait to be regarded as an official portrait of the sovereign and to be reproduced, as a result, in versions and derivations on varying scales and by painters ranging in ability from those who may have been employed in Holbein's workshop to those who can have had no personal contact with him and must have worked from secondary sources. The wall-painting, with its carefully composed Latin inscription (fortunately preserved by Leemput), proclaimed the achievements of the King's parents in settling by their marriage the civil strife of the Wars of the Roses, and the dynasty's present power and future hopes, embodied in Jane Seymour, who produced a male heir to the throne in the year the mural was painted. There is unfortunately no clear description of the Privy Chamber or of the relation of Holbein's design to the decoration of the room, but it is not difficult to imagine the awe with which it struck the beholder.

The King was dressed in the wall-painting in ordinary costume and the derivations from it are not technically repetitions of a state portrait, in which the sovereign wears the robes of state in which he or she opens parliament and in which the regalia is displayed. But in Holbein's last portrait of Henry VIII, in the group painted to commemorate the presentation of their Charter to the Barber-Surgeons Company in 1541,[8] the formidable figure of the King wears the crown and robe of state, carries a sword of state and is seated under a canopy on which the royal arms are embroidered. This presentation of the sovereign as 'the figure of God's majesty, his captain, steward, deputy-elect, Anointed, crowned, planted many years', is close to the standard images in the illuminations at the head of Plea Rolls and other official documents,[9] or embossed on the obverse of the Great Seal.[10] This form of royal icon, which goes back in time beyond the Norman Conquest, is normally perpetuated on a small scale by the limner, engraver or modeller in wax, and life-size presentations are rare. The only extant predecessor of Holbein's terrifying *Henry VIII* on the same scale is the *Richard II* in Westminster Abbey (of which Charles I owned a version); the only important sequels to preserve in this rigidly formal design the presence and all the accessories of majesty are the life-size derivation of Hilliard's early miniature of Elizabeth I[11] and Michael Wright's extremely old-fashioned *Charles II* (285).

5. An early portrait of Henry VIII, close in format to the early royal portraits, was formerly in the collection of H. Clifford Smith (reproduced in the *Connoisseur*, vol. cxxiii (1949), p. 52; sold at Sotheby's, 25 February 1959 (56)).

6. See below p. 57.

7. Ganz, *Holbein*, pl. 135; see catalogue of the exhibition of the Thyssen-Bornemisza Collection at the National Gallery, 1961 (65).

8. R.C. Strong in *Burl. Mag.*, vol. cv (1963), pp. 4-14.

9. These are very fully discussed and illustrated in E. Auerbach, *Tudor Artists* (1954).

10. For a particularly beautiful example, the second Great Seal of Elizabeth I, see E. Auerbach, *Nicholas Hilliard* (1961), pls. 175(a), 177.

11. *Ibid.*, pls. 15, 13.

In the long picture of the ageing Henry VIII with his family (43) the King sits under a canopy and the composition seems to have been conceived as a sequel to the wall-painting. In an elaborate renaissance interior Jane Seymour is resuscitated to sit near her son, but the King's two daughters are significantly set apart from the main line of succession. The glimpse of Westminster in the distance may have been inserted in order to integrate the picture, as it hung in the Presence Chamber at Whitehall, with its actual context and it foreshadows the topographical background in Van Dyck's *Great Piece* of 1632 (150).

From the available sources it is impossible to tell what pictures Henry VIII owned by the painters, native-born or foreign, who at different times were in his service or from whom he commissioned portraits of himself and his family in the last years of his reign.[12] Of his consorts, only portraits of Jane Seymour are recorded in the collection in the sixteenth century. There is no evidence that any of them were serious patrons of the arts, but the Careys and Boleyns had known the Hornebolt family in Flanders and may have introduced them into the King's service, Gerard by October 1528 and Lucas, his son (appointed King's Painter in 1534), by September 1525. The Boleyns, described as 'more Lutheran than Luther', would thereby be supporting a family of artists formerly associated with the court of Margaret of Austria and then active in England before Holbein's second visit to London, and one of the first of those families which fled to this country from religious persecution on the Continent and were to exercise so great an influence on the history of the arts in England.[13]

We may associate with the pictures that witnessed to the strength of his dynasty, Henry VIII's record of some of the dramatic episodes in the early years of his reign. The King probably owned one (22) and possibly the other (23) of the two pictures surviving in the collection of the exciting campaign against the French in Flanders in 1513, when the young King had served beside the Emperor Maximilian I and routed a body of French cavalry. In 1588-9, near to the group of the King's family (43) in the Presence Chamber at Whitehall, hung the two large canvases (24, 25) that illustrate with a mass of detail the progress towards the spectacular meeting with Francis I on the Field of the Cloth of Gold in 1520.[14] The painters of these historical pieces are still irretrievably anonymous.

The influence of Holbein's presentation of Henry VIII is felt in the two principal portraits of his son. In the earlier (44), probably painted just before his father's death, the Prince pauses timidly in an attempt at the terrifying pose struck by his father on the wall of the Privy Chamber; in the full-length derivations, such as that at Petworth (*Fig.* 1), in which Edward is seen as King, under a canopy of state embroidered with the royal arms, this dependence is closer, as it is in the portrait type associated with Guillim Stretes (*e.g.*, no. 49) which probably succeeded the earlier portrait as the official likeness of the King. In Lord Lumley's collection, indeed, it was listed after Holbein's Cartoon for the wall-

12. Two of the derivations, still in the royal collection, from Holbein's portrait in the mural (35, 36) belonged to Charles I, and may have been in the later Tudor collection. The Trustees for Sale valued at £20 at St. James's *King Henry ye 8th at length* (L.R. MS., f. 67), which may have been *en suite* with the full-lengths of his parents cited on p. 9, n. 4. It is not clear how many other portraits of Henry VIII were in the collection by 1550. In the inventory of 1547 was (p. 53) an unfinished portrait of the King, conceivably a version of the design that Ganz (*Holbein*, pl. 158) associated, almost certainly wrongly, with Holbein. The portraits at St. James's in the inventory of 1549-50 (pp. 62, 65) may have been the early portraits referred to above; the inventory of 1547 contains (p. 28) a portrait conceivably identical with one in the inventory of 1549-50 (p. 66). No. 45 in the inventories of 1542 and 1547 was a diptych containing portraits of the King and Jane Seymour. No. 64 in the same inventory was a portrait of the King in an anti-Papal allegorical design.

13. H. Paget, 'Gerard and Lucas Hornebolt in England', *Burl. Mag.*, vol. CI (1959), pp. 396-402. The payments to Lucas provide a good example of the impossibility of determining if such payments to portrait painters at this date were for miniatures, for large portraits, or for both.

14. The references in the early sources are obscure, but it seems that there were other pictures of this type in the collection at an early date. Van der Doort's list of pictures in the First Privy Gallery at Greenwich (*Van der Doort*, p. 195) includes a third large piece removed from Whitehall *bin Wᵣ hnri ta 8 besisit te tauwn bolonia*. This could have been *The Seidge of bulloigne by henᵣ: yᵉ 8* valued at £2. 10s. by the Trustees for Sale at Greenwich (L.R. MS., f. 6 v.) and sold to Maidwell for £8 on 18 October 1649. At Hampton Court in October 1649 the Trustees valued at £5 *Henry yᵉ 8 before bulloyne* (ibid., f. 118), sold to De Critz and others on 18 November 1651 (S.P. 29, 447, 24, 1).

painting and a full-length picture of Henry VIII. Edward VI almost certainly owned the remarkable distorted portrait of himself (*Fig*. III), now in the National Portrait Gallery (1299), which fascinated visitors to the royal palaces in the time of Elizabeth I, as well as an equestrian portrait.[15]

We know little of the royal collection under Mary I. There is no evidence that she owned a version of her portrait by Hans Eworth or of the incisive portrait by Anthonis Mor, both painted in 1554.[16] But at the end of 1553, when negotiations were under way for the Queen's marriage with Prince Philip of Spain, the Queen of Hungary secretly sent over to London a portrait of the Prince 'the one in the blue coat with white wolf skin . . . painted three years ago by Titian. . . . It will serve to tell her what he is like, if she will put it in a proper light and look at it from a distance, as all Titian's paintings have to be looked at.' Unfortunately the Queen of Hungary stipulated that the portrait was to be returned to her 'as it is only a dead thing, when she has the living model in her presence.'[17]

Between 1549–50 and the reign of James I no official inventories survive of any part of the royal collection, and for its appearance in the time of Elizabeth I we have to depend primarily on the accounts of royal houses set down by distinguished visitors from abroad.[18] For the evolution of the official royal portrait, there are three particularly important documents from the Queen's reign. In order to ensure that a reasonable standard was maintained in her portraits, Sir William Cecil drafted in 1562 a proclamation that would forbid painters, printers or engravers to produce a likeness of the Queen until she had given a sitting to 'some speciall conning paynter' who could 'take ye naturall representation of hir Matie'; to this she had been always 'very unwillyng'. In 1584 a draft patent, possibly composed by the Queen's Serjeant-Painter, George Gower, aimed at giving him a monopoly in the production of all forms of 'purtraictes and pictures of our person, phisiognomy, and proporcōn of our bodye' in oils, engravings and woodcuts. A similar monopoly was proposed for Nicholas Hilliard in miniature portraits of the Queen. Finally, in January 1582 the statutes of the Painter-Stainers Company had attempted to discredit the untrained artists who did 'enterprise to portrait, counterfeit, shadow and paint the pictures, proportions, ensigns and arms . . . as well of the Kings and Queens predecessors ancestors to the Queen's most excellent Majesty, as of Her Highness . . .'[19] These three passages have a significance far beyond the age of Elizabeth I. They show the desire that the image by which the sovereign would be known to her subjects should be based on an authorised likeness, drawn from a sitting granted by the sovereign. We learn of an attempt by the Queen or her Serjeant-Painter to restrict to one workshop the production of the sovereign's portraits. And we are told of a thriving and undesirable trade in unreliable historical royal portraits and unauthorised portraits of the Queen.

Elizabeth I owned surprisingly few portraits of herself. The beautiful picture of her as a girl (46) had probably been painted for her father. She had perhaps commissioned in 1569 the pleasing allegory (58) in which Juno, Venus and Pallas retire in confusion before her beauty and accomplishments as she moves, richly dressed and carrying her regalia, from the normal *ambiance* of the state portrait into the fields of classical mythology, set here by the river Thames near Datchet Ferry. In 1613 the Duke

15. The Trustees for Sale valued at £1 *King Edward ye 6.th on horsback* among the pictures at Hampton Court in October 1649 (L.R. MS., f. 123); it was sold to Hunt and Bass on 1 March 1653. The inventories of 1542 and 1547 contain two portraits of Edward VI (46, 47), the second described as 'with the whole stature'. Others appear to have been at Hampton Court and Greenwich in 1547 (pp. 55, 27). Any of these could have been the full-length portrait valued by the Trustees at £5 in September 1649 (Corsham MS., f. 50) and sold to Brown on 7 January 1650.

16. The Eworth is in the Society of Antiquaries (R.A., *Kings & Queens*, 1953 (90), illustrated souvenir, pl. 24); of the Mor three original versions are known (R.A., *Holbein and other Masters*, 1950–1 (200)).
17. *Calendar of State Papers, Spanish*, vol. xi, 1553 (1916), pp. 355, 367, 384. A few pictures are mentioned in an inventory of 1553 (H.M.C., *Salisbury MSS.*, vol. 1 (1883), pp. 127–32).
18. For the most important of them see Bibliography, p. 43.
19. The documents are most conveniently printed in E. Auerbach, *Tudor Artists* (1954), pp. 103, 109, 110.

I. Holbein: *Henry VIII and the Barber-Surgeons*
(detail). Barbers' Company.

II. Holbein: *Henry VII and Henry VIII*.
National Portrait Gallery, London.

III. Artist Unknown: *Edward VI*. National Portrait Gallery, London.

IV. Holbein: *Henry VIII*.
Thyssen-Bornemisza Collection, Lugano.

V. Artist Unknown: *James VI and I*.
Scottish National Portrait Gallery, Edinburgh.

VII. Van Dyck: *Charles I.* Louvre, Paris.

VI. Peake(?): *Henry, Prince of Wales, with John, 2nd Lord Harington.*
Metropolitan Museum, New York.

of Saxe-Weimar saw portraits of the Queen at Somerset House (probably at full-length) and at Whitehall, 'very beautifully painted.'[20] She also assembled a gallery of portraits of her forebears. In 1601, when she was talking with William Lambarde about portraits of Richard II, she mentioned the portrait of him that had been given to her by Lord Lumley, who had prayed 'that I might put it in order with the ancestors and successors' gathered 'in my house and gallery at Westminster'. The Queen almost certainly gave away pictures. There is, for example, no trace in any of the extant records of the collection of the 'person rare, stronge lymbes and manly shape' of Thomas Seymour, whose portrait had been given to the Queen by Sir John Harington.[21]

II. THE EARLY STUARTS

IN the early seventeenth century the chief impression made on those who saw the royal collection was of an abundance of historical pictures, elaborate painted genealogies and English and foreign royal portraits. By the middle of the reign of James I portraits, many of them at length, seem to have been arranged in the long galleries of the King's houses. The English, French and German portraits noted at Greenwich by the Duke of Saxe-Weimar, for example, were probably hanging in the gallery where they were listed by Van der Doort in 1639 as they had been left by Queen Anne of Denmark. There were to be seen portraits of the Queen's German and Danish relations and of Scots and English courtiers: the Chancellor of Scotland, Lord Dunfermline; Lady Grey of Ruthin; the Duke of Richmond; Leicester, the Queen's Lord Chamberlain; Montgomery, one of the King's handsome young favourites in his Garter robes; Tom Derry, the Queen's fool. And, near a portrait of the little Duke of York, the future Charles I in his long white 'coats', hung full-lengths of his cousin Arbella and Eworth's small panel (56) of his grandfather Darnley with Lady Arbella's father.[22] Such processions of full-length portraits were not uncommon on the walls of Elizabethan and Jacobean galleries, and it is not difficult to envisage the terrifying scene between Hamlet, his mother and the Ghost of King Hamlet played in front of the counterfeit presentment of two royal brothers from a set of full-length royal portraits.[23]

When James VI came south in 1603 to claim the crown of Great Britain, he may have brought into the royal collection the panel by Eworth and a portrait of his grandmother, the Countess of Lennox (91).[24] The *Memorial of Lord Darnley* (90), a savage attack on his mother's reputation and a

20. W. B. Rye, *England as seen by Foreigners* (1865), pp. 161, 162. The two portraits could perhaps be identified with two portraits appraised at Somerset House by the Trustees for Sale: *Quene Elezebeth. in her prlam.t Roobes*, valued at £1 and sold to Hunt and Bass on 1 March 1653 (perhaps a derivation from Hilliard's miniature (see above, p. 10)) and *Queene Elezebeth. at Length*, valued at £15 and sold to Jackson and others on 23 October 1651.
This Catalogue went to press before the publication of Mr. Roy Strong's absorbing study of the iconography of Elizabeth I. It remains true that the Queen's portraits played only a small part in the growth of the royal collection (compared, for example, with those of Charles I) and that there is remarkably little evidence of the Queen's personal concern with the development of her portraiture.

21. J. Nichols, *Bibliotheca Topographica Britannica*, vol. I (1780–90), pp. 525–6; Sir John Harington, *Nugæ Antiquæ* (1804), vol. II, p. 329. It is difficult to be certain how many non-royal British portraits were in the collection in the sixteenth and early seventeenth centuries. There are references, in and before the time of Charles I, to portraits of Rosamund Clifford and Jane Shore

(these two should presumably not be taken too seriously), Lady Fiennes, Thomas, 1st Lord Darcy, Gilbert, (7th?) Earl of Shrewsbury, the Earl of Southampton, Lady Burghley, the Earl of Carlisle, Sir Thomas Chaloner and his family in Arcadian dress, Lady Hoby, one of the Earl of Arundel's sons, Mrs. Middlemore, a daughter of the Earl of Perth (presumably Jean, Countess of Roxburghe) and a Lady Stafford. The portrait of Essex which was shown to the Duke of Stettin-Pomerania at Greenwich in 1602 (*Trans. Roy. Hist. Soc.*, N.S., vol. VI (1892), p. 63) may have been a miniature by Isaac Oliver.

22. *Van der Doort*, pp. 196–8.

23. See annotation by J. Dover Wilson in his edition of *Hamlet* (1934), 3.4.53. A glimpse of an early seventeenth-century long gallery, with portraits hanging in it, can be gained in the background of Mytens's portrait (1618) of the Countess of Arundel (R.A., *17th Century Art in Europe* (1938), illustrated souvenir, pl. 88).

24. *A litle picture of ye Earle of Lenox the kings grandfather* hung, *wth a curtaine of greene Taffita sarcenet*, in the Gallery at Oatlands in 1616 (Glynde MSS.).

grim commentary on the state of Scotland in James's infancy, seems to have passed to his Lennox cousins and did not enter the royal collection until the reign of George II. Charles I owned portraits of James IV and his Queen (see p. 84 and no. 115), which may have belonged to his father; he was given portraits of James V (92), Mary of Lorraine (see no. 93) and probably the large group (57) of Darnley and his brother. He possessed a number of portraits of Mary, Queen of Scots (see, for example, no. 116), and at least two smaller ones of Darnley (see no. 56). He was also given by Robert Young the little portrait of James VI (*Fig.* V), at the age of five and holding a hawk, which is now in the Scottish National Portrait Gallery. It may have been painted by Arnold van Brounckhurst, although he was not appointed principal painter to the young King in Scotland until September 1580.[25] King James's most hateful memories would have been stirred by a portrait of George Buchanan which was hanging at Greenwich in 1649;[26] and in the year of his accession he was reported to be putting away the portraits of Elizabeth I and hanging up instead those of his mother.[27]

We could find many parallels on the Continent to what we have seen under the Tudors of the development of the royal portrait, the creation of a succession of standard types, and the repetition of the official likeness. Under the Stuart and early Hanoverian sovereigns the problems remained the same. We have more evidence, visual and documentary, to show how the problems were tackled; and we shall find much care taken in choosing the best available painter to produce, probably on the basis of a very restricted number of sittings, an acceptable and impressive image of the sovereign, and in organising the widespread distribution of the chosen likeness.

James I 'could never be brought to sit for the taking' of his picture.[28] From the first part of his reign the official portraits of himself, his Queen and their three children were produced in the main in the studios of John De Critz, the Serjeant-Painter, and the younger Marcus Gheeradts. In 1606 De Critz was paid for full-lengths of the King, Queen and the Prince of Wales; in 1608 he was paid for a picture of Edward VI and other royal portraits. Gheeradts may have replaced him in royal service; in 1611, as 'his Maties Painter', he was paid for portraits of the King and Queen, Princess Elizabeth and the Duke of York, in 1613 for another portrait of the Princess, and in 1618 for another set of four full-lengths of the whole family.[29] The two painters were closely related and we cannot be sure which was responsible for the type of portrait of James I which should almost certainly be associated at least with the earlier of these payments. Variants of it (see no. 97) bear dates between 1606 and 1610 and the best versions of it are perhaps those in the Prado and at Dulwich. One sitting probably sufficed for all of them.

The portraits painted by De Critz in 1606 were for the Archduke of Austria. Of those paid for in 1611 the portrait of the Duke of York was sent to Scotland and the others to the Margrave of Brandenburg; the set of 1618 was painted for the Duke of Radziwill. But just as there is no evidence that Elizabeth I had a portrait of herself by Gower, so it seems that James I kept for his own collection no version of any of these images. They were designed primarily to be sent abroad: in exchange, for example, for the portraits by Gysbrecht van Veen of the Austrian Archduke Albert and his Archduchess which the Flemish Ambassador gave to James I in 1603,[30] for a portrait of Henri IV of France painted by Bunel and sent to London in 1611, or for portraits of Philip III and his Queen by Pantoja de la Cruz which

25. *Van der Doort*, p. 65; E. Auerbach, *Nicholas Hilliard* (1961), pp. 265–71. This portrait, and another of the same size and type, were still at Hampton Court in the time of Charles II (Charles II, *Hampton Court* (72, 118), but they are not recorded in the collection after 1714. Charles I also owned a trick picture of James I which reflected an image of his consort (*Van der Doort*, p. 33).

26. L.R. MS., f. 5.

27. *Calendar of State Papers, Venetian*, vol. x (1900), p. 10.

28. Sir Anthony Weldon in his *Court and Character of King James*, quoted in D. Nichol Smith, *Characters from the Histories & Memoirs of the Seventeenth Century* (1918), p. 3.

29. E. Auerbach, *Tudor Artists* (1954), pp. 148, 164–5.

30. *Cal. S.P., Venetian*, vol. x (1900), pp. 97–8; Dr. M. de Maeyer, *Albrecht en Isabella en de Schilderkunst* (Brussels, 1955), p. 276.

were seen by the Duke of Saxe-Weimar at Whitehall in 1613. A present to the King of Spain from James I in 1614 included, with fowling-pieces, crossbows, mastiffs, water-spaniels, Irish grey-hounds, cormorants, pied conies, bulls and ambling mares, four full-lengths of the royal family.[31] The official portraits of King James would hang happily beside those of Spanish, French or Flemish rulers. They were all in the tradition of state portraiture evolved in the sixteenth century from the examples of Mor and Titian, and the portraits of James from the first part of his reign in England share with portraits by Clouet, Coello, Pantoja or Pourbus that 'Artificiall comeliness, . . . whē the skilfull Painter in drawing a King or Emperor, expresseth them grave and full of Maiestie, although per-adventure they bee not so naturalie.'[31a] And on the walls of the King's palaces these royal portraits, with those of ambassadors and envoys to his court (*e.g.*, nos. 109 and 112) would have demonstrated his success as self-appointed peace-maker in Europe.

The last extant royal payment to Gheeradts had been in 1618. In that year a new portrait type of James was produced by Paul van Somer (103). By now a fresh group of portrait painters had been attracted from the Netherlands to London, where they received encouragement from the most sophisticated members of King James's court, the great Earl of Arundel, the Earls of Pembroke and Southampton and Sir Robert Kerr. Abraham van Blyenberch (see p. 83) worked for the court, but Charles I probably gave away the portrait which Blyenberch had painted of him[32] and Van Somer seems to have had a monopoly in royal portraits from at least 1617 until his death. His new portrait of James is more modern and relaxed than the earlier portraits of the King. The painter has brought the regalia back into the official portrait and added bits of a smart new suit of Greenwich armour as an additional 'prop' to a reasonably truthful portrait of one who 'in the whole man . . . was not un-comely' and who all his life had longed for the English crown. It seems to have been immediately popular. Derivations from it often include considerable variations in the details of the costume, but as late as 1623, when a different and older head and costume appear, they are tacked on to the original design. It provides, therefore, an early object-lesson in the permutations through which a popular royal portrait could be developed or debased.

Van Somer's portrait of the Queen (105), painted in 1617, was apparently designed to hang in the Gallery next to the Vineyard at Oatlands. It is one of the earliest attempts on this scale in British painting to set a royal figure at comparative ease in an actual landscape setting, and it illustrates the Queen's passion for the chase. The more archaic portrait of her elder son in the hunting field (100) was an earlier variation on this favourite English royal theme.

Towards the end of his reign James I sat to Daniel Mytens, the third and most distinguished of the new painters from the Low Countries.[33] The Prince of Wales made himself to some extent responsible for Mytens's welfare and soon after he succeeded to the throne in 1625 he appointed him 'one of our picture-drawers of our Chamber in ordinarie'. The sober portraits that Mytens had painted of the new King before his accession (*e.g.*, no. 117) lack the courtly glitter of a portrait (113) which had probably been painted by Jacob van Doort in 1624, but his official portraits of the new King are dig-nified, perceptive and, in their sense of form and texture, reminiscent of the Dutch portrait painters whom Mytens would have known in his earlier days at Delft and The Hague. Of the many portraits of Charles I and his Queen for which he was paid, none were for the King himself; all were painted for the King's friends and servants or for despatch overseas. The finest example of Mytens's earliest

31. W. Reid, "The Present of Spain", *Connoisseur*, vol. CXLVI (1960), p. 21.

31a. Haydocke's translation (1598) of G. P. Lomazzo's *Trattato dell' arte* . . . (Milan, 1584), Bk. 1, p. 23. Useful material for the development of the sixteenth-century full-length is to be found in

Marianna Jenkins, *The State Portrait*, Study no. III, College Art Assoc. of America (New York, 1947).

32. See *Van der Doort*, p. 1.

33. Mytens's study, signed and dated 1621, is in the N.P.G. (109); life-size versions are at Knole and Melbourne Hall.

official portrait of the King is that painted in 1627 (against an architectural fantasy composed in the previous year by Hendrick van Steenwyck) for the King's sister-in-law the Duchess of Savoy (*Fig.* VIII). The stance clearly pleased the King. It was retained for some years and it is perhaps evidence for the King's interest in his own portraiture that Mytens received a fresh sitting so that the design could be kept up to date. On the version of the design recently bequeathed to Her Majesty The Queen (118), Mytens proudly inscribes himself as 'Pictor Regius' and states that he had painted the portrait from life in 1628.

The bills that survive provide glimpses of Mytens at work, going down to Greenwich or Nonesuch to work on his portraits of the King and Queen with his sitters near at hand, and describe the tasks ('such service and employment as shall be reasonably required of him') to which a Court painter would be set, apart from the repetition of the official royal portraits. He was expected to copy some of the pictures in the royal collection and to make posthumous portraits of the King's family (see p. 84 and nos. 115, 116) to complete an historical sequence. In 1630 he was paid five pounds for perusing two drawings of the King and Queen which were to be engraved.[34]

The splendours of Charles I's collection of European contemporary and renaissance paintings have perhaps caused us to overlook his abiding concern with more traditional themes in the collection which he had inherited. His father had been interested in historical portraits of his predecessors: in January 1618 he had written to the Barber-Surgeons that he had heard of their 'table of Painting . . . whereon is the Picture of our Predecessor of famous memorie K. Henry the 8th., together w^h diverse of y^r Companie, w^h being both like him and well done Wee are desirous to have copyd'.[35] Charles I owned a number of superb Holbeins (see p. 57 and nos. 26, 27, 29, 31) and in 1624 had been given by the Earl of Arundel Joos van Cleve's portrait of Henry VIII. By the late 1630's the Bear Gallery at Whitehall had become a splendid Caroline version of the traditional Elizabethan and Jacobean long galleries and a valuable object-lesson in the development of the European royal full-length portrait. Along the walls hung French and Spanish full-lengths of the previous century, Henri II by Clouet, Philip II by Mor and the Bunel of Henri IV; Marie de Medici by Pourbus; full-lengths by Miereveld and Honthorst of the Princes of Orange and the Elector Palatine; Van Somer's portraits of King James and of Anne of Denmark in the hunting-field; portraits by Mytens of the King's Scottish ancestors and of Count Mansfeld, the Duke of Brunswick, the Dukes of Richmond and Buckingham, the Earls of Pembroke and Nottingham, the old Marquess of Hamilton and Jeffery the dwarf. Round the doors were small pictures attributed to Leonardo da Murano, Salviati, Schidone and Alessandro Varotari. Next to Titian's *Charles V*, the full-length with a hound now in the Prado, hung Rubens's *Daniel in the Lions' Den* and *Peace and War*, and nearby were five new portraits by Anthony van Dyck.[36]

III. CHARLES I AND VAN DYCK

FROM his youth in Antwerp Van Dyck had been known to the English court and for a few weeks in the winter of 1620-1 he had been in the service of James I. When he returned to London in the early spring of 1632 the King may have felt that he had at last secured a painter exactly fitted to serve him. Elegant, cosmopolitan and polite, he had been trained in the studio of the painter whom the King long admired and he had been deeply influenced by the work of Titian for which the King had an especial love. With such a training, enhanced by his experiences with the aristocracy of Genoa and

34. Many payments to Mytens are printed by Charlotte Stopes in the *Burl. Mag.*, vol. XVII (1910), pp. 160-3.

35. A. B. Chamberlain, *Hans Holbein the Younger* (1913), vol. II, p. 293.

36. The Bear Gallery is described in detail in *Van der Doort*, pp. 2-7.

Flanders, Van Dyck could conjure up images of the King, his family and his court that would delight his aesthetic sense and gratify the Stuart obsession, which the King had inherited undiluted from his father, with the authority of the Stuart monarchy. Van Dyck's sophisticated vision and touch, and his delicate sense of colour, would be all the more seductive in the King's eyes for their subtle evocations of the Venetian Renaissance. But although Charles I had reserved for Van Dyck a special welcome, a knighthood, an annual pension of £200 and a house in Blackfriars to which a causeway was built at which the King could land when he went to see his pictures,[37] Van Dyck was also the last, although the most eminent, of the painters who had come from the Netherlands to work at the English court. When he entered the King's service he was faced with some of the same tasks as his less illustrious predecessors. He 'had no mind' to insert figures of the King and Queen into a large perspective background as Mytens had been content to do,[38] but he had to produce posthumous portraits and, from very soon after his arrival, repetitions, for presentation at home and abroad, of the new portraits which he had painted of the King and Queen.

Moreover we have become so accustomed to think of Van Dyck working at the court of Charles I as the acknowledged heir of Titian and Rubens – 'con l'istesso Titiano maraviglioso' – that we overlook Charles's desire to keep alive the old patterns that had pleased his forebears. In the first group that he painted of the King with Henrietta Maria and their two children (150), Van Dyck was refurbishing the design produced nearly ninety years earlier for Henry VIII (43). Placed at the end of the King's Long Gallery 'towards the Orchard' at Whitehall, the new picture may have made intentionally the same effect on the spectator as the Tudor group in the Presence Chamber and, less obviously, Holbein's wall-painting in the Privy Chamber. The spectator who had seen behind Henry VIII and his children a glimpse of the Great Garden and Westminster Abbey would have seen the same extension of space at the end of the Long Gallery in the view of Westminster and the river beyond the regalia at Charles I's elbow. Likewise Van Dyck's most romantic portrait of the King, the portrait à la chasse in the Louvre (Fig. VII), may seem the quintessence of the cavalier spirit but is fundamentally only a reinterpretation, though of infinite subtlety and grace, of the traditional Stuart hunting picture.[39] The elements of the design, and their broad grouping, are to be found in Van Somer's portrait of the King's mother in 1617 (105). Is Van Dyck's stature as an artist increased or diminished by the further realisation that in the detailed articulation and inter-relationship of the King, the horse and the equerry, Van Dyck relied completely on Rubens?[40] Finally, the double portrait of Charles I and Henrietta Maria, which seems so tender an evocation of their new-found married happiness, is a deliberate re-working, probably carried out at the Queen's express command, of an earlier design by Mytens (119).

Nevertheless the 'Great Piece' of 1632 is much bigger than any of its early Tudor prototypes and Charles I took full advantage of Van Dyck's easy mastery of baroque design on a grand scale. Van Dyck's largest royal pieces were painted to be placed with dramatic effect at the end of the vistas in the royal galleries. We know that Van Dyck's first equestrian portrait of the King, painted in 1633 (143), made a profound impression on a visitor who saw it in 1638, hanging at the end of the Gallery at St. James's. A curtain is pulled back to show a glimpse of sky and landscape and under an archway the King rides into the Gallery. The walls on either side of the Gallery were hung with some of the

---

37. P.R.O., Declared Accounts, A.O.I. 2427/64. I am very grateful to Dr. Margaret Whinney for giving me this reference.

38. Whinney and Millar, p. 69, n. 2. Charles I owned at least two, presumably French, portraits of Henrietta Maria in her youth (Van der Doort, pp. 158, 176).

39. This was independently noted by J. S. Held in "Le Roi à la ciasse', Art Bulletin, vol. XL (College Art Assoc., N.Y., 1958), p. 139.

40. On the oil-sketch in the Mauritshuis for the Triumph of Rome in the Constantine cycle (Olieverfschetsen van Rubens, Rotterdam, 1953 (41), pl. 40).

King's finest pictures and Van Dyck had painted his equestrian portrait of the King in a pose that would evoke in the most educated minds at court memories of Rubens and older memories of Venice and Mantua: memories stimulated by the King who had seen as a young man in Spain Rubens's equestrian portrait of the Duke of Lerma[41] and had placed on the walls of his Gallery the Roman Emperors of Giulio Romano and Titian.

For the Prince's Gallery at Hampton Court Van Dyck painted a few years later the equestrian portrait in the National Gallery (*Fig.* 13); the King kept the exquisite *modello* (144) for the Chair Room at Whitehall. It is not clear how the pictures in the Prince's Gallery were hung, but the portrait may have been placed as the culmination of another vista; its lovely Arcadian landscape may have been considered more appropriate to the pastoral setting of the palace in which it was hung. In this design Van Dyck had painted the King *à cavallo ad imitatione di Carlo Quinto espresso da Titiano*: in imitation, indeed, of another great picture that the King had seen in 1623. But there are reminders of earlier examples in English portraiture and the life-size equestrian royal portrait was not quite new in England. The large equestrian portrait of Henry, Prince of Wales, at Parham[42] does not seem to have belonged to the Crown, but the design of the horse and rider may have been inspired by a life-size equestrian portrait of Henri IV which had been hanging at Greenwich at least since 1613 and contained, which Titian's *Charles V* does not, an attendant carrying his helmet before him.[43] The actual disposition and movement of the horse and rider in Van Dyck's *imitatione di Carlo Quinto* are perhaps nearer to the picture of Prince Henry and to stock English martial engraved portraits of an earlier date, such as Cockson's of the Earl of Essex, than they are to Charles V and his horse in Van Dyck's accepted prototype.

To paint the King in armour was an innovation in English royal portraiture and it provides a significant link between the royal portraits of Titian and Van Dyck. In the two equestrian portraits Charles I is seen as the embodiment of the Renaissance ideal of the warrior and the horseman, while Van Dyck carries out the sixteenth-century injunction that 'the precepts of Arte permit us to represent the Pope, the Emperor, a Souldier . . . with that Decorum which truly belongeth to them . . . the chiefe pointe of the skill [lyeth] not so much in representing the action, which peradventure the . . . Emperor never did, as that which he ought to have donne, in respect of the Maiestie and decorum of his estate.'[43a]

Just before Van Dyck came to London in 1632 he had painted in Brussels, presumably for Henrietta Maria, portraits of her mother, Marie de Medici, her brother Gaston, Duke of Orléans, and the Archduchess Isabella. These he probably brought with him from Antwerp. The portraits of her relations were put by the Queen in the Cross Gallery at Somerset House,[44] where they fitted into an almost complete series of family full-lengths: the Duchess of Orléans by Van Dyck, Henri IV by Ferdinand Elle, and portraits of Louis XIII, the Archduke Albert and his wife, Philip III and Philip IV of Spain with their consorts. Of her husband's ancestors and relations, there were Henry VIII, Elizabeth I, Mary, Queen of Scots, Christian IV, Anne of Denmark and Mytens's new portrait of the Queen of Bohemia (121). James I and Henry, Prince of Wales, were represented by the two posthumous portraits specially painted by Van Dyck (141, 142), who also produced the full-length of the little Prince of Wales (169). Charles I, the culminating figure in this brilliant sequence, was almost certainly represented by a new state portrait (145). Van Dyck had painted the King in the hunting-field,

41. See the catalogue issued by Sotheby's for the projected sale of this picture on 4 May 1962.

42. R.A., *British Portraits*, 1956–7 (43). (*Fig. 11*)

43. *Van der Doort*, p. 195.

43a. Haydocke's translation from Lomazzo, *op. cit.*

44. There is no contemporary list of the pictures in Somerset House, but the pictures in the Cross Gallery were separately listed by the Trustees for Sale in September 1649 (Corsham MS., ff. 55–6) and this probably indicates the hanging of the pictures in happier times.

seated at ease with his family, or as an imperial figure on horseback; he now shows him as the sovereign. Van Somer, in his state portrait of James I (104), had been constrained by the traditional formulae. Van Dyck places the crown, orb and sceptre on a table beside the King, as Van Somer had done in the portrait of 1618 which Van Dyck had characteristically refined for his own posthumous likeness of King James. Now, in 1636, Van Dyck lavished all his elegance of line and Venetian richness of texture on a supremely elegant and majestic image which profoundly affected the future development of the English state portrait: an image, moreover, which recaptures the synthesis, that 'certaine mooving vertue', in Titian's royal portraits between an idealisation of the sitter's royalty of nature with the subtlest and most graceful allusions to his great office.

Van Dyck's sensitive perception and delicate touch are seen most clearly in his smaller royal pieces: the three surviving canvases (146, 148, 149) painted for Bernini's guidance and so much more than the factual record that the sculptor required of his patrons' features; the portrait of Henrietta Maria (147), hung by the King in his Bedchamber at Whitehall; the sumptuous double portrait of the King's nephews, painted when they were in London in 1637 and hanging in the Privy Gallery at Whitehall in a frame decorated with martial trophies; the Villiers boys (153); and the two groups of the royal children, the one (151) painted for Somerset House, the other (152), two years later, for the King's Breakfast Chamber at Whitehall. For this second group three preparatory studies survive which perhaps indicate how Van Dyck put together such a design. When its main layout had been decided he probably made, in the presence of the children, rapid chalk drawings of the pose and dress of each child (*e.g.*, *Figs.* 25, 26). With these beside him he could lay out the group in detail. There is also an oil sketch (*Fig.* 23) for the heads of the youngest children, almost certainly done from life and to be transferred to the final canvas without the need of further sittings from incurably restless sitters.

To those pictures by Van Dyck that survive in the royal collection must be added in the imagination those (see p. 92) that are now dispersed. Except for his Italian period, all the phases of Van Dyck's career were represented in the King's collection. In his subject pictures Van Dyck was moving towards a style charged with his recollections of Titian and a personal refinement that looks away from Rubens and towards the rococo, a fusion already clear in the *Rinaldo and Armida* (Glück, 265) painted for Charles I in Antwerp in 1629 and perfected in the exquisite *Cupid and Psyche* (166) which perhaps conveys more than any other picture what Van Dyck meant to Charles I and with what intelligence he could minister to the King's most ardent emotions. It seems probable that it was to be one of the canvases for the decoration of the Queen's Cabinet at Greenwich; in this room the King wished 'yᵉ faces of yᵉ woemen as beautifull as may bee, yᵉ figures gracious and suelta'.[45] If Psyche's features are those of Van Dyck's mistress, Margaret Lemon, we can understand the King's purchase of Van Dyck's unfinished portrait of that termagant lady (157). That the portrait was a pastiche of one of the Titians he had secured in Spain would have further pleased the King. Finally, in the only surviving sketch by Van Dyck for the last project on which the King set him to work, a series of designs of the history and ceremonial of the Order of the Garter, he is seen in procession with his Knights against an architectural backcloth in the manner of Veronese.

The sketch illustrates once more the cosmopolitan brilliance of the pictures painted by Van Dyck in the service of Charles I. In their distillation of the grand manner and a great tradition to the needs of a particularly sophisticated patron and his family, in their sensitive variation of mood and colour to suit a particular commission, and in their technical brilliance, they can only be compared, within the seventeenth century, with Velazquez's record of the court and family of Philip IV. Nothing earlier

45. See O. Millar, *Rubens: The Whitehall Ceiling* (1958), p. 23. There seems no reference in any of the documents concerning Charles I's collection to the mythologies painted for him by Van Dyck according to Bellori (*Le Vite . . .* (Rome, 1672), pp. 261–2).

in the history of the English royal portrait can stand with Van Dyck's achievement, and later only Gainsborough attained its 'amalgam of magnificence lightened by sophistication',[46] an amalgam wrought, so far as Van Dyck was concerned, by the fusion of a patron's especial needs with his favourite painter's training and inclinations. Certainly Van Dyck almost completely eclipsed in the King's sight other painters working in London. Cornelius Johnson, for example, who may have helped Mytens in producing repetitions of the official portrait of the King, was only intermittently employed by the King, and on unimportant tasks, although he was a royal 'Picture Drawer' all the time Van Dyck was in England.[47] The attitude towards contemporary portrait painters in the mind of Charles I, *tanto amico e rimuneratore de' peregrini ingegni*, and its effect on the future course of painting in England, would have been seen in microcosm in a little room at Whitehall in which the King had placed the self-portraits of Mytens, Rubens and Van Dyck.[48]

After the King's execution in 1649, when his possessions were put up for sale, dealers and collectors from the Continent eagerly sought after his Van Dycks. Richard Symonds wrote that 'in yᵉ yeares 1651 1652 yᵉ things of Vandyke were bought up by the Flemyngs at any rate wᶜʰ were the Kings', and in 1653 Cardinal Mazarin wrote to his agent in London: 'je souhaiterois encore d'avoir des portraits de Vandeck, desquels on à quantité en Angleterre . . . et mesme il y en a de la maison du Roy qui ne sont pas encore vendus.'[49] A few months before Van Dyck's death, Charles II had gone down in his barge to the artist's studio for a sitting.[50] In the Civil War he had been painted, as his father and brother had been, by William Dobson at Oxford (203–5). During his exile he and his brothers had sat to such painters as Hanneman (see p. 115), Honthorst, Philippe de Champaigne, Gonzales Coques, Luttichuys, Wautier (215) and Nason: to painters, that is, who had absorbed much of Van Dyck's manner. Soon after the King was restored to the throne, Peter Lely, who may have been in touch with the exiled court during the Interregnum, received official recognition of his position as the best painter in London, in a grant of the annual pension from the Crown of the two hundred pounds that had formerly been paid to Van Dyck.

IV. THE LATER STUARTS

NEITHER Charles II nor his consort seem to have been particularly attracted by Lely's style. They sat to him on a number of occasions, but although at least two of Lely's full-length patterns of Charles II seem to have been popular[51] the King himself did not own one. Unlike his father, he seemed in-

---

46. D. Mathew, *The Age of Charles I* (1951), pp. 26–7.

47. O. Millar, 'An Attribution to Cornelius Johnson reinstated', *Burl. Mag.*, vol. xc (1948), p. 322, and "Some Painters and Charles I", *ibid.*, vol. civ (1962), p. 330.

48. *Van der Doort*, pp. 37–8.

49. B.M., Egerton MS., 1636, f. 102; Comte de Cosnac, *Les Richesses du Palais Mazarin* (Paris, 1884), p. 195.

50. See R.A., *British Portraits*, 1956–7 (79). An earlier portrait of Prince Charles, not by Van Dyck, *in a sea greene coate*, was valued at £20 by the Trustees for Sale (L.R. MS., f. 122) at Hampton Court in October 1649 and sold to De Critz on 18 November 1651 (S.P. 29/447, 24, 1). After the Restoration the King secured nos. 171 and 179. A portrait by Lievens of Prince Charles and Princess Mary *hand in hand* was valued at £4 by the Trustees for Sale at Oatlands in September 1649 (Corsham MS., f. 10); it was in Charles II's collection (Charles II, *Hampton Court* (71) as by *Lewen*, measurements given as 51 × 40 in.). A group of *Madamozelle &*

ye Kings 2 yongest Children was valued at £10 by the Trustees in the Closet in Somerset House in September 1649 and sold to Baker on 4 February 1651 (Corsham MS., f. 49).

51. Both are in Garter robes. One shows the King advancing to the right, of which the best version, now reduced to a head and shoulders, is at Althorp. Of the other, seated with the regalia beside him, the original belongs to the Duke of Grafton; it may have been given by the King to the Earl of Arlington for his 'gallery hung with pictures at length – on the one side the Royal family from K. Henry the 7th by the Scottish race his eldest daughter down to the present King William and his Queen Mary' (*The Journeys of Celia Fiennes*, ed. C. Morris (1947), p. 150). On 18 June 1662 Pepys was impressed in Lely's studio by an unfinished portrait of the King. When the Painter-Stainers Company wished to commission a set of royal portraits, they resolved at their Court of 6 April 1676 that Wright should paint the Duke of York for them, Greenhill the Duchess, Huysmans the Queen, but Lely the King (the Company's *Booke of Orders and Constitutions*, vol. ii, f. 198).

different to displaying portraits of himself in his own houses. Lely may have painted for the King the portrait of Lady Byron (253) and an unadorned portrait of a later mistress, Nell Gwynn, but he found more constant patrons in the Duke of York and his first Duchess. He had painted James as a boy, with his younger brother and sister, in 1647, when he was in the Earl of Northumberland's custody,[52] and the two portraits in which Lely displays most lavishly his mature Restoration baroque style are those of the Duke and Anne Hyde.[53] A few years later he was painting for them his two most famous series of portraits. The 'Windsor Beauties' (257–66) were painted for the Duchess and were hung by her in the White Room at Whitehall. There they must have made a lustrous impression. The London agent of the Grand Duke of Tuscany reported in 1667 that a series of Lely's portraits of the famous ladies of the day would be *una colletione miracolosa per adornare una stanza con ricche cornici indorate* and fired his master's desire for a comparable set. By now Lely had probably finished for the Duke the series of portraits of the flag-officers who had served under him in the Battle of Lowestoft (see nos. 252 and 254). The Duke placed them in the Great Chamber of his hunting box at Culford. Again, Lely contributed portraits (of Prince Rupert and the Earl of Ossory) to the Grand Duke of Tuscany's *Condottieri piu famosi sul mare*.[54] Of James himself Lely began at least two portraits (239 and 240) which the Duke kept and he presumably painted for him the portraits of his first Duchess (see no. 242), her successor (245) and his eldest daughter (250). James owned his *Penitent Magdalen* (268) and eleven unfinished portraits by Lely were recorded in his collection at St. James's Palace in 1688.[55] Other important royal portraits by Lely (241, 246, 249, 251) first appear in Queen Anne's inventory.

The court of Charles II, and later of his brother James, was probably more cosmopolitan than their father's had been; and whereas almost all the foreign artists and craftsmen who had worked for Charles I had come from the Netherlands, the service of Charles II and James II also attracted painters from France and Italy. The brothers' admiration for their cousin Louis XIV no doubt made them sympathetic towards such 'new Conqu'rors of the *Norman Race*' as the Vignons (see p. 131), Gascars or Simon Verelst (see nos. 293 and 294) with their Frenchified affectation of 'Embroidery, fine Cloaths, lac'd Drapery, and a great Variety of Trumpery Ornaments'. Gascars was the protégé of the King's younger sister Henrietta, Duchess of Orléans, the 'chief support' of the French interest at Whitehall, and his portrait of the Duke of York (*Fig.* IX) epitomises the debased style that these painters brought to London.[56] In Antonio Verrio Charles II welcomed a baroque decorative painter who had seen some of the work done by Le Brun and his team for Louis XIV at Versailles and who designed for Charles and his brother religious schemes (see no. 298) of an entirely Roman Catholic flavour and, in the new state apartments at Windsor, a protracted glorification of Charles II and his Queen, of the Stuart conception of the royal prerogative and of the absolutist principles which Louis XIV embodied and the later Stuarts so warmly supported.

The two most important portrait painters to come to London from the Low Countries after the Restoration were Jacob Huysmans and Willem Wissing. Huysmans, a Catholic and an especial favourite of Catherine of Braganza, displayed on her behalf (particularly in no. 289) the same debased Van Dyckian style that we find in Hanneman's latest pictures.[57] Wissing took over much of Lely's

---

52. Whinney and Millar, pp. 170–1. No. 247 seems to have been among the family portraits (see also nos. 151 and 212) which Henrietta Maria had at Colombes until her death in 1669.

53. Now in the Scottish N.P.G. (901, 1179).

54. See O. Millar, 'The Restoration Portrait', *Journal of the Royal Society of Arts*, vol. CIX (1961), pp. 424–6.

55. B.M., Harl. MS. 1890, f. 85v.; Bathoe, *James II* (1185–95).

56. The portrait, probably painted for the sitter, was at Windsor

in the reign of James II (B.M., Harl. MS. 1890, f. 82v.; Bathoe, *James II* (1098)). It was among the naval portraits given by George IV to Greenwich Hospital. Portraits of the Duchess of Orléans, probably painted in France, belonged to Charles II (Charles II, *Whitehall* (640, 641); Bathoe, *James II* (378)).

57. For example, his *Allegory of Peace* (1664) in the Binnenhof, The Hague. A half-length of the Queen, apparently sent over from Portugal, hung in the King's Bedchamber at Whitehall (Charles II, *Whitehall* (241), measurements given as 46 × 38 ins.).

fashionable practice and painted many portraits of James II and his daughters in a court style closely based on Lely. It was, however, the Scots Roman Catholic, Michael Wright, self-styled 'Pictor Regius', who painted the most remarkable state portrait of the period in his rigidly patterned *Charles II* (285), an unequivocal image of restored monarchy on the throne of Solomon. This conceit would have pleased the King's grandfather. Wright's design owes nothing to Van Dyck, but is in direct descent from Henry VIII by Holbein in the Barber-Surgeons' picture; the immediate prototypes for Wright's design seem to be such earlier pieces as Simon van de Passe's engraving of James I or Willem van de Passe's of Charles I (*Figs.* X, XI) and it demonstrates Lomazzo's dictum that 'the gestures of *Maiestie* are agreeable to those of honor, nobility, magnanimity, liberality, and excellency, all which united together, would be represented . . . especially, as they sit on their thrones and tribunals.'[58] We do not know how Wright's canvas was originally staged, but it would have been admirably suited for setting up at the banquet given by the Earl of Castlemaine to the prelates of Rome in 1686. It may indeed have been a particularly splendid example of the royal portrait which it was customary to give to Ambassadors for the countries to which they were accredited. Charles II gave to Sir Richard Fanshawe when he went as Ambassador to Portugal in 1661 'his picture at length, in his garter robes', which could be shown to the Princess the King was to marry; and in 1669 the Earl of Fauconberg, on an Embassy to Italy, received from the Wardrobe a full-length of the King which he seems to have given to the Duke of Savoy.[59]

Wright was the only British painter working 'in large' who was generously patronised by the later Stuarts. Apart from royal portraits (*e.g.*, 286 and 287), he painted for Charles II John Lacy (288) whose acting had often delighted the King and whose portrait is the first important painting of an English actor in costume. John Riley painted Charles II, James II and his daughters (see no. 329) and, probably for Princess Anne or her father, the remarkable portrait of the aged 'necessary woman' Bridget Holmes (330), in which the conventions of a fashionable court style were deployed, perhaps with a touch of satire, for a most unfashionable sitter. Foreign and Roman Catholic artists had basked in the favour of Charles II and his brother, but they were rudely awakened when James II fled from Whitehall. James II had appointed Verrio to succeed Lely as Principal Painter, but at the Revolution his place was taken by Riley and Godfrey Kneller; Largillierre had been fêted by James II and Mary of Modena but was driven out of England by the jealousy of his rivals.[60] One suspects that Kneller was prominent among them. Arrogant, methodical and efficient, Riley's premature death in 1691 gave him the undisputed inheritance of the position in society formerly occupied by Van Dyck and Lely.

Kneller had painted Charles II in 1678 or 1679, apparently as a result of the success of his portrait of the Duke of Monmouth painted in the earlier year. Slightly later he painted a full-length of Charles II (*Fig.* XII) which is more of a state portrait than any surviving earlier picture of the King,[61] a stiffened derivation from Van Dyck's state portrait of Charles I, with the regalia placed in the same relation to the figure as it had been by Van Dyck and Van Somer. For Charles II Kneller also designed a seated full-length in Garter robes which survived as a pattern in his studio until the time of George II (see nos. 361 and 380). He painted a particularly swagger full-length of James II, just before his accession,

58. Haydocke's translation of Lomazzo, *op. cit.*, Bk. II, p. 31; A. M. Hind, *Engraving in England in the Sixteenth & Seventeenth Centuries*, part II (1955), pls. 154, 174. In the background of the plate of James I the sword of Justice lies across the Bible; in a small engraved derivation (by Faithorne) of Wright's *Charles II*, the King is supported by figures representing the Church and the Law.

59. *The Memoirs of Ann, Lady Fanshawe* (1907), pp. 97, 100; MS.

sold at Sotheby's, 14 April 1959 (429). The expenses of the English resident in Venice in 1669 included £15 for a full-length of the King with its frame (*Cal. S.P. Dom.* (1671), p. 212).

60. Dezallier d'Argenville, *Abrégé de la Vie des plus fameux Peintres . . .* (Paris, 1762), vol. IV, p. 297.

61. A version of the portrait is at the end of Jacob de Witt's sequence of the Kings of Scotland at Holyroodhouse; a version of Kneller's earlier Garter portrait of Charles II is at Redlynch Park.

as Lord High Admiral;[62] after his accession he produced state portraits of the new King and his consort,[63] and painted for the King the masterly 'Chinese Convert' (348). In 1690 he produced his two state portraits of William III (335) and Mary II (338). The portrait of William is the most successful state portrait between the Van Dyck of 1636 and Allan Ramsay's *George III*. The stance is livelier and more energetic than Kneller's earlier state pieces and it is doubtful if any of Kneller's contemporaries in London could have produced so satisfying an image of the new King: 'Some other hand perhaps may reach a Face; But none like thee a finish'd Figure place.'[64] It is very remarkable that he placed the finished figure of William III almost exactly as he had, probably in 1685, drawn Lord Jeffreys as Lord Chancellor.[65] Thereafter he was entrusted with the official likenesses of Queen Anne, George I (whom he had painted as a young man) and George II as Prince of Wales. For nearly forty years, besides painting a number of smaller or less conventional royal portraits, Kneller almost had a monopoly in official portraits of the British sovereigns; and towards the end of his career Addison, thinking of the portraits from 'swarthy Charles' to 'Triumphant Nassau', 'bright Maria' and 'famed Brunswick', wrote to Kneller *On his Picture of the King*: 'Thy pencil has, by monarchs sought, From reign to reign in ermine wrought, And in their robes of state arrayed, The kings of half an age displayed.'

For a longer period than any other portrait painter in the history of British painting, Kneller was the 'speciall conning paynter' on whose likeness, taken from a sitting *ad vivum*, would depend the presentation of the sovereign to his subjects at home and foreign governments overseas. We have two glimpses of his methods. In March 1690 he received two sittings from the King at Kensington to enable him to draw the face for the state portrait. Much later, probably in 1720, Alexander Pope told Lady Mary Wortley-Montagu that Kneller 'thinks it absolutely necessary to draw the Face first, which he says can never be set right on the figure if the Drapery & Posture be finishd before. To give you as little trouble as possible, he proposes to draw your face with Crayons, & finish it up, at your own house in a morning; from whence he will transfer it to the Canvas, so that you need not go to sit at his house. This I must observe, is a manner in which they seldom draw any but Crown'd Heads.'[66] The only royal portrait drawing in crayons by Kneller that survives is of Louis XIV, 'Drawen by the Life' at Versailles in 1684 for the portrait which Kneller was commissioned to paint by Charles II.[67] Such drawings would presumably have been the basis of Kneller's portraits of rulers who visited the English court: Peter the Great (347) in 1698 or the Archduke Charles (346) in the winter of 1703-4. Likenesses snatched by the painter during these brief state visits remind us of the difficulties Mytens may have experienced with Count Mansfeld (126) and the Duke of Brunswick (122) in 1624.

Having made an approved likeness, Kneller could work up in his studio the complete portrait and, from the basis of one original, organise the repetition at the command of the Lord Chamberlain of innumerable copies at fifty pounds a time. The entry in this Catalogue for the state portrait of William III records the making of these copies for Governors overseas, for ambassadors, for the King's friends, for City Companies, the Courts of Law and the Universities. Kneller's factory for the production

62. In the N.P.G. (666). The portrait was probably not that which, with a companion piece of Charles II, Kneller painted in 1684 for the Privy Council Chamber in Holyrood (*The Bannatyne Miscellany*, vol. III (1855), pp. 339–42). I am very grateful to Mr. J. D. Stewart for this reference.

63. The portrait of James is only known through Smith's engraving (Chaloner Smith, pp. 1184–5, no. 143); for Kneller's *Mary of Modena* see R.A., *The Age of Charles II*, 1960–1 (376).

64. Dryden, *To Sir Godfrey Kneller* (1694).

65. The portrait is at Erddig; see J. Steegman, *A Survey of Portraits in Welsh Houses*, vol. I (1957), p. 97, where it is wrongly attributed to Riley.

66. *The Correspondence of Alexander Pope*, ed. G. Sherburn (1956), vol. II, p. 22.

67. A. P. Oppé, *English Drawings . . . at Windsor Castle* (1950), p. 70.
    Pictures of more exotic foreigners appear in the records of the royal collection. Ketel had been paid for pictures of the 'strange man' brought back by Frobisher from his voyage to the North West Passage in 1577. In 1710 Harman Verelst was paid £100 by the Queen (P.R.O., L.C./155, f. 36) for four full-lengths, which were placed at Kensington, of the four Iroquois sachems or Kings who had come to London. The portraits were at Hampton Court in 1835 (555–8), but have since vanished; they may be the versions now at Ingatestone.

of copies of his *William III* alone must have been as well organised and active as Ramsay's or Lawrence's for George III or George IV. It was his first duty as Principal Painter and he never shirked it. In 1717–18, when he lived at Whitton and never came to London 'Except', in his own words, 'Extraordinary occasions in his Majesties and the Royal family servis. and sume particular good frinds', he was concerned with a portrait of George I ordered by the Lord Chamberlain for the Guildhall. The canvas was to be of the same size as an earlier portrait of Queen Anne, for which he had presumably been responsible; when the canvas was dry a sitting from the King could be arranged; and Kneller himself wished to go to the Guildhall to supervise the placing of the portrait and to rearrange portraits of William and Mary.[68]

In addition to the repetition of his royal portraits on the original scale, Kneller took great care over the reproduction of them by the engraver. Very fine contemporary engravings had been issued of Elizabeth I and James I, but they had not necessarily been based on the official portraits. Few of Van Dyck's portraits of the royal family were published in engravings at the time. Later in the seventeenth century, however, some of the more popular Van Dycks of the royal family were issued in mezzotint, and royal portraits by Lely, Wissing, Huysmans or Riley were produced by this new process in some quantity; some of the finest early mezzotints are Abraham Blooteling's after portraits by Lely of Charles II, Catherine of Braganza, the Duke of York and the Prince of Orange. Isaac Beckett produced a mezzotint of Kneller's state portrait of Charles II,[69] and in 1679 Robert White engraved in line his portrait of the King in Garter robes, a print that was put on sale in the same year at White's shop in Bloomsbury Market near the Golden Heart. In 1682 he published an engraving of a portrait by Kneller of the Duke of York. But it was the large velvety mezzotints of John Smith (*e.g.*, *Fig.* XIII), executed and produced under Kneller's eye, that must have enhanced Kneller's fame. From the Garter portrait of Charles II to the official portraits of George II and his wife when they were Prince and Princess of Wales (343, 345), all Kneller's official, and a number of his lesser, royal portraits, down to a plate of Princess Anne engraved in 1720, were published by Smith. Impressions from his plates were bought by collectors and enabled less illustrious folk than the Ambassador to the Great Mogul or the Governor of the Barbadoes to arrange round their walls the kings of half an age.

Kneller ministered to the needs of William III as Van Dyck had to those of Charles I. It may have been that the new joint sovereigns felt that their taking of the throne needed to be justified and their tenure of it repeatedly emphasised; certainly no earlier state portrait had been so methodically distributed as William III's. The original was put up in the Council Chamber at Kensington. It was fashionable in the new King's circle to scoff at the acres of adulation in paint and marble that had been laid out for Louis XIV at Versailles. In 1698 Matthew Prior wrote: 'His house at Versailles is something the foolishest in the world; he is galloping in every ceiling, and if he turns to spit he must see himself in person or his Vicegerent the Sun with *sufficit orbi*, or *nec pluribus impar*. I verily believe that there are of him statues, busts, bas-reliefs and pictures above two hundred in the house and gardens.'[70] It is tempting to try to relate political history to the history of taste by pointing to Verrio's retreat from court and to the destruction in 1688 of the court culture that had produced the ceilings at Windsor; or by quoting the superb rejoinder made by Prior to the guide who had showed him round Versailles and asked him if William III's actions had been recorded as lavishly as those of *Le Roi Soleil*: 'The monuments of my Master's actions are to be seen everywhere but in his own house.'[71] The vast equestrian

---

68. MS. (Box I. 86, DD) acquired by the V. & A. Museum at Sotheby's, 28 May 1956 (1584).

69. Chaloner Smith, p. 25, no. 17. (*Fig. XII*)

70. H.M.C., *Bath MSS.*, vol. III (1908), p. 193.

71. Quoted by Johnson, in his life of Prior in the *Lives of the English Poets*, probably from Prior's *History of His Own Time*, ed. A. Drift (2nd. ed., 1740), p. 42.

IX. Gascars: *James II*. National Maritime Museum, Greenwich.

VIII. Mytens and Steenwyck: *Charles I*. Galleria Sabauda, Turin.

X. Simon van de Passe: *James I.*

XI. Willem van de Passe: *Charles I.*

XII. Beckett after Kneller: *Charles II.*

XIII. Smith after Kneller: *James II.*

portrait of William III (337), painted by Kneller in 1701 for the position it still occupies in the Presence Chamber at Hampton Court, was a tribute to William's activities as a peace-maker at the Peace of Ryswick in which Louis XIV had officially recognised him as King of Great Britain; the likeness of the King seems an heroic reinterpretation of the head in the state portrait of 1690. Iconographically, however, the design inevitably has affinities with painted and sculpted equestrian portraits of Louis XIV at Versailles; moreover it seems to have been conceived to hang in the same relation *vis-à-vis* the royal presence as Mignard's equestrian portrait which now hangs in the Salon d'Hercule at Versailles but was originally in the Throne Room.[72] And the elaborate wall-painting by Kneller at the end of St. George's Hall, of which only a fragment survives (336), would have conveyed the illusion of approaching the King's presence. It was to some extent a sequel to Wright's portrait of Charles II in his state robes and regalia, and in its original setting might have reminded a visitor from France of Henri Testelin's large portrait of Louis XIV in his royal robes, placed in the Grande Salle des Assemblées in the Louvre.[73]

For William's gentle and charming Queen Kneller painted her 'principal Ladies' (351–8). The series provokes inevitable comparison with the set painted by Lely for the Queen's mother, but Kneller's portraits belong to a politer age. A design such as the *Countess of Dorset* (353) may still be reminiscent of court portraiture in the reign of James II, but others, the *Duchess of Grafton* (351) or the *Countess of Ranelagh* (356), are probably the most refined portraits of their kind before the age of Reynolds and Ramsay. Ramsay, indeed, based one of his earlier portraits verbatim on Lady Ranelagh and Fielding took her as a pattern of female charm. Queen Anne seems to have regarded Kneller without enthusiasm. The series of naval portraits (see pp. 142, 151, 152), again taking up a theme by Lely, was probably painted for her husband Prince George, but the sitters were divided between Kneller and Michael Dahl. The Queen may have preferred the Tory Dahl to his Whig rival. She did not care for the equestrian portrait of William III and it must have been a blow to Kneller's pride when the Queen, who did not keep the original or any version of her state portrait, gave to Dahl the commission for the vast equestrian portrait of the Prince (384) for the Queen's Guard-Chamber at Windsor. Dahl was, however, persistently slighted by the Hanoverians. Neither of James II's daughters displayed anywhere in their houses a portrait of their father as King; nor do they appear to have owned a portrait of their step-brother, the little Prince of Wales.

In their dealings with painters working in England, the Stuarts were not solely concerned with their own dull counterfeits, but they viewed landscape painting with a severely practical eye: as a source of topographical records of a town or a palace or as suitable subjects on canvases that could be set into the panelling of a room, over a fireplace or a door. The early Stuarts shared the contemporary interest in topography. The pictures of the principal cities of the world, which the Duke of Saxe-Weimar saw at Theobalds in 1613, had probably been painted for the Cecils as part of the original decoration of the house, but he saw at Whitehall the country of England painted, probably in the form of a map, on three large 'tables' and several views of English castles and palaces. Charles I may have shown a more sophisticated interest in modern landscape painting, but the charm of the only landscape by Rubens that he is known to have possessed, the enchanted *Landscape with St. George* at Buckingham Palace, lies in its idealised evocation of the English landscape and the river Thames. The two views of Greenwich (196 and 197), painted for the King by Stalbemt a few years later, are primarily topographical views of a famous scene from a popular point of vantage; but they are also examples of

72. The Abbé Bourdelot's *Relation* of 1683, quoted in P. de Nolhac, *Versailles Résidence de Louis XIV* (Paris, 1925), p. 272, notices the portrait.

73. Exhibited, Musée des Arts Décoratifs, Paris, *Louis XIV, Faste et Decors*, 1960 (535, pl. LXXVII).

advanced Flemish landscape painting in the age of Rubens, more modern in conception and atmosphere than Stalbemt's earlier and more traditional pictures. Among the pictures painted by Alexander Keirincx for the King were ten views, *after y⁰ Life* and hanging at Oatlands, of the King's houses in Scotland.[74] The King also owned a view of London 'done by Geldorp's man'[75] and a view of Pontefract Castle (see no. 438). A group of five landscapes at Somerset House included views of Nonesuch, Windsor, Highgate Hill and Lewisham.[76]

After the Restoration Charles II commissioned Streeter (317) to record some of the most hazardous moments in his wanderings after the Battle of Worcester. Vorsterman's views of Windsor (417–19) should be associated with the new works on the Castle, and Hendrick Danckerts painted for the King views of his houses and principal sea-ports (see nos. 397–400) and the large classical landscapes (*e.g.*, nos. 402–11) which provided, from over the doors and fireplaces in the royal palaces, glimpses of the Italian scene at the time of Claude Lorrain. The more severely classical pieces by Jacques Rousseau (466–70), the flower pieces by Baptiste and Bogdani (471, 483, 484) and Bogdani's handsome bird pictures (*e.g.*, no. 482) were likewise integral embellishments of William III's new apartments at Hampton Court. James II's patronage of Loten (see no. 413) and the later acquisition of works by Griffier (420), Hennin (421), Knyff (422–6), Van Diest (427–31) and Edema (434–7) combined to make of the royal collection a *locus classicus* for the study of landscape painting under the Stuarts. Bogdani worked for William III and Queen Anne and the Queen bought (see no. 472) his pictures of the birds in the aviary formed by George Churchill at Ranger's Lodge in the Little Park at Windsor.[76a]

V. THE EARLY GEORGES

NEITHER George I nor George II took much interest in their own portraiture. After Kneller's death George II entrusted the official portraits of himself and his consort to Jervas, who in 1723 succeeded Kneller as Principal Painter (see no. 500), Enoch Seeman (508–13) and Shackleton (567–8), whose practice was to be taken over by Allan Ramsay. The King himself only retained versions of Seeman's portraits; the more flamboyant design by Shackleton was distributed extensively between 1750 and 1757 as Kneller's *William III* had been. The royal collection contains evidence for modifying the tradition that George II rarely sat for his portrait, but he showed no enthusiasm for it. The 'most like' of any portraits of 'our late good old King', the vivid impression of him snatched at Kensington by Pine, was still with the painter in 1784; Vanderbank painted an impressive equestrian portrait of George I in 1726 (499) and a brilliant full-length of Caroline of Ansbach in 1736, but neither portrait was for the sitters themselves; and Highmore's relations with the Crown seem to have been intermittent and inconclusive (see no. 518). As we should expect, George II and his father patronised a number of shadowy German court painters, Fountaine (498), Maingaud (514–16), Kayser and Klyher (517),[76b] but in the heart of George II aesthetic perception was no match for military ardour. It was primarily for the King and his younger son, the Duke of Cumberland, that the form of small martial

---

74. They were valued at £30 by the Trustees for Sale at Oatlands in September 1649 (Corsham MS., f. 10) and were sold to Lempett (?=Leemput) on 3 May 1651 for £33.

75. *Ibid.*, valued at £2 10s. and sold to Mallory on 5 April 1650.

76. *Ibid.*, f. 46, valued at £7 10s. and sold to King on 8 November 1649.

76a. William III or Queen Anne probably commissioned the four overdoors by Henry Cooke recorded in her inventory: in the Queen's Drawing Room in her Garden House at Windsor

(Queen Anne, *Windsor*, after store (2, 3) were *Two Pieces of Boys and Goats*, and in the Little Drawing Room at St. James's (*ibid.*, *St. James's* (10, 11)) *Shepherds and Shepherdesses*. James II owned a landscape by Pearce (B.M., Harl. MS. 1890, f. 83v.; Bathoe, *James II* (1147)). A flower piece by Vanzoon was over the fireplace in the Queen's Dining Room at Kensington (Queen Anne, *Kensington* (141)).

76b. Vertue records the success with the King of the Chevalier Rusca, who arrived in 1735 from Cassel (*Notebooks*, vol. III, p. 76).

equestrian portrait was produced, a type that is associated with Morier (see p. 191) and is a base derivation from the great royal equestrian portraits of the seventeenth century. The type became popular and sets of these portraits are not uncommon (a good set, for example, is at Wykeham Abbey); their quality is sometimes reminiscent of such painters as Seymour or Butler. George II or the Duke probably commissioned pictures of military scenes (*e.g.*, 597 and 599) and (no. 598) an extremely interesting survey, perhaps by Thomas Sandby, of the Battle of Culloden. This Hanoverian passion for military subjects was to be an obsession even in the civilised mind of George IV.

VI. CAROLINE OF ANSBACH

GEORGE II's consort, 'For Love of Arts and Piety renown'd', was a much more interesting figure, with a genuine respect for the great minds of the age. She corresponded with Leibniz; Dr. Clarke was her mentor and introduced her to Newton. She set up Clarke's portrait (501) in Kensington, perhaps acquired the portraits of Newton (363), Locke (377) and Wollaston (642), and must have rejoiced to possess Kerseboom's portrait of Boyle (332). In her Grotto or Hermitage at Richmond she placed busts of Clarke by Guelfi and of the others by Rysbrack,[77] and in placing busts of poets and philosophers along the walls of her New Library in St. James's Park,[78] the Queen was following the practice, made popular during the seventeenth century, of embellishing a library with portraits of famous men of letters.

She also had a feeling for the past. By the time of Queen Anne the identities of the early portraits of Kings had been lost, but Queen Caroline reassembled them in her Dressing Room in her private apartments at Kensington.[79] Thereby she was promoting the studies in early English portraiture that we associate later with Walpole, William Cole, Gray, Granger or Kerrich and, in Queen Caroline's day, pre-eminently with George Vertue, who, in his own words, 'collected coppyes in Water Colours of most of the Kings of England that was anywhere to be found from picture Image or limning.' Vertue found the collection of early portraits and historical pictures at Kensington invaluable and in 1734 he went there 'to Observe what pictures are most usefull to mee to work after. amongst the kings heads.'[80] Five years later he saw in the Queen's Closet 'lately brought from Richmond all those rare drawings by Hans Holben' and in 1743 he was authorised by the Lord Chamberlain to make copies from them. As well as bringing Holbein's drawings to light, the Queen was probably responsible for the purchase by the Crown of the magnificent portrait of Sir Henry Guildford (28). She bought a portrait of Elizabeth I (see no. 48) and 'begged' from Lord Cornwallis a set of royal portraits, probably the series from Edward III to Mary I, uniform in style and format and characteristic of the making of such historical pieces late in the sixteenth, or early in the seventeenth, century.[81] The Prince Consort may not have been conscious, when he occupied himself with the Holbein Room, that he was paying honour to the ghost of Caroline of Ansbach.

The Queen also followed the contemporary vogue for imaginary or semi-imaginary historical portraits. Two very early examples of this taste had been the remarkable *Edward III, Black Prince*

77. For contemporary references to this see Pope's *Epistle to Burlington* in *Epistles to Several Persons*, ed. F. W. Bateson (1961), pp. 144–5.

78. M. I. Webb, *Michael Rysbrack* (1954), pp. 154–5.

79. Vertue inv., *Kensington*, ff. 25–6; Horace Walpole, in a letter of 25 January 1795, to Pinkerton, mentions Kensington, 'where most of the remaining royal portraits had been assembled by Queen Caroline' (*Letters*, ed. Mrs. Paget Toynbee, vol. XV (1905),

p. 338).

80. *Notebooks*, vol. I, pp. 4, 54, vol. IV, pp. 65–8, 160, vol. V, p. 21.

81. Rev. J. Granger, *A Biographical History of England . . .* (5th ed., 1824), vol. I, p. 17; Granger wrongly assumed that it was the older portraits that had come from Cornwallis. Cornwallis was presumably the 1st Earl, Groom of the Bedchamber, 1721–2. The series comprises nos. 1, 3, 4, 7, 9, 11, 13, 15, 16, 18, 38, 41, 42, 51, 54 in this Catalogue.

and *Edward IV* painted by Belcamp (198–200) for Charles I. Edward III and the Black Prince may have been needed by the King for a scheme that celebrated the foundation of the Order of the Garter, perhaps the scheme for which Van Dyck produced a sketch, and it is unlikely that the King planned so large a show of kings as Jacob de Witt conjured up for Charles II at Holyroodhouse. Queen Caroline commissioned from William Kent the meagre little episodes from the career of Henry V (505–7) that anticipate the more serious mediaeval subjects painted by West for her grandson. From Rysbrack she commissioned a series of busts in terracotta of royal figures from Alfred to Henry, Prince of Wales. She may have contemplated a Temple of Worthies like that at Stowe, and felt herself to be helping to make amends for the 'unwilling Gratitude' which mankind had hitherto shown, according to Pope, to 'Edward and Henry, now the Boast of Fame, And virtuous Alfred, a more sacred Name'. The earliest figures in Rysbrack's series have the slightly sickly glamour that is familiar from Vertue's engravings of the Normans, Angevins and early Plantagenets. In Merlin's Cave at Richmond the Queen planned a display of figures that included Merlin, Henry VII and characters from Ariosto.[82]

VII. FREDERICK, PRINCE OF WALES

Between Charles I and George IV, Frederick, Prince of Wales, stands as the most enthusiastic royal collector and the most intelligent royal patron. He was deeply interested in the story of Charles I's collection and in noting such pictures as survived from it in his father's possession, and he gave Vertue permission to dedicate to him his projected edition of Van der Doort's catalogue. On his death Vertue wrote: 'no Prince since King Charles the First took so much pleasure nor observations on works of art or artists.'[83] Unlike his father or grandfather he had a feeling for the integration of a work of art into the context of the daily round that foreshadows the sophisticated tastes of his grandson George IV.

He showed a keen interest in his own portraiture. The portraits painted of him during his lonely childhood in Hanover, by painters such as Maingaud, Fountaine or Kayser, are dreary examples of contemporary German portraiture, but immediately after his arrival in London in December 1728 he went to the liveliest studio in London, that of Philippe Mercier. He enjoyed visiting the studios of painters, especially of those recently come from abroad, and in his dealings with artists he was consistently kind and affable. In patronising Mercier he was stimulating the gayest painting then available to a patron in London, a lively Frenchified style (*e.g.*, no. 524) that gave English painters such as Hogarth, Hayman or the young Gainsborough a touch of Pater or Watteau. Although the appearance of harmony in Mercier's *Music Party* (522) is wholly deceptive, it represents something new in English royal portraiture: a genre scene on a small scale which, with the pictures painted for the Prince by Wootton and Philips, encouraged the development of the conversation and sporting piece in English painting at this period and provides an intriguing glimpse of royal diversions in their true setting. Mercier, Wootton and Philips were doing for the Prince of Wales what Zoffany, Stubbs, Landseer or Winterhalter were to do for his successors.

Soon after he had been painted by Mercier the Prince sat to Herman van der Myn, encouraged by the 'general satisfaction' felt by the court with the artist's portrait of the Prince of Orange.[84] In

---

82. See Pope's *Imitation of the First Epistle of the Second Book of Horace* (1737) in ed. of *Imitations* by J. Butt (1939), pp. 195, 225.

83. *Notebooks*, vol. I, p. 14.

84. *Ibid.*, vol. III, p. 69; Van der Myn was paid £63 on 8 September 1735 for his portrait of the Prince of Wales (D. of Cornwall MSS., vol. v). In 1749 Rudolf Studer was paid £64. 2s. for a full-length

of the Prince (*ibid.*, vol. XVII, f. 544). The Princess of Wales and her children had been drawn by Thomas Gibson in 1742 (Vertue, *Notebooks*, vol. III, p. 112). The best portraits of the Prince and Princess from the last years of his life are those by Hudson (1750), now at Cliveden. They were engraved by the younger Faber in 1751 (Chaloner Smith, pp. 305, 354).

1735 Jacopo Amigoni painted three portraits of the Prince for his friends in a light Venetian rococo style that probably pleased the Prince. The version in the royal collection (526) is a tribute to the diversity of his tastes: to the arts and sciences, to thwarted martial ambition beating under a painted breastplate and to literary taste and patronage in the copy of Pope's *Homer* under his hand. In his patronage of English painters the Prince probably liked the rococo swing of his portrait by Highmore (519), painted in 1742, better than the more traditional stance in Richardson's wooden full-length of 1736.[85] In March 1738 the Prince and his wife visited the studio of the fashionable Vanloo and were very pleased with what they saw; in 1739 Vanloo painted the group (538) of the Princess with her family and household which is perhaps the most original royal group since the time of Van Dyck. Three years later he painted portraits of the royal pair (536, 537) which mark a stage in the development of the English state portrait. Vanloo was an experienced court artist and he enlivened the state portrait, which had settled into a state of atrophy before the death of Kneller, with a curving architectural setting, a lively glance and a gay flutter in draperies and curtains: qualities which are essentially French and which Ramsay was to use with a grander sense of scale, more sophisticated colour and deeper sensibility in his portraits of George III and Queen Charlotte. Vanloo's superiority as a painter of state portraits over his contemporaries and rivals in England can best be gauged by comparing his portraits for the Prince with the pair painted by Charles Philips in 1737 (531 and 532).

The Prince is seen at ease with his boon companions in a conversation piece more congenial to Philips's slight talent, in no. 533 with its valuable illustration of an interior at Kew, or in hunting pictures painted for him by Wootton. The three principal sporting pictures, painted for the Prince between 1734 and 1737 (545, 546, 555) to hang at Kew, mark a stage in the development of this genre between Wootton's master Jan Wyck, to whose hunting pictures Wootton's are still very close, and an early picture by Stubbs, such as the *Westminster Hunt* of 1762. Slightly later Wootton painted the three views of Park Place (548–50) which combine accurate topography with a glimpse of elaborately informal perambulations in the country by the Prince and his family. The two vast canvases of 1742, illustrating two of the Duke of Marlborough's most celebrated sieges (551 and 552), show that the Prince was not without his family's deep interest in military history; and Wootton's portrait of the young Duke of Cumberland (554), painted in 1744 in collaboration with Hudson, helped to form the convention of small martial portraits associated with Morier. A much more important work of collaboration by Wootton was the large hunting piece of 1734 (555) which would have brought the Prince, however briefly and indirectly, into contact with Hogarth. A few years earlier Hogarth, whose relations with the royal family were continuously unhappy, had been unable to complete the little royal conversation piece (in the vein later to be worked by Zoffany) for which two *modelli* (see no. 559) survive. Hogarth probably had a sitting from the Prince for this piece and seems to have painted, perhaps soon after their marriage, little full-lengths (562, 563) of the Prince and his wife. They sat in 1745 to Barthelemy Du Pan. In the following year Du Pan painted for them the large group (572) of their children in the gardens of Park Place, which seems to have been a success (they ordered two copies of it); it was a new form of royal child-portraiture that Copley was to perfect for George III in

85. Richardson was paid on 13 September 1737 £147 for two full-lengths of the Prince (D. of Cornwall MSS., vol. VII, f. 164). One of these portraits, at Warwick Castle, is signed and dated 1736; the preparatory drawing for the head, in the Kneller tradition, dated 20 September 1736, is in the British Museum. In 1740 portraits of the Prince and his wife were sent in fine carved frames to Richard Nash at Bath (*ibid.*, vol. IX, f. 183). They are now in the Guildhall at Bath; they appear to be by Seeman and the portrait of the Princess is closely related in design to no. 563. Vertue had noted in 1732 (*Notebooks*, vol. III, p. 57) that the Prince had sat three times to Dandridge: 'the picture of the face which is yet only done is vastly like. and by ye Prince and others thought to be the most striking likeness yet done'. A full-length of the Prince in robes of state, signed by Dandridge and dated 1732, was formerly at Woborn, sold at Christie's, 19 January 1951 (90). The equestrian portrait painted by him for Lord Barrington may be that in the N.P.G. (1164).

1785. The apotheosis of the Prince's iconography came in the huge canvas by Knapton (573), painted soon after the Prince's death, in which he looks down from the wall on the pyramid of children engaged in some of the pursuits that had given him such delight. Knapton had already executed pastels of some of the children (574–6), but these were outclassed by the ravishing set of portraits (580–8) drawn by Liotard for Princess Augusta in her widowhood. When it is remembered that the Prince had discussed with Vertue 'the settlement of an Accademy for drawing & painting', Joshua Reynolds, writing to Miss Weston from Italy on hearing of the Prince of Wales's death, was guilty of an understatement: 'We are all extremely afflicted for the loss of the Prince of Whales (sic) who certainly would have been a great Patron to Painters.'[86]

Although he was on notoriously bad terms with his mother, the Prince had something of her liking for old portraits. Vertue put much of the fruit of his studies in royal iconography into the large engravings of the Kings of England commissioned by the Knaptons for the folio edition of Rapin's *History of England*. The Prince received a finely bound copy of the work from Vertue's hands at Kensington. In 1731 he paid nearly a thousand pounds for the furniture and goods in the great and little houses at Kew[87] which he had acquired from Lady Elizabeth St. André. The goods included a series of historical portraits which Lady Elizabeth had inherited from her great-aunt Lady Capel. The series had come to Lady Capel from her Bennett and Leman ancestors and although it contains few pieces of merit, apart from the portrait of Sir John Parker by Custodis (59), it is interesting as a set of portraits, many inscribed in a uniform way, of which the nucleus may have been formed early in the seventeenth century, possibly by Sir John Leman, whose portrait (69) was presumably among those owned by Lady Capel. The collection had probably been augmented by Lord Capel 'who collected many portraits of Eminent men as well of this Nation as of other parts of Europe.'[88] As if not to be outdone by his mother, the Prince bought before 1750 Holbein's portrait of the 3rd Duke of Norfolk (30). If he acquired the portrait of his ancestor, Prince Henry, in the hunting field (100), it is not difficult to imagine how he would have enjoyed this early Stuart forewarning of Wootton.

The Prince's taste was predominantly for seventeenth-century pictures and his interest in the collections of Charles I may have stimulated him in the acquisition of a superb group of pictures by Rubens and Van Dyck. To the Van Dycks left from the time of Charles I the Prince added the *Portrait of a Man* (160) and the magnificent *St. Martin* (165), both, in different ways, crucial examples of a most important phase in Van Dyck's career; the two lovely female portraits (154, 158) from the short but brilliant period when Van Dyck was working in Brussels; and the double portrait (156) which is an unsurpassed masterpiece of his mature English style.

VIII. GEORGE IV

FOR quality these canvases can stand with the finest acquisitions by Charles I or George IV. George IV, like his grandfather, acquired a number of early portraits and, possibly by inheritance from his uncles, Henry Frederick, Duke of Cumberland (*d.* 1790), and William Henry, Duke of Gloucester

---

86. *Letters*, ed. F. W. Hilles (1929), p. 12. In 1735 the Prince had bought Gawen Hamilton's little *Club of Artists* (1735), now in the N.P.G. (1384).

87. D. of Cornwall MSS., vol. 1 (11); on 26 March 1731 the sum of £957. 7s. 6d. was paid for these goods.

88. Vertue, *Notebooks*, vol. 1, p. 133. In September 1761 Walpole saw the portraits at Kew: 'a room full of old heads in pannels, which have long been in the house; many are imaginary, all very bad' (*Visits*, p. 39; see also *Anecdotes*, vol. 1, p. 47). Among the portraits, in this volume of the Catalogue, which came from Lady Capel's collection, or are presumed to have done so, are: 21, 37, 52, 59, 62–5, 67–70, 72, 75, 76, 78, 81, 85, 101, 134, 280. Some are stated in the inventory of Kensington in 1818 to have come from the 'Old palace at Greenwich'. The only modern single portraits Walpole noted at Kew were of Lords Cobham and Chesterfield, probably by Hudson.

(*d.* 1805), pictures relating to Prince Frederick. He bought two fine religious pieces by Van Dyck (162, 164) and placed at the apex of the royal collection of Van Dycks the famous triple portrait of Charles I (146).[89] During his reign he lent nearly all the important Van Dycks in the collection to exhibitions at the British Institution and by 1835, perhaps in accordance with his plans for the re-arrangement of the pictures at Windsor, the old Queen's Ball Room had been hung with Van Dycks and thus transformed into the famous Van Dyck Room.[90] George IV had also presumably planned the insertion of full-length royal portraits, from James I onwards, high up on the north wall of St. George's Hall. This display, for which he took two Van Dycks (141, 145) and which was completed early in 1832 by the addition of a version of his own official portrait by Lawrence, was the last important essay in a time-honoured royal theme.[91]

IX. MODERN TIMES

SINCE 1830 important early royal portraits have been continuously added to the royal collection. In 1883 Queen Victoria acquired, under pressure, the intriguing *Family of Henry VII* (19) from Strawberry Hill.[92] Of Her Majesty Queen Mary's many additions to the Crown collection the most important were perhaps the little portraits of Frederick, Prince of Wales, and his wife that may be by Hogarth.[93] More recently the early part of the collection has been enriched by pictures of exceptional interest, such as Edward Bower's portrait of Charles I at his trial (208) or, in the portrait of the King by (?) Jacob van Doort (113) and Hogarth's sketch for a royal conversation piece (559), of a quality that would have pleased Charles I, Frederick, Prince of Wales, and George IV.

Finally, in 1961 a group of royal portraits was bequeathed to Her Majesty the Queen by Cornelia, Countess of Craven, from the collection at Hampstead Marshall. Around this collection has long hung the glamour of its presumed associations with Elizabeth, Queen of Bohemia. On 27 August 1769 George Montagu wrote to Walpole: 'I intend to amuse myself at Lord Craven's. It seems the late Lord has been routing out a thousand curious ancestors that have been nailed up in boxes ... ever since the Queen of Bohemia's time; and by the account many of her things she pawned that were brought from Hempsted, and are now ranged about the house – thanks to you, who have taught the world to treat their kin and their goods and chattels with respect, and think they are as good furniture as Mr Reynolds and all our daubers make us pay so dear for.'[94] It is difficult to substantiate the 'account' of the provenance of the Craven pictures. In her Will, drawn up in May 1661, the Queen of Bohemia named her eldest son Charles Louis as her principal heir, but left to Prince Rupert 'tout ce qui nous est deu de l'argent, et ce qui nous est en main, toutes mes principales bagues et vesselles, et autres meubles, qui sont à nous.' Prince Rupert in turn, by Will dated 27 November 1682, left all his goods, including his pictures, to William, Earl of Craven, in trust for his mistress Margaret

89. George IV had made use of some of the royal Van Dycks at Carlton House (see nos. 142, 145, 148, 149). He bought at Henry Hope's sale in 1816 a full-length of Gaston d'Orléans which he placed in the South Ante-Room at Carlton House but gave to the Duke of Orléans in 1829 (Jutsham, *R.*, f. 1; *Carlton House*, 1816 (45)); it is now at Chantilly (Glück, 429).

90. Waagen (1838), vol. I, p. 170; *The Royal Windsor Guide* (1839), p. 37.

91. *Ibid.* (1832), p. 37. Queen Caroline had arranged a set of royal full-lengths in the Queen's Gallery at Kensington (Vertue inv., *Kensington*, f. 22; still to be seen in Pyne, vol. II, Kensington, p. 67) and a comparable display from the time of Queen Victoria

survives in the Picture Gallery at St. James's Palace, in which one portrait (36) has been used in three of the main historical sequences since the time of Charles I. Among George IV's acquisitions of early pictures were nos. 123, 138 (?), 207, 333. From the collection of his brother Frederick, Duke of York, he bought such early historical pieces as nos. 488 and 489.

92. Among other acquisitions by Queen Victoria may be cited nos. 120, 132, 285 (reluctantly), 314, 441, 502, 561.

93. Queen Mary also acquired nos. 117, 269, 315, 531, 532, 553.

94. Walpole's *Correspondence*, ed. W. S. Lewis, vol. X (Yale, 1941), p. 286.

Hughes and Ruperta, his daughter by her. Craven, who was the Prince's executor, was empowered to sell the goods for the benefit of the two women, and may have eventually come into possession of a large part of the Prince's goods.[95] Many of the portraits still at Hampstead Marshall could have belonged to the Queen of Bohemia, but of those that came in the bequest in 1961 this perhaps is only true of the portraits of Charles I (118) and his eldest daughter (170). The other portraits, of Charles II in the Civil War (204) and of the Duke of Gloucester (303) and Charles II in later life (301), are perhaps more likely to have belonged in the first place to Prince Rupert or Lord Craven.

X. CONCLUSION

It will be obvious from these notes that the successive phases of royal patronage form a vital thread in the early history of the British portrait. It could be argued that, after the Civil War and the destruction of the 'Whitehall group' of patrons and connoisseurs at the court of Charles I, the Crown never entirely recovered its position as the main source of patronage and as a leading arbiter of taste. It is true that Henry VIII was, as a patron, essentially unworthy of Holbein and that the names of George I and George II are almost synonymous with indifference, if not with active hostility, towards good painting. It can also be claimed that a royal patron could hardly ever initiate a phase in taste or seek out an artist struggling in obscurity. Charles I's love of Venetian painting and Prince Frederick's apparent liking for French painting sprang from the example of people close to them and helped to popularise, but did not create, a given taste. This would likewise be true of George IV's passion for Dutch and Flemish painting of the seventeenth century or the Prince Consort's respect for Primitives.

In the same way, even the most discerning British royal patrons have gone for their portraits to painters who were well established in London or had recently arrived from Europe with the glamour that continental experience has always held for the English. In employing Holbein, Eworth, Mytens, Van Dyck, Lely, Kneller, Wootton or Vanloo, English sovereigns and princes could not claim that they were helping or discovering a neglected artist; recognition from the Crown would only be granted to an artist who could be described by his contemporaries as the 'wonder of the world', as *Titiani imprimis aemulus* or simply as 'the best artist in England'. Encouragement from the Crown, a place on the royal establishment as Principal Painter or as 'one of our Painters in Ordinary', was the hall-mark of success to portrait painters working in the main tradition of portrait painting in this country from Holbein to Ramsay. There is no mistaking the note of hopeful urgency in Mytens's endeavours in 1618 to 'fynde occasion to drawe the Princes Highnes picture', the importance in Kneller's early years in London of the sittings given to him by Monmouth, Charles II, and the Duke of York, or the *cachet* stamped on the reputation of a smart continental painter when the Prince of Wales and Princess Augusta visited his studio. In his incredibly pompous *Self-portrait* in the Uffizi, Kneller shows off the gold medal given to him by William III to announce his position as a Gentleman of the Privy Chamber and Principal Painter. It was the patronage of the British Crown that attracted Rubens, Van Dyck and countless other foreigners to London; and it is perhaps a measure of the service rendered by the Crown to British painting that a considerable part of the history of British painting must be written round the careers of the painters with whose works this Catalogue is concerned, and that there will be found in it, with very few exceptions, the names of all the painters of importance who worked in England from the age of Holbein to the age of Hogarth.

95. The two Wills are printed in vol. LXXXIII (1863) of the *Camden Society*, pp. 109, 142–4. Walpole saw the Craven collection in 1768 (*Visits*, p. 63) and some of the pictures are mentioned by J. Britton, *The Beauties of England and Wales*, vol. XV (1814), pt. II, pp. 52–7. Among other recent purchases for the royal collection are nos. 60, 99, 339, 350, 423, 527, 543, 544, 641.

NICHOLAS HILLIARD:
DESIGN FOR ELIZABETH I's GREAT SEAL OF IRELAND.
British Museum.

GENEALOGICAL TABLE

en inserted

ork

ridge

ork

ARD III
52–85)

Catherine
(1503)

of Lennox
76)

la
615)

of

e Matilda
51–75)

BIBLIOGRAPHY

References to specialised art-historical and other works, and isolated references in documentary sources, will be found in the individual entries or groups of entries in the Catalogue. This Bibliography contains only the principal manuscript and printed sources that deal specifically with the growth of the royal collection.

I. INVENTORIES AND OTHER CLOSELY RELATED SOURCES

If the source is referred to in the Catalogue in an abbreviated form, the abbreviation is placed in brackets immediately after the title of the source.

THE TUDORS

1. Inventory of pictures etc. in the collection of Henry VIII in the Palace of Westminster, 1542.

MS. in P.R.O., in Vol. 160 of the Miscellaneous Books of the Augmentation Office (abbr. as *1542*). The occasion of the inventory was the appointment in 1542 of Sir Anthony Denny as Keeper of the Palace of Westminster; the inventory was drawn up by the Wardrobe clerk, N. Bristow, and is dated 24 April 1542. Only ff. 53–59, 106 v. and 135 were printed by W. A. Shaw (see below).

2. Inventory of pictures etc. in the collection of Edward VI at Greenwich, Westminster, Hampton Court, Oatlands, Nonesuch, The More, Richmond, Newhall and Bedington.

B.M., Harl. MS. 1419 (abbr. as *1547*). Taken by virtue of a Commission dated 14 September 1547; only the entries for pictures were printed by Shaw.

3. Inventory of pictures etc. in the collection of Edward VI, 1549–50, at St. James's.

B.M., Harl. MS. 1419 (abbr. as *1549–50*). The occasion of this sequel to the inventory of 1547 is obscure.

These three inventories were edited by W. A. SHAW, *Three Inventories of the Years 1542, 1547 and 1549–50 of Pictures in the Collections of Henry VIII & Edward VI* (1937).

An undated Tudor inventory, containing scattered references to pictures and drawn up *c.* 1560 by John Wolde, is among the MSS. at Glynde (see below).

JAMES I

4. Inventory of Anne of Denmark's pictures etc. at Oatlands, 1616.

MS. at Glynde Place, entitled 'An Inventory of her Ma^tyes stuffe in Otelands taken at her Ma^tyes remove in October 1616'.

5. Inventory of Anne of Denmark's pictures etc. at Oatlands, 1617.

MS. at Glynde Place, entitled 'An Inventory of hir Ma^ts owne stuffe in Oatelands taken ye day after remoove from thence being the 7th day of October 1617'.

These MSS, now the property of Mrs. Humphrey Brand, also include a copy of the 1617 inv., apparently made in 1618 and recording alterations and other amendments since October 1617, and miscellaneous notes of the period 1616–28. The MSS. have passed by descent from the Trevor family and should be associated with, and are partly in the hand of, Sir John Trevor, appointed Keeper of Oatlands on 31 August 1603.

CHARLES I

6. List of pictures in the possession of Charles I when Prince of Wales.

MS., probably drawn up *c.* 1624, entitled 'A note of all such pictures as your Highness hath at this present, done by several famous masters' own hands, by the life'; printed from the original in the P.R.O. by W. N. SAINSBURY, *Original Unpublished Papers illustrative of the Life of Sir Peter Paul Rubens* . . . (1859), p. 355. The list is stated by Sainsbury to be partly in the hand of Sir Balthazar Gerbier; a copy is in the B.M., Stowe MS. 185, f. 219.

7. Catalogue of the collections of Charles I, drawn up by Abraham van der Doort.

MS. in Bodleian Library, MS. Ashmole 1514, entitled 'A Book of all such the kings Pictures As are by his Maiests. Especiall appoyntment placed at this present time remayning in Whitehall in the Severall . . . placees followeinge'.

Apparently the draft of a catalogue or 'Register' of the royal collections, concerned mainly with Whitehall, but including draft sections dealing with Nonesuch and Greenwich and copious annotations and amendments.

8. Catalogue of the contents of the Cabinet Room at Whitehall.

MS. in Royal Library. A fair copy, drawn up under Van der Doort's surveillance, of the section in MS. Ashmole 1514 that deals with the Cabinet Room.

9.

MS. in Bodleian Library, MS. Ashmole 1513. A second fair copy, also drawn up under Van der Doort's surveillance, of the contents of the Cabinet Room.

10. Catalogue of the contents of the Chair Room at Whitehall.

B.M., Add. MS. 10112, entitled 'The Booke of the Kings: 40: Pictures and: 12: Statuas placed at this time in the Kings Chare roome . . .'. A fair copy, drawn up under Van der Doort's surveillance, of the section in his MS. that deals with the Chair Room.

These four MSS. (Nos. 7–10 above) were printed, and their relationship discussed, by O. MILLAR, 'Abraham van der Doort's Catalogue of the Collections of Charles I', *Walpole Soc.*, Vol. XXXVII (1960) (abbr. as *Van der Doort*). Van der Doort was probably occupied with his 'Register' from at least 1637; the fair copies were probably written out in 1639; and some of Van der Doort's addenda are dated 1640. Of the copies of Van der Doort's catalogue the most important is that by George Vertue, B.M., Harl. MS. 4718, probably the basis of the edition printed by William Bathoe in 1757 with an Advertisement by Horace Walpole. The copy made by Vertue for Frederick, Prince of Wales (see below, No. 30), is in the Surveyor's Office.

11. Catalogue of pictures etc. at Whitehall and in the Long Gallery at St. James's.

MS. in the Victoria and Albert Museum, MS. 86.J.13, entitled 'A CATALOGUE OF PICTURS'. Probably compiled in 1640, the MS. may have been written by Sir James Palmer and is not closely dependent on Van der Doort's work. It is printed in O. MILLAR, *op. cit.*

THE COMMONWEALTH

12. Valuations of the goods belonging to the royal family.

MS. in P.R.O., Miscellaneous Exchequer Auditors of Land Revenue, L.R.2, 124 (abbr. as L.R.MS.).
A resolution had been passed by the House of Commons on 23 March 1649 that the late King's goods should be inventoried, appraised and (a large part of them) sold, and on 4 July 1649 an Act was passed to this effect (*Acts and Ordinances of the Interregnum*, ed. C. H. Firth and R. S. Rait (1911), vol. II, pp. 160–8). Trustees were appointed, including Jan van Belcamp (see below, p. 111) to make detailed inventories and valuations of all royal goods in all royal residences; they were to make three copies of these 'appraisals' and the L.R. MS. is an almost complete set of original valuations by the Trustees, made between 27 August 1649 and 28 November 1651.

A more complete set of valuations formerly belonged to the Sebright family, but this is now lost; a typescript of it is in the Surveyor's Office.

13. Valuations of royal goods at Oatlands, Windsor, Wimbledon and Somerset House.

MS. in the possession of Lord Methuen at Corsham Court (abbr. as Corsham MS.). The third set of original valuations for these parts of the royal collection.

A number of later copies of the valuations, loosely known collectively as the Commonwealth Sale Catalogue, are known. In one, B.M. Harl. MS. 7352, sent by Thomas Coke (see below) to the (2nd?) Earl of Oxford, the names of buyers and the prices they paid for royal goods are inserted. These appear to be reasonably accurate when they are compared with a bundle of original certificates to the Treasurers for the Sale recording the day by day sale of goods between 15 August 1649 and 1 February 1653 (P.R.O., S.P.29/447, 24, 1).

A mass of other material for the Sale is to be found among the State Papers in the P.R.O., *e.g.* in S.P. 28/282–5; 28/350 (9); 29/447,24; and in the S.P. Domestic in the printed Calendars.

Valuable documentary material on the formation and dispersal of the collection of Charles I is to be found in: A. LUZIO, *La Galleria dei Gonzaga venduta all'Inghilterra nel 1627–28* (Milan, 1913), and Le COMTE DE COSNAC, *Les Richesses du Palais Mazarin* (Paris, 1884).

The *Diary* of John Evelyn (ed. E. S. de Beer (1955) and the notebooks of Richard Symonds, especially B.M. Egerton MS. 1636, contain references to royal pictures in the hands of dealers and agents in the Interregnum.

THE RESTORATION

14. Declarations of former royal goods to the House of Lords' Committee.

MSS. in House of Lords (abbr. as H. of L. MSS), calendared in H.M.C., *Seventh Report*, part 1 (1879), pp. 88–93.

A Committee of the Lords had been appointed on 9 May 1660 with full powers to recover as much as they could of the royal goods. On 12 May they issued an order that within seven days all in possession of any such goods should bring them to the Committee and between 10 and 28 May they received Declarations from those who held, or knew the whereabouts of, former royal possessions. Valuable transcripts of the House of Lords material by Mr. Francis Needham were given to the Surveyor's Office.

15. Inventory of goods recovered by Colonel William Hawley.

B.M., Add. MS. 17916 (abbr. as Col. Hawley). The Colonel had been authorized by the Lords' Committee to receive information concerning royal goods, to seize and secure them and to deliver them to Whitehall; the MS. is, at least in part, a register of pictures etc. recovered by him and so delivered, and entries in it are dated between 1 June 1660 and 16 August 1661.

The Commissioners appointed to recover the King's goods were active until at least February 1673; there is material on their activities in the State Papers and in the *Calendar of Treasury Books*. A list of pictures and other works of art handed over by Lord Lisle on 8 and 10 September 1660 is in the National Library of Wales (MS. 6596D, 2nd part) and in the Penshurst MSS. (1160, 14).

THE LATER STUARTS

16. Inventory of Charles II's pictures etc. at Whitehall and Hampton Court.

MS. in Surveyor's Office, in two parts, entitled 'An Inventory of all his Maties Pictures in White-Hall' and 'An Inventory of all his Maties Pictures in Hampton-Court'. Probably drawn up *c.* 1666–7.

The documents dealing with the purchase of pictures by Charles II from William Frizell in 1660 and 1662, and lists of the pictures, are in B.M. Add. MS. 23199, the lists on ff. 28–31; these documents were published and discussed by B. R E A D E, 'William Frizell and the Royal Collection', *Burl. Mag.*, vol. LXXXIX (1947), pp. 70–5.

The gift of pictures to Charles II by the States-General of Holland in November 1660 was discussed by D. M A H O N, *ibid.*, vol. XCI (1949), pp. 303–5, 349–50, vol. XCII (1950), pp. 12–18, 238; a volume of engravings was issued in Amsterdam, V A R I A R U M   I M A G I N U M   A   C E L E B E R R I M I S   A R T I F I C I B U S   P I C T A R U M   C Æ L A T U R Æ   E L E G A N-T I S S I M I S   T A B U L I S   R E P R Æ S E N T A T Æ, *Ipse Picturæ partim* . . . C A R O L O   I I . . . *dono missæ sunt.*

17. Inventory of Henrietta Maria's goods at Colombes, 1669.

MS. in P.R.O., SP. 78/128, ff. 209–25, entitled, 'An inventory of all the Goods Plate, And Household Stuffe belonging to the late Queene the Kings Mother begun to bee taken att Colombe the last of October 1669, and finished the fifth of November 1669.'

Taken after the Queen's death in August 1669 to assist in establishing Charles II's claim to many of the pictures etc. in her possession. The negotiations were in the hands of Sir Leoline Jenkins, who presumably caused the inv. to be drawn up, and others who had been joined with him in a Commission of 27 September 1669 (*Cal. S.P.Dom.* (*1668–9*), pp. 503–4).

18. Inventory of the goods of James II, when Duke of York, at Culford Hall, 1671, and Whitehall, 1674.

MS. 891 in Bodleian Library. The two sections are entitled 'Goods of his Royall Highnesse the Duke of York at Culford hall in the charge of Maddam Elliott: 23 Octob^r 1671' and 'Goods of his Roy^ll Highnesse . . . in the custody and Charge of Phillip Kinnersley Yeom of his R^ll High^s wardrobe of Beds: the first of June 1674'.

19. Inventory of James II's pictures in 1688 at Whitehall, Windsor, Hampton Court, and in the custody of The Queen Dowager, Catherine of Braganza, at Somerset House.

B.M., Harl. MS. 1890. An inventory of royal goods entitled 'I N V E N T O R Y   O F   H I S   M A J E S T Y S   G O O D S   1688'. The first folio is dated 15 February 1688 (o.s.). Pictures and statues etc. occupy ff. 45–89, a section signed by William Chiffinch, Keeper of the King's Closet.

Vertue's copy of this MS. is in the B.M., MS. 15752; this served as the basis for the edition printed for W. Bathoe in 1758 (abbr. as Bathoe, *James II*).

In the Surveyor's Office is a MS. closely dependent, and probably based, on James II's inv., drawn up in the reign of William III, who appears on f. 40 substituted for James II as the owner of the pictures at Windsor.

20. Inventory of William III's pictures etc. at Kensington, 1697.

B.M., Harl. MS. 7025, ff. 188–94, entitled 'A List of his Majesty's Pictures, as they are now placed in Kensington House. – 1697' (abbr. as *Kensington*, 1697).

21. Inventory of William III's pictures etc. at Kensington, 1700, and Hampton Court.

B.M., Harl. MS. 5150, the two sections entitled 'List of His Majesties Pictures as they are now Placed in Kensington House 1700' and 'Pictures in the Kings Private appartm^ts at Hampton-Court'.

References to pictures in William III's collection are scattered throughout the *Journal* of Constantijn Huygens the younger and in invs. of the furnishings of Kensington in 1697 and 1699/1700 (TH. H. LUNSINGH SCHEURLEER, 'Documents on the Furnishing of Kensington House', *Walpole Soc.*, vol. XXXVIII (1962), pp. 15–58).

22. Inventory of Queen Anne's pictures at Kensington, Hampton Court, Windsor, St. James's and Somerset House.

MS. in Surveyor's Office, entitled 'A LIST OF HER MAJESTIES PICTURES IN KENSĪGTON HAMPTON COURT AND WINDSOR CASTLE' (abbr. as Queen Anne).

Drawn up by or for Peter Walton, Surveyor and Keeper of the pictures, probably between 1705 and 1710. Copious notes are added, apparently during the Queen's lifetime and probably *c.* 1710–12, by Thomas Coke, Vice-Chamberlain of the Household, recording later movements and rearrangements of the pictures.

An early copy of the section relating to Kensington is in the B.M., MS. 17917; a later copy of the whole is also in the B.M., MS. 20013. A list of pictures at Kensington in Vertue's MSS., B.M. MS. 19027, ff. 12–13, is close to relevant sections of No. 22.

23. Inventory of Queen Anne's pictures.

MS. in Surveyor's Office, entitled 'A List of the Pictures Belonging to the Crown, Taken By Mr. Walton when the Duke of Kent was Lord Chamberlain' [*i.e.,* 1704–10].
An early eighteenth-century MS., based on No. 22, with differences in detail, unaware of Coke's notes, and therefore perhaps derived from a copy of No. 22; on f. 9 v. is a reference to a picture being moved and replaced in 1728.

24. Inventory of Queen Anne's pictures.

MS. in Surveyor's Office, entitled as No. 23. A later eighteenth-century MS., very close to No. 23 and perhaps copied from it.

The MS. was given to Horace Walpole in 1775 by Topham Beauclerk. It contains annotations by Walpole, at one point dated 1776, and longer remarks by him, dated 1783, on the fly-leaves.

THE EARLY GEORGES

25. Inventory of pictures at Somerset House, 1714.

B.M., Add. MS. 19933, entitled 'The Pictures in the Store Rooms at Somerset House October:28:1714'. Still to some extent dependent on the numbering established in No. 22.

A list of pictures hanging in the Earl of Oxford's lodgings at St. James's, January 1715, is among the Lothian MSS. at Melbourne Hall (H.M.C., *Cowper MSS.*, vol. III (1889), pp. 112–13).

26. Inventory of pictures etc. at Windsor, 1724.

MS., in P.R.O., L.C.5.202 (ff. 323–33), entitled 'An Inventory of the Goods in the kings Royall Palace at Windsor – taken on ye 2^d Day of May Ann^o Dom. 1724. by Mrs Anne Marrott'. A perfunctory list, still dependent on No. 22.

27. Inventory of the pictures at Windsor.

MS. in B.M. Reading Room, Press Mark c.119 h.3, entitled 'A List of Pictures in Windsor Castle'. It closely follows Nos. 22 and 26 and appears to be a careless copy of an original inv. of the time of Queen Anne which had been annotated and amended over a number of years, at least up to 1736.

'A Catalogue of the Pictures in the Great Appartment of Windsor Castle', composed by Dr. Derham, Canon of Windsor 1716–35, was lent to Thomas Hearne in May 1733 and is printed in his *Remarks and Collections*, vol. XI, ed. Rev. E. H. Salter, *Oxford Hist. Soc.*, vol. LXXII (1922), pp. 198–205. A MS. list of pictures at Windsor, of the same period, is in the Surveyor's Office.

28. Inventory of pictures etc. at Kensington, Hampton Court, Windsor and St. James's.

B.M., Stowe MS. 567, entitled 'Royal Pictures at Kensington Hampton Court Windsor & St James's.' MS. in French, probably drawn up early in the reign of George I, probably before 1723.

29. Inventory of George II's pictures at Kensington.

MS. in Surveyor's Office entitled 'A Catalogue taken of the Pictures, which are, in their Majesties Publick, and Private, Lodgings. in the Palace at Kensington.' References occur in the MS. to the removal of pictures in 1736.

30. Inventory of the pictures at Kensington, Hampton Court and Windsor.

MS. in Surveyor's Office, entitled 'The COLLECTIONS of PICTURES PAINTINGS &c. at KENSINGTON HAMPTON-COURT and in the CASTLE of WINDSOR 1750' (abbr. as Vertue inv.).

The vol. is one of the three made by George Vertue (perhaps written by an amanuensis) for Frederick, Prince of Wales, apparently in 1750 (*Notebooks*, vol. I, p. 13) '. . . 3d book contain an account I had taken of all the pictures now at the palaces of Kensington. Hampton Court – and Windsor

Castle, for all which I had visited and seen purposely by his Highnes order. and also had the assistance of the House-keepers books . . .'

The inv. is in three main sections:

I. 'A Catalogue taken of the Pictures . . . in the Publick and Private Lodgings of the Palace of Kensington. 1732. by Heny Lowman'. The catalogue was, however, made after 1736 and after the death of Queen Caroline in 1737 and was probably only based on the inv. of 1732.

II. 'Extract of an Inventory of his Majesty's Pictures at his Palace of Hampton Court. in the Charge of the House-keeper 1750'.

III. 'At the Royal Palace and Castle, at Windsor. Pictures in the Appartments Described'. Probably also composed in 1750.

31. Vertue's inventory of the contents of Queen Caroline's Closet at Kensington.

B.M. MS. 15752 is Vertue's original draft (see No. 19), of which the last section is entitled '. . . an account of all the paintings, Limnings Drawings H. Holbein at Kingenton Palace in the Queen's Closet described by G.V.1745'. This catalogue is printed at the end of Bathoe's edn. of James II's catalogue (1758), but it is stated at the end to have been 'taken at Queen CAROLINE's command, by Mr. VERTUE, in September, 1743.'

It is followed in Bathoe's volume by a short 'CATALOGUE OF THE Principal PICTURES, STATUES, &c. at Kensington Palace'.

In the Surveyor's Office are Horace Walpole's copies of Bathoe's two volumes on the collections of Charles I and James II. They contain annotations by Walpole and, at the end of the 1758 volume, very important addenda to the list of pictures at Kensington. These seem to be of varying dates; one section is dated 2 June 1763.

A volume of miscellaneous papers relating to Kensington Palace is in the B.M., MS. 20101; it contains references to pictures, 1728–61. Queen Caroline's Accounts in the Royal Archives contain a few references to pictures and artists.

The *Notebooks* of George Vertue (see below) contain very numerous references to the royal collection.

FREDERICK, PRINCE OF WALES

There is no formal inv. of the Prince's possessions. Descriptions of his collections are to be found in Vertue's *Note-books* and lists of some of his pictures etc. in Vertue's miscellaneous papers, B.M. MS. 19027, especially ff. 20–24v. Pictures are mentioned in Sir William Chambers's description (see below) of Kew (1763).

Some of the Prince's payments to artists and craftsmen survive in the Royal Archives, but his expenditure, and that of his wife, is recorded in detail from 1728 onwards in a long series of volumes in the Duchy of Cornwall Office (abbr. as D. of Cornwall MSS).

GEORGE III

32. Inventory of pictures at Windsor.

Nos. 32–36 are in a MS. vol. in the Surveyor's Office, probably all in the same hand, but perhaps not all of the same date.

No. 32 occupies ff. 1–29 and is entitled 'A Catalogue of the Pictures in His Majesty's Palace at Windsor taken in the Year 1776'. It is, however, very close indeed to Pote's account of 1749 (see below), or even to No. 30 (III), and probably still records the pictures as they were in the reign of George II or very early in the reign of George III.

33. Inventory of pictures at St. James's.

Occupying ff. 30 v.–46 of the above, untitled (abbr. as Geo. III, *St James's*). Probably drawn up c. 1785.

34. Inventory of pictures at Buckingham House.

Occupying ff. 49–68 of the above, mutilated and untitled (abbr. as Geo III, *Buck. Ho.*) Probably drawn up c. 1790–5; it agrees very closely with a list in the B.M., Add. MS. 6391, which is dated 8 November 1796 and was probably extracted from No. 34.

35. Inventory of pictures at Windsor.

Occupying ff. 69–100 v. of the above, untitled. The account is still close to Pote's of 1768 (see below) but variations from it seem to indicate that No. 35 records the pictures at Windsor c. 1780–6. A few pencil notes were added, probably nearer 1790.

36. Inventory of pictures at Hampton Court.

Occupying ff. 101 v.–135 v. of the above, untitled (abbr. as Geo. III, *Hampton Court*). Probably of approximately the same date as No. 35; pencil notes were added slightly later.

37. Inventory of pictures at Kew.

MS. in Surveyor's Office entitled 'A Catalogue of His Majesty's Pictures at Kew House' (abbr. as Geo. III, *Kew*). Probably drawn up c. 1800–5, but with slightly later pencil notes by the compiler of Nos. 47 and 48.

A MS. in the Surveyor's Office, entitled 'A Catalogue of the Pictures at Kew House', is probably a rough draft for No. 37.

38. Inventory of the pictures at Kensington.

MS. in Surveyor's Office, entitled 'A Catalogue of His Majesty's Pictures at Kensington Palace' (abbr. as Geo. III, *Kensington*). Probably drawn up c. 1785–90, but with later pencil notes.

39. Removals of pictures.

MS. in Surveyor's Office, entitled 'A Catalogue of Pictures sent from the Queen's Palace, St James's, Kensington & Hampton-Court Palaces, and Kew House, to His Majesty at Windsor Castle. 1804 & 1805' (abbr. as Geo. III, *Removals*).

The title probably only covers ff 1–14 (except f. 9 v. which records moves on 24 July 1795); certainly ff. 17 v.–20 v contain a separate list of pictures brought to Buckingham House from St. James's at the time of the fire, 25 January 1809.

40. Francis Legge's lists of pictures at Windsor, 1813, 1816.

MS. in Surveyor's Office in two volumes, the first entitled 'A Catalogue of His Majesty's collection of Paintings in Windsor Castle, according to the present arrangement . . . In two parts. compiled by F.L. 1813'.

The second volume is entitled 'A Catalogue of His Majesty's collection of Paintings in Windsor Castle, according to the present arrangement . . . compiled by F.L. 1816'. Both volumes also include a mass of biographical and other historical matter.

41. Inventory of pictures at Windsor.

Nos. 41 and 42 are in a MS. vol. in the Surveyor's Office, probably all written by the same hand.

No. 41 occupies ff. 84–109 and is entitled 'Now in Windsor Castle. from Mr. Legge's Catalogue'. It is closely based on the second volume of No. 40, but there are slightly later pencil annotations, including a passage on f. 109 which is signed with indecipherable initials.

42. List of pictures etc. bought by George III.

Occupying ff. 61–83 of the above, in three sections.

I. On ff. 61–73, entitled 'Catalogue of Paintings of the Italian School all in fine preservation, and in Carved Gilt Frames in modern & Elegant Taste. Bought by His Majesty in Italy, & now chiefly at Kew'.

II. On ff. 74–80, entitled 'Catalogue of the Flemish & Dutch Schools all in fine Preservation, in new gilt carved Frames. in Elegant Taste'.

III. On ff. 81–83, Addenda and Corrigenda to I and II.

These are the lists generally held to be of the pictures bought by George III with the collection of Consul Smith in 1762,

but the lists are not original and must have been compiled from MSS. that are now lost. The Italian section was printed by SIR L. CUST in the *Burl. Mag.*, vol. xxiii (1913), pp. 150–62, 267–76, and the Dutch and Flemish lists by SIR A. BLUNT, *Venetian Drawings . . . at Windsor Castle* (1957), pp. 19–23.

The volume of which Nos. 41 and 42 form part also contains, ff. 1–60, a copy of James II's inv. (No. 19 above), probably based on the version of it drawn up in the reign of William III; later notes record collation between this text and the original Harl. MS. 1890 in the B.M.

43. Inventory of the pictures etc. at Kensington, 1818.

MS. in Surveyor's Office, entitled 'Catalogue of the Pictures in the Palace at Kensington. 1818'.

The volume forms, with Nos. 44 and 46, a set of catalogues, uniform in size, form and binding and all written by the same hand; the numbered items in No. 43 run from 1 to 658. Faulkner (see below) states (p. 357) that the catalogue was composed at the command of George, Prince of Wales (the future George IV), who ordered Benjamin West to make a survey of the whole collection. The three volumes should, therefore, be attributed to West in his official capacity as Surveyor of Pictures, a post which he held until his death in 1820, though William Seguier was also concerned at this date with royal catalogues. No. 43 contains later notes, some certainly dating from the reign of William IV.

44. Inventory of the pictures etc. at Buckingham House and St. James's Palace, 1819.

MS. in Surveyor's Office, dated 1819 on the cover, a sequel to No. 43, and entitled (items 659–1010) 'Catalogue of the Pictures at the Late Queens House Saint James's Park' and (for items 1011–1088) 'Catalogue of the Pictures at Saint James's Palace'. Clearly composed after the death of Queen Charlotte on 17 November 1818; in items no. 985–8, however, George III is described as 'His late Majesty', which may indicate that the catalogue, at least in part, was written after his death on 24 January 1820.

Material on the collection of George III is also to be found in the Royal Archives. In the Royal Library is a set of drawings to scale, indicating the arrangement of pictures on the walls of some of the rooms at Buckingham House early in the reign of George III. A later set of drawings, recording the disposition of pictures in certain rooms at Windsor, is also in the Royal Library.

GEORGE IV

45. Inventory of pictures etc. at Carlton House, 1816.

MS. in Surveyor's Office, entitled 'A CATALOGUE of PICTURES, forming the Collection of HIS ROYAL HIGH-NESS THE PRINCE-REGENT, in CARLTON-HOUSE. December, 1816'.

Drawn up by Michael Bryan, probably with advice from Sir Thomas Lawrence. In 1817 Bryan submitted an account for £105 'For making sundry Catalogues of the Collection, and for making a valuation of the same, in conjunction with Sir Thomas Lawrence'; the account was settled on 12 August 1819 W.R.A., Geo 27003).

Later 'Remarks' in the inv. include notes by Benjamin Jutsham (see below) on later movements of the pictures; many of these notes are dated and were made between 7 June 1817 and 1 November 1830. Jutsham also kept the inv. up to date by adding items 532–604, *i.e.*, up to and including acquisitions in the early part of 1823.

Various other later notes are scattered throughout the MS.

Labels, written in the same hand as No. 45, giving the relevant number in the inv. and describing it as the New Catalogue of 1816, were fixed to the back of the pictures recorded in it; many of these labels survive.

46. Inventory of the pictures etc. at Carlton House, 1819.

MS. in Surveyor's Office, entitled 'Catalogue of The Prince Regents Pictures, in Carlton House, June 1819'.

The third of the volumes which made up (see Nos. 43 and 44) the survey initiated by the Regent. The items are numbered from 1 to 550, but there is a later continuation (see below) from 551 to 688.

47. Inventory of the pictures etc. at Carlton House.

MS. in Surveyor's Office, entitled 'CATALOGUE OF HIS MAJESTY'S PICTURES IN CARLETON PALACE'.

Drawn up very soon after the accession of George IV in

1820. It is compiled in very much the same way as No. 46, but the items run continuously from 1 to 688. The compiler of the catalogue added later notes recording movements of pictures etc. up to 1834. No. 47 is written in the same hand as No. 48; they were presumably compiled by William Seguier who in 1820 had succeeded West in the Surveyorship and held the post until his death in 1843. The catalogue probably originally ended at no. 598; the later items are more briefly described but include purchases and movements from at latest May 1826 onwards and the latest entries, though probably all recording pictures belonging to George IV, were added after his death in 1830.

Nos. 46 and 47 are closely connected. Doyne C. Bell,[1] using No. 47, copied the additional items 551–688 from it into No. 46. No. 46 had presumably been completed in June 1819 and very little had been added to it by the original compiler; and Bell seems to have had both texts in front of him in bringing No. 46 into line with No. 47.

Also in the Surveyor's Office is a secondary and untitled MS., drawn up by the same hand as No. 47, of the pictures at Carlton House. It appears to have been written immediately after the death of George IV (26 June 1830) and probably before 5 October 1830.

48. Inventory of the collection of George IV and William IV at Kensington, Buckingham Palace, St. James's, Kew and Hampton Court.

MS. in the Surveyor's Office, entitled 'CATALOGUE OF HIS MAJESTYS PICTURES'. Drawn up by the same hand and in the same form as No. 47 and perhaps complementary to it. The catalogue is divided into six sections:

I. Kensington Palace. Items running from 1 to 658, copied from No. 43 with occasional variations and with later notes recording movements of pictures between 2 October 1828 and 22 September 1838.

II. Buckingham Palace. Items running from 659 to 1010, copied from No. 44, but with later notes recording movements between 14 July 1824 and 17 December 1835.

III. St. James's Palace. Items running from 1011 to 1088, copied from No. 44, but with later notes recording movements between 6 July 1828 and 19 December 1835.

IV. Kew Palace. Items running from 1089 to 1223. Based on No. 37, which contains notes by the compiler of No. 48; later notes record movements between 12 July 1825 and 1835.

V. Hampton Court. Items running from 1224 to 1264, a continuation of the above, but incomplete and perhaps based on an earlier list.

Taken with No. 47 these five sections of No. 48, probably compiled c. 1825, provide a reasonably complete inv. of the royal collection with the exception of the pictures at Windsor. In sections I–IV No. 48 perpetuated an official numbering of the pictures; these numbers are still to be seen stamped on the back of royal pictures with the cipher of George IV.

VI. Hampton Court. An independent section, entitled 'Catalogue, of His Majesty's Pictures 1835, Beginning in the Kings Guard Chamber, Hampton Court Palace'. Drawn up in the same manner as the remainder of the volume, but more perfunctorily; the inv. may be incomplete. It includes pictures taken to Hampton Court in December 1835, so the date in the title may be deceptive.

There are in the Surveyor's Office two copies of No. 48. The first is entitled 'CATALOGUE OF HER MAJESTY'S PICTURES. COPY 1844'. A pencil note at the beginning of the copy of section VI of No. 48 states that 'This Catalogue was made when the Parliament passed a vote for opening the Palace to the Public'.

The second copy is entitled 'CATALOGUE OF THE KING'S PICTURES. 1834'. The date is misleading as the volume is a complete copy of No. 48 and records events later than 1834.

There is a great deal of material on George IV's activities as a collector in the Royal Archives. The most important single source for his collections are the day-books (now in the Surveyor's Office) kept by Benjamin Jutsham in which are recorded the daily arrivals at, and despatchings from, Carlton House of works of art of all kinds. There are three volumes:

I. Volume entitled '1806 An Account of Furniture &c Received and Deliver'd By Benjamin Jutsham On Account of His Royal Highness The Prince of Wales at Carlton House' (abbr. as Jutsham, *R/D*). Recording the daily receipt of works of art etc. between 31 December 1806 and 21 June 1816, and the despatch of goods between 7 January 1807 and October 1820. Jutsham clearly had No. 45 at his elbow and annotated it frequently.

II. Volume entitled later 'INVENTORY OF FURNITURE ETC. GEORGE IV' (abbr. as Jutsham, *Receipts*). Recording the daily receipt of works of art etc. between 23 June 1816 and 7 December 1829.

III. Volume untitled (abbr. as Jutsham, *Deliveries*), recording the works of art etc. sent away from Carlton House between 23 October 1820 and 4 February 1830.

A copy was made by John Roberts in 1861 or 1867 of the references to pictures in these volumes; this was lent by Doyne Bell from the Lord Chamberlain's Office to J. Hollis who took another copy, dated 6 March 1875.

A fourth volume by Jutsham in the Surveyor's Office is a record of Privy Purse payments, entitled 'Bills on Account of Privy Purse for Expences of Armory &c' (abbr. as Jutsham, *PP*); it contains a few references to pictures.

Jutsham (*d.* 1836) is recorded as Inspector of Household Deliveries to George IV from 1803 to 1830 and continued until his death to serve William IV in the same capacity.

---

1. An official of the Privy Purse from 1851 to his death in 1888.

QUEEN VICTORIA

49. Acquisitions made by Queen Victoria and the Prince Consort.

A set of three MS. volumes in the Surveyor's Office:

I. Volume entitled 'CATALOGUE OF HER MAJESTY'S PRIVATE PICTURES, MINIATURES, ENAMELS &c. &c.' A detailed record of the Queen's acquisitions, whether by gift or purchase, between 1827 and Christmas, 1856.

II. Volume, untitled, continuing the record of the Queen's acquisitions between 1857 and Christmas, 1862.

III. Volume entitled 'List of Pictures presented to or purchased by His Royal Highness Prince Albert'. Drawn up in the same form as nos. I and II, recording the Prince's acquisitions between 1839 and January 1847.

A fair copy of III was made by Thomas Cockerill in 1845, but only as far as item 188.

50. List of the Prince Consort's pictures at Windsor, 1862.

MS. in Surveyor's Office, entitled 'List of Pictures at Windsor Castle the property of His Royal Highness The Prince Consort – March 1862'.

51. The inventory of pictures in the collection of Queen Victoria.

The great survey in the Surveyor's Office (abbr. as *V.R.inv.*) of the entire royal collection of pictures (see above pp. 7, 8); initiated by the Prince Consort, carried out by Richard Redgrave as Surveyor and, after 1882, continued by his successor, Sir J. C. Robinson.

The survey involved an accurate description of each picture on a separate sheet, with notes on its history and condition; to each sheet of the original of the survey was affixed a photograph[1] of the picture. Each sheet was signed by the Surveyor and Redgrave's successors have continued to annotate and work on his original sheets; the results of Doyne Bell's researches on earlier invs. were added to them;

and the whole survey, with its new series of numberings, is a landmark in the history of the collection and Surveyorship. A copy of the original is also in the Surveyor's Office.

The individual sections of the original survey were made up as follows.

I. Windsor Castle. Nos. 1–1901, on sheets dated between January 1859 and 9 July 1879. The volumes of the copy bear the date 1878.

II. Buckingham Palace. Nos. 1–1643, on sheets dated between 8 October 1850 (*sic*.) and 1 June 1878. The volumes of the copy bear the date 1877.

III. Hampton Court. Nos. 1–1077, on sheets dated between February 1858 and 23 November 1876. The volumes of the copy bear the date 1872.

IV. St. James's Palace. Nos. 1–94, on sheets dated between March 1858 and 4 January 1871. The copy bears the date 1871.

V. Kew. Nos. 1–62. One sheet is dated 4 April 1863, the remainder in 1870; they are still in their original bound volume. There is also a copy in the Surveyor's Office.

VI. Stud Lodge. Nos. 1–27, on sheets dated 1868–9 and still in their original bound volume, dated by Redgrave 29 April 1870.

The format of Redgrave's survey was perpetuated in the following addenda to it:

VII. Holyroodhouse. Nos. 1–67, in their original volume, dated 1884; the entries are signed by Robinson. There is also a copy in the Surveyor's Office.

VIII. A copy of section VI with additional nos. 28–52. The pictures had, however, by now been moved to Cumberland Lodge and the volume is entitled 'CUMBERLAND LODGE. CATALOGUE. 1896'.

IX. A bound volume of the pictures at Cumberland Lodge in 1896, closely dependent on section VIII.

In the Surveyor's Office is a Register, recording the receipt and removals of works of art belonging to The Queen in two volumes, running from 7 June 1879 to 13 May 1909; up to November 1887 it appears all to be in the hand of Doyne Bell. There is also in the Office a list of loans by the Queen to annual exhibitions of old masters at the R.A., 1870–81. Much material on the royal collection in and since the time of Queen Victoria is to be found in the Queen's *Journal*, in the Royal Archives, in the P.R.O. (Lord Chamberlain's papers), in the records of the Lord Chamberlain's Office and the Privy Purse, and in the notebooks of Sir George Scharf at the N.P.G.

An inv. of the pictures at Buckingham Palace was prepared for the Lord Chamberlain's Office in 1911 by Messrs. Trollope. A MS. inv. of the pictures at Marlborough House in 1925 is in the Surveyor's Office.

---

1. These were taken by Thurston Thompson, William Bambridge, William Johnson and E. Kemp.

II. PRINTED BOOKS

I. EARLY ACCOUNTS OF THE ROYAL COLLECTION

The following are the more important early catalogues of royal pictures and accounts of royal palaces containing references to the pictures.

For the Tudor collection, valuable lists of, or references to, works of art in royal palaces, extracted from the journals of distinguished visitors, are printed in:

RYE, W. B. *England as seen by Foreigners* (1865).
The following are also useful: the 'Journey through England and Scotland made by Lupold von Wedel', 1584–5, translated by G. von Bülow, *Trans. Roy. Hist. Soc.*, N.S., vol. IX (1895), pp. 223–70; *Thomas Platter's Travels in England 1599*, translated and ed. C. Williams (1937); 'Diary of the Journey of Philip Julius, Duke of Stettin-Pomerania, through England in the Year 1602', ed. G. von Bülow, *Trans. Roy. Hist. Soc.*, N.S. vol. VI (1892), pp. 1–67; *Queen Elizabeth and some Foreigners*, ed. V. von Klarwill (1928).

FIENNES, Celia. *Journeys through England*, ed. C. Morris (1947).

England in 1710. From the Travels of Z. C. von Uffenbach, trans. and ed. by W. H. Quarrell and Margaret Mare (1934).

DEFOE, D. *A Tour through England and Wales*, 3 vols. (1724–7), ed. G. D. H. Cole, 2 vols. (1928).

VERTUE, G. *Notebooks*, 6 vols. with index vol., *Walpole Soc.* vols. XVIII (1930), XX (1932), XXII (1934), XXIV (1936), XXVI (1938), XXIX (1947), XXX (1955).

BICKHAM, G. *Deliciæ Britannicæ; or, The Curiosities of Kensington, Hampton Court, and Windsor Castle . . .*, 2nd edn. (1742).

POTE, J. *The History and Antiquities of Windsor Castle . . .* (1749).

DODSLEY, R. and J. *London and its Environs Described*, 6 vols. (1761).

CHAMBERS, SIR W. *Plans, Elevations, Sections, and Perspective Views of the Gardens and Buildings at Kew . . .* (1763).

WALPOLE, H. *Anecdotes of Painting* (1762–71), ed. J. Dallaway and R. N. Wornum, 3 vols. (1888).
— 'Journals of Visits to Country Seats, &c.', *Walpole Soc.*, vol. XVI (1928), pp. 9–80.

[MARTYN, T.] *The English Connoisseur*, 2 vols. (1766).

A Catalogue of the Pictures, &c. in His Majesty's Royal Apartments, Kensington Palace (1778).

PENNANT, T. *Some Account of London*, 3rd edn. (1793).

LYSONS, D. *The Environs of London . . .*, vol. III (1795), supplementary vol. (1800).

PYNE, W. H. *The History of the Royal Residences*, 3 vols. (1819), severally dedicated to the Queen, the Regent and the Duke of York. The original water-colour drawings for the plates, by such artists as C. Wild, Cattermole and Stephanoff, are in the Royal Library.

FAULKNER, T. *History and Antiquities of Kensington* (1820).

HAZLITT, W., *The Pictures at Windsor Castle* (1823), *Works*, ed. A. R. Waller and A. Glover, vol. IX (1903).

British Galleries of Art (1824).

WESTMACOTT, C. M. *British Galleries of Painting and Sculpture, . . .* (1824).

PASSAVANT, J. D. *Kunstreise durch England und Belgien* (Frankfurt-am-Main, 1833).

WAAGEN, G. F. *Works of Art and Artists in England*, 3 vols. (1838).
— *Treasures of Art in Great Britain*, 3 vols. (1854).
— *Galleries and Cabinets of Art in Great Britain* (1857).

The Royal Gallery of Pictures, being a Selection of The Cabinet Paintings in Her Majesty's Private Collection at Buckingham Palace, published under the superintendence of John Linnell (1840).

[SEGUIER, W.] *Catalogue of Her Majesty's Pictures in Buckingham Palace* (1841).

JAMESON, MRS. *A Handbook to the Public Galleries of Art in and near London*, 2 vols. (1842).

A Descriptive Catalogue of the Pictures, Busts, Bronzes, &c. in the Corridor of Windsor Castle (1843).

A Descriptive Catalogue of the Pictures, . . . deposited in the Corridor of Windsor Castle (1845).

WAAGEN, G. F. *Descriptive Catalogue of a Collection of Byzantine, early Italian – German – and Flemish Pictures, belonging to His Serene Highness Prince Louis D'Ottingen Wallerstein* (1848).
— *Descriptive Catalogue of a Collection of Byzantine, early Italian, German, and Flemish Pictures, belonging to His Royal Highness Prince Albert . . .* (1854).

NASH, J. *Views of the Interior and Exterior of Windsor Castle* (1848). Some of the original water-colours survive in the Royal Library; those by, for example, Haghe, D. Morrison and J. Roberts illustrate pictures hanging on the walls of the interiors.[1]

GRUNDY, J. *The Stranger's Guide to Hampton Court Palace and Gardens* (1849).

UWINS, T. *Catalogue of The Pictures in Her Majesty's Gallery at Buckingham Palace, . . .* (1852).

LAW, E. *The History of Hampton Court Palace*, 3 vols. (1888–91).

HOPE, W. H. St. John. *Windsor Castle, An Architectural History*, 2 vols. (1913).

CUST, Sir L. *Notes on Pictures in the Royal Collection* (1911). Reprint of *Notes* I–XX on royal pictures published in the *Burlington Magazine;* Cust later published, up to 1918, a further twenty *Notes* in the same periodical.

SMITH, H. Clifford. *Buckingham Palace* (1930).

1. Nineteenth century photographs of royal interiors are a useful source; photographic illustrations were published, for example, by Disderi in *Windsor Castle* (1867) and B. B. Woodward, *Windsor Castle Picturesque and Descriptive* (1870).

II. LATER CATALOGUES OF THE ROYAL COLLECTION

Catalogue of the Paintings, Sculpture, and other Works of Art, at Osborne (1876); a *Handbook* to Osborne, with a catalogue of the pictures, by A. I. Durrant (n.d.) was published in the reign of Edward VII.

[COLE, A. S.] *A Catalogue of the Works of Art at Marlborough House . . . and at Sandringham Norfolk belonging to Their Royal Highnesses the Prince and Princess of Wales* (1877).

LAW, E. *A Historical Catalogue of the Pictures in the Royal Collection at Hampton Court . . .* (1881).

[ROBINSON, SIR J. C.] *Catalogue of the Pictures in Her Majesty's Gallery and the State Rooms at Buckingham Palace* (1885).

Catalogue of Pictures in State Rooms, St. James's Palace (1894).

LAW, E. *The Royal Gallery of Hampton Court* (1898). This is very close in detail to Law's volume of 1881; thereafter Law produced a volume of illustrations, *Masterpieces of the Royal Gallery of Hampton Court* (1904) and a succession of official Guides to the Palace which include lists of the pictures (*e.g.*, in 1882, 1907, 1908, 1925, 1926, 1927).

LOGAN, Mary. *Guide to the Italian Pictures at Hampton Court* (1894).

LAW, E. *Kensington Palace . . . an Historical Guide . . .* (1899). Revised editions appeared in 1903, 1907 and 1926 and the material on pictures was incorporated into the author's Guide to *The London Museum at Kensington Palace . . .* (1912).

[CUST, Sir L.] *Catalogue of Paintings and Drawings in Buckingham Palace*, privately printed (1909).

Guide to . . . Windsor Castle, privately printed (1903), later revisions issued in 1906, 1907 and 1909.

CARTWRIGHT, Julia (Mrs. ADY). *Hampton Court* (1910).

Catalogue Raisonné of the Pictures in the possession of King George V in the Picture Gallery and the Royal Closet and on the Chapel Stairs at Buckingham Palace, privately printed (1920).

KONODY, P. G., CONWAY, Sir M., CUST, Sir L. *The King's Pictures* 3 vols. (n.d., *temp.* George V).

Catalogue Raisonné of the Pictures in the possession of King George V in the State Apartments and Principal Private Apartments at Windsor Castle (1922).

LAW, E. *Kew Palace Illustrated a Popular Guide . . . with a Catalogue of the Pictures* (1924).

BAKER, C. H. COLLINS. *Catalogue of the Pictures at Hampton Court* (1929).

— *Catalogue of the Principal Pictures in the Royal Collection at Windsor Castle* (1937).

Exhibition of The King's Pictures, R.A. (1946–7), with illustrated souvenir.

I have made no attempt to list the more ephemeral Guide-Books to the royal palaces which have been issued from the eighteenth century to the present day and often contain lists of pictures. They are, on the whole, very unreliable compared with the inventories and should be used with the greatest caution. Miss Olwen Hedley has compiled an invaluable check-list of the Windsor Guides issued in the eighteenth and nineteenth centuries.

ABBREVIATIONS

Where an inventory is listed, a reference is given to the numbered description of inventories on pp. 35–42 above.

Bathoe, *Charles I.*	*A Catalogue and Description of King Charles the First's Capital Collection. . .* Printed for W. Bathoe (1757).
— *James II.*	*A Catalogue of the Collection of Pictures, &c. belonging to King James the Second; To which is added, A Catalogue of the Pictures and Drawings in the Closet of the late Queen Caroline . . . and also of the Principal Pictures in the Palace at Kensington.* Printed for W. Bathoe (1758).
Beckett, *Lely.*	R. B. Beckett, *Lely* (1951).
B.F.A.C.	Burlington Fine Arts Club.
Bickham.	G. Bickham, *Deliciæ Britannicæ*, 2nd edn. (1742).
B.M.	British Museum.
Buckeridge.	B. Buckeridge, *An Essay towards an English School*, with English edn. (1706 and later) of R. de Piles, *Abrégé de la Vie des Peintres, . . .* (Paris, 1699).
Buckingham Palace, 1841, 1852, 1909, 1920.	See the printed catalogues listed above, pp. 43–4, under these dates.
Burl. Mag.	*The Burlington Magazine.*
Cal. S.P.Dom.	Calendar of State Papers, Domestic.
Cal. Tr. Bks.	Calendar of Treasury Books.
Cal. Tr. Papers.	Calendar of Treasury Papers.
Carlton House, 1816.	Inventory no. 45.
Carleton Palace.	Inventory no. 47.
Chaloner Smith.	J. Chaloner Smith, *British Mezzotinto Portraits*, 4 vols. (1878–83).
Charles II, *Hampton Court, Whitehall.*	Inventory no. 16.
Col. Hawley.	Inventory no. 15.
Collins Baker, Hampton Court.	C. H. Collins Baker, *Catalogue of the Pictures at Hampton Court* (1929).
— *Lely.*	— *Lely and the Stuart Portrait Painters*, 2 vols (1912).
— *Windsor.*	— *Catalogue of the Principal Pictures in the Royal Collection at Windsor Castle* (1937).
Corsham MS.	Inventory no 13.
Cust, *Van Dyck.*	Sir L. Cust, *Anthony van Dyck* (1900).
D. of Cornwall MSS.	MSS. in the Duchy of Cornwall Office, see above p. 39.
Edward VI (*1549–50*).	Inventory no. 3.
Eng.	Engraved.
Exh.	Exhibited.
Faulkner.	T. Faulkner, *History and Antiquities of Kensington* (1820).

Celia Fiennes.	C. Fiennes, *Journeys through England*, ed. C. Morris (1947).
Ganz, *Holbein.*	P. Ganz, *The Paintings of Hans Holbein* (1950; enlarged edition, 1956).
— *KdK.*	— *Hans Holbein D.J.*, Klassiker der Kunst (Stuttgart and Leipzig, 1912).
Geo. II, *Kensington.*	Inventory no. 29.
Geo. III, *Buck. Ho.*	Inventory no. 34.
— *Hampton Court.*	Inventory no. 36.
— *Kensington.*	Inventory no. 38.
— *Kew*	Inventory no. 37.
— *Removals.*	Inventory no. 39.
— *St. James's.*	Inventory no. 33.
Glück.	G. Glück, *Van Dyck*, Klassiker der Kunst (Stuttgart, 1931).
Granger.	Rev. J. Granger, *A Biographical History of England . . .* , 5th edn., six vols., (1824).
Henry VIII (*1542, 1547*).	Inventories nos. 1 and 2.
H. of L. MSS.	Inventory no. 14.
Hookham Carpenter.	W. Hookham Carpenter, *Pictorial Notices . . . a Memoir of Sir Anthony Van Dyck . . .* (1844).
Mrs. Jameson.	Mrs. Jameson, *A Handbook to the Public Galleries of Art in and near London*, 2 vols. (1842).
Jutsham, *Deliveries.*	Benjamin Jutsham's book of Deliveries, see p. 41.
— *PP.*	— book of Privy Purse Payments, see p. 41.
— *R/D.*	— book of Receipts and Deliveries, see p. 41.
— *Receipts.*	— book of Receipts, see p. 41.
Kensington, 1697.	Inventory no. 20.
— 1818.	Inventory no. 43.
Law, *Holbein, Van Dyck.*	E. Law, *Pictures by Holbein & Van Dyck at Windsor Castle;* the two sections were published together in 1902, incorporating the earlier work on Van Dyck (1899).
— *Kew* (1924).	— *Kew Palace Illustrated . . . with a Catalogue of the Pictures* (1924).
— 1881, 1898.	— *An Historical Catalogue of the Pictures in the Royal Collection at Hampton Court . . .* (1881) and *The Royal Gallery of Hampton Court* (1898).
L.R.MS.	Inventory no. 12.
Parker.	K. T. Parker, *The Drawings of Hans Holbein . . . at Windsor Castle* (1945).

Pigler. A. Pigler, *Bogdány Jakab* (Budapest, 1941).

P.R.O. Public Record Office.

Pyne. W. H. Pyne, *The History of the Royal Residences*, 3 vols. (1819).

Queen Anne. Inventory no. 22.

Queen's House, 1819. Inventory no. 44.

R.A., *King's Pictures.* Royal Academy, *Exhibition of The King's Pictures* (1946–7).

Sainsbury. W. N. Sainsbury, *Original Unpublished Papers . . .* (1859).

Schaeffer. E. Schaeffer, *Van Dyck*, Klassiker der Kunst (Stuttgart and Leipzig, 1909).

Schmid. H. A. Schmid, *Hans Holbein der Jüngere*, Tafelband (Basel, 1945), Textband, 2 vols. (Basel, 1948).

Sebright MS. MS. formerly in the possession of the Sebright family; see Inventory no. 12.

Smith. J. Smith, *A Catalogue Raisonné of the Works of the most eminent Dutch, Flemish and French Painters; . . .* part III (1831); and Supplement to the Catalogue Raisonné . . . , part IX (1842).

V. & A. Victoria and Albert Museum.

Van der Doort. Text of Inventories nos. 7–11, ed. O. Millar, *Walpole Soc.*, vol. XXXVII (1960).

Vertue. G. Vertue, *Notebooks*, 6 vols. with index vol., *Walpole Soc.*, vols. XVIII (1930), XX (1932), XXII (1934), XXIV (1936), XXVI (1938), XXIX (1947), XXX (1955).

Vertue inv. Inventory no. 30.

V.R. inv. Inventory no. 51.

Waagen (1838). G. F. Waagen, *Works of Art and Artists in England*, 3 vols. (1838).

— (1854). — *Treasures of Art in Great Britain*, 3 vols. (1854).

Walpole, *Anecdotes.* H. Walpole, *Anecdotes of Painting*, ed. J. Dallaway and R. N. Wornum, 3 vols. (1888).

— *Visits.* — 'Journals of Visits to Country Seats, &c.', *Walpole Soc.*, vol. XVI (1928), pp. 9–80.

Waterhouse, *Painting in Britain.* E. K. Waterhouse, *Painting in Britain 1530 to 1790* (1953).

Whinney and Millar. M. Whinney and O. Millar, *English Art 1625–1714* (1957).

Windsor, 1922. *Catalogue Raisonné of the Pictures . . . at Windsor Castle* (1922).

W.R.A., Geo. Georgian Papers in the Royal Archives at Windsor.

CATALOGUE

CATALOGUE

Artists Unknown : Early Portraits

1. EDWARD III

Windsor Castle (233). Panel: 22¾ × 17⅞ in., 57,8 × 44,1 cm.

Inscribed: ·EDWARDVS·· iii.

Head and shoulders, wearing a crown and an ermine robe.

Probably part of the set of royal portraits secured by Queen Caroline from Lord Cornwallis (see above pp. 9, 27); see no. 2.

Literature: Collins Baker, *Windsor*, p. 101.

This type, for which see also no. 2, was perhaps based on the effigy on the King's tomb in Westminster Abbey; versions are at Albury and at Trinity College, Cambridge, and another was in the collection of the Duke of Leeds.

2. EDWARD III

Windsor Castle (3039). Panel: 18¼ × 14½ in., 46,4 × 36,8 cm.

Inscribed: EDWARDVS· III.

Head and shoulders.

At Kensington in 1818 two portraits of Edward III are recorded (284, measurements given as 23 × 15½ in., and 633, measurements given as 22½ × 17¾ in.) which are presumably to be identified with nos. 1 and 2. No. 2 was later at Hampton Court (915) and St. James's.

Literature: Law, 1881, 1898 (577).

A version of the same type as no. 1, probably painted in the second half of the sixteenth century. Neither of the portraits of Edward III now in the royal collection can be identified conclusively with the 'Old painting of K. Ed. 3ᵈ' recorded by Vertue in the Library at Windsor in the early 1720's (*Notebooks*, vol. I, p. 121).

3. RICHARD II

Windsor Castle (235). Panel: 22⅝ × 17 in., 57,5 × 43,2 cm.

Inscribed: RICARDO· ·II.

Head and shoulders wearing a crown.

Probably part of the set of royal portraits secured by Queen Caroline from Lord Cornwallis; recorded at Kensington in 1818 (634).

Literature: Sir G. Scharf, *Observations on the Westminster Abbey Portrait*... (1867), pp. 5–7; Collins Baker, *Windsor*, p. 107.

Presumably a derivation from the famous full-length portrait of the King at Westminster Abbey. Other versions of no. 3 are at Anglesey Abbey, Albury and in the National Portrait Gallery (565).
Charles I seems to have owned a copy of the portrait at Westminster Abbey. The Trustees for Sale valued at £2 at Hampton Court in October 1649 *Richard yᵉ 2ᵈ at length* (L. R. MS., f. 120 v.) which was sold to De Critz and others on 18 November 1651 (S.P. 29/447, 24, 1). It was re-covered at the Restoration and placed in the Queen's Gallery at Hampton Court (Charles II, *Hampton Court* (26): *Richard the 2ᵈ sitting in a Chayre with a Crowne on his head*, measurements given as 82 × 50 in.), but seems to have left the royal collection early in the eighteenth century; it may have been the portrait drawn by Giuseppe Grisoni and engraved by Vertue in 1718 as in the collection of John Talman (measurements given as 83 × 41 in.). It does not seem to have been identical with the portrait of Richard II discovered by Lord Lumley and given by him to Elizabeth I (see above p. 13).

4. HENRY IV

St. James's Palace. Panel: 22⅞ × 17⅝ in., 58,1 × 44,8 cm.

Inscribed: HENRICVS · iiii.

Head and shoulders wearing a gold chain from which is suspended a badge with a lion rampant, holding a red rose in his right hand and a sceptre in his left.

Probably part of the set of royal portraits secured by Queen Caroline from Lord Cornwallis. Both portraits of Henry IV in the royal collection (see no. 5) were recorded at Kensington in 1818 (167,630), but only one seems to be recorded in the eighteenth century. No. 4 is closer than no. 5 in format and in the calligraphy of the inscription to the other portraits in Queen Caroline's set; it was later at Buckingham Palace (506).

A version of the standard portrait of Henry IV; others are in the National Portrait Gallery (310), in the collections of the Duke of Leeds and Sir George Bellew and at Euston, Bessels Leigh and Albury. A version at Hampton Court, Herefordshire, later in the collection of the Earl of Essex and now at Anglesey Abbey, was engraved by Vertue and the type had been used by Renold Elstrack for the portrait in the *Baziliologia* of 1618. The source of the portrait has not been identified, but the pattern is very close to a wood engraving of Charles IV of France in the *Cronique abregee des faits, gestes et vies illustres des Rois de France*... (Lyons, 1555).[1]

5. HENRY IV

Windsor Castle (237). Panel: 23 × 17¾ in., 58,4 × 44,1 cm.

Inscribed: HENRICVS·· iiii.

See no. 4. If no. 4 was the portrait acquired with Lord Cornwallis's set by Queen Caroline, no. 5 may have been the portrait recorded, presumably at Kensington, on 5 April 1729 (?) (B. M., Add. MSS. 20101, f. 56: *The head of K. Hary. 4ᵗʰ Gilt frame*) and in Her Majesty's Dressing Room at Kensington in the reign of George II (Vertue inv., *Kensington*, f. 25; and see *Notebooks*, vol. IV, p. 65). It is possible, therefore, that Queen Caroline had secured a portrait of Henry IV before she acquired the set from Lord Cornwallis, which would therefore have contained a duplicate of it.

Literature: Collins Baker, *Windsor*, p. 105.

A version of no. 4.

1. I am very grateful to Mr. Roy Strong for drawing my attention to this.

6. HENRY V (*Plate 2*)

Windsor Castle (239). Panel: 22¼ × 14¼ in., 56,5 × 36,2 cm.; the painted surface is 21½ × *c.* 13½ in.

Inscribed later: HENRY THE FIFTH.

Head and shoulders in profile to the left against a patterned background, wearing a jewelled gold chain and raising his left hand on which are three rings.

See above, p. 9. Probably the portrait recorded in the collections of Henry VIII and Edward VI (*1542, 1547* (49): . . . *a table with the picture of King Henry the V*th . . .); and among the *Nyne old heades* at Whitehall in the time of Charles I (*Van der Doort*, p. 27: . . . *a Sidefaced picture without a beard in a black capp . . . in a decayed greene habbitt & reede velvett Sleeves & a collo*r *about his Should*rs *painted uppon a reed ground uppon a board. in a reed painted and guilded frame*). The portrait cannot be identified safely in the documents relating to the Sale, but was apparently recovered at the Restoration (see Col. Hawley, f. 50) and placed once again at Whitehall (Charles II, *Whitehall* (134): *Henry 1*st (sic.) *in a black cap and a greene garm*t. *A side Face*); later at Kensington.

Literature: Vertue, *Notebooks*, vol. I, p. 54, vol. IV, p. 65; Walpole, *Anecdotes*, vol. I, p. 31; R. A., *British Primitive Paintings*, 1923 (77); Collins Baker, *Windsor*, p. 106.

Presumably painted in the same workshop as nos. 8 and 14, perhaps in the late fifteenth century. The source of the portrait may have been a medal, the effigy of the King in Westminster Abbey (from which the head was stolen in 1546) or a votive portrait in miniature or on the scale of life in which the King appeared as a donor. It became the standard type of Henry V in sets of royal portraits (*e.g.*, no. 7) and versions are at Eton College, Hatfield, Stanford Park, in the Queen's College, Oxford, in the Society of Antiquaries, in the National Portrait Gallery (545) and in the collection of Sir G. Bellew; a considerably later derivation is at Knebworth. The type was used by Renold Elstrack for the portrait in the *Baziliωlogia* of 1618 and no. 6 was engraved by Vertue, with considerable variations, when it was at Kensington. The repainting on no. 6 is not so disturbing as on other panels of this type and some original quality is visible. The ear was apparently painted at first slightly smaller and further to the right; there are slight *pentimenti* in the upper lip and left hand. See also no. 7.

7. HENRY V

Windsor Castle (228). Panel: 22⅝ × 17 in., 57,5 × 43,2 cm.

Inscribed: HENRĬCVS· ·V·

Probably part of the set of royal portraits secured by Queen Caroline from Lord Cornwallis; recorded at Kensington in 1818 (636); later at St. James's.

A poor derivation from no. 4.

8. HENRY VI (*Plate 4*)

Windsor Castle (241). Panel: 22¼ × 14 in., 56,5 × 35,6 cm.; the painted surface is 21⅝ × 13½ in.

Inscribed later: HENRY THE SIXTH.

Head and shoulders against a patterned background, with clasped hands and wearing the collar of the Lancastrian order of SS from which hangs a jewelled pendant; the upper corners are filled with gold spandrels on which are painted the arms of France and England.

See above, p. 9. Probably the portrait recorded in the collections of Henry VIII and Edward VI (*1542, 1547* (50): . . . *a table with the picture of King Henry the VI*th . . .); and among the *Nyne old heades* at Whitehall in the time of Charles I (*Van der Doort*, p. 27: . . .

*saide to be kinge Henrie the 6th in a decayed greenish collo*r *roabes. lined with white armin in a black capp houlding both his hands one over anoth*r *in a reede painted guilded frame*). The portrait cannot be identified safely in the documents relating to the Sale, but was apparently recovered at the Restoration and placed once again at Whitehall (Charles II, *Whitehall* (117): *A King of England holding his hands togeather having 3 Rings on one hand*); later at Kensington.

Literature: Vertue, *Notebooks*, vol. I, p. 54, vol. IV, p. 65; Walpole *Anecdotes*, vol. I, p. 34; R. A., *British Primitive Paintings*, 1923 (79); Collins Baker, *Windsor*, p. 106.

Presumably painted in the same workshop as nos. 6 and 14, and perhaps by the same hand as no. 14. There is a very early, probably original, alteration to the shape of the hat, which was at first narrower and higher. The gilded spandrels seem to be part of the original design. The flesh is heavily over-painted but there are traces of original handling and drawing. The portraits of Henry VI seem to have been subjected to considerable variations, but they may be derived ultimately from the same source. Portraits at Hatfield, Albury, Sudeley Castle, King's College, Cambridge, and in the National Portrait Gallery (546) are close to no. 8 in design; and see no. 9. The pattern was also the source of a 'Founder's' portrait of Henry VI at Eton College. No. 8 was engraved by Vertue when it was at Kensington. A slightly different type is represented at the National Portrait Gallery (2457) and in the Society of Antiquaries.

9. HENRY VI

Windsor Castle (227). Panel: 22¾ × 17½ in., 57,8 × 44,5 cm.

Inscribed: HENRĬCVS VI.

Probably part of the set of royal portraits secured by Queen Caroline from Lord Cornwallis; recorded at Kensington in 1818 (638); later at Windsor and St. James's.

A poor derivation from no. 8.

10. EDWARD IV (*Plate 3*)

Windsor Castle (231). Panel: 26¾ × 18⅞ in., 67,9 × 47,9 cm.; the painted surface is *c.* 26¼ × 18⅜ in., 66,7 × 46,7 cm.

Inscribed later: *K Edward y*e *4*th.

Head and shoulders, in a black cap and rich brocaded gown, holding a ring in his hands.

See above, p. 9. Probably the portrait in the collections of Henry VIII and Edward VI (*1542, 1547* (52): . . . *a table with the picture of King Edward the I I I*jth . . .) and among the *Nyne old heades* at Whitehall in the reign of Charles I (*Van der Doort*, p. 27: . . . *a Lardge*r *picture . . . without a beard putting a ring uppon his left hand . . . Saide to be king Edward y*e *4*th *in a reed & guilded frame*). The portrait cannot be identified safely in the documents relating to the Sale, but was apparently recovered at the Restoration and placed once again at Whitehall; its identity had, however, become confused (Charles II, *Whitehall* (135) as *Henry 5*th *holding up his hands with a ring*,[1] measurements given as 26 × 18 in.); later at Kensington.

Literature: Vertue, *Notebooks*, vol. IV, p. 65; Walpole, *Anecdotes*, vol. I, p. 46; Collins Baker, *Windsor*, p. 102; R. A., *British Portraits*, 1956–7 (3).

No. 10 has more of the appearance of an *ad vivum* portrait than the other portraits in this group. It is the best preserved panel in the set, although the outline of the cap has been slightly enlarged at a later date and the lower part of the panel has been damaged and repainted; it is also on a larger scale. The gilded spandrels are part of the original design. The handling seems markedly Flemish. No. 10 may have

1. The type was engraved as Henry V in the eighteenth century.

been the source of the more conventional and much weaker portraits of the King in the standard sets, *e.g.*, no. 11 and at Albury, Anglesey Abbey, Corpus Christi, Cambridge, the Society of Antiquaries and (formerly) in the collection of the Duke of Leeds. A very bad copy is at Petworth (315); a respectable version was sold at Christie's, 9 February 1951 (149); a later derivation is at Knebworth. Vertue's engraving, made when no. 10 was at Kensington, was the source of numerous derivations.

11. EDWARD IV

Windsor Castle (243). Panel: 22⅝×17⅛ in., 57,5×43,5 cm.

Inscribed: EDWARDVS iiii.

Head and shoulders wearing a black cap and an embroidered gown.

Probably part of the set of royal portraits secured by Queen Caroline from Lord Cornwallis; recorded at Kensington in 1818 (640).

Literature: Collins Baker, *Windsor*, p. 102.

Probably ultimately derived from no. 10.

12. ELIZABETH WOODVILLE

Windsor Castle (2011). Panel: 14¾×10⅜ in., 37,5×26,4 cm.; originally, however, it was a smaller, round-topped panel, *c.* 13¼×7⅞ in.

Half-length, resting her folded hands on a ledge in front of her.

Probably the portrait recorded in the collections of Henry VIII and Edward VI (*1542, 1547* (51): . . . *the picture of Quene Elizabeth king Edward's wiff*) and among the *Nyne old heades* at Whitehall in the time of Charles I: . . . *in a black and gould habbitt with a goulden dresing on her heade being the Princess of Elizabeth. Regina Edwardi* (*Van der Doort*, p. 30, measurements given as 12×8 in.). After the Restoration it is very difficult to disentangle in the inventories of the royal collection the references to no. 12 and the other small female portraits of the same date and type, such as no. 17 or nos. 296, 297, 303, 304 at Hampton Court; this group was in the King's Privy Gallery at Whitehall in the reign of Charles II (Charles II, *Whitehall* (116, 124, 127, 128, 129): no. 124 is described as *A womans head in a golden dress and a red ground behind her. The Frame arched*, measurements given as 12×8 in.) and at Kensington in 1818 (probably no. 132), by which time no. 12 had been enlarged to its present size (the others in the set were nos. 2, 4, 131, 133 in this inventory; see Pyne, vol. II, *Kensington*, p. 54). Later at Hampton Court (300).

Literature: Law, 1881, 1898 (585); Collins Baker, *Windsor*, p. 104.

The panel has been heavily overpainted, but originally was an early portrait of the Queen and probably the source for such later derivations as no. 13.

13. ELIZABETH WOODVILLE

Windsor Castle (245). Panel: 23×17½ in., 58,4×14 cm.

Inscribed: ELIZABETH REGINA REGIS EDWARDI QVARTI.

Half-length with her hands folded.

Probably part of the set of royal portraits secured by Queen Caroline from Lord Cornwallis; recorded at Kensington in 1818 (642).

Literature: Collins Baker, *Windsor*, pp. 104–5.

A derivation from a type of portrait of which no. 12 is a very early version. Similar derivations are at Dunham Massey, Queens' College, Cambridge, and in the Ashmolean Museum (Mrs. R. L. Poole, *Catalogue of Portraits . . .*, vol. I (1912), p. 167).

14. RICHARD III (*Plate* 5)

Windsor Castle (247). Panel: 22¼×14 in., 56,5×35,6 cm.; the painted surface is 21½×13½ in.

Head and shoulders against a patterned background, wearing a jewelled gold chain and an elaborate jewelled brooch in his cap and placing with his left hand a ring on the little finger of his right hand; in the gold spandrels in the upper corners are monochrome profiles of a crowned man and of a woman (?).

See above, p. 9. Probably the portrait recorded in the collections of Henry VIII and Edward VI (*1542, 1547* (82): . . . *a table with the picture of Kynge Richard the third . . .*), and among the *Nyne old heades* at Whitehall in the time of Charles I (*Van der Doort*, p. 27: . . . *Kinge Richard the third . . . putting a ring on his right hand in a reed painted and guilded frame . almost Soe bigg as yᵉ life.*). The portrait cannot be identified safely in the documents relating to the Sale, but was apparently recovered at the Restoration and placed once again at Whitehall (Charles II, *Whitehall* (133): *Richard 3ᵈ putting a ring on his finger*); later at Kensington.

Literature: Vertue, *Notebooks*, vol. I, p. 54, vol. IV, p. 65; Walpole, *Anecdotes*, vol. I, p. 47; R. A., *British Primitive Paintings*, 1923 (78); Collins Baker, *Windsor*, p. 108; R. A., *British Portraits*, 1956–7 (1).

Presumably painted in the same workshop as nos. 6 and 8 and perhaps by the same hand as no. 8. It is not known whether the portrait was based on any contemporary image of Richard III, but it is the source for the standard image of his countenance and does not seem to show any elements of propaganda. Versions, all of which seem later, are in the National Portrait Gallery (148) and at Hatfield (see G. Harriss, *The Mystery of Richard III*, Hatfield House Booklet No. 3), Welbeck (336), Albury, Anglesey Abbey, Swynnerton, Capesthorne, formerly in the collections of the Duke of Leeds and Commander Dunn, and at Bramshill (sold at Sotheby's, 16 July 1952 (25)). No. 14 seems to have been extensively overpainted, but there are traces of original drawing and quality. The outline of the right shoulder was altered at a very early date. No. 14 was engraved by Vertue when it was at Kensington.

15. LADY MARGARET BEAUFORT, COUNTESS OF RICHMOND AND DERBY

Windsor Castle (262). Panel: 23×17¾ in., 55,9×45,1 cm.

Head and shoulders, holding in her hands an open book and wearing the costume of a widow or vowess.

Probably part of the set of royal portraits secured by Queen Caroline from Lord Cornwallis; recorded at Kensington in 1818 (637).

Literature: Collins Baker, *Windsor*, p. 109.

A derivation from the standard portrait of Lady Margaret, of which the best version is probably that at St. John's College, Cambridge. The prototype of the portrait cannot date from before the last years of the fifteenth century; for this and the other versions see J. Goodison, *Catalogue of Cambridge Portraits*, vol. I, *The University Collection* (1955), pp. 2–3, to which can be added versions at Swynnerton, Capesthorne and in the collection of Mr. G. Baron Ash. There are at Sledmere another version and a seventeenth century pastiche of it, which is a portrait of Frances Howard, Duchess of Richmond and Lennox. The type which is clearly related to, and perhaps dependent on, Pietro Torrigiano's bronze effigy in Westminster Abbey, was also used for full-length variants, *e.g.*, a kneeling portrait at St. John's College, Cambridge; a version of this seems to have been in the collection of Edward VI (*1549–50*, p. 62: . . . *the picture of the Duches of Richmonte and Darbie sitting upon her knees*). In the collections of Henry VIII and Edward VI seems also to have been a version of the standard portrait (*1542, 1547* (48)): ... *the picture of Henry the seventh his mother being Countess of Richemont* ...); this was presumably the portrait recorded among the *Nyne old heades* at Whitehall in the time of Charles I: ... *the Picture ... of Kinge Henrie yᵉ 7ᵗʰˢ Moother. In a white mourning dressing habbitt Houlding a Black booke in her hands* ... (*Van der Doort*, p. 28), and it seems to have been recovered at the Restoration but not to be recorded in the royal collection after 1714.

16. HENRY VII

Windsor Castle (249). Panel: 22⅝ × 17¼ in., 57,5 × 43,8 cm.

Inscribed: ·HENRICI· ·VII·

Head and shoulders, wearing the collar of the Garter and holding a red rose in his right hand.

Probably part of the set of royal portraits secured by Queen Caroline from Lord Cornwallis; apparently recorded at Kensington in 1818 (639).

Literature: Collins Baker, *Windsor*, p. 107.

Probably derived from a portrait type (probably *c.* 1490–1500) of which there are variants at Helmingham Hall, Christ Church, Oxford, in the Society of Antiquaries (two versions; see R. A., *Kings and Queens*, 1953 (62, 63)), in the collection of Mr. N. Davenport and in the Musée Calvet, Avignon. Very similar derivations are at Albury, Anglesey Abbey, Nostell Priory and in the Tyrwhitt-Drake collection. A portrait of the King is recorded in the collections of Henry VIII and Edward VI (*1542, 1547* (42)) and in the inventory of 1549–50 two portraits of him appear (*Three Inventories ...*, ed. W. A. Shaw, (1937), p. 62). One of these was presumably the portrait among the *23 litle heads* at Whitehall in the time of Charles I: ... *An ould Picture of kinge Henrie yᵉ 7ᵗʰ with 2 hands In a furrd gowne and a black capp In a black and green painted and guilded frame* (*Van der Doort*, p. 28, measurements given as 12½ × 9 in.).

17. ELIZABETH OF YORK (*Plate 6*)

Windsor Castle (251). Panel: 15¼ × 11 in., 38,7 × 27,9 cm.; the painted surface is *c.* 14¾ × 10½ in.

Head and shoulders, holding a white rose in her hands and wearing a 'gable-hood'.

A portrait of the Queen is recorded in the collections of Henry VIII and Edward VI (*1542, 1547* (43): ... *the picture of Quene Elizabeth* ...). Charles I owned two versions of the type. Among the *Nyne old heades* at Whitehall was ... *Kinge Henrie the 7ᵗʰ his Queene In a black and goulden dressing houlding in her hand a litle white roase. In a blue painted guilded frame;* and among the *23 litle heads* ... *Kinge Henrie the 7ᵗʰˢ Queene picture with a litle white roase in her hand, and a black and gould dressing In a reede & guilded frame* (*Van der Doort*, p. 28; the measurements of the latter are given as 14½ × 9 in. and it hung with a portrait of Henry VII). In the reign of Charles II two portraits were again at Whitehall (Charles II, *Whitehall* (236), measurements given as 22 × 17 in. and a confusion in the title; and (130): *Henry 7ᵗʰ Queene with a white Roase in her hand*, measurements given as 14 × 10 in.). Of these no. 236 does not seem to be recorded in the royal collection after 1714 (but see no. 12), but no. 130 is probably to be identified with our no. 17 and seems to have been later at St. James's and Kensington, where it was definitely hanging in 1818 (163).

Literature: Vertue, *Notebooks*, vol. IV, p. 75; Walpole, *Visits*, p. 15; Collins Baker, *Windsor*, p. 105.

A very early, probably contemporary, but much overpainted version of the standard portrait of the Queen, which probably dates from *c.* 1502 and of which there are a number of versions, *e.g.* at Trinity College, Cambridge, Christ Church, Oxford, in the National Portrait Gallery (311), at Hatfield, Dunham Massey, Anglesey Abbey, Nostell Priory and in the Tyrwhitt-Drake collection, and formerly at Bramshill, sold at Sotheby's, 16 July 1952 (24); another was sold at Christie's, 10 December 1954 (152). One of Charles I's versions of the type was presumably the source for the miniature in his collection of family portraits which was *Coppied by Haskins after an auncient ould Cullored peece* (*Van der Doort*, p. 109).

18. ELIZABETH OF YORK

St. James's Palace. Panel: 22⅞ × 17½ in. 58,1 × 44,5 cm.

Inscribed: ELIZABETH. REGINA. MATAR. HENRICI. OCTAV.

Probably part of the set of royal portraits secured by Queen Caroline from Lord Cornwallis; recorded at Kensington in 1818 (641); later at Buckingham Palace (505).

A later derivation from the standard portrait, of which no. 17 is a very early example.

19. THE FAMILY OF HENRY VII WITH ST. GEORGE AND THE DRAGON (*Plate 1*)

Windsor Castle (2054). Panel: 56 × 57½ in., 142,2 × 146,1 cm.

In a landscape, in which are two fantastic buildings, the Saint attacks the dragon before the captive Princess Cleodolinde, his broken tilting spear lies on the ground. In the foreground are two tents or canopies. The roofs of the tents are divided into red and white stripes and decorated with roses and portcullises; on the apex of the tents, composed of orbs, *fleur-de-lys* and roses, are two angels, and the bases of the apexes are inscribed: on the left VIVAT ..., and on the right VIVAT REGINA III ... In the foreground an angel draws open the flap of each tent to show on the left, Henry VII, kneeling with three sons, and on the right Elizabeth of York, kneeling with four daughters. The King and Queen wear royal crowns, their children crowns of a less elaborate form; all nine figures are robed and wear chains round their shoulders from which indeterminate orders and jewels are suspended. On two draped prie-dieux lie, before the King, an open book, sceptre and orb; before the Queen an open book and an orb.

Recorded by Vertue, probably in 1726 (*Notebooks*, vol. II, p. 20: 'also a large square old picture of 5 princes kneeling & 4 Ladyes. an Angel coming down to the King above is S. George on horseback & the dragon under'), among 'Old Pictures left in the Gallery' at Tart Hall. This house belonged to William, Earl of Stafford (*d.* 1734) and many of the pictures therein had descended to him from the collection of the Earl of Arundel (see no. 28); no. 19 is not, however, identifiable in the inventories of Lord Arundel's collections. Apparently still in the Stafford collection in 1743 (*ibid.*, vol. V, p. 27); later in the collection of James West (*d.* 1772) and bought in 1773 by Horace Walpole (see his letter of 7 April 1773 to William Cole, *Correspondence*, ed. W. S. Lewis, vol. I (1937), pp. 265, 305), but, at the Strawberry Hill sale of 1842, 21st day, 18 May 1842 (26), reserved and retained at Strawberry Hill in the possession of the 7th Earl of Waldegrave (*d.* 1846); passed to his widow (*d.* 1879) and thence to her last husband, Lord Carlingford, by whom it was sold at Strawberry Hill in 1883; purchased from Graves by Queen Victoria at Sir J. C. Robinson's earnest entreaty (P.R.O., L.C. 1/405).

Literature: Vertue, *Notebooks*, vol. IV, p. 167, vol. V, p. 27; *The English Connoisseur* (1766), vol. II, p. 15—16; Walpole, *Anecdotes*, vol. I, pp. 31–3; Sir J. C. Robinson and Sir G. Scharf, *Proceedings of the Society of Antiquaries*, second series, vol. X (1883–5), pp. 8–12 (29 November 1883); Sir G. Scharf, 'On a Votive Painting of St. George and the Dragon ...', *Archaeologia*, vol. XLIX (1886), pp.

243–300 (paper read 29 November 1883); Collins Baker, *Windsor*, pp. 119–20.

Stated by Walpole (*loc. cit.*) to have been an altarpiece at the royal palace at Sheen. Henry VII frequently occupied Sheen and, after it was burnt in 1498, rebuilt it as Richmond Palace. Scharf suggested (*loc. cit.*) that no. 19 was painted for a royal chapel dedicated to St. George and drew attention to the protracted tournament held at Sheen by the King in 1492, when a combat took place over a grant of arms by Garter. Walpole and Vertue had both thought the votive figures to be Henry V, Catherine of Valois and their family. No. 19 is almost certainly Flemish and was probably painted *c.* 1505–9, *i.e.*, after the death of Elizabeth of York in childbirth and during the lifetime of her husband; the armour worn by St. George could hardly be earlier than this period. Behind the King his three sons Arthur, Henry and Edmund are presumably represented, and behind the Queen their daughters Margaret, Elizabeth, Mary and Catherine; Edmund and Elizabeth it should be noted, died very young and Catherine only lived for a few hours. The votive figures should thus be seen as royal symbols and not as portraits. The individual heads are slightly worn, but none of them seem to be the work of a painter who had seen any of the sitters in the flesh. The two youngest daughters are shown without the hoods worn under crowns by the other female figures. The red rose of Lancaster and the portcullis of Beaufort are combined on the tents with the scarlet and white Lancastrian livery, which are also the colours of St. George. For Henry VII's contribution to the development of St. George as the patron Saint of England, see Scharf (*op. cit.*) who also drew attention to other instances in British royal iconography of votive figures assembled under the protection of their patron Saints: attention should perhaps be drawn particularly to the Wilton Diptych (for Richard II), to the Trinity Altarpiece by Van der Goes (for James IV), to the great window in St. Margaret's, Westminster, originally intended for Henry VII's chapel in Westminster Abbey, and to a miniature of Henry VII kneeling with the sovereigns of Europe before St. George (B.M., Add MS. 25698, f. 3).[1] The panel has suffered considerably in the past, but well preserved areas, such as the angels at the apex of the tents, seem to be of good quality. Scharf noted in 1863 copies of the two votive groups on separate panels in the possession of Sir John Stephen Barrington Simeon; a pair of such panels is also at Syon.

20. ARTHUR, PRINCE OF WALES (?) (*Plate* 7)

Windsor Castle (254). Panel: 15⅜ × 11 in., 39,1 × 28 cm.

Head and shoulders, with both his hands displayed, wearing a collar composed of knots and roses and a badge, apparently bearing the figure of St. John the Baptist, in his cap.

Traditionally known as a portrait of Prince Arthur. In the collections of Henry VIII and Edward VI two portraits of Prince Arthur are recorded (*1542, 1547* (32): . . . *the picture of Prince Arthure* and (98): . . . *the picture of Prince Arthure wering like a rede cappe with a broche upon it and a collor of red and white roses*. No. 20 may be identical with the latter, which seems to be the portrait recorded among the *Nyne old heads* at Whitehall in the time of Charles I as: . . . *the Picture . . . of kinge Henrie the 8th when he was young painted with 2 hands with a reed capp and a Coller aboute his neck of white & reed rosees. In a reed painted and guilded frame* (Van der Doort, p. 28). This seems to have been recovered at the Restoration, to have been hung again at Whitehall, but with another identity: *Henry the 7 when a youth, with a red cap on his head* (Charles II, *Whitehall* (118), measurements given as 16 × 11 in.). The later references to the portrait are very hard to

disentangle, but it seems to have been (as Henry VII) at Kensington and St. James's[1] and was almost certainly at Kensington in 1818 (158).

No. 32 in the early Tudor inventories may have been the portrait among the *23 litle heads* at Whitehall in the time of Charles I: . . . *Princ Arthure in his minoritye In a black capp and goulden habbitt houlding in his right hand a white gillifloore in a reed pintit guilded frame* (Van der Doort, p. 30, measurements given as 23 × 7 in., presumably in error for 11 × 7 in., and described as *a whithall peece*). This was almost certainly the portrait hanging at Whitehall in the reign of Charles II (Charles II, *Whitehall* (115): *Prince Arthur*, measurements given as 11 × 7 in.), but not apparently recorded in the collection after the time of James II.

It was perhaps yet another portrait that was recorded at Oatlands in October 1616 and October 1617: *a litle auntient picture of prince Arthur* (Glynde MSS., no. 35 in later inventory), valued at five shillings at Oatlands on 13 September 1649 by the Trustees for Sale (Corsham MS., f.11: *ye Picture of Prince Arthur*) and sold to T. Greene on 19 April 1650 (P.R.O., S.P. 29/447, 24, 1).

Literature: Sir G. Scharf, 'Remarks on some Portraits from Windsor Castle, Hampton Court, and Wilton House', *Archaeologia*, vol. XXXIX (1863), pp. 245–71 (read 21 February 1861), 457–63; Collins Baker, *Windsor*, pp. 100–1; E. Auerbach, *Tudor Artists* (1954), p. 47.

There is apparently no certain extant painted portrait of Prince Arthur with which no. 20 can be compared. If it is to be identified with no. 98 in the early Tudor inventories (see above) it could probably be accepted as a likeness of the Prince. Only that portrait's apparent later transformation into a portrait of the Prince's younger brother raises the possibility that it may be an early portrait of Henry VIII. No. 20 can perhaps be tentatively accepted as a portrait of Prince Arthur, painted just before his death on 2 April 1502. It is much repainted, but appears to be fundamentally a contemporary portrait.

21. JOHN HOWARD, FIRST DUKE OF NORFOLK (1430?–1485)

Windsor Castle (230). Panel: 22⅞ × 17⅞ in., 58,1 × 45,4 cm.

Head and shoulders wearing the ribbon of the Garter.

Inscribed: . . . HANNES HOWARD *dux Norff:/* . . [*ca*] *sus apud* BOSWORTH, and later: THE DUKE OF NORFOLKE / KILLED AT BOSWORTH FEILD. At the same period inscribed with the famous message written on the Duke's lodgings before he left to join Richard III and shown to the King just before the Battle of Bosworth (Shakespeare, *Richard III*, Act V, Sc. III): *Jockey of norfolk be not too bold / For Dickon thy master is bought / and sold.*

Among the early portraits, formerly in the collection of Lady Capel, acquired at Kew (on the back is a seventeenth-century label of the same type as on the back of no. 70 and an illegible (eighteenth century) inscription); seen there by Walpole in September 1761 (*Visits*, p. 39: . . . 'probably an original picture, undoubtedly of the time'); later at Kensington.

Literature: Walpole, *Anecdotes*, vol. I, p. 47; Collins Baker, *Windsor*, p. 109.

Probably painted in the second half of the sixteenth century; the earlier inscription is probably contemporary. A more painterly version at Arundel uses the same head, but is of a slightly different design and includes the hands and the Garter badge (D. Piper, 'The 1590 Lumley Inventory: . . . I', *Burl. Mag.*, vol. XCIX (1957), p. 228).

A zealous Yorkist, Knight of the Garter (1472), Admiral of England, Ireland and Aquitaine; he was High Steward at Richard III's coronation and was killed at Bosworth.

---

1. Mr. Roy Strong kindly gave me this reference.

1. Vertue, *Notebooks*, vol. IV, p. 75; Walpole, *Visits*, p. 15.

Artists Unknown: Early Tudor History Pieces

22. THE MEETING OF HENRY VIII AND THE EMPEROR MAXIMILIAN I (*Plate* 8)

Hampton Court (524). Panel: 39×81 in., 99,1×205,7 cm.

The composition is divided into three phases. In the foreground Henry VIII is greeting Maximilian I; both are in armour and on horseback and are labelled: ɪᴍᴘᴇʀᴀᴛᴏʀ / ᴍᴀxɪᴍɪʟɪᴀɴˢ and ʜᴇ̄ʀɪᴄᴠs ᴏᴄᴛᴀᴠᴠs / ʀᴇx‑ᴀɴɢʟɪᴀ̄–. Their followers are drawn up behind them. Beyond, the King and Emperor, still on horseback, are seen between bodies of their infantry drawn up by their encampments, near four cannon; the tents and the sovereigns' horses are decorated with the royal arms and the imperial eagle. Further back the combined English and imperial forces are engaged with the French at the battle of the Spurs. In the distance are the towns of Thérouanne and Tournay, inscribed respectively ᴛᴇʀᴠᴀɴᴇ and ᴛᴏʀɴᴀʏ, under siege.

Recorded at St. James's House in the inventory of 1549–50: *Item a table wherein is conteined the Seging of Torney and Turwyn* (*Three Inventories . . .*, ed. W. A. Shaw (1937), p. 63); seen at Whitehall in 1613 by the Duke of Saxe‑Weimar: 'The meeting of the Emperor Maximilian I, and Henry VIII ... before Tournay; on a large table – an old and beautiful picture' (W. B. Rye, *England as seen by Foreigners* (1865), p. 160). No. 22 cannot be identified with certainty in the records of Charles I's collection, but the CR brand was recorded on the back in 1869 (*V.R. inv.*) before the present cradling was applied to the back of the panel. Recovered at the Restoration and placed in store at Whitehall (Charles II, *Whitehall* (488)); seen at Whitehall by Evelyn: 'The Juncture with *Maximilian* the Emperor, Militating and receiving Pay under the Banner of St. George' (*Numismata* (1697), p. 159); later at Hampton Court, Somerset House and Kensington.

Literature: Waagen (1854), vol. II, p. 367; Law, 1881, 1898 (331); Collins Baker, *Hampton Court*, pp. 148–9; N. Beets, 'Cornelis Anthonisz, I', *Oud‑Holland*, vol. LVI (Amsterdam, 1939), pp. 160–84.

Nos. 22 and 23 record episodes in the English campaign against the French in Flanders in 1513. The English vanguard had invested Thérouanne on 27 June; on 1 August they were joined by Henry VIII with the main body of the army and on 12 August Maximilian I arrived in the English camp. After their success at Guinegate (no. 23) Thérouanne capitulated and was handed over to the Emperor by Henry VIII. On 21 September Tournay surrendered. No. 22, probably by a Flemish painter, may have been painted for Henry VIII as a formal record of this successful campaign and of his meeting with the Emperor. The battle in the distance is reminiscent of a passage in Anthonisz's woodcut of 1553 (*Fig.* 6) of the siege of Thérouanne, but no. 22 cannot safely be attributed to him. Gold leaf is used in the painting of the armour of men and horses. The cannon prominently shown in front of the allied camps may be four of the famous twelve great pieces of English artillery, the Twelve Apostles, which were taken on this campaign. In 1527 a payment of £4. 10s. was made to 'Maistr' Hans', who is presumed to have been Holbein, for a monumental picture of the siege of Thérouanne which was to be part of the decorations planned as the background for festivities held at Greenwich on 5 May 1527 at the time of the preparation of a treaty between England and France (E. Auerbach, *Tudor Artists* (1954), pp. 11–12).

23. THE BATTLE OF THE SPURS (*Plate* 9)

Hampton Court (517). 51¾×103¾ in., 131,4×263,5 cm.

Inscribed, probably slightly later: *The Bataile of / Spvrrs. anno. / 1513.*

In the background is a hilly landscape with the town of Thérouanne in the distance, inscribed *Terwaen*; in front of the town, by a ruined abbey (?), is the English camp; the cross of St. George is painted on some of the tents and some of the others appear to bear the Tudor colours of green and white. Other encampments can be seen in the distance and near a castle on the right. In the foreground the English cavalry is routing the French forces. On the extreme left are trumpeters whose instruments are decorated with the royal arms. In the centre of the composition Henry VIII receives the surrender of an opponent, probably intended for the Chevalier Bayard, who was captured in the action. The King's armour and that of his opponent are gilded and the King's horse‑armour is decorated with the royal arms. On the King's left a struggle for the French standard is taking place. In the foreground is a (? French) warrior (perhaps the Duc de Longueville) whose horse's armour is richly decorated with mythological scenes, including the Rape of Europa.

Apparently first recorded in the royal collection in 1613, when the Duke of Saxe‑Weimar noted in Whitehall, after referring to no. 22: 'The battle before Assumcourt [*sic*] between the said Henry VIII and the King of France; on a large table, which also is a beautiful picture' (W. B. Rye, *England as seen by Foreigners* (1865), p. 160). Probably *the battaile of spors*, valued at £8 by the Trustees for Sale at Hampton Court in October 1649 (L. R. MS., f. 121) and sold to De Critz and others on 18 November 1651 (S.P. 29/447, 24, 1). Recovered at the Restoration and placed in the King's Privy Gallery at Whitehall (Charles II, *Whitehall* (142)), where it was recorded by Evelyn: 'The Battles of *Spurrs*, though of an Inferior Pencil . . .' (*Numismata* (1697), p. 159); later at Windsor.

Literature: Vertue, *Notebooks*, vol. I, p. 78; Walpole, *Anecdotes*, vol. I, pp. 58–9 (n. by Dallaway), 62; Waagen (1854), vol. II, p. 367; Law, 1881, 1898 (339); Collins Baker, *Hampton Court*, pp. 149–50; N. Beets, 'Cornelis Anthonisz, I', *Oud‑Holland*, vol. LVI (1939), pp. 160–84.

See no. 22. On 16 August 1513 a strong mounted contingent of French troops was routed by a small body of English cavalry in an action near Guinegate known as the 'Battle of the Spurs'. Henry VIII was present and Maximilian I served under him as an English soldier; Maximilian and his men were 'armed in on sute with redde crosses'. The English spears, seen prominently behind the King, 'fought valiantly with the Frenchmen and threw downe their standarde'. The Duc de Longueville and Bayard were captured. No. 23 seems as likely to be by an Italian as a Flemish hand and the treatment of the armour suggests that it was painted reasonably near the event and possibly for Henry VIII. Redgrave noted (*V.R. inv.*, 22 June 1872), that, in relining, the CR brand had been revealed on the original canvas and that the head of the French warrior in a helmet on the right, looking back at his page, had been shown to be a later insertion, replacing a head that had been cut out of the original canvas. The background is partly derived from Anthonisz's woodcut of 1553 (*Fig.* 6; see no. 22), but Beets's attribution of no. 23 to him is not acceptable.

24. THE EMBARKATION OF HENRY VIII (*Plate* 10)

Hampton Court (515). 66½×135¾ in., 168,9×346,7 cm.; the canvas has probably been stretched at the top in lining.

The fleet is seen setting sail from Dover; five principal vessels are in the foreground with others beyond. On the left is Dover Castle and in the distance the coast of France. Salutes are being fired from two forts in the foreground. Troops are putting off for the ships. The five principal vessels fly streamers with St. George's cross and are decorated with shields bearing St. George's cross and Tudor emblems. The large ship in the foreground has the royal arms on the stern and carries royal standards on the deck; the ship on the extreme right also carries royal standards. The ship on which the King is seen standing on the deck, surrounded by courtiers, trumpeters and Yeomen of the Guard, has the royal arms on stern and forecastle and royal standards on the deck; the sails and streamers are painted in gold leaf and the sails are covered with a rich damask pattern. The green and white Tudor colours are seen repeatedly on flags, shields and streamers.

Nos. 24 and 25 are not recorded in the earlier Tudor inventories, but they are presumably referred to in the restoration, recorded in the Declaration of Account of the Paymaster of the Works for the year 1588–9, of the Presence Chamber at Whitehall, where 'all the discourse of King Henries Coronacion and his going to Bulleyne' were cleaned and varnished 'with a special Vernishe made without sente' (P. R. O., E. 351/3223).[1] They were seen at Whitehall in 1613 by the Duke of Saxe-Weimar: '. . . there are two large tables with many figures painted from life . . .' (W. B. Rye, *England as seen by Foreigners* (1865), p. 159), but they were later moved to the King's First Privy Gallery at Greenwich. No. 24 is recorded there in the time of Charles I: . . . *Wr king henri te 8 is in his shipin tu kras te se vor vranz* (Van der Doort, p. 195); it was valued at Greenwich by the Trustees for Sale at £20 (L. R. MS., f. 61: *ye ships. goeing to. Bulloigne*) and sold to Captain Stone and others on 23 October 1651; it was declared by John Stone to the House of Lords Committee on 17 May 1660 to be in his possession (H. of L. MSS.). Placed in the King's Privy Gallery at Whitehall (Charles II, *Whitehall* (143): *Henry 8 going to Bullen with his fleete*, measurements given as 64 × 149 in.), where it was seen by Pepys on 25 December 1662. Thereafter at Windsor.

Literature: Vertue, *Notebooks*, vol. I, p. 106, vol. II, p. 29, vol. IV, p. 119; Walpole, *Anecdotes*, vol. I, pp. 58–9 (n. by Dallaway), 62, *Correspondence*, ed. W. S. Lewis, vol. IX (1941), pp. 69, 99; J. Topham, 'A Description of an Antient Picture in Windsor Castle', (*Archaeologia*, vol. VI (1782), pp. 179–220 (read 21 June 1781)); Waagen (1838), vol. II, p. 117, (1854), vol. II, p. 366; Law, 1881, 1898 (337); Collins Baker, *Hampton Court*, p. 149; N. Beets, 'Cornelis Anthonisz, I' *Oud-Holland*, vol. LVI (1939), pp. 160–84; R. A., *King's Pictures* (505); Waterhouse, *Painting in Britain*, p. 4.

On 31 May 1520 Henry VIII had embarked from Dover, with his Queen and a vast retinue, for the personal meeting with Francis I recorded in no. 25. The little portrait of the King in no. 24 seems, however, to be dependent ultimately on Holbein's full-length of 1537 (see no. 216) and certainly does not show the King as he was in 1520. That nos. 24 and 25 do not appear in the inventory of 1547 may indicate that they were painted not earlier than *c.* 1550; this is perhaps confirmed by the costumes in the foreground of no. 24. No satisfactory attribution has been put forward for them. Holbein's name was first attached to them in the time of James II (B. M., Harl. MS. 1890, f. 48; Bathoe, *James II* (86)), and Evelyn classed them with 'those admirable Paintings of *Holbein* in his *Majesty's Privy-Chamber at White-Hall*' (*Numismata* (1697), p. 159). Vertue and Walpole could not accept this, and Waagen ((1854), vol. II, p. 366) recognized them as Netherlandish. J. G. Nichols seems to have been the first to put forward tentatively (in 1862; *Archaeologia*, vol. XXXIX (1863), p. 28) the name of Vincent Volpe. There is, however, nothing to support this suggestion and Waagen's opinion has been recently endorsed by Dr. Auerbach ('Vincent Volpe, the King's Painter', *Burl. Mag.*, vol. XCII (1950), p. 227). Beets's attribution (*loc. cit*) to Anthonisz has not received support, but it is perhaps significant that his brother Anthonis compiled in 1546 the roll of ships in the B. M. and the Pepysian Library. It is, however, certain that

more than one artist worked on nos. 24 and 25. In no. 24 the figures in the foreground appear all to be by the same hand, which is close to the hand that painted the figures in the right foreground of no. 25; the smaller figures in the background are close to, but not necessarily by the same hand as, the figures in the background of no. 25, which seem slightly finer and fresher in quality. No. 24 is more homogeneous in appearance than no. 25, but the ships were probably painted by another hand than the figures. In no. 24 the King is presumed to be aboard the *Henri Grace-de-Dieu*, but the ships have not been satisfactorily identified and the largest vessel in the King's squadron on this occasion was the *Great Bark* (for the vessels in no. 24 see W. Laird Clowes, *The Royal Navy*, vol. 1 (1897), pp. 405–8). The view of Dover is from the southwest point of the harbour; the two forts in the foreground would therefore be the Archcliff and the Black Bulwarks. If the measurements given in Charles II's inventory (see above) are correct, no. 24 has been slightly cut on one or both of its sides. A slightly later copy, sold at Christie's, 1 May 1911 (94), is now in the possession of the Earl of Scarbrough.

In the eighteenth century the Tudor historical pictures in the royal collection were the objects of deep interest in antiquarian circles. The Society of Antiquaries commissioned a large water-colour copy of no. 24, which was painted by S. H. Grimm in 1779. This reproduction is still with the Society and in 1781 the Society published a large engraving of it by Basire. No. 24 was, with nos. 22, 23 and 25, lent to the Society by George III. By 1828 the Society was under the impression that they had been given to it, but George IV wished to have them moved to Windsor and they returned to the royal collection from the Antiquaries on 2 December 1828 (*The Letters of King George IV*, ed. A. Aspinall (1938), vol. III, pp. 435–6; Jutsham, *Receipts*, f. 265).

25. THE FIELD OF THE CLOTH OF GOLD
(Plate 11)

Hampton Court (520). 66½ × 135⅞ in., 168,9 × 347,3 cm.; the canvas appears to have been stretched at the top and on the two sides.

In the left foreground Henry VIII is seen riding into Guisnes with his forces and retinue, attended by Yeomen of the Guard and six Pages of the Chamber. Above him flies a dragon. In the right centre of the composition is the special building put up for the reception of Henry VIII and his Queen, Catherine of Aragon; in front of it are the two fountains also erected for the occasion. Behind the temporary palace are the King's golden dining tent and the ovens and tents in which the King's meals were prepared. Beyond the dining tent is seen the meeting of Henry VIII with Francis I, dismounted in front of a rich golden tent and, on the right, the tournament field; the jousting is watched by the two Kings and their Queens and in the corner of the field stands the Tree of Honour on which were displayed the shields of the contestants. In the right foreground is a large tent, decorated with the Tudor rose, in which a banquet is taking place, possibly attended by the King's sister Mary and her second husband the Duke of Suffolk; the litter behind this tent, surrounded by mounted ladies-in-waiting, probably contains Catherine of Aragon. The tents used by lesser members of the royal suite stretch into the distance. In the extreme distance can be seen Calais and Ardres, with the Castle of Hammes surrounded by water.

See no. 24. No. 25 is recorded in the King's First Privy Gallery at Greenwich in the time of Charles I: *Wijthal pis . . . a larg pis opan klaht ramufft aut auff Wijthal bin king hnri da 8 entrin tu bolonia (Van der Doort*, p. 195); it was possibly the picture valued at Greenwich by the Trustees for Sale at £30 (L. R. MS., f. 61 : *A Picture of yᵉ Seidge. of Bulloigne*) and sold to Captain Stone and others on 23 October 1651; and it was declared by John Stone to the House of Lords Committee on 17 May 1660 to be in his possession (H. of L. MSS.). Placed in the King's Privy Gallery at Whitehall (Charles II, *Whitehall* (144): *Henry 8 going into the Towne of Bullen*, measurements given as 64 × 148 in.), where it was seen by Pepys on 25 December 1662. Thereafter, with no. 24, at Windsor.

Literature: Vertue inv., *Windsor*, ff. 9–10, *Notebooks*, vol. IV, pp. 146–7; Walpole, *Anecdotes*, vol. I, pp. 58–9 (n. by Dallaway), 62; Sir J. Ayloffe 'An Historical Description of an ancient Picture . . .', *Archaeologia*, vol. III (1775), pp. 185–229 (read 29 March 1770); Waagen (1838), vol. II, p. 117, (1854), vol. II, p. 366; Law, 1881, 1898 (342); Collins Baker, *Hampton Court*, p. 150; N. Beets, 'Cornelis Anthonisz, I', *Oud-Holland*, vol. LVI (1939), pp. 160–84; R. A., *King's Pictures* (506); S. Anglo, 'Le Camp du Drap d'Or . . .', *Les Fêtes de la Renaissance*, II (Paris, 1960), pp. 113–34, and a paper read to the Society of Antiquities, 7 December 1961.

No. 25 should be read as a sequel to no. 24. It is a very carefully compiled record of the festivities that took place during the meeting of Henry VIII and Francis I between Guisnes and Ardres, just within the English Pale. The English King had arrived at Guisnes from Calais on 5 June 1520 and is probably seen in no. 25 in the procession to the actual meeting with Francis I two days later. The two sovereigns took leave of each other on 24 June, after a week of banquets, masques, jousting and martial sports. No. 25 seems to be only a moderately accurate resumé of some of the details of the meeting and of its settings. It could be compared with the contemporary account in Edward Hall's *Chronicle* (ed. of 1809, pp. 604–20). A good modern account is to be found in J. S. Brewer's introduction (pp. lxviii–lxxxi) to *Letters and Papers . . . of the Reign of Henry VIII*, vol. III, pt. I (1867), but the most valuable recent analysis of the events is to be found in S. Anglo, *op. cit*. The temporary palace had been built by English artisans, under the surveillance of Sir Edward Belknap, to house the royal suites. Many of the riders close to the King in the royal procession are clearly portraits, but they have not all been satisfactorily identified. The two principal horsemen in front of the King are clearly Sir Thomas Wriothesley, Garter King of Arms (d. 1534), and Thomas Grey, 2nd Marquess of Dorset (1477–1530), carrying the Sword of State. Cardinal Wolsey, whose crossbearer is some way ahead, rides beside the King. Of the four horsemen behind the King, the one on the extreme left is Charles Brandon, 1st Duke of Suffolk (d. 1545). Beside him rides, apparently, the Earl Marshal; his features are very close to those of the 3rd Duke of Norfolk (see no. 30), but neither he nor his father, the 2nd Duke, who was Earl Marshal in 1520, were present, and this rider may be Henry Bourchier, 2nd Earl of Essex (d. 1539), who was Marshal of the King's train. Other prominent figures present at the event were John Russell, 1st Earl of Bedford (1486?–1555), and Sir Henry Guildford (see no. 28), who might be the two riders on the right in the rank behind the King; Sir John Gage (see no. 66), George Nevile, 3rd Baron Abergavenny (1471?–1535), and George Talbot, 4th Earl of Shrewsbury (1468–1538). In the procession on 7 June Henry VIII rode in cloth of silver on a bay horse; in no. 25 he is shown in cloth of gold and on a white horse. The King's head has clearly been cut out and reinserted. Ayloffe (*loc. cit.*) stated that this had been done by the Earl of Pembroke (probably the 5th Earl, though Ayloffe is confused on this point) when the picture was thought to be about to be sold abroad in the Interregnum; but Thomas Locke in a letter to Sir Dudley Carleton, 18 March 1621, describing the audience given by James I to the Spanish Ambassador in the Gallery at Whitehall, states that the Ambassador's followers were in the next

room: 'where are many good peeces . . ., amongst others . . . King Henry VIII his going into Bolloigne . . . out of these were many pieces cutt where the Spaniards received any disgrace . . . In the other the king's head cutt off . . .' (quoted in Smith, *Supplement*, p. 242). The dragon in the sky is presumably the firework in the shape of a dragon or salamander which was released on 23 June. No. 25 is considerably finer in quality than no. 24, and is certainly the work of more than one hand. The group of figures (including two Oriental (?) trumpeters) in the foreground of the right half of the composition, and in front of the artificial palace, is distinct from the rest of the composition and is by the hand which is closest to the figures in the foreground of no. 24.[1] The palace and the fountains, which are described in many of the contemporary accounts, may have been painted by another hand; but it is possible that the nucleus of no. 25 was a record of these celebrated creations. For a comparison between the painted record in no. 25 with the accounts in contemporary descriptions, see S. Anglo, *op. cit*. The fluently painted figures in the right foreground are painted over the fountain and pillar and the front of the palace, as if the painted record of the structures was completed before the figures were set in. The remainder of the figures in the foreground are by another hand, but yet another artist seems to have been responsible for the more important portraits. The figures in the background (including those in the dining tent on the extreme right) appear to be by yet another hand; and this hand was probably not responsible for the buildings and tents. There are slight *pentimenti* in the roof of the château at Guisnes. It can perhaps be suggested that no. 25 was completed considerably after the events it records and possibly on the basis of documentary records. Dr. Anglo pointed out, especially in his paper (see above), that the general topographical lay-out and the details of Guisnes Castle are inaccurate; that the palace and fountains agree reasonably well with what is said in contemporary descriptions; that the procession is a summary only of the actual cavalcade; but that the tournament is radically unlike the actual setting constructed for the tilt. Despite its mutilation, the head of the King seems to be dependent on Holbein's image.

The Society of Antiquaries commissioned a water-colour copy of no. 25 from E. Edwards, of which in 1774 the Society published an engraving by Basire. Edwards's drawing (signed and dated 1771) was presented by the Society to George III (*The Society of Antiquaries, Notes on its History . . .* (1951), p. 67).

Hans Holbein the Younger

1497/8–1543. Born at Augsburg and trained by his father, Hans Holbein the elder. He was in Basel by 1515; during a period at Lucerne, 1517–19, he probably visited North Italy; became a member of the painters' Guild at Basel, 25 September 1519, and a citizen in the following July. Holbein visited France in 1524 and went to England in the late summer of 1526. In August 1528 he was back in Basel, but by 2 September 1532 he was once more in London. By 1536 he was in the service of Henry VIII. He visited Brussels, France and Basel in 1538. During his first visit to England Holbein does not seem to have painted portraits for the King, although he may (see no. 22) have carried out decorative undertakings for the Revels. During his second visit he was

---

1. It is at this point that no. 25 perhaps comes stylistically close to Anthonisz, but Beets's attribution (*loc. cit.*) of no. 25 to him does not take into account the presence of more than one hand in the picture.

prolific as a decorative painter and a graphic artist. His drawings for goldsmith's and jeweller's work include designs for jewelry for Henry VIII and Princess Mary and for Garters and decorative weapons. In 1537 he painted the fresco of the Tudor family in the Privy Chamber at White-hall (see no. 216). He painted single portraits of the King, Jane Seymour, Edward VI and Anne of Cleves (Ganz, *Holbein*, pls. 135, 138, 146, 148, 178), but no portraits by Holbein can be identified in the records of the early Tudor collection apart from Christina of Denmark in the National Gallery (2475), painted for Henry VIII on the basis of sittings in Brussels in March 1538. The portrait is thought to have been given by the King to Henry Fitzalan, Earl of Arundel (M. Levey, *The German School*, N.G. (1959), pp. 54–7).[1]

Important works by Holbein, however, entered the royal collection at a later date. Sir Adam Newton, formerly Tutor to Henry, Prince of Wales, presented to Charles I before his accession the portrait of Erasmus in the Louvre (Ganz, *Holbein*, pl. 66) which the King later gave to the Duc de Liancourt in an exchange. A number of portraits were attributed to Holbein in the collection of Charles I. The *Portrait of a Woman* in the Mauritshuis (275; *ibid.*, pl. 68) bears Charles I's brand on the back; it was perhaps *A Picture of a woman done by Holben*, valued at £40 by the Trustees for Sale at Greenwich (L. R. MS., f. 5 v.) and sold to Wright for £41 on 21 May 1650. Charles II owned the portraits of Robert Cheseman and a *Man with a Hawk* in the Mauritshuis (276, 277, *ibid.*, pls. 109, 162). Both were in the King's Closet at Whitehall (Charles II, *Whitehall* (308); B. M. Harl. MS. 1890, f. 61 v.; Bathoe, *James II* (505, 507)); they were taken to Holland by William III.

26. DERICH BORN (1510?–after 1549) (*Plate* 16)

Windsor Castle (64). Panel: $23\frac{3}{4} \times 17\frac{3}{4}$ in., 60,3 × 45,1 cm.; a little of the original unpainted edge is visible on all four sides of the panel.

Head and shoulders, leaning on a stone ledge on which is inscribed: DERICHVS SI VOCEM ADDAS IPSISSIMVS HIC SIT / HVNC DVBITES PICTOR FECERIT AN GENITOR / DER BORN ETATIS SVÆ 23. ANNO 1533. Behind are tendrils of the same vine (?) as appears in the background of nos. 28 and 31.

The history of no. 26 is difficult to disentangle. The panel bears the CR brand so can be presumed to have belonged to Charles I. It is not, however, identifiable in the documents relating to his collection and may have been given by the King to the Earl of Arundel, of whose passion for Holbein the King would have been aware. No. 26 is probably identifiable with a picture in the Arundel inventory drawn up in Amsterdam in 1655 (P. R. O., Del. 1/VII, f. 700: *holbein Derichius a Born*; see M. F. S. Hervey, *The Life . . . of Thomas Howard, Earl of Arundel* (1921), p. 481). No. 26 was hanging in the King's Closet at Whitehall soon after the Restoration (Charles II, *Whitehall* (321): *Holbin A young man in a black cap & blacke habit laying one hand on yᵉ other To yᵉ wast.*). Its entry (or re-entry) into the royal collection is recorded by Colonel Hawley (f. 17: *A young mans picture to yᵉ wast in A Blacke Cap and A Blacke habite Leaning wᵗʰ one hand upon yᵉ othʳ done by holbin*); the date of this source is obscure and this reference may not be incompatible with a letter from Sir William Temple to Charles II from Brussels, 9 March 1666: 'I . . . beg your Majesty's pardon in sending over a picture of Holpeyn's, which was esteemed by my Lord Arundel among the best of that hand in his collection. M. Ognati has undertaken to leave it at your Majesty's feet . . .' (T. P. Courtenay, *Memoirs of . . . Sir William Temple* (1836), vol. I, p. 79); this letter

would at least account for the presence in Charles II's collection of a picture by Holbein that had belonged to Arundel. No. 26 was probably taken by William III to Kensington, where it can perhaps be identified with no. 30, 32 or 53 among the pictures on the Staircase there in 1697 (B. M., Harl. MS. 7025, ff. 193, 194); and was probably hanging in the Queen's Gallery in the following reign (Queen Anne, *Kensington* (71): *Alberto Duro. A mans head in a black Cap with 2 Hands*; B. M., Stowe MS. 567, f. 11 v. as by 'Gennet'). At Windsor early in the reign of George III.

Literature: Waagen (1838), vol. I, p. 178, (1854), vol. II, pp. 430–1; A. Woltmann, *Holbein und seine Zeit*, vol. I (Leipzig, 1874), pp. 369–70, vol. II (1876), p. 156; Law, *Holbein*, pp. 9–10; Ganz, *KdK.*, 100; A. B. Chamberlain, *Hans Holbein the Younger* (1913), vol. II, pp. 17–20; U. Christoffel, *Hans Holbein D.J.* (Berlin, 1924), pp. 96–8; W. Stein, *Holbein* (Berlin, 1929), pp. 232–4; Collins Baker, *Windsor*, p. 160; Schmid, Tafelband (1945), p. 31 (81); Textband (1948), vol. II, pp. 367, 384–5, 388; R. A., *King's Pictures* (15), *Holbein and Other Masters*, 1950–1 (25); W. Pinder, *Holbein der Jüngere . . .* (Cologne, 1951), p. 88; F. Grossmann, 'Holbein Studies – I', *Burl. Mag.*, vol. XCIII (1951), p. 40; Ganz, *Holbein*, p. 241 (69).

There is a vertical crack running through the nose. There is some loss of original paint down this crack, down the edges of the panel and in the costume; there are small rubbed areas in the hair, in the shirt-collar and in the costume, and the background is worn in a number of places. But the surface is, in general, in good condition. There are alterations in painting to the outlines of the hair, of the cap (on the left), and of the shoulders. The portrait seems to have been painted first on the gesso ground, and the background then to have been painted up to it.

The sitter was a merchant from Cologne and a member of the Hansa Steelyard community in London, where he was recorded as late as 1549; in 1536 he had supplied war materials for the suppression of the Rebellion in the North. A small portrait, originally a roundel and now an oval, by Holbein of the same sitter in the same year is in the Pinakothek in Munich (1083; Ganz, *Holbein*, pl. 117).

27. JOHANNES FROBEN (1460–1527) (*Plate* 12)

Hampton Court (323). Panel: $21\frac{3}{4} \times 12\frac{3}{4}$ in., 55,2 × 32,4 cm., including a later addition at the top of $2\frac{1}{2}$ in.; the original unpainted edge is visible on the three other sides.

Half-length, nearly in profile to the right, behind a ledge on which is inscribed: IOANNES FROBENIVS TYP. HHOLBEIN P. (initials in monogram).

Stated to have been bought, presumably with the companion portrait of Erasmus (no. 39), by the 1st Duke of Buckingham from Michel Le Blond, *c.* 1625. Presented to Charles I by the Duke: the CR brand is on the addition at the top of the panel and on the back is a partly illegible label of the type applied by Van der Doort: *This picture of ffrobenus/was delivered to his Maᵗⁱᵉ by/yᵉ Duke of Buckingham before . . . Ile of Ree.* The Duke presumably gave the pictures to the King in the summer of 1627, before setting sail on 27 June for the Isle of Rhé; they were placed in the Cabinet Room at Whitehall, where no. 27 is described as: *Don by Hollben . . . the Picture of Frobenius with his printing Tooles by . . . in a black frame . . .* (Van der Doort, p. 84; the measurements were probably given in one of his MSS. as 21 × 12½ in.). The Trustees for Sale valued the pair (*Fobanus & Erasmus in 2 pictures*) at £200 (L. R. MS., 162 v.; in the Sebright MS. they are attributed to Holbein): *Froben* was sold for £100 to Colonel Hutchinson on 24 May 1650, *Erasmus* for the same sum, on the same day, to Milburne. The pair was recovered at the Restoration and hung in the King's Closet at Whitehall (Charles II, *Whitehall* (333, 336), measurements of both given as 21 × 12 in.): they may have been the 'Two incomparable heads of *Holbein*' seen by Evelyn at Whitehall on 6 December 1660 (*Diary*, ed. E. S. de Beer (1955), vol. III, p. 263). The pair was thereafter at Kensington, and was taken to Hampton Court on 20 November 1833.

---

1. For Edward VI's ownership of Holbein's portrait-drawings and their subsequent history, see K. T. Parker, *The Drawings of Hans Holbein . . . at Windsor Castle* (1945), pp. 7–20.

Literature: C. Patin, *Relations Historiques et Curieuses de Voyages* (Paris, 1674), pp. 170–1 ('... tous deux de la main d'Holbein leur bon amy'); Vertue, *Notebooks*, vol. I, p. 55; Walpole, *Anecdotes*, vol. I, pp. 76 (confused), 344; Waagen (1838), vol. II, p. 116, (1854), vol. II, p. 363; R. N. Wornum, *Some Account of the Life and Works of Hans Holbein* (1867), pp. 138–40; A. Woltmann, *Holbein und seine Zeit*, vol. I (Leipzig, 1874), p. 289, vol. II (1876), pp. 49, 164; Law, 1881, 1898 (603), *Holbein*, pp. 27–8; Ganz, *KdK*, 207; A. B. Chamberlain, *Hans Holbein the Younger* (1913), vol. I, pp. 162, 166–8, 183–4, vol. II, pp. 329–30; W. Stein, *Holbein* (Berlin, 1929), p. 84; Collins Baker, *Hampton Court*, p. 74; R. A., *King's Pictures* (2); Schmid, Textband (1948), vol. I, p. 181; R. A., *Holbein and Other Masters*, 1950–51 (4); Ganz, *Holbein*, pp. 227–9 (33); Kunstmuseum, Basel, *Die Malerfamilie Holbein in Basel*, 1960 (168).

It is not impossible that no. 27 and the companion portrait of Erasmus were the component parts of the diptych described in the list of Holbein's works in the MS. (in Basel) *Humanae Industriae Monumenta* by Remigius Faesch (1595–1667).[1] Charles Patin certainly thought that the portraits in the diptych were those he had seen in Whitehall in 1672.[2] The two panels are of the same size. X-ray (1960) revealed, moreover, that in the original background of no. 39, under the later architectural perspective, the curtain, of which a small part appears in no. 27, continues across behind Erasmus, as if the two sitters were to be seen against a common background. If they did not form the diptych mentioned by Faesch, they must have made up another such diptych. The X-ray also showed that no. 27 is of considerably better quality than had hitherto been suspected, with more modelling in the costume than is visible to the naked eye, and *pentimenti* round the outline of the figure against the background of the same kind that are found in, for example, nos. 26 and 28. The ledge in the foreground is painted over the finished sleeve and represents therefore probably a second stage in the composition and not a *pentimento*. It seems possible that no. 27 may be an original portrait by Holbein, painted at Basel *c.* 1522–3, which was joined to no. 39 at a very early date. In Van der Doort's catalogue they are clearly hanging apart, and they were never, so far as is known, hinged together again. By then they had been enlarged. The CR brand is on the addition to no. 27 and the perspective background was not removed from this addition when it was taken off the original panel in 1927 (see Sir L. Cust, 'The Portrait of Frobenius ...', *Apollo*, vol. V (1927), pp. 249–52). The perspective backgrounds were probably painted immediately after the additions had been made, probably *c.* 1629 and at the command of Charles I, and almost certainly by Hendrick van Steenwyck. Vertue, indeed, stated (*loc. cit.*) that the backgrounds had been painted by Steenwyck in 1626, and Walpole declared (*op. cit.*, p. 344) that Steenwyck's name and the date 1629 were on the background of no. 27. This background included an inking-pad and a box of printer's dies, perhaps the *printing Tooles* mentioned by Van der Doort (see above). No. 27 seems without doubt to be the finest version of Holbein's portrait of Froben. There are two copies in the Öffentliche Kunstsammlung at Basel (357, 1910); a copy in the collec-

1. 'Erant 2. tabulae junctae, ligamentis ferreis ut aperiri et claudi potuerint, in tabula dextra Effigies Johan. Frobenii Typographi, in altera Erasmi sine dubio ab ipso Erasmo in gratiam et honorem Frobenii, quem impense amabat, et eidem ab Erasmo oblatae, unde et eidem dextram cessit: Ex his tabulis nobis exempla paravit pictor non imperitus Joh. Sixtus Ringlinus Basil. An. 1648, quae extant inter effigies nostras' (quoted in Woltmann, *op. cit.*, vol. II, p. 49). The date of the copies painted for Faesch is the most serious obstacle to identifying nos. 27 and 39 with the original diptych.

2. 'Opinor hasce duas effigies ERASMI & Frobenii eas esse quas in cimelarchio Regis Londini observasse memini, an. 1672.' (in the material on Holbein prefixed to Patin's edition of 1676 (Basel) of Erasmus's *Praise of Folly*).

tion of Earl Fitzwilliam appears to have been painted in England *c.* 1640, perhaps by a painter such as Remigius van Leemput, and records the background as it had been painted by Steenwyck; a drawing at Hatfield may be of the same date; and there is also a copy in the Bodleian Library. A very good small roundel in the collection of Sir Thomas Merton (Ganz, *Holbein*, pl. 96) seems to have been based on no. 27 or on a lost original of the type.

Froben was one of the finest printers of his time, closely associated in Basel with Holbein, who did much book-illustration and decorative work for him, and with Erasmus, who lived in Froben's house in Basel and whose works, from 1514 onwards, were printed by him.

28. SIR HENRY GUILDFORD (1489?–1532) (*Plates* 17–19)

Windsor Castle (65). Panel: $32\frac{1}{2} \times 26\frac{1}{8}$ in., 82,6×66,4 cm.; the panel may have been reduced by *c.* $1\frac{3}{4}$ in. on the left.

Inscribed on the later *cartellino*: *Anno.* D:MCCCCCXVII.*/ Etatis. Suæ. xl ix:*

Half-length, wearing the collar of the Garter and clasping in his right hand his staff of office, probably as Comptroller of the Household; in the background a curtain is pulled back to reveal the tendrils of a climbing vine (?). In his cap is a brooch etched with a design of a clock and surveying instruments.

Almost certainly the portrait recorded in the collection of John, 1st Baron Lumley (*d.* 1609): *Of sir Henry Guilfourd, Coumptroller to k: H:8. | drawne by Hance Holbyn*, with, later in the same inventory, *Of the La: Guilfourd, wife to sir Henry Guilfourd Coumptroller. drawne by haunce holbyn* (Sir L. Cust, 'The Lumley Inventories', *Walpole Soc.*, vol. VI (1918), pp. 24, 26). They may have come into Lumley's possession from his father-in-law, the 12th Earl of Arundel (see no. 49); the *cartellino* was originally (see below) the distinctive type which Lumley caused to be painted on his portraits (see D. Piper, 'The 1590 Lumley Inventory ... I', *Burl. Mag.*, vol. XCIX (1957), p. 227). The two portraits probably passed by descent into the collection of Lumley's great-nephew Thomas Howard, Earl of Arundel, where they were etched by Hollar (Parthey, 1409, 1410; see M. F. S. Hervey, *The Life ... of Thomas Howard, Earl of Arundel* (1921), pp. 57, 482); they are recorded in the Arundel inventory drawn up in Amsterdam in 1655 (P. R. O., Del. 1/VII, f. 701: *holbein ritratto d'al Cavaglier Guilford* and *ritratto della Moglie sua;* on f. 702 occurs: *holbeen – Ritratto del Cavaglier Guiltfort in piccole*) and probably passed through Arundel's son William, Viscount Stafford, to the latter's grandson William, Earl of Stafford, in whose house, Tart Hall near St. James's Park, they were seen, apparently in 1726, by Vertue (*Notebooks*, vol. II, p. 19) '... on bord. (with their orig. frames) highly finishd & labourd ...' Vertue reported later (*c.* 1735, *ibid.*, vol. IV, p. 40) that the male portrait had been bought by the Crown, perhaps soon after Lord Stafford's death in January 1734;[1] placed in the King's Gallery at Kensington; taken to Carlton House on 7 August 1812 (Jutsham, *R/D*, f. 217), but only in store there in 1816 (383; the 1816 label is still on the back of the frame); later at Hampton Court.

Literature: Vertue, *Notebooks*, vol. IV, p. 65, vol. V, p. 49; Walpole, *Anecdotes*, vol. I, p. 93; Waagen (1838), vol. II, p. 116, (1854), vol. II, pp. 362, 430; A. Woltmann, *Holbein und seine Zeit*, vol. I (Leipzig, 1874), pp. 343–4, vol. II (1876), p. 155; Law, *Holbein*, pp. 1–4; Ganz, *KdK*, 72; A. B. Chamberlain, *Hans Holbein the Younger* (1913), vol. I, pp. 299, 313, 316–21; W. Stein, *Holbein* (Berlin, 1929), pp. 150–2, 155–6, 316; Collins Baker, *Windsor*, p. 157; R. A., *King's Pictures* (6); Schmid, Textband (1948), vol. I, p. 83, vol. II, pp. 290–1, 300; R. A., *Holbein and Other Masters*, 1950–1 (8); W. Pinder, *Holbein der Jüngere* ... (Cologne, 1951), p. 69; Waterhouse, *Painting in Britain*, pp. 6–7; E. Auerbach, *Tudor Artists* (1954), pp. 11, n. 5, 70; Ganz, *Holbein*, p. 232 (44).

1. The inscription on the back of the panel, identifying the sitter, was probably put on at this period.

Holbein's preparatory drawing is at Windsor (Parker, 10); the face has been appreciably lengthened by the artist when he transferred it to the panel. A small copy (?) in a roundel is at Detroit (Ganz, *Holbein*, p. 244 (76)) and another was in 1936 in the P. Strauss collection in New York. A later miniature copy of the head is at Windsor; the latter is close in detail to Hollar's etching. A reduced copy of the whole design was in the McCormick collection, Chicago. The original companion portrait of Mary, Lady Guildford, Sir Henry's second wife, is now in the City Art Museum at St. Louis, Missouri (*Fig.* 2). The sitter's age (27) and the date (1527) are inscribed on it, the curtain-rod appears to continue across from the portrait of her husband, and the same vine (?) appears in the background. The inscription on the *cartellino* on no. 28 was applied at a later date, over the *cartellino* presumed to have been put on when the portrait belonged to Lumley; under the inscription can still be discerned the calligraphy distinctive of Lumley's *cartellini*. If the existing inscription is correctly read as giving Guildford's age as 49, this does not tally with the accepted date of his birth; Vertue omitted, on the three occasions when he transcribed the inscription, the last two digits of the inscribed age. No. 28 is in a very pure condition; much gold paint has been used in the costume and the collar of the Garter, and there is gold leaf in the badge on the cap. There seem to be traces of alterations in the outline of the shoulders. The figure seems first to have been painted before the blue background, which was then worked up to it and also to the curtain and rod; the foliage would have been painted at the next stage. The objects engraved on Guildford's badge are the components of the 'Typus Geometriae,' an iconographic formula used by Dürer in his *Melencolia I* of 1514 (E. Panofsky, *The Life and Art of Albrecht Dürer* (Princeton, 1955), pp. 156-7.[1]

A favourite of Henry VIII, whose friendship he retained all his life. He held numerous posts in the King's service from the time when he was a squire of the body; he was Master of the Horse (1515-22), Comptroller of the Household and attended the King at the Field of the Cloth of Gold; and was created a Knight of the Garter in 1526. In 1527 he authorised, in his official capacity as Comptroller, the payments to the Master Hans, who is assumed to be Holbein, for decorative work at Greenwich.

29. A MERCHANT OF THE GERMAN STEEL-YARD: 'HANS OF ANTWERP' (*Plate* 14)

Windsor Castle (68). Panel: $24 \times 18\frac{7}{16}$ in., 61×46.8 cm.

Half-length seated at a table, holding a letter in his left hand and cutting the string that ties it with a knife in his right hand; before him lie coins, a seal (on which appears to be the letter *W*) and a quill pen resting on a sheet of paper. On the paper is inscribed: *Anno Dns 1532 auf 26 July | Aetatis . . .*; there is an illegible inscription (see below) on the letter in the sitter's hand.

Secured in Germany by Sir Henry Vane and given to Charles I, who placed it in the Chair Room at Whitehall: *Done by Holbin . . . upon a Crackt board the Picture of a Merchant . . . cuting wᵗʰ A knife the sealing Thred from the lere a Seale lying by him upon a greene Table* (Van der Doort, p. 69; p. 225 *. . . in a Carved gilt frame . . .*). It is not possible to identify no. 29 with certainty in the documents dealing with the Sale: the pictures valued by the Trustees for Sale at St. James's on 16 February 1649 included: *A mans picture* at £45 (L. R. MS., f. 162 v.; Sebright MS., p. 214 as by Holbein) sold to Captain Geere on 14 May 1650 (S.P. 29/447, 24, 1); *A man wᵗʰ a Cap – pr holbin* at £20 (L. R. MS., f. 163 v.) sold to Bass and others on 19 December 1651 (S.P. 29/447, 24, 1); *A mans picture in black* at £120 (L. R.

MS., f. 165; Sebright MS., p. 219, as by Holbein) sold to Belcamp on 6 December 1650 (S.P. 29/447, 24, 1); and *A Picture done by Holben* at £40 (L. R. MS., f. 166) sold to Turbridge on 30 April 1650 for £44. No. 29 was certainly recovered at the Restoration and was placed in the King's Closet at Whitehall (Charles II, *Whitehall* (309)); recorded in the Queen's Closet at Windsor in the time of Queen Anne (Queen Anne, *Windsor* (90)).

Literature: Vertue, *Notebooks*, vol. IV, p. 119; Walpole, *Anecdotes*, vol. I, p. 84; Waagen (1838), vol. I, p. 178, (1854), vol. II, p. 431; R. N. Wornum, *Some Account of the Life and Works of Hans Holbein* (1867), pp. 258-9; A. Woltmann, *Holbein und seine Zeit*, vol. I (Leipzig, 1874), p. 368, vol. II (1876), pp. 155-6; Law, *Holbein*, pp. 5-7; Ganz, *KdK.*, 96; A. B. Chamberlain, *Hans Holbein the Younger* (1913), vol. II, pp. 8-14, 295-7; W. Stein, *Holbein* (Berlin, 1929), pp. 13, 226, 229-30; Collins Baker, *Windsor*, p. 158; Schmid, *Tafelband* (1945), p. 28 (55, 56), Textband (1948), vol. I, p. 84, vol. II, pp. 357, 367; R. A., *King's Pictures* (12), *Holbein and Other Masters*, 1950-1 (27); Ganz, *Holbein*, pp. 238-40 (62-64).

The identity of the sitter has not been conclusively established. In the early years of the nineteenth century (*e.g.*, in Legge's lists of pictures at Windsor in 1813 and 1816, and in Dallaway's notes (1826) to Walpole's *Anecdotes* (*q.v.*, vol. I, p. 80 n. 2)) he is described as Holstoff, a German merchant. This may have been due to a misreading of the inscription in the letter in the sitter's hand which Woltmann (*op. cit.*) read as: *Dem ersamen Hannsen Von anwerpen . . . upn Stallhoff zu handen.* This in turn led to the possible identification of the sitter with the goldsmith Hans of Antwerp. John or Hans of Antwerp, also referred to in 1541 as John van der Gow, had apparently been in England since 1515 and was paid for goldsmith's work for the Crown between 1537 and 1547; this included work for Princess Mary and the making of Garter insignia. On 7 October 1543 he witnessed Holbein's Will (see Sir L. Cust, 'John of Antwerp . . .', *Burl. Mag.*, vol. VIII (1906), pp. 356-60). The inscription indicates, moreover, that the sitter was one of the merchants of the Hansa Steelyard in Thames Street (see no. 26). Holbein designed for the goldsmith an elaborate cup (Schmid, Tafelband, pl. 133) which bore the inscription HANS VON ANT. The same sitter is almost certainly represented in a smaller portrait by Holbein at Schloss Blankenburg (Ganz, *Holbein*, pl. 102) on the back of which is an early inscription giving the date 1532 and the age 34; and may also be represented in another small portrait in the Victoria and Albert Museum ((P. 158-1910; *ibid.*, pl. 101), inscribed with the age 34.

Van der Doort's description (see above) indicates that the panel has been for a long time in an unsatisfactory state. There are at least four major vertical cracks; the panel has been repainted round all the edges, and there is extensive repaint, covering areas of lost original paint: primarily in the cap and hair, down the beard into the costume, in the costume, in the lower left background, and on the table, including the pen and paper. The face and central part of the beard, the front of the shirt, the fold on and above the right elbow and (except for local damages) the hands, are in good condition. No. 29 is, with the portrait of Georg Gisze in Berlin, the only portrait by Holbein of a merchant of the Steelyard to be dated 1532. The two portraits must therefore have been painted soon after his return to London in September 1532. The accessories in no. 29 appear in some of Holbein's other portraits of the merchants, *i.e.*, Dirk Tybis (Vienna) and Cyriacus Kale (Brunswick) of 1533 and Derich Berck (Metropolitan Museum) of 1536 (Ganz, *Holbein*, pls. 105, 106, 130).

30. THOMAS HOWARD, THIRD DUKE OF NORFOLK (1473-1554) (*Plate* 20)

Windsor Castle (59). Panel: $31\frac{5}{8} \times 24\frac{1}{4}$ in., 80.3×61.6 cm.

---

1. I am grateful to Mr. Roy Strong for drawing my attention to this.

The original inscription in the background has been almost entirely obliterated and overpainted; it originally read as follows: [. THOMAS . DVKE OF.] NORFOLK. MARSH [ALL. / . AND .] TRESVRER OF INGLOND[E.] / THE [.L]X [VI.] YERE [O]F HIS AGE.[1]

Half-length, wearing the collar of the Garter and holding in his right hand the Earl Marshal's baton and in his left the staff of Lord Treasurer.

Presumably painted for the Duke in 1538–9. It passed by descent to his great-great-grandson Thomas, Earl of Arundel; it was carefully depicted, with a portrait by Holbein of the Duke's son, the Earl of Surrey, by Philip Fruytiers in the background of his water-colour (1643) of the Arundel family which may record a scheme by Van Dyck for a large family group (see R. A., *British Portraits*, 1956–7 (551)); it was drawn by Vorsterman as a preparatory study for his engraving (A. M. Hind, *Catalogue of Drawings by Dutch and Flemish Artists . . . in the British Museum*, vol. II (1923), p. 148); and it appears in the Arundel inventory drawn up in Amsterdam in 1655 (P.R.O., Del. 1/VII, f. 702: *holbein. Ritratto de Tomaso Howard Ducha de Nordfolk;* see also M. F. S. Hervey, *The Life . . . of Thomas Howard, Earl of Arundel* (1921), p. 482). Presumably the portrait sold in an anonymous sale in Amsterdam on 23 April 1732, where it fetched fl.1120: in 1744 Vertue saw in London 'a sale of Pictures. Thomas Duke of Norfolk painted on bord. by H. Holben the same picture I saw several years ago brought from Holland – valud then 200¹¹s'; this was presumably the sale to which Vertue had referred earlier, probably in 1735: . . . 'if this the original Qᵘ – however as it is to be sold. they value at a high price – 200¹¹ – and has stood unsold. (lately was put to an Auction there it went at 300 pounds –)' (*Notebooks*, vol. III, p. 122, vol. IV, p. 83). It seems to have been acquired by Frederick, Prince of Wales, and was mentioned among his pictures by Vertue in July 1750 (B. M., MS. 19027, f. 21: 'the Duke of Norfolk. Ld. Treasurer. H. Holben. painted'); recorded at Leicester House by Walpole (*Anecdotes*, vol. I, p. 83, n. 3); at Windsor early in the reign of George III.[2]

Literature: Waagen (1838), vol. I, 178, (1854), vol. II, p. 430; R. N. Wornum, *Some Account of . . . Hans Holbein* (1867), pp. 342–4; A. Woltmann, *Holbein und seine Zeit*, vol. I (Leipzig, 1874), pp. 470–1, vol. II (1876), pp. 57, 156; Law, *Holbein*, pp. 15–20; Ganz, *KdK.*, 123; A. B. Chamberlain, *Hans Holbein the Younger* (1913), vol. II, pp. 171, 197–200; U. Christoffel, *Hans Holbein D.J.* (Berlin, 1924), pp. 118–20; W. Stein, *Holbein* (Berlin, 1929), pp. 314–16; Collins Baker, *Windsor*, pp. 159–60; Schmid, *Tafelband* (1945), p. 34 (106), Textband (1948), vol. II, pp. 368, 376, 383–5, 389; R. A., *King's Pictures* (10), *Holbein and Other Masters*, 1950–51 (12); W. Pinder, *Holbein der Jüngere . . .* (Cologne, 1951), pp. 70, 80–1; Ganz, *Holbein*, p. 250 (103); R. A., *British Portraits*, 1956–7 (9).

The original inscription in gold, painted on a green background, can still be read in places, but has been partly removed; the whole background has been overcleaned and then apparently overpainted with a thin glaze of a duller green than the original. The background appears already to have been in its present condition in 1862 (*V.R. inv.*), though the inscription may then have been more legible. Much of the modelling over the gold leaf on the Earl Marshal's baton has been worn off. There are two versions of no. 30 at Arundel. They bear, with minor variations, the inscription given above; neither of these versions, which are both on panel, are of the same high quality as no. 30. Also at Arundel is a copy extended to a full length and an (eighteenth-century ?) variant of no. 30 which has been endowed with a later swagger. A copy at Castle Howard has a patterned background; another full length extension is at Gorhambury.

1. The sections in square brackets have been transcribed from the picture of no. 30 as it is seen hanging in Fruytiers's water-colour (see above).

2. It is improbable that no. 30 is referred to in an obscure reference in the list of pictures at Kensington in the reign of George II appended to Bathoe, *James II:* 'Holbein. Lord Arundel or Howard' (no. 4 in this list and described by Walpole, *Anecdotes*, vol. I, p. 83, as 'much inferior').

A version is at Naworth Castle. A pen drawing in reverse, attributed to J. Wiericx, is in the Albertina.

The Duke was closely related to the royal house, uncle to Anne Boleyn and Catherine Howard, and one of the most powerful men of his time: Lord High Admiral (1513–25), Lord High Treasurer (1522–47), Earl Marshal (1533), Knight of the Garter (1510) and god-father to Edward VI. Sent to the Tower for High Treason in 1546, his execution was only prevented by Henry VIII's death; he was in prison during the reign of Edward VI, but fully restored by Mary I.

31. WILLIAM(?) RESKIMER (*Plate* 15)

Windsor Castle (3019). Panel: 18¼ × 13¼ in., 46,4 × 33,7 cm. The original unpainted edges have been preserved on all four sides; the original painted surface is 17½ × 12½ in.

Half-length, almost in profile to the left, with both his hands in front of him; behind are tendrils of the same vine (?) that is seen in the background of nos. 26 and 28.

Presented to Charles I by Sir Robert Killigrew (d. 1633) and placed in the Cabinet Room at Whitehall: *Don by Hollben . . . in an ould defaced gilded frame . . . a side faced Gentleman out of Cornwall . . . with a long peaked Beard houlding both his hands before him, some part of a Vine painted by . . . upon a defaced Crackt Board* (*Van der Doort*, p. 82); the CR brand, now concealed by cradling, and a paper label that may have been of the type applied by Van der Doort, were recorded in 1859 (*V.R. inv.*). It is impossible to identify no. 31 among possible pictures attributed to Holbein in the valuations drawn up by the Trustees for Sale, but some of the more likely pieces are mentioned at this point in the history of no. 29; no. 31 was certainly recovered at the Restoration (Col. Hawley, f. 18 v.), possibly from Philip, Lord Lisle, later 3rd Earl of Leicester, who sent in on 10 September 1660 a group of pictures that included *A man wᵗʰ a red beard by Holben* (Penshurst MSS., 1160, 14); placed in the King's Closet at Whitehall. Probably taken by William III to Hampton Court: among the pictures in the King's Private Apartments in 1700 was (22): *Gennet Mans head black Cap on 2 hands* (B. M., Harl. MS. 5150, f. 14); this was probably identical with: *Gennet. A mans head wᵗʰ a red beard and black Cap Side Face* in the Closet below Stairs in the following reign (Queen Anne, *Hampton Court* (50)) and, with the same attribution, in 1750 (Vertue inv., *Hampton Court*, f. 8). Certainly at Hampton Court (later inv. no. 325) in the reign of George III.

Literature: Walpole, *Visits*, p. 80; Waagen (1838), vol. II, p. 116, (1854), vol. II, p. 363; A. Woltmann, *Holbein und seine Zeit*, vol. I (Leipzig, 1874), pp. 333, 375, vol. II (1876), p. 128; Law, 1881, 1898 (610), *Holbein*, p. 29; Ganz, *KdK*, 113; A. B. Chamberlain, *Hans Holbein the Younger* (1913), vol. I, pp. 299, 333–4; W. Stein, *Holbein* (Berlin, 1929), p. 273; Collins Baker, *Hampton Court*, pp. 72–3; Schmid, *Tafelband* (1945), p. 32 (92), Textband (1948), vol. II, p. 364; R. A., *King's Pictures* (25), *Holbein and Other Masters*, 1950–51 (180); Ganz, *Holbein*, p. 241 (71).

Probably painted c. 1532–33, early in Holbein's second English period. The preliminary drawing at Windsor (Parker, 31) is inscribed: *Reskemeer a Cornish Gent:*, and the painting follows it very closely. There are two vertical cracks on the right side of the panel and areas of repaint in the right background and down the shoulder; the blacks are rubbed in the shadows; but the panel on the whole is in good condition and the head and hands are very well preserved.

The sitter is almost certainly one of the sons of John Reskimer of Merthen, and a member, therefore, of a very old Cornish family. The elder son, John Reskimer, with whom the portrait was traditionally identified, seems to have been engaged in local activities in Cornwall at the time no. 31 was painted; but his younger brother William was Page of the Chamber in 1532, was thereafter almost continuously at court and in 1546 became a Gentleman-Usher.

32. 'NOLI ME TANGERE' (*Plates* 22–5)

Hampton Court (383). Panel: $30\frac{1}{4} \times 37\frac{3}{4}$ in., $76,8 \times 94,9$ cm. The panel has been made out at the sides and the original painted surface is $30\frac{1}{4} \times 37\frac{5}{16}$ in.

In the foreground Christ forbidding the Magdalen to touch Him; behind her is the open tomb with the two angels in white sitting by the grave-clothes; beyond are SS. Peter and John returning to Jerusalem from the empty tomb and in the distance are Calvary and Jerusalem (St. John XX, 1–17).

Not recorded in the royal collection before 2 September 1680 when Evelyn saw, in the Private Lodgings at Whitehall: '(& in my esteeme) above all the *Noli me tangere* of our *B: Saviour* to *M: Magdalen*, after his *Resurrection*, of *Hans Holbeins*, than which, in my life, I never saw so much reverence & kind of Heavenly astonishment, expressed in Picture' (*Diary*, ed. E. S. de Beer (1955), vol. IV, pp. 216–7). It is possible that no. 32 had belonged to Henrietta Maria and came to Charles II at her death in 1669; among the pictures over the chimney in the Cabinet by her Bedchamber at Colombes was *A Noli me Tangere* which was *To be taken away unknowne to Madame* (P. R. O., S.P. 78/128, f. 219). In the reign of James II it was still hanging in the Private Lodgings, apparently in the King's Closet, at Whitehall (B. M., Harl. MS. 1890, f. 62; Bathoe, *James II* (520); the original James II number (521) is painted on the panel). Thereafter at Kensington.

Literature: A. Woltmann, 'Holbein at the National Portrait Exhibition', *Fortnightly Review*, vol. VI (1866), p. 158; Law, 1881, 1898, (599); H. Knackfuss, *Holbein der Jüngere* (Leipzig, 1896), p. 68; Law, *Holbein*, pp. 31–2; L. Baldass, *Kunstgeschichtliche Anzeigen* (Innsbruck, 1911), p. 104; Ganz, *KdK*, 80; A. B. Chamberlain, *Hans Holbein the Younger* (1913), vol. I, pp. 95–8; U. Christoffel, *Hans Holbein D.J.* (Berlin, 1924), p. 123; W. Stein, *Holbein* (Berlin, 1929), pp. 216, 218; Collins Baker, *Hampton Court*, p. 73; R. A., *King's Pictures* (158); Schmid, Tafelband (1945), Text-band (1948), vol. II, pp. 326, 386, 392–3; W. Pinder, *Holbein der Jüngere* . . . (Cologne, 1951), p. 48; F. Grossmann, 'Holbein Studies – II', *Burl. Mag.*, vol. XCIII (1951), p. 111; Ganz, *Holbein*, p. 223 (22); Kunstmuseum, Basel, *Die Malerfamilie Holbein in Basel*, 1960 (186); L. Baldass, *Zeitschrift für Kunstwissenschaft*, vol. XV (Berlin, 1961), p. 95; City of Manchester Art Gallery, *German Art, 1400–1800*, 1961 (97); M. Levey, C. White and F. Grossmann in *Burl. Mag.*, vol. CIII (1961), pp. 487, 493–4.

Although Holbein's name has been attached to no. 32 in the records of the royal collection since 1680 it has only been accepted in his *oeuvre* by scholars since 1895.[1] Woltmann had attributed it in 1866 (*op. cit.*) to Bruyn. In November 1871 Dr. A. von Zahn had told Redgrave (*V.R. inv.*) that he thought it a fine Holbein of the Basel period. The varied views on the authorship and dating of the panel are clearly set out in the catalogue of the exhibition at Basel in 1960 (*loc. cit*). The dating has probably been confused by the assumption that no. 32 could be identified with a picture in Henry VIII's collection (*1542, 1547* (33) . . . *a table with the picture of our Lorde appering to Mary Magdalen*) and that it had therefore probably been painted in England. But there is no evidence that the picture in Henry VIII's collection was by Holbein and, more significant, no. 32 cannot be identified in the documents dealing with the collection of Charles I, who does not, indeed, seem to have owned a picture of this subject. If such a panel as no. 32 had been in his collection it would, moreover, probably have been branded. It is therefore possible to date no. 32 on evidence of style alone and this would seem to place it perhaps slightly earlier than is usually thought: in about the period of, or just after, Holbein's visit to France in 1524.[2] This date would explain the synthesis of reminiscences

. By A. Bayersdorfer in *Kunsthistorische Gesellschaft* . . ., vol. I (1895).
2. It is not inconceivable, indeed, if no. 32 came to England from France, that it had been painted by Holbein in France in 1524.

of Baldung and Burgkmair and, in the figure of Christ and in the sky, of Holbein's earlier religious works, such as the altarpiece of the Passion in Basel of *c.* 1520 (Ganz, *Holbein*, pls. 16–30) and the Oberried Altarpiece of 1520–1 (*ibid.*, pls. 35–44), with a classical influence which links *Noli Me Tangere* with Holbein's later woodcuts, and with the influence of Italian High Renaissance painting which is clearly felt in the figure of the Madalen. In type she is close to the female portraits of 1526 (*ibid.*, pls. 69–70), and may indeed have been painted from the same very appropriate model. Approximate parallels have been found in no. 32 to details in Holbein's graphic work; the figure of St. Peter is perhaps akin to the figure of Samuel in the drawing (*c.* 1530) for a fresco in the Town Hall at Basel (*ibid.*, fig. 52) and that of Christ reappears in reverse, with minor variations, in one of the little episodes on Holbein's title-page to Miles Coverdale's translation (1535) of the Bible, and, in the same sense but also with variations, in a woodcut of *c.* 1543 (Schmid, Tafelband, pl. 202). There appear to be *pentimenti* in no. 32 in the position of Christ's left hand and possibly in the drawing of the opening of the tomb. There are alterations in painting to the upper right outline of the Magdalen, where an area of white (? drapery) has been painted out between the shoulder and elbow. An unusual iconographical element in the design is the presence of six (and possibly originally seven) crosses on Calvary. A copy belonged (1951) to the Rev. Stuart Adams.

After Hans Holbein the Younger

33. PORTRAIT OF THE ARTIST

Hampton Court (969). $30\frac{1}{4} \times 25\frac{1}{2}$ in., $76,8 \times 64,8$ cm.; there are later additions on both sides and at the bottom and the original canvas was *c.* $26 \times 20\frac{7}{8}$ in.

Head and shoulders in a black cap.

Probably first recorded in the Supper Room at Kensington in the reign of George II (Vertue inv., *Kensington*, f. 12: *A Copy of The head of Hans Holben painter*).

Literature: Law, 1881, 1898 (857); Collins Baker, *Hampton Court*, p. 169.

Apparently an early-eighteenth-century derivation, perhaps painted for Queen Caroline, of the painter's *Self-portrait* of 1543. The source of the *Self-portraits* was probably the drawing in the Uffizi (Ganz, *Holbein*, p. 14); no. 33 could have been derived from one of the miniature versions (*e.g.*, *ibid.*, pls. 186, 187).

34. HENRY VIII

Windsor Castle (73). Panel: $39\frac{1}{4} \times 29\frac{1}{4}$ in., $99,7 \times 74,3$ cm.

Three-quarter-length, his gloves in his right hand and holding with his left the chain on which his dagger is suspended.

Recorded at Kensington in 1818 (161: *Half length Portrait of Henry the Eighth Holbein* . . .)

Literature: Waagen (1838), vol. I, p. 178, (1854), vol. II, p. 432; A. Woltmann, *Holbein und seine Zeit*, vol. II (Leipzig, 1876), p. 20; Law, *Holbein*, pp. 13–14; Ganz, *KdK*, 222; A. B. Chamberlain, *Hans Holbein the Younger* (1913), vol. II, pp. 103–4; N. Beets, 'Cornelis Anthonisz, II', *Oud-Holland*, vol. LVI (1939), pp. 199–221; Schmid, Textband (1948), vol. I, p. 91, vol. II, pp. 374, 396; Collins Baker, *Windsor*, p. 161; R. A., *King's Pictures* (9); Ganz, *Holbein*, p. 249 (96).

A very early derivation from Holbein's original portrait of the King, painted in 1537 on the wall of the Privy Chamber at Whitehall (see no. 216). This wall-painting was the source of such early full-length portraits as those at Chatsworth, Belvoir, Petworth and (probably the finest) the Walker Art Gallery, Liverpool. Three-quarter and half-length derivations, with variations in detail, are equally common; the finest is probably that in the National Gallery, Rome, of 1539–40 (Ganz, *Holbein*, pl. 147). No. 34 may have been painted during the King's lifetime, and is still close in technique to Holbein; it is possible that the head of the King is derived from a sitting later than that which formed the basis of the wall-painting. See also no. 35. The attribution of no. 34 to Cornelis Anthonisz, put forward by Beets (*loc. cit.*), does not seem tenable.

35. HENRY VIII

Windsor Castle (266). Panel: $36\frac{1}{4} \times 29\frac{1}{2}$ in., $92,1 \times 75$ cm.

Three-quarter-length, his gloves in his right hand and holding with his left the chain on which his dagger is suspended.

In the collection of Charles I (the CR brand is on the back). Among the pictures valued at Hampton Court on 3–5 October 1649 by the Trustees for Sale were two portraits of Henry VIII, one of which may be identifiable with no. 35: *Henry ye 8th* valued at £8 (L. R. MS., f. 121 v.) and sold to Jackson and others on 23 October 1651; and *The Picture of King Henrÿ ye 8th*, valued at £1 (*ibid.*, f. 123) and sold to De Critz and others on 18 November 1651. No. 35 was hanging in the Queen's Gallery at Hampton Court in the reign of Charles II (Charles II, *Hampton Court* (1): *Henry 8 holding his gloves in his right hand at Halfe length*, measurements given as 36×30 in.); and is almost certainly the portrait in the Old Gallery at Windsor in the reign of Queen Anne (Queen Anne, *Windsor* (129): *Holbin. King Henry ye 8th to ye waste over y^e door to y^e back Stairs*).

Literature: Collins Baker, *Windsor*, p. 163.

A competent but simplified later sixteenth-century derivation from the same source as no. 34, but clearly later and one stage further from Holbein in technique and quality.

36. HENRY VIII

St. James's Palace. $94\frac{1}{4} \times 58\frac{1}{4}$ in., $239,4 \times 148$ cm.; there are additions at the top and on both sides; the original canvas was *c.* 82×36 in.

Full-length standing, his gloves in his right hand and holding with his left the chain on which his dagger is suspended.

Probably the portrait recorded in the set of royal portraits in the Cross Gallery at Somerset House in September 1649, when it was valued at £30 by the Trustees for Sale (Corsham MS., f. 56: *King Henry ye 8. at Length*); sold to Col. Webb on 29 October 1649; probably the *Large peece of Henry ye 8th*, valued at £30 and declared to the House of Lords Committee on 18 May 1660 as in the possession of John Cade (H. of L. MSS.). Recorded in the Cross Gallery at Somerset House in the time of Queen Anne (Queen Anne, *Somerset House* (25)) as by Holbein and with a note by Thomas Coke recording its slightly later move to the Blue Room at St. James's, where it was noted in the following reign (B. M., Stowe MS. 567, f. 70: *. . . en habit Bleu*). Later at Kensington in the set of royal full-lengths in the Queen's Gallery (Vertue inv., *Kensington*, f. 22); removed to St. James's by order of the Lord Chamberlain on 13 March 1824.

Literature: Walpole, *Anecdotes*, vol. I, p. 83.

A derivation, probably painted in the second half of the sixteenth century, from the same source as no. 34. The background on the original canvas seems to have been overpainted at the time when the additions were made; at Kensington in 1818 (257) the canvas was already its present size. The additions were probably made so that no. 36 could hang harmoniously with the other full-lengths in the Queen's Gallery at Kensington (see Pyne, vol. II, *Kensington*, p. 67).

37. HENRY VIII

Hampton Court (326). Panel: $18\frac{1}{2} \times 15\frac{1}{4}$ in., $47 \times 38,7$ cm. The panel seems to have been cut down all round.

Half-length, resting his hands on a red cushion before him, his gloves in his right hand.

Among the early portraits, formerly in the collection of Lady Capel (on the panel is her seal), acquired at Kew; possibly the portrait recorded in the King's Dressing Room at Hampton Court (Geo. III, *Hampton Court* (*King Henry the 8th*); Pyne, vol. II, p. 58, *. . . painted by Hans Holbein*); definitely at Hampton Court in 1835 (324).

Literature: Waagen (1838), vol. II, p. 116; Law, 1881, 1898 (606); Collins Baker, *Hampton Court*, p. 76.

An early derivation of respectable quality from the same source as no. 34, probably painted later in the sixteenth century. The red cushion in front of the King may be an early example of a favourite element in the copying of early royal portraits on this scale (*cf.*, nos. 41, 42 and 54).

38. HENRY VIII

Windsor Castle (255). Panel: $22\frac{5}{8} \times 17\frac{3}{8}$ in., $57,5 \times 44,1$ cm.

Inscribed: ·HENRICVS· ·viii·

Head and shoulders, wearing a jewelled chain.

Probably part of the set of royal portraits secured by Queen Caroline from Lord Cornwallis, and possibly the portrait recorded at Kensington in 1729 (?): *The head of K. Henry 8th in a new Gilt frame Cleand* (B. M., Add. MS. 20101, f. 56); certainly at Kensington in 1818 (644).

Literature: Collins Baker, *Windsor*, p. 163.

Probably derived from the same source as no. 34. Derivations on this scale are common, *e.g.*, at Penicuik and Boughton.

39. ERASMUS (1466–1536) (*Plate* 15)

Hampton Court (324). Panel: $21\frac{1}{2} \times 12\frac{7}{8}$ in., $54,6 \times 32,7$ cm., including a later addition at the top of $2\frac{1}{2}$ in.; the original unpainted edge is visible on the three other sides.

Half-length, resting his hands on a book.

See no. 27, with which it was placed by Charles I in the Cabinet Room at Whitehall: *Done by Holben . . . Erasmus Rotterdamus in a high black frame . . . fellow to the aforesaid peece of ffrobenius* (Van der Doort, p. 85, measurements given as 21×13 in.); the CR brand and a (possibly contemporary) label were thought in 1859 to have been removed (*V.R. inv.*). See no. 27 for the later history of the pair.

Literature: The references given for no. 27 also apply to no. 39. For no. 39 see particularly Law, 1881, 1898 (597); Collins Baker, *Hampton Court*, pp. 73–4; H. A. Schmid, *Die Werke Hans Holbein in Basel* (1930), p. 64; P. Ganz, 'Die Erasmusbildnisse von Holbein', *Gedenkschrift zum 400. Todestag des Erasmus* (Basel, 1936), p. 260; R. A., *King's Pictures* (3), *Holbein and Other Masters*, 1950–51 (3); Kunstmuseum, Basel, *Die Malerfamilie Holbein in Basel*, 1960 (169).

No. 39 still has the background, presumed to have been painted when the panel was enlarged, probably soon after it entered Charles I's collection (see no. 27). The background shows bookshelves behind the sitter and the interior of a large Gothic church; it is very close in style to Hendrick van Steenwyck and Waagen recorded ((1838), vol. II, p. 116) Steenwyck's name on the background and the date 1629. There is no trace of this today. The curtain which in 1927 was revealed in the background of no. 27 continues across the original background of no. 39; its outline can be seen with the naked eye. The X-ray revealed, however, a difference in handling between the areas of curtain in the two panels. Nor are there any traces of alterations in the painting of no. 39 as there are in no. 27; the top of the cap is painted over the original green curtain. The paint in no. 39 is thinner and less rich than in no. 27. No. 39 is of good quality and is probably a contemporary derivation, painted within Holbein's orbit, from Holbein's portrait of Erasmus of this type, of which the finest version, dated 1523, is at Longford Castle (Ganz, *Holbein*, pl. 64); of this type numerous versions, variants and derivations exist (*e.g.*, *ibid.*, pp. 235-8). There seems no contemporary evidence for the original ownership of the diptych. If it can be assumed that it was formed by joining to an original portrait of Froben a version of a standard *Erasmus* specially painted as a pendant, it could have originated with either of the sitters. It has been traditionally stated that after Froben's death Erasmus secured the portraits and hinged them together as a lasting memorial to their friendship (Chamberlain, vol. I, p. 166) and it is perhaps more logical to assume that the portraits may originally have belonged to Froben rather than to Erasmus.

The famous scholar and humanist, who paid a number of visits to England and in 1499 saw the royal children at Eltham. During his residence at Basel, 1521-9, he was closely associated with Froben and Holbein.

40. ELIZABETH CHEYNE, LADY VAUX (*c.* 1505?-1556)

Hampton Court (337). Panel: $14\frac{15}{16} \times 11\frac{1}{4}$ in., $38 \times 28,6$ cm.

Half-length, wearing at her bosom a jewel decorated with an image of the Madonna and Child enthroned, holding a pink in her right hand and a cherry (?) in her left.

Possibly a picture recorded at Whitehall in the time of James II: *One of King Henry the Eighths Queenes with a Gilliflower in her hand* (B. M., Harl. MS. 1890, f. 59; Bathoe, *James II* (410)). This seems to have been at Hampton Court in 1700 (Harl. MS. 5150: *Gennet Henry the VII^ths Queen*) and in the time of Queen Anne: *Gennet. A small Womans head wth a July Flower in her hand* (Queen Anne, *Hampton Court* (31); Vertue's inventory of Hampton Court in 1750, f. 7, describes the picture in almost the same terms and repeats the attribution to Clouet). Recorded as a portrait of Lady Vaux in the King's Dressing Room at Hampton Court in the reign of George III (Geo. III, *Hampton Court*).

Literature: Waagen (1838), vol. II, p. 117, (1854), vol. II, p. 361; Law, 1881, 1898 (591); A. Woltmann, *Holbein und seine Zeit*, vol. I, (Leipzig, 1874), pp. 333, 424, vol. II (1876), p. 128; A. B. Chamberlain, *Hans Holbein the Younger* (1913), vol. II, pp. 86, 87; Ganz, *KdK*, 221; Collins Baker, *Hampton Court*, pp. 74-5; Schmid, *Tafelband* (1945), p. 33 (96), vol. II (1948), pp. 390-1; R. A., *Holbein and Other Masters*, 1950-1 (172); F. Grossmann, 'Holbein Studies – I', *Burl. Mag.*, vol. XCIII (1951), p. 40; Ganz, *Holbein*, pp. 246-8 (90).

Although attempts have been made to claim no. 40 as an original, it seems to be a very painstaking copy of a lost original of *c.* 1535, probably made early in the seventeenth century. This is confirmed by X-ray (1961), which reveals no trace of autograph quality. The slightly smaller, and possibly superior, version in Prague is probably also a copy and may be the one recorded in the collection of the 2nd Duke of Buckingham: *By Holbein . . . The picture of Madam de Vaux* (*A Catalogue of the . . . Collection . . . of George Villiers, Duke of Buckingham . . .*, printed by W. Bathoe (1758), p. 16, measurements given as 18 × 12 in.). Holbein's preparatory drawing for the original portrait is at Windsor (Parker, 25), with a drawing of Lord Vaux (Parker, 24). Parker points out that in the drawing of Lady Vaux 'the outlines in metal-point are drawn, as if for transfer to the panel, sharply and incisively'.

Elizabeth, daughter of Sir Thomas Cheyne, married in 1523 Thomas, 2nd Lord Vaux of Harrowden.

Artists Unknown : Tudor Royal Portraits

41. CATHERINE OF ARAGON

Windsor Castle (253). Panel: $22\frac{5}{8} \times 17\frac{1}{2}$ in., $57,5 \times 44,5$ cm.

Inscribed: CATERINA PRIMA VXOR HENRICI OCTAVI.

Head and shoulders.

Probably part of the set of royal portraits secured by Queen Caroline from Lord Cornwallis; recorded at Kensington in 1778, in Sir Henry Ellis's MS. *Memoranda* (1822), and in 1818 (643).

Literature: Collins Baker, *Windsor*, p. 101.

A version of a standard type. Other versions are in the National Portrait Gallery (163), at Merton College, Oxford, at Petworth (423) and in the collection of Mrs. Eric Thompson. The type may have originated with a three-quarter-length which is associated with Johannes Corvus (*c.* 1510-20) of which there is a version at Northwick Park (see Walker Art Gallery, Liverpool, *Kings and Queens of England*, 1953 (4), illustrated souvenir, pl. 16).

42. ANNE BOLEYN

Windsor Castle (257). Panel: $23 \times 16\frac{7}{8}$ in., $58,4 \times 42,9$ cm.

Inscribed: ANNA BOLLINA VXOR · HENRICI · OCTAVI.

Head and shoulders, wearing round her neck a gold pendant in the shape of a B.

Probably part of the set of royal portraits secured by Queen Caroline from Lord Cornwallis; recorded at Kensington in 1818 (645).

Literature: Collins Baker, *Windsor*, p. 100.

A derivation from a standard type of portrait of the Queen, of which there are versions in the National Portrait Gallery (668), in the National Gallery of Ireland (549; with the same roll of brocade in front) and in the collections of Mrs. Eric Thompson and Major C. E. Radclyffe; the last is probably a contemporary portrait of the Queen (R. A., *Kings and Queens*, 1953 (75), illustrated souvenir, pl. 17).

A portrait of *Queene Anna: of Bulloigne*, valued at £1 by the Trustees for Sale at Hampton Court in October 1649 (L. R. MS., f. 124) and sold to Murray and others on 23 October 1651, may have been the source of a miniature in Charles I's collection of *Queene An: of Buloin in a black dressing adorn'd wth pearls wch was Coppied by Haskins after an oyle Cullored. peece.* (*Van der Doort*, p. 109).

43. THE FAMILY OF HENRY VIII (*Plate* 27)

Hampton Court (510). $66\frac{3}{4} \times 140\frac{1}{4}$ in., $169,5 \times 356,9$ cm.; there are two later additions at the top, the first *c.* $5\frac{1}{2}$ in. and the second *c.* $2\frac{1}{2}$ in. (see below).

A group of five full-length royal figures under a slightly raised colonnade, supported on carved and gilded columns; the ceiling is decorated with Tudor roses and the wall with an intricate design in carved and gilded wood-panelling. Through archways at each end of the colonnade are glimpses of the Great Garden at Whitehall Palace with the King's Beasts. Through the left opening is seen the end of a richly decorated building, which may be the Banqueting House in the Orchard, or, less likely, a wing of the Prince's Lodgings, and, in the distance, the Westminster Clock-house; through the right opening is seen the north transept of Westminster Abbey and one of the corner turrets of Henry VIII's tennis court. In the archway on the left is a serving-maid (?) and on the right a fool with a monkey perched on his shoulders. In the centre of the composition, under a richly decorated canopy of state (bearing the royal arms and a tablet inscribed with the monogram HR. VIII), Henry VIII is seated, placing his right hand on Prince Edward, later Edward VI; Jane Seymour is seated on the King's left. On the left of the group stands Princess Mary, later Mary I, on the right Princess Elizabeth, later Elizabeth I.

Probably painted for Henry VIII. The accounts of the Paymaster of the Works for the year 1588–9 for the restoration of the Presence Chamber at Whitehall provide for varnishing 'with a special Vernishe made without sente' the pictures in the room (see nos. 24 and 25), which included: 'a greate table containing Kinge Henrie, Prince Edwarde and the ij ladies his daughters Pictors' (P. R. O., E. 351/3223).[1] No. 43 was seen at Whitehall in 1602 by the Duke of Stettin-Pomerania and may be the picture recorded by Sandrart at Whitehall and as by Holbein: 'Er hat auch sehr künstlich gemacht König Heinrichs drey hinterlassene Prinzen und Prinzessinnen als Eduardum, Maria und Elisabeth, die auch eben daselbst zu sehen seyn' (*Academie...*, ed. A. R. Peltzer (Munich, 1925), p. 100). In the time of Charles I it hung in the Privy Gallery at Whitehall: ... *a Longe peece painted with gould where King Henrie y⁰ 8th sitts with his Queene and his Sonn ... on his right Side: and his two daughtrs ... at each Side: and a foole at the left Side in the doore with a Jaconaps on his Shouldr and on the other side a waiteing woeman ...* (Van der Doort, p. 31); valued by the Trustees for Sale in 1649 at £15 (L. R. MS., f. 9) and sold to Col. Webb on 27 October 1649. Declared to the House of Lords Committee on 18 May 1660 in the possession of John Cade (H. of L. MSS.) and apparently first attributed at this time to Holbein; placed in the King's Privy Gallery at Whitehall (Charles II, *Whitehall* (107): *Henry 8 sitting in a chayre Queene Jane ...*, measurements given as 54 × 133 in.); later at Windsor (Vertue inv., *Windsor*, f. 10).

Literature: Vertue, *Notebooks*, vol. II, p. 29, vol. IV, p. 119; Walpole, *Anecdotes*, vol. I, pp. 58–9 (n. by Dallaway); Waagen (1854), vol. II, p. 366; J. G. Nichols, *A Catalogue of the Portraits of King Edward VI...* (1859), pp. 10–11, 'Remarks upon Holbein's Portraits of the Royal Family...', *Archaeologia*, vol. XL (1866, read 1863), pp. 79–80; Law, 1881, 1898 (340); F. M. O'Donoghue, *A Descriptive... Catalogue of Portraits of Queen Elizabeth*, (1894), p. 2; Collins Baker, *Hampton Court*, pp. 75–6; N. Beets, 'Cornelis Anthonisz, II', *Oud-Holland*, vol. LVI (1939), pp. 199–221; R. Edwards, *Early Conversation Pieces* (1954), pp. 18, 155; D. Piper, *Connoisseur Period Guides, Tudor* (1956), p. 48.

Probably painted *c.* 1545. Edward VI and Elizabeth I seem slightly younger than in nos. 44 and 46. The Queen seated by the King has been identified (*e.g.*, by Law, *op. cit.*) as Catherine Parr, but is almost certainly Jane Seymour, represented as the mother of the King's heir. The portrait of her is presumably based on Holbein's standard image of her (*e.g.*, Ganz, *Holbein*, pl. 138). The other portraits, on the other hand, appear to be *ad vivum*, though the presentation of the King is obviously reminiscent of Holbein. The painter of no. 43 has not been identified, but it is one of the most important works from the period immediately after Holbein's death. As a royal group and a dynastic record it is to some extent a sequel to Holbein's wall-painting in the Privy Chamber at Whitehall (see above, p. 11) and the precursor of the group at Sudeley Castle (see no. 58), of no. 150 and also, to a more limited extent, of no. 285. Although the setting of no. 43 is probably imaginary, the background seen through the two archways constitutes a topographical record rare at this period. The rails and the King's Beasts with their vanes were a notable feature of the Great Garden: '... different animals carved in wood, with their horns gilt, are set on top of the columns, together with flags bearing the Queen's arms'. Among the beasts represented in no. 43 are the Griffin (Edward III), the Yale (Beaufort), the White Greyhound (Richmond), and possibly the Hind and the

Greyhound. At least from the time of Dallaway (*loc. cit.*) the fool in the background, who is in dark green with red stockings, has been identified as Will Somers, the King's jester, but this cannot be accepted as conclusive. Gold leaf is used in the architectural setting and in all the royal figures. The picture was clearly originally narrower. The earlier of the two additions at the top includes an extension of the original forms of architectural detail; the second contains a feigned relief of a mask and fruit in a much later style.

44. EDWARD VI (*Plate 21*)

Windsor Castle (69). Panel: 42¼ × 32¼ in., 107,3 × 81,9 cm.

Inscribed, at a slightly later date and in the same hand as no. 46: *Edwardus Sextus Rex | Angliæ*.

Three-quarter-length standing, resting his left hand on his sash and clasping a dagger in his right; from a chain round his shoulders is suspended a jewel decorated with the Prince of Wales's crown and feathers. The sculptured decoration of the embrasure of the window on the left includes a roundel, possibly of Marcus Curtius, who appears in a roundel in relief, inscribed MARCVS. CVRCIVS. ROMAN[VS], on the base of the column in the background. Through the window is seen a landscape with deer in a park and a large early Tudor building beside a church.

Probably painted for Henry VIII. It is not known at what date no. 44 was enlarged into a full-length (see below), but it was certainly before Van der Doort's catalogue was drawn up. No. 44 may be identical with a portrait in Edward VI's collection (*1547* (150): ... *a table w' the picture of the whole stature of the kyngs Ma'ie in a gowne like crymsen satten furred with Lucernes with a curtene of white sarconet*) which is not recorded in the inventory of 1542. It was engraved by Simon van der Passe for the *Baziliωlogia* of 1618 and the *Herωologia* of 1620; in the marginalia in the Rosenwald-Mariette copy of the latter a seventeenth century annotation gives *from Whitehall Halbens* as the source of the plate (A. M. Hind, *Engraving in England in the Sixteenth and Seventeenth Centuries*, part II (1955), pp. 130, 152). Recorded in the Privy Gallery at Whitehall in the reign of Charles I: *A whitehall peece ... Kinge Edward the 6th at length. in a reed Sattin Coate lined wth white furr and in white suite In a wodden guilded frame* (Van der Doort, p. 32; the CR brand is on the back); valued by the Trustees for Sale at £10 (L. R. MS., f. 9) and sold to King on 8 November 1649. Presumably recovered at the Restoration, but not identifiable in Charles II's inventory; recorded in the Privy Gallery in the reign of James II (B. M., Harl. MS. 1890, f. 48; Bathoe, *James II* (89)) as by Holbein, an attribution that persisted until the nineteenth century; later at Kensington.

Literature: Vertue, *Notebooks*, vol. III, p. 94, vol. IV, pp. 65–6, vol. V, p. 77; Walpole, *Anecdotes*, vol. I, p. 83; Waagen (1838), vol. I, p. 178 (not accepting the attribution to Holbein), (1854), vol. II, p. 431; J. G. Nichols, *A Catalogue of the Portraits of King Edward VI...* (1859), pp. 6–7; Ganz, *KdK.*, 223; Collins Baker, *Windsor*, p. 162; N. Beets, 'Cornelis Anthonisz, II', *Oud-Holland*, vol. LVI (1939), pp. 199–221; R. A., *King's Pictures* (7), *Holbein and Other Masters*, 1950–1 (17); E. Auerbach, *Tudor Artists* (1954), p. 87.

Probably painted not long before the King's accession on 28 January 1547; in the version at Petworth (see below), which bears a *cartellino* with the date 1547 and seems to show him as King, the jewel at his breast no longer bears the Prince of Wales's crown and feathers. The painter of no. 44 has not been identified, but seems without doubt also to be the painter of no. 46. Stylistically the two portraits are very alike and the likeness is confirmed by X-ray; in particular the original construction of both panels included the application of narrow strips of canvas (*c.* ¾ in. wide) under the gesso on the surface of the panels (in the head) to reinforce the joins in the wood. Although there are in the King's stance in no. 44 inevitable reminiscences of Holbein's celebrated presentation of Henry VIII, nos. 44 and 46 are not strikingly

---

1. I am deeply grateful to Sir John Summerson for this reference, and for providing the information on the topographical details in the background. The document was printed by J. W. Goodison in *Burl. Mag.*, vol. XC (1948), p. 264.

Holbeinesque in handling or construction, and the technique seems to be Flemish or Franco-Flemish. The landscape behind seems Flemish in quality, and Dr. Auerbach (*loc. cit.*) has drawn attention to the similarity in the choice of decorative accessories between no. 44 and the illumination, probably carried out by a very accomplished Netherlandish miniature painter, of a letters patent of 21 July 1547. Beets's attribution of no. 44 to Anthonisz does not seem acceptable, but he reproduces (*loc. cit.*, p. 206) an early woodcut after it. In the painting of the furred coat in no. 44, red is glazed over a layer of tin leaf applied to the gesso. The panel seems to have been cut on all four sides. There may have been an earlier design for the right background as there appear to be traces of a circular relief, like that of Marcus Curtius, in the column. There are also *pentimenti* in the fingers of the right hand and possibly in the cuffs. There seem also to have been alterations to the mouldings at the bottom of the wall on the left and to the King's legs. A patch of red below the coat at the left is perhaps a survival from the carpet on which the King was standing when the panel was extended to a full-length. The panel was still a full-length in the time of Walpole (*loc. cit.*: '... very badly converted into a whole figure since the time of Holbein'; and see Vertue, *Notebooks*, vol. IV, pp. 65–6), but was of its present size by the time the list of pictures at Windsor in 1813 was drawn up. Its appearance in its enlarged state (there was also an extension at the top) can be seen in Vertue's water-colour of 1745 in the Royal Library (A. P. Oppé, *English Drawings ... at Windsor Castle* (1950), p. 98 (627)), which was bought from Vertue by Frederick, Prince of Wales; or from the copy at Audley End which Vertue saw at Billingbear (*Notebooks*, vol. V, p. 83).

No. 44 may have been regarded as the official portrait of the young King before the invention of the type associated with Stretes (no. 49). The full-length version at Petworth (*Fig.* 1) shows the King after his accession (see above) in front of a canopy of state bearing the royal arms. The landscape background appears on the right of the composition and more of the landscape is seen on the left, which seems to confirm that no. 44 has been cut down (C. H. Collins Baker, *Catalogue of the Petworth Collection of Pictures ...* (1920), p. 58). That it is by another hand may indicate that no. 44 was painted by an artist who was only in England for a short time. An inferior version is in the collection of Sir Danvers Osborn and another, at half-length, is at Dalmeny. A version is at Christ's Hospital and the type appears in the background of Verrio's vast group-portrait at Christ's Hospital; Vertue stated (*Notebooks*, vol. III, p. 94) that Scheemakers's brass statue of Edward VI, erected at St. Thomas's Hospital in 1739 was 'principally modelld' from no. 44. The head in a portrait of the King at Loseley (dated 1549 on the contemporary frame) approximates to no. 44. The house in the background, which Vertue stated (*ibid.*, vol. V, p. 83) to have been one of the houses in which the King had been nursed, has not been identified.

45. EDWARD VI

St. James's Palace. 93 × 58 in., 236,2 × 147,3 cm.

A copy of no. 44, extended to a full-length; recorded at St. James's in 1870 (*V.R. inv.*) as having been made, presumably *c.* 1865 (see no. 175), by J. B. Williamson for the set of royal portraits at St. James's.

46. ELIZABETH I WHEN PRINCESS (*Frontispiece*)

Windsor Castle (2010). Panel: 42⅞ × 32⅛ in., 108,9 × 81,6 cm.

Inscribed, in the same hand as no. 44 and therefore at a slightly later date: *Elizabetha | [?Filia] Rex | Angliæ.*

Three-quarter-length standing, holding a book in her hands, in a richly jewelled dress with an elaborate jewel at her throat and another at her breast, and wearing four large rings on her hands; another book is open on a table beside her.

Probably painted for Henry VIII; recorded in Edward VI's collection (*1547* (151): *... a table with the picture of the ladye Elizabeth her grace with a booke in her hande her gowne like crymsen clothe of golde withe workes*). It was seen at Whitehall by such visitors as Hentzner in 1598 and the Duke of Saxe-Weimar in 1613 (W. B. Rye, *England as seen by Foreigners* (1865), pp. 161, 281). Hanging in the Privy Gallery in the time of Charles I: *A whitehall peece ... the Picture of Queene Elizabeth when shee was young to the waist in a reed habbitt houlding a blewe booke in both her hands and an othr booke lyeing uppon the table. In a guilded wodden frame* (Van der Doort, p. 33; the CR brand is on the back); valued by the Trustees for Sale at £10 (L. R. MS., f. 9) and sold to Jackson and others on 23 October 1651. Recovered at the Restoration and placed in the Third Privy Lodging Room at Whitehall (Charles II, *Whitehall* (203), with an attribution to Holbein which persisted until the nineteenth century); later at Kensington, Windsor, St. James's and Hampton Court (280).

Literature: Walpole, *Anecdotes*, vol. I, p. 86; Waagen (1838), vol. II, p. 118 (disagreeing with a current attribution to Cranach), (1854), vol. II, p. 361; R. N. Wornum, *Some Account of the Life and Works of Holbein* (1867), pp. 269–70; F. M. O'Donoghue, *A Descriptive ... Catalogue of Portraits of Queen Elizabeth* (1894), p. 1; Collins Baker, *Windsor*, pp. 120–1; R. A., *King's Pictures* (24), *Holbein and Other Masters*, 1950–1 (144); Waterhouse, *Painting in Britain*, p. 10; E. Auerbach, *Tudor Artists* (1954), pp. 71, 76.

Presumably painted *c.* 1546, at the same period, and almost certainly by the same hand, as no. 44. There are traces of considerable alterations during painting. There are *pentimenti* in the right hand, especially in the fingers resting on the book, and in the position of the book. There are alterations in the book beside the Princess and on the wall immediately above it, where a balustrade (?) and a complex capital (?) incorporating carved rams' heads have been painted out. The curtain seems likewise to belong to a second stage in the development of the design; it is painted over the wall of which a section appears above the book, and the moulding on the wall originally continued behind the Princess into a curved recess to the right. These alterations do not seem dissimilar to those in no. 44, and the two portraits, especially since the cleaning of no. 44 in 1959, seem very close in technique, in tone and in their fundamentally un-Holbeinesque modelling and presentation. There is an early eighteenth-century copy of no. 46 in the Queen's College, Oxford.

47. ELIZABETH I (*Plate* 38)

Hampton Court (293). Panel: 22½ × 17¼ in., 57,2 × 43,8 cm.; perhaps slightly reduced on the right.

Head and shoulders, wearing a richly jewelled dress, head-dress and veil, holding a feather fan in her right hand.

See no. 48; at Kensington in 1818 (629), with an attribution to De Heere.

Literature: Waagen (1854), vol. II, p. 361; Law, 1881, 1898 (616); F. M. O'Donoghue, *A Descriptive ... Catalogue of Portraits of Queen Elizabeth* (1894), p. 133; Sir L. Cust, 'Marcus Gheeraerts', *Walpole Soc.*, vol. III (1914), p. 25; Collins Baker, *Hampton Court*, p. 42.

A version, apparently contemporary, of a portrait probably painted in the early 1580's; the same type appears in the portrait presented in 1588–9 to Cambridge University (J. W. Goodison, *Catalogue of Cambridge Portraits*, vol. I (1955), pp. 11–12) and seems to be the work of an English or Anglo-Netherlandish hand or workshop. There are traces of a different pattern underneath the present pattern on the sleeves, and there are alterations on both shoulders.

48. ELIZABETH I (*Plate* 39)

Windsor Castle (2613). Panel: $23\frac{1}{4} \times 17$ in., $59,1 \times 48,2$ cm.

Head and shoulders, wearing a richly jewelled dress, head-dress and veil, holding in her right hand the badge of the Garter, the 'Lesser George', which is suspended from her shoulders on its blue ribbon; the sleeves of her dress are embroidered with roses, her corsage with roses and fleurs-de-lis.

A portrait of Elizabeth I is recorded in the Queen's Dressing Room at Kensington in the reign of George II: *A head of Queene Elizabeth* (Vertue inv., *Kensington*, f. 25). This was presumably the portrait mentioned at Kensington, probably in 1729: *The head of Q. Eliz. in a Gilt frame bought at Mr Cokes* (B. M., MS. 20101, f. 56), but it could be identified with no. 47 or no. 48. No. 48 was definitely at Kensington in 1818 (29), with an attribution to Marcus Gheeradts which persisted into the nineteenth century, and was later at Hampton Court (273).

Literature: Law, 1881, 1898 (619); F. M. O'Donoghue, *A Descriptive . . . Catalogue of Portraits of Queen Elizabeth* (1894), p. 5; Collins Baker, *Windsor*, p. 104.

Apparently a contemporary portrait, showing the Queen towards the end of her life. It may have been based on an *ad vivum* image, and the type does not seem to be one of the more familiar likenesses of the Queen. The prominence with which the Queen displays the Garter badge is almost certainly deliberate. In the Dedication of Marcus Gheeradts the elder's *Procession of the Knights of the Garter* (1576) the Order is stated by Thomas Dawes, Rouge Croix Pursuivant, to have been 'lastly purged, from divers superstitious ceremonies and customs, by the godly zeale of your highnes, and now used, the glorie of God, in mainteining of unitie and concorde among Christian Princes & Nobilitie'. The background seems to have been overpainted.

Guillim Stretes (or Scrots etc.)

fl. 1537–53. Flemish portrait painter, appointed in 1537 *peintre en titre* to Mary of Hungary, Regent of the Netherlands. In January 1546 he was granted an annuity of £62. 10s. by Henry VIII, whose service he had probably entered in 1545. The annuity was continued by Edward VI, certainly until June 1553; Stretes may have left England at the death of Edward VI.

Attributed to Guillim Stretes

49. EDWARD VI (*Plate* 33)

Hampton Court (1246). Panel: $65\frac{3}{4} \times 35\frac{3}{4}$ in., $167 \times 90,8$ cm.; there is an addition on the right of *c*. $\frac{1}{4}$ in.

Inscribed on an early *cartellino: Kinge Edward. 6.*

Full-length standing, holding his gloves in his right, and his sword-belt with his left, hand.

Recorded in the collection of John, 1st Baron Lumley (*d.* 1609): among his *Pyctures carying the ffowrme of the whole Statuary*, was *The Statuary of his sonne king Edward the sixt, Drawne by* (Sir L. Cust, 'The Lumley Inventories', *Walpole Soc.*, vol. VI (1918), p. 21), which was later recorded in the Lodging Rooms at Lumley Castle and finally sold in the sale of the Earl of Scarbrough's possessions at Lumley Castle on 18 December 1807 (9) (*ibid*, pp. 31, 34). The *cartellino* (see above) is of the type painted on Lord Lumley's pictures, see D. Piper, 'The 1590 Lumley Inventory . . . I', *Burl. Mag.*, vol.XCIX (1957), pp. 224–31. Although drawn up in 1590, additions were made to the inventory for a year or two after that date. Thereafter the picture passed into the possession of William Beckford (it is recorded in an inventory of his pictures in 1846) and was bequeathed to the Duke of Hamilton; noted at Hamilton House by Sir Henry Ellis (MS. *Memoranda of Original Royal Portraits* (1822 and later) in

office of Surveyor of The Queen's Pictures); sold with the Hamilton Palace Collection at Christie's, 17 June 1882 (43), as by Holbein, and purchased by Queen Victoria; later at Windsor (2025).

Literature: Collins Baker, *Hampton Court*, pp. 76–7; E. Auerbach, 'Notes on some Northern Mannerist Portraits', *Burl. Mag*, vol. XCI (1949), pp. 221–2, 'Holbein's Followers in England', *ibid.*, vol. XCIII (1951), pp. 45–50; Waterhouse, *Painting in Britain*, pp. 12–13; E. Auerbach, *Tudor Artists* (1954), pp. 77–8.

A good version of perhaps the most important official portrait of Edward VI, which has been convincingly associated by Dr. Auerbach (*op. cit*) with Guillim Stretes or Scrots. The type may have originated in 1550, when negotiations were set on foot for a marriage between the King and the eldest daughter of Henri II of France. Portraits of the couple were exchanged in 1550, and early in 1551 the King's Council was reported to be sending over to France 'a certain painting, a portrait of the King of England, which the Vidame requested to be allowed to present to the King, his master' (*Calendar of State Papers, Spanish*, vol. X, *1550–52* (1914), p. 217). Versions of no. 49 are in the Louvre (2481A) and in the Museum at Roanne (2546); the latter is traditionally stated to have been given by the sitter to the Maréchal de St. André, who had been sent to London in July 1551 to confer upon the King the Order of St. Michael (F. Déchelette in *L'Echo du Sud-Est*, Lyons, 8 and 9 November 1948). The version in the Louvre bears a later inscription *Sir A. More. pinxt*. Payments to Stretes are recorded in March 1552 for two 'great tables' of the King, both of which were for English Ambassadors abroad. The type was thus clearly a popular one and many reductions and variants exist. A bust version in the possession of Lord Fairhaven is inscribed with the date 29 September 1550; other such reductions are at Audley End, Boughton, Ingatestone, Gainsborough Old Hall, Braemore and in the Devonshire and Tyrwhitt-Drake collections (and see nos. 50 and 51). Small full-length copies are at Welbeck and Helmingham; and a version sold at Sotheby's, 11 June 1947 (76), had an inscription in English, Greek and Latin suggesting it was painted for despatch abroad. Another, at three-quarter-length and sold at Sotheby's, 2 July 1958 (41), bore the date 1551 and an inscription proclaiming the King as Defender of the Faith and head of the English Church. A seated variant is at Hinton Charterhouse. It is possible that no. 49 came into Lord Lumley's possession from his father-in-law, Henry Fitzalan, 12th Earl of Arundel, who was Lord Chamberlain (1546–50) to Henry VIII and Edward VI and High Constable at King Edward's Coronation.

After Guillim Stretes

50. EDWARD VI

Windsor Castle (265). Canvas: $17\frac{7}{8} \times 12\frac{7}{8}$ in., $45,4 \times 32,7$ cm.

Head and shoulders.

In 1598 Paul Hentzner saw at Hampton Court a portrait of Edward VI (W. B. Rye, *England as seen by Foreigners* (1865), p. 203); this could have been the portrait valued by the Trustees for Sale at Hampton Court in October 1649 at £2: *Edward ye 6. being a head* (L. R. MS., f. 121 v.), which was sold to William Latham and others on 23 October 1651. On 15 and 17 May 1660 Emmanuel De Critz reported to the House of Lords Committee that Latham had entrusted him with, among other pictures, *A head of Edward the 6th*, valued at £2 (H. of L. MSS.), and it was presumably this portrait that hung later in the Third Privy Lodging Room at Whitehall (Charles II, *Whitehall* (237): *Edward the 6th To the Wast*, measurements given as 17 × 15 in.); probably later at Windsor and Kensington and certainly at Kensington in 1818 (165), when it was stated to be on paper on wood.

Literature: Collins Baker, *Windsor*, p. 103.

An early derivation from Scrots's full-length of the King (see no. 49). Engraved by Vertue when it was at Kensington. Redgrave recorded (*V.R. inv.*, 16 February 1861) an inscription which has since been removed: *Eduardvs 6th Rex Angs* . . ., and the portrait seems to have been slightly reduced.

51. EDWARD VI

Windsor Castle (225). Panel: 22½ × 16⅞ in., 57,2 × 42,9 cm.

Inscribed: EDWARDVS VI.

Head and shoulders.

Probably part of the set of royal portraits secured by Queen Caroline from Lord Cornwallis; recorded at Kensington in 1818 (646); later at St. James's.

A later derivation from no. 49.

Gerlach Flicke

d. 1558. German portrait painter, who came, probably from Osnabrück, to England *c.* 1545 and died in London.

After Gerlach Flicke

52. SIR PETER CAREW (1514–75)

Hampton Court (270). Panel: 23¼ × 18¼ in., 59,1 × 46,4 cm.; 2⅞ in. at the bottom may be an addition. A horizontal crack is repaired at the back with a strip of canvas apparently cut from a portrait and showing a fragment of ermine-lined drapery.

Inscribed later: SR PETER CAREW KNiGHT 3 / SONNE TO SR WILLIAM / CAREW BVRiED AT WATERFORD iN / iERLAND ANO 1575. This has been copied from an earlier, and now almost entirely obliterated, inscription to the right of the head.

Head and shoulders in a plumed cap and a slashed white doublet.

Probably among the early portraits, formerly in the collection of Lady Capel, acquired at Kew; recorded at Kensington in 1818 (555 . . . *Brought from the Old Palace at Greenwich*).

Literature: Law, 1881, 1898 (615); Mary F. S. Hervey, 'Notes on a Tudor Painter . . .', *Burl. Mag.*, vol. XVII (1910), p. 72; Collins Baker, *Hampton Court*, p. 56.

A copy from the half-length portrait, formerly in the collection of the Marquess of Lothian, now in the National Gallery of Scotland (1934) and generally accepted as by Flicke, *c.* 1550 (see R. A., *British Portraits*, 1956–57(5)). No. 52 is extensively worn and repainted, but traces of original quality, especially in the hair and beard, seem to indicate that it is at least a contemporary copy.

Soldier and courtier; Gentleman of the Privy Chamber to Henry VIII; he plotted against Mary I, but came back into favour in the reign of her successor. The last years of his life were spent in Ireland.

Anthonis Mor

1519–75. Portrait painter; a native of Utrecht, he worked in Antwerp, Italy, Spain and Portugal. In 1554 he came to London and painted the portrait of Mary I, presumably for Philip II of Spain.

After Anthonis Mor

53. MARY I

Windsor Castle (70). Panel: 36¾ × 29⅞ in., 93,3 × 75,9 cm.

Three-quarter-length, seated in a chair, holding a book in her left, and her gloves in her right, hand; on the edge of the hanging behind her are woven the initials MR.

The provenance of no. 53 is obscure It may be the picture mentioned by Vertue in the reign of George I (in 1724?): 'the half lenght picture of Queen Mary. I. is now at Richmond in the princess house' (*Notebooks*, vol. I, p. 133), which would indicate that it may have been purchased by Queen Caroline; certainly at Windsor in 1851 (see Waagen (1854), vol. II, p. 431).

Literature: Collins Baker, *Windsor*, p. 240.

A derivation, with differences in detail and presumably painted later in the sixteenth century, from Mor's portrait of 1554 (see no. 54). A reference by Vertue (*Notebooks*, vol. II, p. 143) seems to refer to one of Mor's original versions of this portrait: 'in the Royal Collection of Pictures belonging to the Crown. I have seen a Picture . . . of Queen Mary a half length painted curiously on a pannel . . . being (on one corner) thus inscribd Anton More pinxit 1554'.

54. MARY I

Windsor Castle (264). Panel: 22½ × 17⅛ in., 57,2 × 43,5 cm.

Inscribed: MARiA · REGINA · FILLiÆ · HENRICI · OCTAVI.

Head and shoulders.

Probably part of the set of royal portraits secured by Queen Caroline from Lord Cornwallis; recorded at Kensington in 1818 (648).

Literature: Collins Baker, *Windsor*, p. 240

A derivation from the three-quarter-length of the Queen by Mor of which there are versions, both signed and dated 1554, in the Prado (2108) and at Castle Ashby (R. A., *Holbein and other Masters*, 1950–51 (200), illustrated souvenir, pl. 13). Similar derivations are in the National Gallery of Ireland (400) and Durham Cathedral Library and at Knole and Anglesey Abbey. The type was engraved by Frans Huys with the date 1555.

55. MARY I

St. James's Palace. 94¾ × 58¼ in., 240,7 × 148 cm.

Full-length standing, resting her left hand on a chair and holding a handkerchief in her right hand.

Recorded at St. James's in 1865 (*V.R. inv.*).

A nineteenth-century derivation, probably from the same source as no. 54, and presumably painted for the set of royal portraits at St. James's.

Hans Eworth

1520–1574? The contemporary documents associated with Eworth's career in this country are inconclusive, and the pictures ascribed to him in such sixteenth-century sources as the Lumley Inventory have not been identified; but an *oeuvre* built up round portraits signed with a particular form of monogram *HE* illustrates a fairly logical artistic development from the late 1540's to the late 1560's and is reasonably associated with the Flemish portrait and decorative painter who entered the Painters' Guild in Antwerp in 1540, probably came to England in 1545, received a grant of denization in 1550 and seems to have worked for the Revels as late as 1573–4.

The Trustees for Sale valued at £20 among the pictures at Hampton Court in October 1649: *King Edward ye 6th at Length. by Hans Hueet* (L. R. MS., f. 122 v.) which was sold to Latham and others on 23 October 1651. Eworth's signed and dated (1554) portrait of Mary I belongs to the Society of Antiquaries (R. A., *Kings and Queens*, 1953 (90), illustrated souvenir, pl. 24); Charles I was given by the Earl of Suffolk the miniature version of this, now in the possession of the Duke of Buccleuch (R. A., *British Portraits*, 1956–57 (613)) and himself seems to have altered the attribution in his catalogue from *Hanc Seward* to *An: More* (*Van der Doort*, p. 110).

56. HENRY STEWART, LORD DARNLEY, AND HIS BROTHER CHARLES STEWART, EARL OF LENNOX (*Plate 34*)

Windsor Castle (2014). Panel: 25 × 15 in., 68,5 × 38,1 cm.

Signed: *HE* (in monogram), and inscribed: THES BE THE SONES OF THE RIGHTE HONERABLES THERLLE OF LENOXE A̅D̅ / THE LADY MARGARETZ GRACE COVNTYES OF LENOXE A̅D̅ ANGWYSE, / 1563 / HENRY STEWARDE LORD DA̅R: / LEY AND DOWGLAS, ÆTATIS, 17, / CHARLLES STEWARDE / HIS BROTHER, ÆTATIS, 6,

Full-lengths standing in the same positions as in no. 57, but with a spacious beamed interior behind them.

Perhaps painted for the boys' parents and thus probably passed by descent from their mother (see no. 91) to her grandson James VI and I; probably hanging in the Queen's Gallery at Greenwich in his reign and certainly recorded there in 1639: 'upon the right light in little at length the king's grandfather with his brother the lady Arabella's father in his coat in a perspective chamber wherein a green table' (*Van der Doort*, p. 198, measurements given as 25 × 14 in.; the CR brand on the back (noted in *V.R. inv.*) is now covered); valued by the Trustees for Sale in September 1649 at £6 (L. R. MS., f. 7: . . . *at Length in little*) and sold to Murray and others on 23 October 1651. Recovered at the Restoration (Col. Hawley, f. 35 v.) and hung in the Long Matted Gallery at Whitehall (Charles II, *Whitehall* (17): . . . *in Little*); later at Kensington and Hampton Court (318), successively as by Holbein, 'Gennet' and Lucas de Heere.

Literature: Vertue, *Notebooks*, vol. IV, pp. 70–1, 74; Walpole, *Anecdotes*, vol. I, p. 154, *Visits*, p. 80; Waagen (1854), vol. II, p. 363; Law, 1881, 1898 (639); Sir L Cust, 'The Painter HE', *Walpole Soc.*, vol. II (1913), pp. 32–3; Collins Baker, *Windsor*, p. 112; R. A., *King's Pictures* (22), *Holbein and Other Masters*, 1950–1 (42); Waterhouse, *Painting in Britain*, p. 17.

The relation between no. 56 and its life-size prototype (no. 57) is difficult to establish, but if the latter can be accepted as the work of Eworth, no. 56 would be an autograph reduction, setting the figures against a more ambitious background, taken from a design by Hans Vredeman de Vries.[1] In no. 56 there are slight *pentimenti* in Lord Darnley's legs, in the right hand of the younger boy and in the left outline of his 'coats'. There are also traces of carved decoration (?) under the present ceiling in the interior in the background. The differences between the figures in the two versions are almost negligible; the most obvious is the absence of the whistle (?) round the younger boy's neck and of the daggers at the belts of both boys. Though no. 56 has suffered local damages, the heads are in very good condition and of very fine quality. This, and the slight differences between the heads in the two versions, may indicate that no. 56 was based on fresh sittings. These differences are particularly marked in the head of the

younger brother. If the larger version is not by Eworth, the heads in the smaller version would obviously have been *ad vivum* portraits fitted into an already established composition. The inscriptions in the two compositions are almost identical. No. 56 was probably painted fairly soon after Darnley's seventeenth birthday.

Charles I owned two other portraits of Lord Darnley. Both are now in the collection of Lord Bolton (R. A., *Holbein and Other Masters*, 1950–1 (34, 36)) and both have the CR brand on the back. The first, signed by Eworth and dated 1555, also has on the back a contemporary label recording the presentation of the portrait to Charles I by the Duke of Lennox on 15 February 1639/40. The second portrait (*c.* 1562) does not seem necessarily to be by Eworth. The two portraits seem respectively to have been valued by the Trustees for Sale at £2 at Greenwich in September 1649 (L. R. MS., f. 6: *The Lord Darnelij*, sold to Latham and others on 23 October 1651) and for thirty shillings at Hampton Court in October 1649 (*ibid.*, f. 123 v.: *King James. father*, sold to Bagley and others on the same day). They were recovered at the Restoration and hung at Hampton Court (Charles II, *Hampton Court* (114, 180)), but are not recorded in the royal collection after 1714.

Attributed to Hans Eworth

57. HENRY STEWART, LORD DARNLEY, AND HIS BROTHER CHARLES STEWART, EARL OF LENNOX (*Plate 35*)

Holyroodhouse. 80¼ × 40½ in., 204 × 102,9 cm.

Inscribed: THES BE THE SOÑES OF THE RIGHTE HONERABLES / THERLLE OF LENOXE AND THE LADY MARGARETZ / GRACE COVNTYES OF LENOXE A̅D̅ ANGEWYSE / AN° DO̅ / M.D. LXII / HENRY STEWARDE LORD DARNL [ ] / AND DOWGLAS, AETATIS SVAE X[ ] / CHARLES STEWARDE HIS / BROTHER, AETATIS SVAE VI,

Full-lengths standing by a table; Lord Darnley, a watch round his neck and his gloves in his left hand, rests his right hand on the shoulder of his younger brother, who wears 'coats' and holds a cap in his left hand.

Probably in the collections of John, 1st Baron Lumley (*d.* 1609), and Robert Cecil, 1st Earl of Salisbury (*d.* 1612). The inventory of Lord Lumley's collection in 1590 included: *The Statuary of the Lorde Darneley aft'ward k. of scotts & his brother Charles Stewarde in one table* (Sir L. Cust, 'The Lumley Inventories, *Walpole Soc.*, vol. VI (1918), p. 22). Pictures from Lumley's collection passed to that of Lord Salisbury and an inventory of the contents of Salisbury House in 1629 includes, in the Great Chamber: *1 picture of the Lord Darneley and his brother with a curtaine of purple taffata fringed with gold*; in an inventory of Salisbury House of 25 March 1640 the picture appears in the same position, but it does not appear at Salisbury House in an inventory of 1645–6 (Hatfield Estate Papers, Boxes, C. 8, C. 9, C. 4).[1] The picture may have been given to Charles I by William Cecil, 2nd Earl of Salisbury (1591–1668); the Trustees for Sale, probably in September 1649, valued at £8 among the pictures from Whitehall: *Lord Darnely wth Charles. steward his brother at Leng* (L. R. MS., f. 8). It appears to have been in the Bear Gallery at Whitehall and thus to have entered the collection just after Van der Doort had completed that part of his catalogue. It was sold to Jackson and others on 23 October 1651, but was recovered at the Restoration, when it was in the possession of Thomas Beauchamp (H. of L. MSS.), and hung in the Queen's Gallery at Hampton Court (Charles II, *Hampton Court* (14), measurements given as 79 × 39 in.); later at St. James's, Kensington and Hampton Court (512), usually as by Lucas de Heere.

---

1. I am very grateful to Sir John Summerson for pointing this out to me.

1. I am very grateful to Mr. David Piper for these references.

Literature: Vertue, *Notebooks*, vol. IV, pp. 70-1; Walpole, *Anecdotes*, vol. I, p. 154, *Visits*, p. 15; Sir L. Cust, 'The Painter HE', *Walpole Soc.*, vol. II (1913), p. 33; R. A., *Holbein and Other Masters*, 1950-1 (43); City of Manchester Art Gallery, *16th Century Portraits . . .*, 1953 (9); Waterhouse, *Painting in Britain*, p. 17.

Painted in a water medium on material of an extremely fine texture, overlaid with an oil varnish at a slightly later date. The surface is very worn, especially round the edges, on the floor, in the costumes and the heads, although there remain traces of considerable refinement in execution. There appear to be *pentimenti* in the younger boy's costume, in which a white sash (?), hanging from his waist, appears to have been painted out, and in Darnley's right foot; his left foot seems to be unfinished. The condition of the canvas[1] makes it almost impossible to attribute it with certainty, but there seems at the moment no reasonable alternative to accepting it as by Eworth and thus as his earlier version of a design which he repeated with variations in the following year (no. 56). The inscriptions are almost identical in both pictures. Vertue (*loc. cit.*) gave the age of Lord Darnley as *XVII*, but probably based this reconstruction on his knowledge of the smaller version. Lord Darnley's seventeenth birthday took place on 7 December 1562. In any case the composition probably dates from late in 1562, when Darnley and his mother were released from confinement. No. 57 may have been painted for Darnley's parents or possibly for Lord Lumley. To Charles I it would have been a welcome addition to the series of historical and family portraits that he had assembled in the Bear Gallery, where it would have hung near no. 116. The figure of Darnley was engraved by Vertue while it was at St. James's.

58. ELIZABETH I AND THE THREE GOD-DESSES (*Plate* 32)

Hampton Court (301). Panel: 27⅞ × 33¼ in., 70,8 × 84,5 cm. The panel may have been slightly cut on the left.

Signed and dated: *1569* | *HE* (initials in monogram). On the original frame is inscribed: IVNO POTENS SCEPTRIS ET MENTIS ACVMINE PALLAS | ET ROSEO VENERIS FVLGET IN ORE DECVS | ADFVIT ELIZABETH IVNO PERCVLSA REFVGIT | OBSTVPVIT PALLAS ERVBVITQ VENVS,

The Queen, wearing a richly embroidered and jewelled dress, on which the Tudor rose is the dominant motif, with a watch or picture-box suspended from her waist, emerges (under an arch decorated with the Queen's initials, roses and fleurs-de-lis) from an interior; she is attended by her ladies-in-waiting, wears her crown and holds the orb and sceptre; in the room behind her is a frieze with the Tudor arms and a canopy, on which the Queen's arms are embroidered. Before the Queen's advance are the three goddesses in confusion: Juno with the peacock, Pallas with helmet, spear and shield, and Venus seated with Cupid on her discarded garments. Behind Venus is her chariot with harnessed swans and in the distance a view of Windsor Castle. On the ground are the abandoned emblems of Juno, Venus and Cupid.

Presumably painted for the Queen; seen at Whitehall by Otto, Prince of Hesse, in 1611. Valued at £2 among the pictures *out of the Gallaries at Grenewch* by the Trustees for Sale (L. R. MS., f. 6:

Queene Elezebeth. Venus & Juno & Pallas); sold to Hunt and Bass on 1 March 1653, but recovered at the Restoration and placed in the King's Gallery at Hampton Court; later at Kensington.

Literature: Vertue, *Notebooks*, vol. IV, pp. 36, 66; Walpole, notes in Bathoe, *James II*, part II, p. 48, *Anecdotes*, vol. I pp. 154-5; Waagen (1854), vol. II, p. 361; Law, 1881, 1898 (635) and p. 316; F. M. O'Donoghue, *A Descriptive . . . Catalogue of Portraits of Queen Elizabeth*, (1894), p. 2; Sir L. Cust, 'The Painter HE', *Walpole Soc.*, vol. II (1913), p. 37; Collins Baker, *Hampton Court*, p. 47; R. A., *King's Pictures* (13); F. A. Yates, 'Queen Elizabeth as Astraea', *Journal of the Warburg and Courtauld Institutes*, vol. X (1947), pp. 27-82; R. A., *Holbein and Other Masters*, 1950-1 (205); E. Auerbach, 'Portraits of Elizabeth I', *Burl. Mag.*, vol. XCV (1953), p. 201; Waterhouse, *Painting in Britain*, p. 17; E. Auerbach, *Tudor Artists* (1954), pp. 106, 131; *Le Triomphe du Maniérisme Européen*, Rijksmuseum, 1955 (50); R. A., *British Portraits*, 1956-7 (22); E. Wind, *Pagan Mysteries in the Renaissance* (1958), p. 79.

No artist's name seems to have been attached to the picture until the time of Vertue, who in his *Notebooks* (*loc. cit.*) and in his inventory of the pictures at Kensington (f. 21) took the monogram to be that of Lucas de Heere. 'Deheere' was inserted in Bathoe's edition (1758) of James II's catalogue (934), but no artist had been given in the original MS. of the catalogue (B. M., Harl. MS. 1890, f. 78). Since Cust's attempt (*op. cit*) to reconstruct the *œuvre* of Eworth, no. 58 seems to have been accepted unequivocally as by Eworth. The calligraphy of the inscription, however, does not seem to be that in which the monogram *HE* is written on portraits generally accepted as by Eworth. Stylistically, moreover, the panel does not seem consistent with the developments in Eworth's handling and presentation in the 1560's. The same problem arises with *The Family of Henry VIII* at Sudeley Castle (R. A. *Holbein and Other Masters*, 1950-1 (202) (*Fig.* 3)), which is perhaps by the same hand and can hardly be much earlier than *c.* 1575. It is not impossible that both panels are by De Heere, painted soon after his arrival in England in 1568. They seem to show more immediately French and Flemish influences than would have survived in this late phase of Eworth's career. The composition is an elaborate example of court flattery: the Queen has not only taken over the conventional role of Paris in judging the goddesses, but has by her own beauty and accomplishments, which combine the attributes of all the goddesses, put them and their separate qualities to shame. In the words of Professor Wind (*loc. cit.*), 'to compliment a prince on his universality by comparing his judgement to that of Paris, became a fixed formula of Renaissance euphuism'; the same authority quotes examples of such compliments addressed to Elizabeth I, for example in the verses celebrating her visits to Cambridge (1564) and Oxford (1566). The iconography of no. 58 should also be related to the cult of the Virgin Queen and to the use for the Queen of the Virgo-Astraea symbol; the illustration of this in the play *Histrio-Mastrix* (of 1589?) is strikingly close to the theme of the panel at Sudeley Castle, and the theme of the revised Judgment of Paris, in which the principal part is taken over by the Virgin Queen, is well illustrated in Richard Barnfield's *Cynthia* (1595) (for this see F. A. Yates, *op. cit.*, especially pp. 60-1). The view of Windsor Castle (from the South East?) is slightly fanciful but is perhaps the earliest painted record of the Castle. There appear to be *pentimenti* in the neck, head and right wing of Juno's peacock which may at first have been slightly larger. The original decoration of the frame survives, with the inscription, but a small decorative feature, perhaps a painted or carved roundel, has been removed from the middle of each side and from the four corners.

1. There are at least two long tears in the canvas. These may have been caused by Colonel Pride's soldiers during the Interregnum. Thomas Beauchamp stated at the Restoration that he had 'restored & amended ye breakeings & other defaceinge' done to some of the royal pictures and statues then in his care. At some stage the top of the canvas was enlarged by *c.* 6 in. (at Kensington in 1818 (429) the measurements were given as 86 × 41 in.). This addition was removed in 1864 (*V.R. inv.*).

Hieronimus Custodis

fl. 1589–93. Portrait painter, presumably a native of Antwerp, thought to have died in or before 1593, probably in London.

59. SIR JOHN PARKER (*Plate* 40)

Hampton Court (288). Panel: 31 × 25½ in., 78,7 × 64,8 cm.

Signed: *Jeronimo Custodis Antverpiensis | Fecit 10° Augusty*, inscribed: PRO FIDE ET PATRIA, and dated: ANNO DNI, 1589.

Half-length, wearing a gorget, raising his sword in his right hand; a coat of arms is painted in the upper right corner.

Possibly among the early portraits, formerly in the collection of Lady Capel, acquired at Kew; recorded at Hampton Court in 1842 (Mrs. Jameson (668)) as a portrait of Sir Robert Cave.

Literature: Law, 1881, 1898 (803); Collins Baker, *Hampton Court*, p. 31; Waterhouse, *Painting in Britain*, pp. 20–1.

No. 59 was painted at the same time as portraits by Custodis of the 3rd Lord Chandos and Elizabeth Brydges, his daughter. Both are at Woburn and are dated 8 July 1589. A third, unsigned, portrait at Woburn, of Frances, Lady Chandos, is also dated 1589 and is almost certainly by the same hand. No. 59 is damaged at the bottom and top of the panel; a large area of original paint is missing from the lower left corner. The sitter is almost certainly Sir John Parker of Ratton, Sussex, a Gentleman Pensioner and Captain of St. Denis Castle in Cornwall. The arms are those granted to his grandfather, Sir John Parker (*d.* 1558).[1]

Artist Unknown

60. JEPHTHAH'S DAUGHTER (*Plates* 28–30)

Windsor Castle (3078). Panel: 16½ × 73 in., 41,9 × 186,7 cm.

Jephthah, returning from his victory over the Ammonites, is greeted by his daughter and her companions, playing on musical instruments; her subsequent death, in fulfilment of her father's vow, is seen taking place in a garden on the right (Judges XI. 29–40). In the distance is seen the rout of the Ammonites and, on the horizon, a view of Windsor Castle from the south.

Sold at Sotheby's, 2 June 1954 (60), and purchased by Her Majesty The Queen for the royal collection in 1955.

Probably painted *c.* 1560–80. The quality and the types of the figures seem to be slightly Flemish. The view of Windsor, with the cusped wall, the houses within the walls, the parish church (?) and the 'Garden Plot,' seems remarkably accurate. It is possible that the windmill in the middle distance, the early Tudor house with its walled garden in the foreground and the distant farmhouse on the right record buildings in the Little Park in the sixteenth century, such as the keeper's lodge (shown on Norden's Survey of 1607), or Great Frogmore and Frogmore Farm, which were just outside the Park.

Artists Unknown: Late Sixteenth- and early Seventeenth-Century Portraits

61. JAMES, 'THE ADMIRABLE', CRICHTON (1560–85?)

Holyroodhouse. 30 × 24 in., 76,2 × 61 cm.

Half-length, resting his left hand on a book and holding a sword in his right hand.

Possibly acquired with the portraits formerly in the collection of Lady Capel at Kew or by George III: *The admirable Creighton* is inserted in pencil into the list of pictures in the Privy Chamber at Kensington in his reign (Geo. III, *Kensington*); later at Hampton Court (335), but sent to Holyrood by command of Queen Victoria in March 1864.

Literature: Mrs. Jameson (300).

No. 61 is probably the only sixteenth-century version of a portrait type associated with Crichton. Copies, which seem later, are at Lennoxlove, Malahide, Airth and in the Bute collection. The type was engraved by Hall for Pennant's *Tour through Scotland* (1774). The versions usually bear a memorial inscription taken from John Johnston's *Heroes* of 1603 (information supplied by the Scottish National Portrait Gallery in connection with the version at Airth). No. 61, which is certainly Italian, could be a portrait of Crichton painted in North Italy, where he had established a legendary reputation as scholar and swordsman.

In his youth a fellow-pupil under George Buchanan with the young James VI; from 1577(?) to his death he travelled in France and Italy and from 1580 was mainly in Venice, Padua and Mantua.

62. SIR GEORGE CROKE (1560–1642)

Hampton Court (267). 22¼ × 17⅜ in., 56,5 × 44,1 cm.

Inscribed later: IVDGE CROOKE.

Head and shoulders in the robes and cap of a Justice of the King's Bench.

Probably among the early portraits, formerly in the collection of Lady Capel, acquired at Kew; recorded at Hampton Court in 1842 (Mrs. Jameson (246)).

Literature: Law, 1881, 1898 (621); Collins Baker, *Hampton Court*, pp. 43–4.

Probably related to the type of which there is a three-quarter-length version in the Inner Temple, inscribed with the sitter's age (66) and dated 1626, and which was probably the source of an engraving by Hollar.

Judge and law reporter, Serjeant-at-law, King's Serjeant (1623) and Justice of the Common Pleas (1623) and of the King's Bench (1628); a firm opponent of the King's interference with judicial procedure in the 1630's.

63. ALICE SPENCER, COUNTESS OF DERBY (*d.* 1637)

Hampton Court (343). Panel: 39 × 33¾ in., 85,7 × 60,3 cm.

Inscribed later: COVNTES OF DARBY.

Three-quarter-length, wearing a high ruff and a necklace decorated with pendant monograms made up of the letter A.

Among the early portraits, formerly in the collection of Lady Capel, whose seal is on the panel, acquired at Kew; recorded at Kensington in 1818 (63: *Portrait of the Countess of Derby. Zucchero*).

Literature: Law, 1881, 1898 (572); Sir L. Cust, 'Marcus Gheeraerts', *Walpole Soc.*, vol. III (1914), p. 32; Collins Baker, *Hampton Court*, p. 45.

Probably painted *c.* 1580–90. The portrait was attributed by Cust (*op. cit.*) to Marcus Gheeradts the younger; it is in the style associated with the studios of the Gheeradts and De Critz families.

Daughter of Sir John Spencer of Althorp; she married shortly before 1580 Ferdinando Stanley, 5th Earl of Derby, and later, as his third wife, the 1st Viscount Brackley.

1. I am deeply grateful to Mr. T. Tremlett and his colleagues at the Society of Antiquaries for their help in identifying the arms.

64. THOMAS FANSHAWE (1533–1601)

Hampton Court (268). Panel: 22⅞ × 17¾ in., 58,1 × 46 cm.

Head and shoulders, wearing a ruff and a tall hat.

Probably among the early portraits, formerly in the collection of Lady Capel, acquired at Kew; recorded at Kensington in 1818 (285) as a portrait of Sir Nicholas Bacon (1509–79).

Literature: Law, 1881, 1898 (667); Collins Baker, *Hampton Court,* p. 43.

In 1931 a later inscription, . . . NICHOLAS BACON, was removed and on the basis of a portrait at Bratton Fleming the sitter was identified as a member of the Fanshawe family; the portrait was probably painted *c.* 1590–1600 and thus represents Thomas Fanshawe, rather than his son Sir Henry (1569–1616). A version was sold at Christie's, 14 April 1950 (134), as a portrait of Lord Burghley.

Queen's Remembrancer of the Exchequer (1568).

65. PORTRAIT OF A MAN *called* SIR GEORGE FERMOR (1561–1612)

Hampton Court (271). Panel: 22½ × 20⅛ in., 57,4 × 51,1 cm.

Inscribed: [*Ætatis suæ*] . 40

Head and shoulders, wearing a ruff; in the upper left corner is a crest, probably that of Fermor of Easton Neston.

Possibly among the early portraits, formerly in the collection of Lady Capel, acquired at Kew; recorded at Hampton Court in May 1860 (*V.R. inv.*).

Literature: Law, 1881, 1898 (618); Collins Baker, *Hampton Court,* p. 42.

No. 65 is very much repainted. The sitter is thought to be Sir George Fermor of Easton Neston, who served under the Prince of Orange in the Netherlands and was knighted by the Earl of Leicester in 1586. It is unlikely, however, that no. 65, in which the sitter's age is given as 40, could have been painted as late as 1601, and the sitter may be an older member of the Fermor family.

66. SIR JOHN GAGE (1479–1556)

St. James's Palace. 90 × 60¼ in., 229 × 153 cm.; there are very early additions on all four sides and the original canvas was *c.* 86 × 51 in.

Inscribed: MESSIRE IEAN GAGE Sʀ DE FVRLE. CHEVAL / DE L'ORDRE DE LA IARTIERE DV CONSEIL / D'ESTAT D'HENRŸ. 8ᴱ EDOARD· 6ᴱ ET MARIE / ROIS D'ANGLE-TERRE ET DE LEVR CONSEI̅ / SVPREME DE GVERRE LIEVTENANT GENERAL / AVEC CHARLES DVC DE SVFFOLKE DE L'ARMEE DVD / ROŸ HENRŸ [A LA] SIEGE ET PRISE DE BOULOGNE EN FRA / CONSTABLE DE LA TOVR DE LONDERS

Full-length standing in Garter robes; the royal arms are embroidered on a banner behind him. The white staff in his right hand could be that of any of the three offices in the Household that he held (see below), but is probably that of the Lord Chamberlain.

Recorded in the reign of Charles II in the Long Matted Gallery at Whitehall (Charles II, *Whitehall* (73): Sʳ *John Gage (Knᵗ of the Garter in Hen: 8ᵗʰ time) in his robe);* later at Hampton Court, St. James's and Hampton Court (320).

Literature: Vertue, *Notebooks,* vol. II, p. 78; Walpole, *Visits,* p. 15; Law, 1881, 1898 (341).

Apparently painted *c.* 1620–30. The portrait may have been based on a portrait-drawing of the school of Holbein;

Holbein's drawing of Sir John Gage at Windsor (Parker, 78), however, is of a different type. A version, probably also painted in the seventeenth century, is at Firle and another of the same period was at Hengrave Hall and was sold there, 15–25 September 1952 (1765).

Statesman and military commander; Vice-Chamberlain (1528) and Comptroller of the Household (1540) to Henry VIII, Captain of the royal guard and Lord Chamberlain (1553) to Mary I.

67. SIR THEOBALD GORGES (d. 1648). *Identity uncertain.*

Hampton Court (287). Panel: 22⅞ × 17¾ in., 58,1 × 46 cm.: there is an addition of 1¾ in. on the right.

Inscribed on a scroll: *Vertutis præmiū, non fortunæ Elimosinā.*

Head and shoulders in a black costume, wearing an ear-ring; the arms of Gorges are in the upper left corner.

Probably among the early portraits, formerly in the collection of Lady Capel, acquired at Kew; perhaps to be identified with *An Ancient Portrait* at Kensington in 1818 (514, measurements given as 23 × 18 in. on panel; a label with the number 514 is attached to the back of this panel).

Literature: Law, 1881, 1898 (712); Collins Baker, *Hampton Court* p. 46; R. Gorges, *The Story of a Family . . .* (1944), pp. 110–12.

Probably painted *c.* 1590–1600. The panel is in a very unsatisfactory state, cut down the left side (one of the supporters in the heraldic achievement is missing) and very worn. It seems, however, to have been an *ad vivum* portrait. There appear to be original *pentimenti* in the drawing of the collar; the nose seems to have been repainted and altered in shape.

The sitter is thought to be Sir Theobald Gorges, one of the bearers of the Green Canopy at the funeral of Anne of Denmark, M.P. for Cirencester and a royalist.

68. ROBERT DUDLEY, EARL OF LEICESTER (1532?–1588)

Hampton Court (289). 22¾ × 17¾ in., 57,8 × 45,1 cm.

Inscribed later: EARLE OF LECISTER.

Head and shoulders, wearing the ribbon of the Garter, a furred cloak and a jewelled band in his hat.

Probably among the early portraits, formerly in the collection of Lady Capel, acquired at Kew; recorded at Kensington in 1818 (575) as *From the Palace at Greenwich.*

Literature: Law, 1881, 1898 (614); Collins Baker, *Hampton Court,* p. 43.

An unimportant derivation of a three-quarter-length, of which a good version is at Hatfield, showing the Earl as Lord Steward, a post to which he was appointed in 1584. In this prototype the Earl wears the chain of the Garter; the ribbon in no. 68 is apparently painted in later over the costume.

The favourite of Elizabeth I, whose chequered and distinguished career ended in his appointment as Governor of the United Provinces in 1586.

69. SIR JOHN LEMAN (1544–1632)

Hampton Court (904). 49⅝ × 42¼ in., 126,1 × 107,3 cm.; there are additions on the right and at the top; the original canvas was 44 × 35½ in.

Inscribed: ANNO DOMINI. 1616. / ÆTATIS SVÆ. 71

Three-quarter-length, wearing the red fur-lined robe of an Alderman of the City of London and the Lord Mayor's chain of office, resting his right hand on a chair and holding his gloves in his left hand; in the background are his arms.

Presumably (see p. 30) among the early portraits, formerly in the collection of Lady Capel, acquired at Kew; recorded at Kensington in 1818 (70) with an attribution to 'Zucchero'.

Literature: Law, 1881, 1898 (757); Collins Baker, *Hampton Court,* p. 46.

Probably painted to commemorate his election as Lord Mayor on 29 October 1616. Falkner (p. 36) attributed the portrait to 'Levinus' and Pyne (vol. II, *Kensington,* p. 51) to 'Leevines'. It is conceivable that the portrait is by Levinus de Vogelaare (see no. 90); though nothing is known of his work at this date it has affinities with the portraits in no. 69 and his was a most unusual name to have been attached to a portrait without evidence.

Member of the Fishmongers' Company. Alderman (1605), Sheriff (1606) and Lord Mayor (1616–17) of London.

70. CHARLES HOWARD, SECOND BARON HOWARD OF EFFINGHAM AND FIRST EARL OF NOTTINGHAM (1536–1624)

Hampton Court (286). Panel: $22\frac{3}{4} \times 17\frac{1}{2}$ in., $57,8 \times 44,5$ cm.

Inscribed later: EARLE OF NOTINGHAM.

Head and shoulders, wearing a skull cap, the ribbon of the Garter and a fur-lined cloak.

Probably among the early portraits, formerly in the collection of Lady Capel, acquired at Kew; recorded at Kensington in 1818 (556) as one of the *Curious Portraits. Brought from the Old Palace at Greenwich.* On the back of the panel is a seventeenth-century label: *9 Earle of Notingham* and giving measurements.

Literature: Law, 1881, 1898 (620); Collins Baker, *Hampton Court,* p. 42.

Probably a version of a standard portrait; the type seems to have been used for the portrait of Nottingham in the group of the Somerset House Conference of 1604 in the National Portrait Gallery (665), which may be by Pantoja de la Cruz. A version is in the set of historical portraits in the Brown Gallery at Knole.

Lord Chamberlain (1574–85) and Lord High Admiral (1585–1618) among many other important posts in a long and distinguished career; commander of the English fleet in the defeat of the Spanish Armada in 1588. His portrait was painted for the Crown by Daniel Mytens (see below, p. 84).

71. CARDINAL WOLSEY (1475?–1530)

Hampton Court (1088). Panel: $17\frac{7}{8} \times 15$ in., $45,4 \times 38,1$ cm.

Half length in profile to the left.

Stated by Law (*loc. cit.*) to have been bought for the royal collection *c.* 1850 when the Jacobean mantelpiece in which it was fixed was brought from a house in Hampton Wick.

Literature: Law, 1907 (911), 1925 (I).

No. 71 is totally repainted and it is impossible to determine its date; it is clearly a small version, probably of a late period, of the standard portrait of Wolsey, of which there is a version in the National Portrait Gallery (32) and many versions elsewhere. In the details of costume no. 71 is close to the type engraved by Houbraken and S. Harding and may, indeed, have been based on one of these prints.

Thomas Wolsey, builder of Hampton Court, the most powerful man in England until his fall after the divorce of Henry VIII from Catherine of Aragon.

72. PORTRAIT OF A MAN *called* SIR GEORGE CAREW (*d.* 1545)

Hampton Court (344). Panel: $35\frac{5}{8} \times 30\frac{1}{4}$ in., $98,1 \times 76,8$ cm.

Inscribed later: GEORGE CAREW ANO $\overline{\text{DNI}}$ ÆTA SVÆ 54 1563. This appears to have been copied from a much earlier, overpainted and probably contemporary, inscription, of which traces are visible to the right of the head: . . . SVÆ / 54.

Half-length, holding his gloves in his right hand and his sword-belt with his left hand.

Probably among the early portraits, formerly in the collection of Lady Capel, acquired at Kew; recorded at Kensington in 1818 (30: *Portrait of Sir George Carew. Holbein*).

Literature: Law, 1881, 1898 (573); Collins Baker, *Hampton Court,* p. 55.

No. 72 seems to be an original portrait. If the date in the later inscription is correct, it cannot be by Flicke (as was suggested by Collins Baker, *loc. cit.*) who had died in 1558, although it is clearly suggestive of his style. The sitter may later have been identified as Sir George Carew, elder brother of Sir Peter Carew (no. 52), who was in command of the *Mary Rose* in the war against France and was drowned when she foundered going out of Portsmouth Harbour. This identification cannot, however, be reconciled with the date in the inscription, which seems correct for the style and costume of the portrait, nor with an established portrait of Sir George Carew at Weston Park (Ganz, *Holbein,* pl. 163).

73. PORTRAIT OF A YOUNG MAN

Hampton Court (913). Panel: $22\frac{3}{4} \times 17\frac{1}{4}$ in., $57,8 \times 43,8$ cm.

There seem to be traces of an original inscription: A⁰ . . .

Head and shoulders in a white shirt and furred cloak.

Possibly among the early portraits, formerly in the collection of Lady Capel, acquired at Kew; apparently recorded at Kensington in 1818 (512: *A Mans Portrait in a Fur Dress*).

Literature: Law, 1881, 1898 (575); Collins Baker, *Hampton Court,* p. 43.

Probably painted *c.* 1590.

74. PORTRAIT OF A MAN

Hampton Court (914). $22\frac{5}{8} \times 17\frac{1}{8}$ in., $57,5 \times 43,5$ cm.

Head and shoulders in black, wearing a black ear-ring.

Possibly among the early portraits, formerly in the collection of Lady Capel, acquired at Kew; probably to be identified at Kensington in 1818 (652: *Head of a Young Man in a Black Dress;* Faulkner, p. 400 '. . . with ear-rings').

Literature: Law, 1881, 1898 (708); Collins Baker, *Hampton Court,* p. 46.

Probably painted *c.* 1590; the surface appears to be extremely worn.

75. PORTRAIT OF A MAN

Hampton Court (942). Panel: $31 \times 24\frac{1}{2}$ in., $78,7 \times 62,2$ cm.

Inscribed: A⁰ Domiñ. 1617. Ætatis Suæ, 72.

Half-length, wearing a gorget, holding his sword in his left hand and resting his right on a helmet.

Perhaps among the early portraits, formerly in the collection of Lady Capel, acquired at Kew; recorded at Hampton Court in 1849 (*The Stranger's Guide* (866)).

Literature: Law, 1881, 1898 (807); Collins Baker, *Hampton Court,* p. 47.

The style is perhaps suggestive of the work of Robert Peake the elder (*d.* 1626?).

76. PORTRAIT OF A YOUTH

Hampton Court (943). Panel: 31 × 25 in., 78,7 × 68,5 cm.

Inscribed: *Ætatis Suæ 17. / A° DONI* 1617. and GENVS ET GENIVS; both inscriptions were repeated at a later date.

Half-length, holding a glove in his left hand and resting his right hand on his hip.

Probably among the early portraits, formerly in the collection of Lady Capel, acquired at Kew; recorded at Kensington in 1818 (56) as by Lucas de Heere and stated by Faulkner, p. 365, to be a portrait of Henry, Prince of Wales.

Literature: Law, 1881, 1898 (854); Collins Baker, *Hampton Court*, p. 46.

Formerly suggested as a portrait of Charles I, who was born in 1600, but to whom the portrait bears little resemblance; the style may not be unlike that of John De Critz the Elder.

77. PORTRAIT OF A MAN

Hampton Court (279). Panel: $30\frac{5}{8} \times 24\frac{1}{2}$ in., 77,8 × 62,2 cm.

Inscribed: *Ætat. suæ . . 34.*

Half-length, holding his dagger in his right hand and a sword in his left.

Stated to have been at Penshurst and acquired from there by William IV; recorded in 1842 by Mrs. Jameson (660) at Hampton Court as a portrait of Shakespeare.

Literature: J. H. Friswell, *Life Portraits of William Shakespeare* (1864), pp. 99–100; Law, 1881, 1898 (709); Collins Baker, *Hampton Court*, p. 169; M. H. Spielmann, 'The Portraits of Shakespeare' in article on Shakespeare in the *Encyclopædia Britannica*.

Probably painted in England and, to judge by the costume, *c.* 1620–5; no. 77 need not therefore be seriously considered as a portrait of Shakespeare. The panel is very coarsely painted and has been repainted, particularly in the head, to enhance, apparently, the hoped-for likeness to Shakespeare.

78. PORTRAIT OF A YOUNG MAN

Hampton Court (1315). $22\frac{5}{8} \times 17\frac{5}{8}$ in., 57,5 × 44,8 cm.

Inscribed: *repugnantia.*

Head and shoulders wearing a ruff and a red sash.

Possibly among the early portraits, formerly in the collection of Lady Capel, acquired at Kew; recorded at Buckingham Palace (1169) in 1876 (*V.R. inv.*, where it is stated to have come from 'the old palace at Greenwich'); later at Windsor (2581).

A portrait of very coarse quality, and apparently very damaged, painted in England *c.* 1620.

79. PORTRAIT OF A WOMAN

Windsor Castle (1604). Panel: $19\frac{1}{16} \times 14\frac{3}{8}$ in., 48,4 × 36,5 cm.

Head and shoulders in black, wearing a small ruff.

It is impossible to identify no. 79 in the earlier sources, but it was recorded at Windsor in 1871 (*V.R. inv.*).

Literature: Collins Baker, *Windsor*, p. 113.

Attributed by Collins Baker (*loc. cit.*) to Eworth and suggested by Cust (note in *V.R. inv.*) as a portrait of Frances Brandon, Duchess of Suffolk, to whom the sitter bears little resemblance. No. 79 has been heavily repainted in the costume and background, but seems fundamentally to be Flemish in character. It was probably painted in England *c.* 1560. A portrait at Petworth (Collins Baker, *Catalogue of the Petworth Collection of Pictures* (1920), pp. 42–3 (194)) appears to represent the same woman on a larger scale and is inscribed with the date 1560 and her age (24); there is a version of this portrait in the Duke of Sutherland's collection.

80. PORTRAIT OF A WOMAN

Windsor Castle (2479). Panel: $30\frac{3}{4} \times 22\frac{5}{8}$ in., 78,1 × 57,5 cm.

Half-length in black, holding her gloves in her right hand and a red rose in her left; at her waist hangs a cameo in a rich jewelled setting and round her wrists are bracelets decorated with an armillary sphere.

Purchased by Queen Victoria in 1843 from the 3rd Earl of Bessborough and stated to have been placed in Prince Albert's apartments in Buckingham Palace (1148).

Literature: Collins Baker, *Windsor*, p. 110.

No. 80 was bought by Queen Victoria as a portrait of Mary I. At a later date it was suggested, *e.g.*, by Cust (note in *V.R. inv.*), that the sitter was Margaret, Countess of Lennox; this (see no. 91) seems equally unlikely. The portrait, which is damaged and repainted, was presumably painted in England *c.* 1575.

81. PORTRAIT OF A WOMAN: 'JANE SHORE'

Hampton Court (901). Panel: $39 \times 29\frac{1}{2}$ in., 99,1 × 74,9 cm.

Inscribed later: BAKERS WİFE MİSTRİS TO A KİNG.

Half-length, wearing a high ruff and clasping her hands to her waist.

Among the early portraits, formerly in the collection of Lady Capel, whose seal is on the panel, acquired at Kew; recorded at Kensington in 1818 (27: *A Female Portrait. Lucas de Heere*).

Literature: Law, 1881, 1898 (793).

Apparently painted in England *c.* 1580; it has no connection, therefore, with Jane Shore (*d.* 1527?), mistress of Edward IV.

82. PORTRAIT OF A WOMAN

St. James's Palace. $94\frac{1}{4} \times 58\frac{1}{4}$ in., 239,4 × 148 cm.

Full-length standing, holding a fan in her right hand, wearing a richly jewelled dress and long strings of pearls over her shoulders; the regalia are on a table to the left.

Recorded at St. James's in 1865 (*V.R. inv.*) as a portrait of Elizabeth I and with an attribution to De Heere.

Literature: F. M. O'Donoghue, *A Descriptive . . . Catalogue of Portraits of Queen Elizabeth* (1894), p. 19.

Probably painted in the nineteenth century for the set of royal portraits at St. James's and based on a portrait of *c.* 1580–1600, wrongly identified as Queen Elizabeth I.

83. PORTRAIT OF A WOMAN

Hampton Court (919). Panel: $44\frac{3}{4} \times 35$ in., 113,7 × 83,8 cm.

Dated: *1601.*

Half-length, holding a fan in her right hand.

Presented to George IV by Lord Stowell: received at Carlton House in March 1812 (Jutsham, *R/D*, f. 189) and recorded at Carlton House in store in 1816 (373: the 1816 label was noted (*V.R. inv.*) on the back of the frame in 1861); later at St. James's.

Literature: Law, 1881, 1898 (802).

No. 83 seems basically to be the type of portrait usually associated with the workshops of Marcus Gheeradts or John de Critz, but the costume appears to have been repainted and is generally suspect in texture.

84. PORTRAIT OF A WOMAN

Windsor Castle (224). Panel: 23 × 17½ in., 58,4 × 44,5 cm.

Head and shoulders in a white dress, with her hair piled up high and embellished with jewels.

Recorded at Kensington in 1818 (649), apparently as a pendant to no. 97.

Literature: Collins Baker, *Windsor*, p. 100.

Probably painted *c.* 1605–10. Formerly thought, understandably, to represent Queen Anne of Denmark, but the identification does not seem wholly convincing; it was also suggested (*e.g.*, by Collins Baker, *loc. cit.*) that the portrait may be of Anne Vavasour, a member of Queen Elizabeth's household.

85. PORTRAIT OF A WOMAN

Holyroodhouse. Panel: 44 × 32½ in., 50,8 × 83 cm.

Three-quarter-length standing, holding a book in her left hand and resting her right arm on a chair.

Possibly among the pictures, formerly in the collection of Lady Capel, acquired at Kew (the remains of a seal, which may have been Lady Capel's, were recorded on the panel in 1858 (*V.R. inv.*)). Recorded at Buckingham House in 1819 (801) as *Portrait of Lady Jane Grey 'a Book in her hand'*; later at St. James's. Sent to Holyrood by command of Queen Victoria in 1864.

Formerly (*e.g.*, in *V.R. inv.*) stated to be a portrait of Mary, Queen of Scots. At some date, possibly early in the eighteenth century, no. 85 had been almost completely overpainted, presumably to make such an identification more plausible. The original portrait on the panel, a female portrait painted in London *c.* 1610–20, can be clearly seen under the later overpaint. The chair seems to have been left in its original state and is of Jacobean design.

86. PORTRAIT OF A GIRL

Windsor Castle (1601). 22½ × 17½ in., 57,2 × 44,5 cm.

Inscribed, probably slightly later: *Suprœma Conju . . .*

Head and shoulders wearing a ruff, a sprig of honeysuckle in her hair and a jewelled S suspended from her ear-rings.

Recorded at Frogmore in 1871 (*V.R. inv.*).

Literature: Collins Baker, *Windsor*, p. 111.

Formerly described as a portrait of Elizabeth, Queen of Bohemia, by Van Somer. Probably painted in England *c.* 1615–18 and in an Anglo-Netherlandish style reminiscent of Van Somer.

87. PORTRAIT OF A WOMAN (*Plate* 37)

Hampton Court (299). 85¼ × 53¼ in., 217 × 135,3 cm.; stretched in lining.

Full-length standing in a wooded landscape in a loose white Oriental dress, richly embroidered with birds and flowers, and in a Persian head-dress and long veil; a ring is suspended from her neck on a black thread; she wears another ring on her right thumb and pearls round her right arm, and places a chaplet of flowers on the head of a stag; behind her is a tree bearing fruit and birds and two inscriptions: *Iniusti Justa*

querela and *Mea sic mihi*; there is a third inscription by the stag's head: *Dolor est medicina (e)d[o]lori.* On a cartouche is inscribed a sonnet:

> The restles swallow fits my restles minde,
> In still revivinge still renewinge wronges;
> her Just complaintes of cruelly unkinde,
> are all the Musique, that my life prolonges.

> With pensive thoughtes my weeping Stagg I crowne
> whose Melancholy teares my cares Expresse;
> hes Teares in sylence, and my sighes unknowne
> are all the physicke that my harmes redresse.

> My onely hope was in this goodly tree,
> which I did plant in love bringe up in care:
> but all in vanie [*sic*], for now to late I see
> the shales be mine, the kernels others are.

> My Musique may be plaintes, my physique teares
> If this be all the fruite my love tree beares.

Vertue states (*Notebooks*, vol. IV, p. 77) that 'Sr John [Stanley], some time ago recover'd to the Crown the picture of Qu. Elisabeth in a strange fantastick habit. (when he was deputy chamberlain to Qu. Anne.[1] which had K. Ch. 1 Mark behind it.' It had been 'bought as rubbish in Moor fields. by a Painter'. It was placed at St. James's (Queen Anne, *St. James's*, note by Thomas Coke: *In the Blew Room . . . over ye Doors . . . Queen Elizabeth in fancy dress . . .*) and later at Kensington in the Queen's Gallery of full-length portraits of sovereigns (Vertue inv., *Kensington*, f. 22); moved to Hampton Court, 12 September 1838.

Literature: Vertue, *Notebooks*, vol. II, pp. 48–9, vol. IV, pp. 65, 77; Walpole, *Anecdotes*, vol. I, pp. 162–3; Pyne, vol. II, *Kensington*, pp. 68–9 and seen in pl.; Law, 1881, 1898 (349); F. M. O'Donoghue, *A Descriptive . . . Catalogue of Portraits of Queen Elizabeth* (1894), p. 23; Sir L. Cust, 'Marcus Gheeraerts', *Walpole Soc.*, vol. III (1914), p. 27, pl. xxiv; Collins Baker, *Lely*, vol. I, pp. 23–4, *Hampton Court*, p. 64; R. A., *King's Pictures* (11); Miss F. Yates, 'Boissard's Costume-Book and two Portraits', *Journal of the Warburg and Courtauld Institutes*, vol. XXII (1959), pp. 365–6.

The identification of no. 87 with Queen Elizabeth persisted until the time of Law (*loc. cit.*); the name of 'Zucchero' (varying with that of Holbein) was attached to it as early as the reign of George I (B. M., Stowe MS. 567, f. 69 v.). Vertue thought the verses were by Spenser, but Walpole (MS. notes in Bathoe, *James II*, pt. II, p. 48) thought 'these silly romantic lines are of her Majesty's own composition'. The more recent identification with Lady Arbella Stuart (1575–1615), supported by Cust (*loc. cit.*) and very tempting, cannot stand comparison with established portraits of her. If Vertue was correct in stating that the portrait had belonged to Charles I (the CR brand was presumably removed in relining), no. 87 could have been tentatively identified with a portrait of 'the Lady Arbella at length in an embroidered habit' which had hung in the Queen's Gallery at Greenwich (*Van der Doort*, p. 196), but the measurements are given as 78 × 46 in. There was in the same Gallery at Greenwich 'A lady's picture at length in white lawn masking habit' (*ibid.*, p. 197, measurements given as 86 × 54 in.); this may have been *The Lady shorley at Length. in phantastick habitt*, valued among the pictures in the Queen's Gallery at £6 by the Trustees for Sale (L. R. MS., f. 7), sold to Murray and others on 23 October 1651 and not apparently recovered at the Restoration; in 1613 the Duke of Saxe-Weimar had seen at Somerset House the portrait, apparently at length, of 'A beautiful Turkish lady' (W. B. Rye, *England as seen by Foreigners* (1865), p. 163). But Lady Shirley (*b.* 1593), a noble Circassian, and

---

1. Sir John Stanley, Bart., was secretary to the Lord Chamberlain, 1689–99, 1700–14.

daughter of Ismael Khan, married to Sir Robert Shirley, an envoy in the service of the Shah of Persia, did not arrive in London until 1611. On the calligraphy of the inscription and on what is left of the texture of the paint, no. 87 can be held to be by Gheeradts the younger and placed in date near to the 'Ditchley' portrait of Elizabeth I in the National Portrait Gallery (2561). The sitter may be wearing a costume designed for a court masque, but remains unidentified; her costume is based on Boissard's 'Virgo Persica' in his *Habitus Variarum Orbis Gentium* of 1581. No. 87 has been extensively rubbed and, especially in the background, heavily repainted, and the outline of the dress down the sitter's left side has been drastically simplified; the overlapping folds of the dress and its fringes have been painted out and the adornments on the veil almost entirely obliterated.

88. PORTRAIT OF A WOMAN

Hampton Court (928). 35⅜ × 31¾ in., 89,9 × 80,6 cm.; stretched in lining.

Half-length, resting her left hand on a chair and wearing a richly embroidered costume, with a view of a landscape in the background.

Possibly among the early portraits, formerly in the collection of Lady Capel, acquired at Kew; recorded at Kensington in 1818 (508).

Literature: Law, 1881, 1898 (796); Collins Baker, *Hampton Court*, p. 82.

Probably painted *c.* 1620. Attributed by Collins Baker (*loc. cit.*) to Gilbert Jackson, but the state of the canvas makes its attribution very difficult: there appear to be later alterations to the drawing of the chair in relation to the arm; the gold decoration on the chair and curtains seems to be later or to have been coarsely strengthened; the outline of the head may also have been altered and the hair made more luxuriant.

89. PORTRAIT OF A WOMAN

Hampton Court (898). 29½ × 24 in., 75 × 61 cm.

Half-length, apparently in mourning, wearing white with black ribbons.

Probably among the early portraits, formerly in the collection of Lady Capel, acquired at Kew; recorded at Kensington in 1818 (152: . . . *in a Widows Dress. C. Jansen*).

Literature: Law, 1881, 1898 (860); Collins Baker, *Hampton Court*, p. 46.

Painted *c.* 1635 by an artist of very provincial character, influenced by the Anglo-Netherlandish style.

Livinus de Vogelaare

The painter of no. 90 is perhaps to be identified with one Lieven de Vogeleer, who became a Freeman of the Antwerp Guild in 1551, rather than with a painter of this name recorded in Brussels in 1600.

90. THE MEMORIAL OF LORD DARNLEY
(Plate 31)

Holyroodhouse. 56 × 88¼ in., 132,1 × 224,2 cm.

Signed: *Livinus Voghelarius* . . . The remainder of the signature is obscure, but does not seem to read as *me fecit* which was apparently Vertue's final reading (see below).

The iconography is very carefully organised and its points are driven home in a succession of inscriptions. Some of these are now very obscure and the sections of them that traduced the name of Mary, Queen of Scots, or referred to her part in Lord Darnley's murder have been erased.[1] Lacunae and obscurities in the inscriptions have been made good from the version at Goodwood (see below) and are printed in square brackets.

The effigy of Lord Darnley rests on a tomb in a chapel, possibly the interior of the old chapel at Holyrood, in front of an altar on which is a small statue of the Victorious Christ. On the wall to the right of the altar is inscribed: TRAGICA ET LAMĒTABILIS ĪTERNECIO / SERNISSI HĒRICI SCOTORV̄ REGIS. Under the three windows hang banners bearing the royal arms of Scotland, a white saltire charged with a ducal crown, and Darnley's arms (Aubigny, Stewart, Lennox, Mar, Albany, Ross, Angus and Douglas). On a paper, mounted on a tablet hanging on the wall of the chapel, is inscribed:

EN SVBSEQVĒTIV̄ HEROV̄ EFFIGIES VIVAS HĒRICVS EIS NOĪS IS FAMA DIGNᴹᴬ NVPER SCOTIÆ REX A COMITE BOTHWELLO SVISQ CŌIVRATIS [COSĒTIĒTE CŌIVGE]
REGINA] ATROCISSĪE CŒSVS VNA CV̄ SVO SERVO CAMERARIO.
[QVÆ REGINA MOX AB ĪTEREPTO AMĀTISSIO FIDISSIOQ MARITO SVO SE EIDĒ BOTHWELLO VXORĒ IV̄XIT]. DĒPTVS
EST PRVDĒTISS... HIC SPECIOSISSIMˢQ PRICEPS NŌ SINE MAGNᴼ
CIVIV̄ SVORV̄ DOLORE IVCTVQ CV̄ ĀNOS VIXERAT TĀTV̄ 21 CVIVS AĪAM DEˢ SVSCIPIAT SIBI IN GLORIAM

IACOBVS EIˢ NOĪS 6ˢ ĪTERĒPTI HĒRICI FILIVS DEI GRĀ REGNI ILLIVS IĀ REX ÆTATIS ĪTER[FACIEDV̄] HOC MĒSIV̄. 16.
QVĒ CŌSERVET DEˢ ĪCOLᴸVMĒ LŌGÆVV̄ [RE]GNOQ FŒLICISSIO

MATTHEˢ COMES LĒNOXÆ DE SĀGVINE REGV̄ SCOTORV̄ SVPERIORV̄ DVORV̄ PRICIPV̄ PATER ET AVVS ÆTATIS INTER
FACIĒDVM HOC ANNIS · 50

DŃA MARGARETA DOWGLAS ILLIVS VXOR COMITESS. LĒNOXÆ VNICA FILIA AC HÆRES ARCHI. COMITIS ĀGVSS.
ET MARGARETE SCOTORV̄ REGINÆ SENIORIS FILIÆ HĒRICI SEPTIMI ANGLIÆ REGIS SVPERIORV̄ DVORVM PRICIPV̄ MATER ET AVIA ÆTATIS INTER FACIENDVM HOC ANNIS 51.

CAROLVS STVART ILLORV̄ FILIVS ÆTATIS INTER FACIENDV̄ HOC ANNIS VNDECIM

On a tablet hanging behind Lord Darnley's effigy is inscribed:

[IN] INTERITVM EXCELLENTISS... HĒRICI SCOTORV̄
REGIS
CARMEN HEROICVM

QV[Ē IĀ] DEPICTV̄ VIDEAS HAC MOLE IACĒTE GRĀNDE BRITANORV̄ QVŌDĀ RES[PIĒ]DVIT ASTR [V̄RV̄]
EN [HER]OS DARNLEIVS ERAT FLOS[ILLE] DECOR[V̄]

1. Although Redgrave (*V.R. inv.*, 24 February 1866) was informed that 'this was done of late years', it may have been done in the time of James VI. Vertue, in his *Observations* (see below), had stated that the inscriptions were defaced.

QVI MODO REGINA RVTILĀS VXORE MARIA
SCOTORV̄ CELEBRV̄ REX EST MEMORABILIS ORT[S]
SACRATO BRITONV̄ LVXIT DE STĒMATE REGV̄
INDOLE MAGNIFICA VENERĀDI CVLTOR HONEST[I]
INGENIO [PRÆ]STĀS LĪGVARV̄ NVMINE FVSVS
FLOSCVLVS [EL]OQVII LITERIS INSIGNITER [AL]TVS
MVSIC[S] ARMIPOTĒS ANIMOS[S] MITIS IN OMNES
[INNVMERO C]ELSÆ FLOREBAT MVNERE MĒTIS

CORPORIS ENCOMI[I]S QVĀT' QVĀQVE BEAT[S]
VVLTVS [MĒBRORV̄] VARIO SVPERĀTE DECORE
MICVIT CERTÈ CŒLESTIS IMAGINIS INSTAR
EXTITIT HEV VITÆ BREVIS. HEV FINIS[Q] DOLĒDI
QVAM CV̄ SORS ĀNIS VNO TVLIT ESSE VIGĪTI
ET PATER INFĀTIS FVERAT CV̄ PRĪCIPIS ALMI,
SPE REX EXIMIA MIRA [PIETATE] MARITVS
OCCIDIT, Ô [TRISTIS SORS CŌ] SPIRĀTE MARIA
CŌIVGE REG[IA TRVCV̄LETO VVLNERE (CÆSVS?)]
OCCIDIT HOC RVTILV̄ LVME SED [CORPORE TANTVM?]
MĒNTE DEO VIVIT [LOCO QVOQ.] VIVIT HONORE.

On a similar tablet on the extreme right of the wall is inscribed:

OPERIS HVI[S] CAVSA

QVOD HOC FIERI FECERV̄T HONORATISS: COMES
LENOXÆ ET DÑA MARGARETA DOWGLAS ILLIVS
VXOR LŌDINI MĒSE IANVARII. A° DÑI 1567 VT NIMIS
QVI IĀ SENESCĒTES SI ĀTE EXCELLĒTISS: SCOTOR
REGIS ILLOR PROLIS ÆTATĒ PERFECTĀ HAC VITA
PRIVARĒTVR. AB EIS MONIMĒTV̄ HABERET IS QVO
ATROCISSIĀ CAEDES NVPER REGIS PR̄IS NŌ EXCLVDIT
ILLI[S] E MEMORIA DONEC DE[S] EADĒ FACIAT PER ILLV̄
VINDICARI

The effigy of Lord Darnley is in armour and supported at his head by two unicorns holding the crown of Scotland; at his feet lies a wolf, which was one of his supporters. On the sarcophagus are Darnley's paternal and feudal arms, with the crown above them and surrounded by the collar of St. Michael, flanking the royal arms of Scotland, surrounded by the collar of the Thistle. Also on the sarcophagus are two reliefs.[1] One, showing the murder, on the night of 9 February 1567 at Kirk o' Field, of Darnley and his servant as they are dragged from their bed, is inscribed CÆDIS DICTI REGIS ET SERVI / SVI IN LECTIS. The other, showing their bodies lying in the garden, is inscribed POST CÆDEM IN HORT[O / REPERIV̄TVR PROSTRATI]

The infant James VI kneels in prayer in royal robes, with his sceptre before him, crowned and wearing the collar of the Thistle. From his lips issues a scroll inscribed: EXVRGE DÑE ET VINDICA SANGVINEM INNOCENTEM REGIS / PATRIS MEI MEQ TVA DEXTERA DEFENDAS ROGO.
Behind him kneel his grand-parents, Matthew Stewart, 4th Earl of Lennox (1516–71), and the Countess of Lennox (see no. 91), and his uncle, their son, Charles Stewart (see nos. 56, 57). From their lips issues a scroll inscribed: EXAVDI DNE CLAMŌRE NR̄M ET VIDICA SĀGVINĒ INŌCĒTĒ REGI[S] CHAR[MI] FILII NR̄I DA REGI FILIO SVO PIA FORTVNA VITĀ[Q] LŌGĀ P[S]CAM[R] VIDICA DÑE SĀGVINĒ INOCĒTĒ REGIS ERIS MEI : ME VIDICTÆ TVÆ ISTRVMĒTV̄ FACIAS ORO.
In the corner is an inset picture of the encounter at Carberry Hill (15 June 1567); Mary, Queen of Scots, is seen surrendering to the insurgent lords, above whose forces is borne the famous banner, held before the Queen's sight, on which was shown Darnley's murdered corpse and the inscription

1. Vertue described these in his Observations as 'quite defaced'.

IVDGE AND REVENGE MY [CAVSE] O LORD. In the distance the Earl of Bothwell can be seen riding from the field according to the terms of the Queen's surrender. Two stages of his flight are seen, inscribed Boithwillis departing and Boithwill fleand. Around the frame of the inset picture is inscribed: ARMATI PRODEVNT SCOTOR REGINA TRADITORQVE BOTHWELLVS CONTRA QVOS VENIVNT REGNI ILLIVS PROCERES LAMENTABILE / HOC QVOD VIDEAS FERENTES VEXILIVM PROFLIGATVS BOTWELLVS AD DV̄RARV̄ / IN CASTELLO FVGIT : REGINA NERO HABITV [SIMPLICI] DEFORMATA SE IN MANVS NOBILIVM DEDIT, IN / QVORVM CŌVENTV DICTVM EST [JVDICIVM?] IN CÆDES SVRSE PRINCIPES DVOS /

Apparently passed by inheritance, presumably through Charles Stewart, to the Dukes of Lennox and Richmond: in the Wardrobe of Pictures at Cobham Hall, in an inventory taken in 1672 of the possessions of the last Duke of Lennox and Richmond, was A peice of the Tomb of King James' father (Archaeologia Cantiana, vol. XVII (1887), p. 405); thence, through the Duke's sister, Lady Katherine O'Brien, to her son's widow, Lady Sophia O'Brien, and to her son by her second marriage, Thomas Fermor, 1st Earl of Pomfret, Master of the Horse to Queen Caroline.[1] It was presented, probably in 1736, to Queen Caroline by Lord Pomfret; placed at Kensington and later at Hampton Court and Windsor (441).

Literature: Vertue, Notebooks, vol. II, p. 25, vol. IV, p. 124, vol. VI, p. 105; Walpole, Anecdotes, vol. I, pp. 183–4; R. A., British Portraits, 1956–7 (21).

Painted, according to one of the inscriptions (see above), for the Earl and Countess of Lennox in London in January 1567/8. James VI was sixteen months old in October 1567. In 1727 James Anderson, the historian and antiquary, drew up for the 2nd Earl of Oxford a description of the picture, with remarks upon it, and the Earl also caused a watercolour copy of the picture to be made. Vertue had difficulty in reading the signature. This had apparently been discussed with Sykes, who had repaired the picture, and also 'upon a review. by several' at Kensington, soon after the canvas had come into the royal collection and when the Duke of Richmond had brought up for comparison the version now at Goodwood, which seems slightly later, which he had recently discovered at Aubigny. In D. Jacques, A Visit to Goodwood ... (1822), pp. 101–27, are printed, as an appendix, Vertue's detailed Observations on the two versions, partly based on Anderson's description.[2] Vertue also examined both versions with Enoch Seeman, and his engraving of the Goodwood version was published by the Society of Antiquaries in 1750. There are slight variations between the two versions, principally in the colour of James VI's robes and in the figure and accessories of the recumbent effigy of Darnley, but Vertue stated in his Observations that this area in the royal version had been particularly severely damaged and that when it was repaired 'some parts of it, hereabout especially were entirely new painted over'. Vertue also mentions a description, probably of the Goodwood version, 'made out at large by Mr Folkes', presumably Martin Folkes, the antiquary. Vertue also noted, of the figure of the infant James VI: 'at first the robe he has on was white satten silk. but when it was repaired by order – the painter made them robes purple – which is false because in fact the robes of the Kings of Scotland is white – and alwayes was so used.' This seems to apply to the Goodwood, and not to the royal, version.

1. On 31 March 1727 Sir John Clerk had noticed it in the Earl of Pomfret's collection. Redgrave noted (addition to V.R. inv., 24 February 1866) that the frame in which it then hung was decorated with the arms of the Earl of Pomfret.

2. A copy of Vertue's original printed Observations is in the library at Goodwood.

The iconography was clearly worked out with the greatest care, presumably by the Earl and Countess of Lennox, and the composition should be read as a damning indictment of the part played by Mary, Queen of Scots, in the murder of her husband, their son, and of her association with the Earl of Bothwell; as a reminder to their grandson, James VI, of his father's murder and his mother's infamous conduct; and as a cry for vengeance on Darnley's murderers. The point of view contained in the picture has an exact literary parallel in the writings of George Buchanan, and especially in the account, in his *Rerum Scoticarum Historia*, of the *Tyrannous Reign of Mary Stewart* (for which see the extremely useful edition by W. A. Gatherer (1958)). His account of the actual murder (*ibid.*, p. 116) is, for example, almost a description of the two reliefs on Darnley's tomb. Buchanan was the principal propagandist of the anti-Marian party and a friend of its leaders, including Lennox, with whom he was associated after the murder of Darnley in the concoction of libels against the Queen. He was appointed tutor to the infant James VI who later did all he could to suppress and discredit Buchanan's works and to undo the damage done therein to his mother's memory. The defacing of the highly defamatory statements in the inscriptions in this picture may thus have been done at James's instructions or in support of his views.

Artists Unknown: Early Stuart Royal Portraits

91. LADY MARGARET DOUGLAS, COUNTESS OF LENNOX

Holyroodhouse. 94 × 55¼ in., 239 × 140,3 cm. The canvas has been enlarged on all sides and the original canvas was *c.* 75¾ × 47¾ in.

Inscribed on a tablet: THE LADY MARGARET. HIR GRACE / LATE WIFE TO MATHEW ERLLE / OF LENNOX REGENT OF SCOTLANDE / AND MOTHER TO HENRY KINGE / OF SCOTLAND / *Aetatis 55 A⁰ Dn̄i. 1572.*

Full-length standing with a Griffon at her feet, holding her gloves in her left hand and resting her right on a table on which stands a clock, in the form of a *tempietto* and with the dial surmounted by a hound supporting a shield on which appear to be the royal arms of Scotland.

Probably passed by descent to the sitter's grandson James VI and I; placed in the Queen's Gallery at Greenwich where it was recorded in 1639: . . . *a schotis ladi at langt in morning habit and a klock opan de tabel in a guldit fram* (Van der Doort, p. 196, measurements given as 74×52). The Trustees for Sale valued at £4 at Greenwich in September 1649 *The Ladye Margrett at Length. wife to yᵉ Regent of scotland* (L. R. MS., f. 7), which appears to have been recovered at the Restoration and placed in the Third Privy Lodging Room at Whitehall (Charles II, *Whitehall* (204): *The Lady Margaret,* measurements given as 75×52 in.); later at Windsor, Hampton Court (513) and St. James's.

Literature: Vertue, *Notebooks,* vol. II, p. 67, vol. IV, p. 74; Waagen (1838), vol. II, p. 117; Law, 1881, 1898 (559).

The portrait is almost certainly to be identified with that in Charles I's collection (see above), though it is perhaps odd that the sitter's identity was not recorded in 1639. The tablet appears to be early, but the date and age given on it do not tally with the Countess of Lennox's birth in 1515.[1] Nor is a

1. Charles I owned a miniature of her, stated to be by Nicholas Hilliard, which was apparently dated 1575 and gave her age as 53 (Van der Doort, p. 111); it has been suggested by Dr. E. Auerbach (*Nicholas Hilliard* (1961), pp. 68–9) that a miniature in the Mauritshuis is the miniature from Charles I's collection.

comparison of her features with those in an undoubted portrait of the Countess (no. 90) wholly convincing. It is, however, possible that the tablet, around which there is a definite change of texture, was applied early in the seventeenth century and that mistakes were made in the Countess's age or in the date of the portrait. There seem to be alterations in both hands, possibly in the legs of the table and in the right outline of the dress. If the portrait does represent the Countess, she is presumably seen in mourning after the death of her husband on 4 September 1571.

92. JAMES V

Windsor Castle (238.) Panel: 20½ × 15½ in., 52,1 × 39,4 cm.; there are apparently additions at the top of 1 in., at the bottom of *c.* 2⅛ in., and on the right of *c.* 1½ in. The original panel was probably *c.* 17¼ × 14 in.

Half-length, wearing the collar of the Thistle and resting his clasped hands on a cushion. On the background are painted the royal arms of Scotland and a tablet with the initials I R S.

Stated to have been given to Charles I: . . . *upon a Board king James. the 5ᵗʰ of Scotland his Picture wᵗʰ the Scottish Armes by, beeing in white habbitt with a black Capp and goulden Cloth Coate wᵗʰ a Coulloʳ wᵗʰ Sᵗ Andrews Crosse about his shoulder wᵗʰ both his hands one over another* (Van der Doort, p. 65, measurements given as 17×14 in.; no. 92 can therefore not be identified certainly with the small portrait of James V that is reported to have hung in the bedroom of the young James VI at Stirling (D. H. Wilson, *King James VI and I* (1956), p. 19). Valued at ten shillings by the Trustees for Sale (L. R. MS., f. 67 v.; it was then apparently, according to the Sebright MS., in the Armoury at St. James's); recorded in store at Whitehall in the time of Charles II (Charles II, *Whitehall* (517), measurements given as 17×14 in.); later at Kensington.

Literature: Elias Ashmole, *The Institution . . . of the Most Noble Order of the Garter* (1672), p. 99; Vertue, *Notebooks,* vol. V, p. 37; Collins Baker, *Windsor,* p. 125.

Probably painted *c.* 1540, but so extensively repainted that it is impossible to assess its quality. It is in reverse from the more familiar type of portrait of James V, of which a version is in the Scottish National Portrait Gallery (686).

93. PORTRAIT OF A WOMAN *called* MARY OF LORRAINE, QUEEN OF SCOTLAND

Holyroodhouse. Panel: 41⅛ × 30 in., 104,5 × 76,2 cm. The panel bears a later addition at the bottom of *c.* 7 in., and the original portrait, *c.* 26 × 23 in., seems to have been let into a larger panel at an early date.

Half-length holding a book in her right hand and wearing an elaborate jewel at her breast.

Inscribed at a later date: MARIA . DE . LORAINE . PAR LA / GRACE . DE . DIEV ROYNE DES . COSSE / FILLE . DE CLAVDE DVC . DE . GVISSE. Probably at the same date the arms of Lorraine, under a royal crown and with the inexplicable date 1611, were added.

Recorded at Kensington in the reign of Queen Anne (Queen Anne, *Kensington,* Store (185): *Maria de Loraine with a red Book in her hand*); seen by Walpole at St. James's in 1758 (*Visits,* p. 15). At Hampton Court in 1858 (*V.R. inv.,* no. 315, where it was stated to have been found at St. James's in January 1852 in a room occupied by the Hon. Mrs. Leigh, to have been cleaned and restored by direction of H.M. Board of Works and placed in the public rooms at Hampton Court. Mrs. Leigh, Lord Byron's famous half-sister Augusta, had died in St. James's in October 1851).

Literature: Law, 1881, 1898 (617).

No. 93 has been so extensively overpainted that it is imposs-ible to assess its age or its original quality or the grounds on which it was identified by the later inscription and arms as a portrait of Mary of Lorraine. It is, however, improbable as a portrait of her and therefore cannot be safely identified with any of the portraits of her in the collection of Charles I. A portrait given to the King in Scotland in 1633 seems to have been a full-length on panel (*Van der Doort*, pp. 172, 181). This was probably the portrait (*Queene of scotland. of yᵉ house of Guese*) valued at £2. 10s. by the Trustees for Sale at Somerset House in September 1649 (Corsham MS., f. 39) and sold to Norris for £3 on 12 November 1649; and not the portrait (*Queene Regent of. scotland, of yᵉ house of Guise*) valued at £10 by the Trustees at Hampton Court in October 1649 (L. R. MS., f. 118) and sold to De Critz and others on 18 November 1651 (S.P. 29/447, 24, 1); this had probably belonged to Elizabeth I.

94. MARY, QUEEN OF SCOTS

Windsor Castle (16). 86½×51½ in., 217,2×131 cm.; slightly stretched in lining and apparently enlarged *c.* 1½ in. on the right.

Full-length standing in mourning costume, with the royal arms of Scotland behind her, holding a crucifix in her right hand, a prayer book in her left hand and wearing a cross and a rosary; behind her, on the right, are her two ladies, Jane Kennedy and Elizabeth Curle (see below), and on the left a representation, inscribed AVLA FODRINGHAᴹY of the Queen's execution at Fotheringay Castle on 8 February 1587.

The canvas bears three long inscriptions: (1) at the top:

MARIA SCOTIÆ REGINA ANGLIÆ, ET HYBERNIÆ VER [E] / PRINCEPS ET HÆRES LEGITIMA IACOBI MAGNÆ BRITAN/NIÆ REGIS MATER, QVAM SVORVM HÆRESI VEXATAM / REBELLIONE OPPRESSAM, REFVGY CAVSA VERBO ELIZ / REGINÆ ET COGNATÆ INNIXAM. IN ANGLIAM ANᴼ / 1568 DESCENDENTEM, 19. ANᴼˢ CAP-TIVAM PER/FIDIA DETINVIT, MILLEQ CALVMNŸS TRADVXIT / CRVDELI SENATVS ANGLICI SENTENTIA / HÆRESI INSTIGANTE, NECI TRADITVR / AG 12, KAL. MART. 1587 A SERVILI / CARNIFICE OBTRVNCATVR. ANᴼ / ÆTAT. REGNIQ. 45.

(2) below the scene of execution: REGINAM SERENISSᴹ REGVM / FILIAM VXOREM, ET MATREM, / ASTANTIBVS, COMMISSARIIS / ET MINISTRIS R. ELI: CAR=/NIFEX SECVRI PERCVTIT: / ATQ VNO ET ALTERO / ICTV TRVCVLENTER SAV=/CIATÆ, TERTIO EI CAPVT / ABSCINDIT /

(3) at the foot of the canvas: SIC FVNESTVM ASCENDIT TABVLATVM REGINA QVONDAM GALLIARVM / ET SCOTIÆ FLORENTISSIMA INVICTO SED PIO ANIMO TIRANNIDEM / EXPROBRAT. ET PERFIDIAM FIDEM CATHOLICAM PROFITETVR. ROMANÆQ / ECCLESIÆ SE SEMPER FVISSE ET ESSE FILIAM PALAM PLANEQ TESTATVR

Recorded at Windsor, probably in the Princess's Drawing Room, in the reign of James II, among the pictures that had not belonged to Charles II: *Gennete. Mary Queene of Scotts. at length* (B. M. Harl. MS. 1890, f. 82 v.; Bathoe, *James II* (1101)); in the reign of Queen Anne it appears in this room as: *Genett. Mary Queen of Scotts at length wᵗʰ yᵉ beheading her* (Queen Anne, *Windsor* (212)).

Literature: New Gallery, *Royal House of Stuart*, 1889 (38–40); Sir L. Cust, *Notes on the Authentic Portraits of Mary Queen of Scots* (1903), pp. 91–112; A. Lang, *Portraits and Jewels of Mary Stuart* (1906), pl. xv; Collins Baker, *Windsor*, pp. 115–18.

Probably a copy, painted early in the seventeenth century, of the Memorial Portrait, now at Blair's College, Aberdeen. The Memorial Portrait is thought to have been commis-sioned by Elizabeth Curle (*d.* 1620), one of the two of the Queen's ladies who had waited on her to the scaffold; it had been bequeathed by her to the Scottish College at Douai. If the inscriptions on the Memorial Portrait are contemporary it cannot have been painted before the accession of James VI to the throne of Great Britain in 1603. There are slight varia-tions in detail between no. 94 and the version at Aberdeen: the form of the inscription at the top of the canvas is different; in the version at Aberdeen the names of the two mourning ladies are inscribed above them; and there are slight varia-tions in the figure of the Queen, in the royal arms and in the little execution scene. Another version belongs to the Earl of Darnley, and a copy of part of the Memorial Portrait was set into the monument to Elizabeth and Barbara Curle in the Church of St. Andrew, Antwerp. It is possible that the Memorial Portrait was based on the 'Sheffield' portrait (see no. 116).

95. MARY, QUEEN OF SCOTS

Holyroodhouse. 75½×43¾ in., 191,8×111,1 cm.

Full-length standing, resting her left hand on a table.

Formerly in the collection of William II, King of Holland, sold in The Hague, 9 September 1851 *et seq.* (162); purchased by the Lord Chamberlain in 1894.

Literature: Sir L. Cust, *Notes on the Authentic Portraits of Mary, Queen of Scots* (1903), p. 145.

Formerly attributed to Zuccaro, no. 95 is a late, probably eighteenth-century, work, presumably derived ultimately from the type associated with François Clouet.

96. JAMES VI and I

Hampton Court (900). 33⅞×22⅛ in., 86×56,2 cm.

Inscribed later: [. . . Re]x Scotorum

Half-length in a ruff, wearing a richly jewelled band and clasp in his hat.

Conceivably at Kensington in the reign of George II (*e.g.*, Vertue inv., f. 23: *A Man's head with a ruff & white waistecoat* or *A Young [ ] head with a lace ruff*) and recorded there in 1818 (611: *Portrait of One of the Kings of Scotland*).

Literature: Law, 1881, 1898 (761); Collins Baker, *Hampton Court*, p. 53.

Presumably painted *c.* 1587. The canvas has clearly been cut, certainly on the left where part of the inscription has been cut off, and probably on the three other sides. A portrait of the King as a young man, with a portrait of his consort, was seen at Richmond by Peter Eisenberg in 1614 (W. B. Rye, *England as seen by Foreigners* (1865), p. 172).

97. JAMES I

Windsor Castle (223). Panel: 22⅞×17⅝ in., 58,1×44,8 cm.

Head and shoulders wearing the ribbon of the Garter and a very elaborate jewel in his hat.

Recorded at Kensington in 1818 (647), apparently as a pendant to no. 84.

Literature: Collins Baker, *Windsor*, p. 111.

A reduced copy, of no importance, from a standard type of portrait of the King of which many variations exist, *e.g.*, at Dulwich (548, where the same jewel appears), formerly in the collections of the Earl of Ellesmere and Lord Harcourt (the latter dated 1606), in the Prado (1954), in the National Maritime Museum (dated 1610) and in the Scottish National Portrait Gallery (561). A very similar derivation is in the National Portrait Gallery (548). The original has been associated with the studios of John De Critz and Marcus Gheeradts the younger (Waterhouse, *Painting in Britain*, p. 27; R. A., *Kings and Queens*, 1953 (113)).

98. ANNE OF DENMARK

Windsor Castle (3062). Panel: 43½ × 34⅜ in., 110,5 × 87,3 cm.

Dated *1614* and inscribed with the motto: *La mia grandezza dal eccelso*.

Half-length, in a richly embroidered dress, holding a feather fan in her right hand. Her jewels include the crowned S and the crowned monogram C4 (see no. 106).

Apparently first recorded in 1687 at Whitehall (B. M., Harl. MS. 1890, f. 60 v.; Bathoe, *James II* (461)) with an attribution to Paul van Somer: *Queen Anne halfe length in a Farthinghall. A picture of Queen Ann* had been recovered at the Restoration (Col. Hawley, f. 6). At Windsor in the time of George III as by 'Jansen' and later at Hampton Court (265) and St. James's.

The portrait was painted before the arrival of Van Somer in London and in style and calligraphy is suggestive of Marcus Gheeradts the younger (see p. 80). A full-length version at Woburn Abbey (Sir L. Cust, 'Marcus Gheeraerts', *Walpole Soc.*, vol. III (1914), pl. VIII) has a different background, with a view of a garden, but could also be by Gheeradts. No. 98 may have been cut down. There are possible *pentimenti* in the jewels, in the attachment of them to the Queen's dress and hair, and in the drawing of the wired ruff. The background and, to a lesser extent, the figure have been overpainted. For further uses of the motto in the Queen's portraits see no. 105.

99. HENRY, PRINCE OF WALES (*Plate 41*)

Windsor Castle (3077). Panel: 22⅝ × 17⅝ in., 57,5 × 44,8 cm.

Head and shoulders in the robes of the Garter and wearing three very elaborate jewels in the plumed hat of the Order.

Stated to have been in the collection of the Winder family of Vaynor Park, Montgomeryshire; passed ultimately into the possession of Mrs. E. B. Cooke; purchased by Her Majesty The Queen for the royal collection in 1956.

Possibly painted in 1604. It is closely related to a full-length of the Prince, painted in that year, in the collection of the Earl of Mar and Kellie; the calligraphy of the inscriptions on that portrait is of the type used by Robert Peake, with whom, therefore, no. 99 can be associated.

100. HENRY, PRINCE OF WALES, IN THE HUNTING-FIELD (*Plate 36*)

Hampton Court (327). 75 × 65 in., 190,5 × 165,1 cm.; stretched in lining.

The Prince, dressed in hunting costume and wearing a very fine jewelled George, has dismounted from his horse, which is held by a groom, to deliver the *coup de grâce* to a stag whose antlers are held by the young Earl of Essex; the arms of the Prince and the Earl are suspended behind them, and in the background are an enclosed park with deer and a view of a town and a castle.

Conceivably acquired by Frederick, Prince of Wales; first recorded in the collection of George III in the Wardrobe at St. James's (George III, *St. James's*, f. 38: *Prince Henry with his attendance suposed the Earl of Essex*); removed in 1809 to Buckingham House (787), where the Prince was at one time described as the Earl of Leicester;

sent to Windsor in 1821 by order of George IV; thereafter at Hampton Court (1835 inv. (317) as by Lucas de Heere) and identifying the attendant as Lord Harrington.

Literature: T. Pennant, *Some Account of London* (1793), pp. 116–17; 5th ed. (1813), pp. 156–7; Walpole, *Anecdotes*, vol. I, pp. 210–211, n. by Dallaway; Law, 1881, 1898 (400); Sir L. Cust, 'Marcus Gheeraerts', *Walpole Soc.*, vol. III (1914), p. 28, pl. xxxiv; Collins Baker, *Hampton Court*, p. 65; R. A., *King's Pictures* (5).

Probably painted *c.* 1606–7 (Essex was absent from England for two years from the end of 1607). It is a later adaptation, possibly by a different hand, of the composition painted in 1603 (*Fig.* VI), formerly at Wroxton Abbey and now in the Metropolitan Museum (R. A., *British Art*, 1934 (135); *Commemorative Catalogue* (1935), p. 11), which is probably by Peake, shows variations in the landscape, and in which Prince Henry's companion is John, 2nd Lord Harington. There has been confusion between the portraits of Prince Henry and of his younger brother Charles, but no. 100 certainly represents the elder boy; the costume would be too early for the younger Prince and the features agree with accepted portraits of Prince Henry (see no. 99). In style the composition comes very close to Robert Peake, who was a member of the Prince's Household in 1610. The composition, like no. 105, is eloquent of the early Stuarts' passion for the chase and both versions of the design were probably painted as grateful records of days in the hunting-field, perhaps on the estates of friends; the earlier group may record a hunt with the Haringtons at Burley-on-the-Hill (Law, *loc. cit.*).

Robert Devereux, 3rd Earl of Essex (1591–1646), son of Elizabeth I's unfortunate favourite, was restored in blood and honours in 1604 and was a companion of Prince Henry in his youth; he bore the Sceptre with the Dove at the Coronation of Charles I and was Lord Chamberlain, 1641–2, but was never in sympathy with the King's policy and became in 1642 'General of the Army of the Parliament'.

John de Critz the Elder

1552?–1642. Came to England in 1568, the son of a refugee who had fled from the religious persecutions in Flanders. As Serjeant-Painter (1605–42) he was responsible for decorative work in the royal palaces, at royal funerals, and on the royal ships, barges and coaches, but from 1606 he also received payments for contemporary and posthumous royal portraits and for repairing pictures in the royal collection.

After John de Critz the Elder

101. SIR FRANCIS WALSINGHAM (1530?–1590)

Hampton Court (290). 22½ × 18 in., 57,2 × 45,7 cm.

Inscribed later: sᴿ FRANCES WALSINGHAM.

Head and shoulders, wearing a ruff and a black cap.

Probably among the early portraits, formerly in the collection of Lady Capel, acquired at Kew; recorded at Kensington in 1818 (573) as coming *from the Old Palace at Greenwich*.

Literature: Law, 1881, 1898 (613); Collins Baker, *Hampton Court*, p. 43.

A version of a standard portrait. In the *Herωologia* of 1620 the type is engraved, presumably by William de Passe, for the portrait of Walsingham and is annotated in the seventeenth-century marginalia in a copy in the Rosenwald collection,

National Gallery of Art, Washington, as *from Jo: de Critz* (A. M. Hind, *Engraving in England in the Sixteenth and Seventeenth Centuries*, part II (1955), p. 154, pls. 74, 87). De Critz's letters to Walsingham from Paris in 1582 indicate that he was or had been in Walsingham's service (*Cal. S. P. Dom., Add. Elizabeth–James I*, pp. 56, 68, 77–8) and the portrait probably dates from *c.* 1585. Versions are at Ingatestone, in the set of historical portraits in the Brown Gallery at Knole and, perhaps the best, in the National Portrait Gallery (1807); another was sold at Christie's, 10 July 1931 (107).

Secretary of State (1573–90) and an expert on foreign affairs, who successfully organised secret-service activities against the Queen's enemies at home and abroad.

Marcus Gheera(e)dts the Younger

1561/2–1636. Born in Bruges and brought to London in 1568 by his father, who was a religious refugee. Hollar's etching (1644) of Gheeradts's *Self-portrait* of 1627 describes him as '*Illustrissimis & Serenissimis Principibus Beatæ memoriæ* Elizabethæ & Annæ . . . Reginis *Servus*'. He or his father painted a little portrait of Elizabeth I at Welbeck (see R. A., *British Portraits*, 1956–7 (15)) and in the last years of the Queen the younger artist carried out decorative and heraldic painting for the Wardrobe. Between 1609 and 1618 he was paid for royal portraits (including one of Philip II of Spain) for presentation or for despatch abroad, and although in 1618 he was described as 'picture drawer to his Maiesty' he seems to have been particularly associated with Anne of Denmark. He was referred to in 1617 as 'her Majesties painter' and two years later he was among the tradesmen and artificers who attended her funeral. His position at court was probably jeopardised, many years before the arrival of Van Dyck, by the success of Van Somer and Mytens. His son Henry's miniature copy of Feti's *Dream of St. Peter* (Kunsthistorisches Museum, Vienna), belonged to Charles I, and Gheeradts himself had copied the picture 'in oyle Cullo^{rs}', probably when it was in the royal collection.
It is almost certain that nos. 87 and 98 above should now be included in Gheeradts's œuvre.

102. LOUIS FREDERICK, DUKE OF WURTEMBERG (1586–1631)

St. James's Palace. 88¾ × 44¼ in., 225,4 × 113 cm.; in lining *c.* 1 in. has been turned over on the left, ¾ in. at the bottom and 1 in. on the right, and there is an addition at the top of 3½ in.

Signed: *gerardi Brugiense fece/1608* (it is possible that the beginning of the signature has been lost) and inscribed on the early *cartellino*: . . . *Witenburg* / . [*16*] *08;* there are traces on the floor of an eighteenth-century inscription giving the sitter's name.

Full-length standing, holding his hat in his right hand.

Probably painted for James I or Anne of Denmark; the Duke of Saxe-Weimar noticed at Somerset House in 1613 portraits of the Duke of Wurtemberg and his wife (W. B. Rye, *England as seen by Foreigners* (1865), p. 162), and the former may have been the portrait that hung in the following reign in the Queen's Gallery at Greenwich (where the pictures had remained undisturbed since the time of Anne of Denmark): '. . . at length the Duke of Wurtemberg all in black in a cloak with his right hand upon his sword . . . by a green table' (*Van der Doort*, p. 198, measurements given as 84 × 52 in.). No. 102 can be identified in Charles II's inventory at Hampton Court (7, measurements given as 88 × 54 in.), where it has remained

(508) until recently. Notes in chalk on the back date from the eighteenth century when the picture hung over the chimney in the Prince of Wales's Drawing Room.

Literature: Law, 1881, 1898 (59), *The Haunted Gallery* . . . (1926), p. 33; Collins Baker, *Hampton Court*, p. 64; D. Piper, 'Some Portraits by Marcus Gheeraerts II . . .', *Proceedings of the Huguenot Soc. of London*, vol. XX, no. 2 (1959–60), p. 219.

The identity of the sitter has been in doubt. The portrait must represent one of the sons of Frederick VI, Duke of Wurtemberg, K.G., who died in 1608. His elder son and successor, John Frederick, is not recorded in England in that year, but he sent over his younger brother Louis Frederick with his father's Garter insignia. Louis Frederick was in England for three months in the autumn and early winter of 1608, was hospitably entertained by James I, and may have sat to Gheeradts while he was in London. His portrait in the Society of Antiquaries bears a very close resemblance to no. 102.

Paul van Somer

c. 1576–1621/2. Born in Antwerp and recorded in 1604 in Amsterdam, working as a history and portrait painter, in 1612 and 1614 at Leyden, at The Hague in 1615 and Brussels in 1616. By December 1616 he was in London. From 1618 until his death he was a neighbour of Mytens and Abraham van Blyenberch, and he was buried at St. Martin-in-the-Fields on 5 January 1622. From at least 1617 he was employed on royal portraits and payments for them continued to be made to his widow after his death. He seems to have been particularly associated with Anne of Denmark: on 4 February 1620, for example, a warrant was issued for payment to him of £170 for pictures made for the late Queen, and he had been in attendance as 'picture maker' at her funeral. In 1620 he seems to have paid a visit to the Low Countries. In addition to the portraits still in the collection, Charles I owned the portrait in the Tate Gallery (T. 398) of the Countess of Kent; a full-length of Tom Derry; and *The Lord Lyle to ye knees*. They were all ascribed to Van Somer by the Trustees for Sale.

103. JAMES I (*Plate* 43)

Holyroodhouse. 94⅛ × 54¾ in., 269,6 × 139,1 cm.; there are later additions of 9½ in. at the top and 2¾ in. at the bottom and *c.* 1 in. of the original painted surface is turned over down both sides.

Inscribed on the contemporary, but damaged, *cartellino*: *Jacobus D: G: Mag: Bri . . . / fran: et Hiberniæ Rex / 1618* (the last digit is obscure).

Full-length standing, holding in his right hand the badge of the Garter and resting his left hand on a table on which are the crown, sceptre and orb; the King wears the gorget of a suit of Greenwich armour which bears the initials IR and is piled on the floor beside him.

Presumably painted for the King; hung in the following reign in the Bear Gallery at Whitehall: *Done by Paul van Somerr . . . King James. the 6th in a black suite at length with a corslet about his neck* (*Van der Doort*, p. 5, measurements given as 85 × 58 in.); valued at £20 by the Trustees for Sale (L. R. MS., f. 8) and sold to Jackson and others on 23 October 1651. Probably the full-length of King James that was valued at the same price and declared by Thomas Beauchamp to the House of Lords Committee at the Restoration (H. of L. MSS.); thereafter at Hampton Court (455). It is impossible accurately to disentangle the references in the early sources to full-lengths of James I.

Literature: Vertue, *Notebooks* vol. II, p. 67, vol. IV, p. 73; Walpole, *Anecdotes,* vol. I, p. 210; Pyne, vol. II, pp. 63–4; Law, 1881, 1898 (308).

Vertue, who made a drawing of the portrait at Hampton Court in August 1735, and Walpole read the date as 1615, but 1618 seems the correct reading and is the date on the version at Hampstead Marshall which may have been painted for the King's daughter Elizabeth. The portrait was regarded as the official presentation of King James: it was the source of copies and variants (*e.g.,* no. 110 and at Euston Hall), and was perhaps connected with Francis Delaram's large engraving (Hind, *Engraving in England . . .,* vol. II, p. 224, pl. 126). A copy of the head was painted by John Hoskins in miniature (*Van der Doort,* p. 111) and is still at Windsor (*Fig.* 7); Van Dyck based his portrait of the King (no. 141), which confusingly bears the date 1617, on no. 103. Another popular type of portrait of James (*e.g.,* at Grimsthorpe, Drumlanrig (exh. Liverpool, *Kings and Queens of England,* 1953 (16)) and formerly at Bramshill Park, sold at Sotheby's, 16 July 1952 (43)) seems to have been a slightly later adaptation of Van Somer's design with variations in costume and accessories; and further developments of Van Somer's pattern are perhaps to be seen in a portrait in the Museum at Malmö and in a full-length, with a different head, of which there are versions at Newbattle Abbey and Hatfield (1623). It is possible that a gorget and a reinforcing beaver of Greenwich armour in the Armories, Tower of London, are connected with the armour shown in the present portrait (exh. Tower of London, 1951 (68)).

104. JAMES I (*Plate* 45)

Windsor Castle (3079). 89 × 58¾ in., 226,1 × 149,2 cm.

Full-length, standing in robes of State, wearing the crown and the insignia of the Garter and holding the orb and sceptre; through the casement (on which is painted the royal motto DIEV ET MON [DROIT]) is seen the façade of the new Banqueting House.

Presumably painted for James I, but not to be identified with certainty in Charles I's collection; *King James at Length* was valued at £12 by the Trustees for Sale at Hampton Court early in October 1649 (L. R. MS., f. 118), was sold to Emmanuel De Critz and others on 18 November 1651 (S.P. 29/447, 24, I), and was declared by him to the House of Lords Committee, 15 May 1660 (H. of L. MSS.). Probably in Charles II's collection: *Paul Van Somer King James. To the Feete* (Charles II, *Whitehall* (206), measurements given as 90 × 59 in.) and thereafter at Windsor, Kensington and Hampton Court (514). See nos. 103 and 141 for the difficulty of disentangling references in early sources to full-lengths of James I.

Literature: Vertue, vol. II, p. 29; Walpole, *Anecdotes,* vol. I, p. 210; Law, 1881, 1898 (763); Collins Baker, *Lely,* vol. I, p. 31, vol. II, p. 108, *Hampton Court,* p. 152; Mrs. R. L. Poole, *Catalogue of Portraits . . ., vol.* II (1925), p. xvi.

Probably painted *c.* 1620. The rendering of the Banqueting House records the general appearance of the new building and is accurate in certain details, but is rather a garbled version of what was being built; the artist may be forgiven for not understanding the unfamiliar architectural language in which Inigo Jones was speaking. There seems no grounds for associating the portrait (see Mrs. Poole, *loc. cit.*) with the warrant (30 January 1623) for payment to Richard Greenbury of £30 for a full-length of the King, although passages in the canvas have a richness of texture that is not usually found in Van Somer's portraits.

105. ANNE OF DENMARK (*Plate* 42)

Windsor Castle (2966). 104½ × 82 in., 265,4 × 208,3 cm.

Signed and dated: *P. van somer* | *A⁰ 1617* and inscribed on the contemporary, though slightly damaged, *cartellino*: *Anna D G Magna[e] Britan[niæ]* | *Franciæ et Hiberniæ Regina* | *Aetatis suæ 43 Anno* | *Dni. 1617.*

Full-length, standing in the park at Oatlands in hunting costume with five black and white Italian greyhounds who bear her initials AR on their collars; a negro groom in scarlet and gold embroidered livery holds her horse; Oatlands House is seen in the distance; an owl, symbol of Wisdom, perches on a tree above; there is a blaze of light in one part of the sky and a scroll, on which is inscribed LA MIA GRANDEZZA DAL ECCELSO, floats above the Queen's head.

Painted for the Queen and listed at Oatlands on 7 October 1617: *In yᵉ gallery next yᵉ vineyard her Maᵗˢ owne picture, wᵗʰ her horse by her, done at large,* with a slightly later annotation, *sent to the prince to Sᵗ Jeyms 8. Mʳᶜʰ 1618* (Glynde MSS.); recorded in Charles I's collection when he was Prince of Wales (Sainsbury, p. 355) and later in the Bear Gallery at Whitehall (*Van der Doort,* p. 5: . . . *In a Landskipp wher the house of Oatelands is painted*); valued at £20 by the Trustees for Sale (L. R. MS., f. 8 v.) and sold to Jackson and others on 23 October 1651. Recovered at the Restoration and thereafter at Whitehall, Windsor, Kensington and Hampton Court (780).

Literature: Celia Fiennes, *Journeys,* p. 359; Walpole, *Anecdotes,* vol. I, p. 210; Law, 1881, 1898 (346); Collins Baker, *Lely,* vol. I, pp. 28–9, vol. II, p. 108; *Hampton Court,* pp. 151–2, *Windsor,* p. 299; R. A., *King's Pictures* (19); Waterhouse, *Painting in Britain,* p. 34; R. A., *British Portraits,* 1956–7 (37); Whinney and Millar, p. 19.

The canvas can be dated within narrow limits in 1617 as it was presumably painted before 7 October (see above) and after the beginning of the year, according to the Old Style, on 25 March. In the same year Inigo Jones completed, among his alterations at Oatlands for the Queen, the classical gateway (for which the drawing is in the Burlington-Devonshire collection at the R.I.B.A.) which is prominent in the landscape. The canvas is therefore a tribute to the Queen's love of building and patronage of Inigo Jones as well as a display of her passion for the chase and a deliberate advertisement of the Divine Guidance with which she felt herself inspired. It is perhaps relevant that above the portrait, when it hung in the Bear Gallery, was placed a picture attributed to Salviati of three angels holding palms and garlands of flowers. The motto was a favourite with the Queen (see no. 98). In an early copy at Lamport the landscape is extended at the right. See also no. 202. *Queen Ann and her dogs* was among the portraits listed in Sarah, Duchess of Marlborough's possession in London (MS. at Althorp). Van Somer's design was woven in reverse by Francis Poyntz (1672) at Mortlake in the series of royal portraits in tapestry at Houghton Hall (H. A. Tipping, *English Homes,* Period V, vol. I (1921), p. 101).

106. ANNE OF DENMARK (*Plate* 44)

Hampton Court (591). 92 × 58⅛ in., 233,7 × 147,6 cm.; stretched in lining; the original painted surface is 90½ × 57½ in.

Inscribed: ANNA D. G. MAGN[AE] | BRITANIÆ. FRANCI [AE] | HIBERNIÆ REG[INA] | ÆTATIS SVÆ 44

Full-length standing, resting her left hand on a table and holding in her right a feather fan; the most elaborate jewels in her ruff are made in the shape of a crowned S (perhaps an allusion to her mother, Sophia, Queen of Denmark), a crowned monogram C4 (given to her in 1611 by her brother Christian IV) and the IHS under a Cross. In the background is an elaborate architectural fantasy.

Presumably painted for the Queen or her husband; valued at £15 by the Trustees for Sale at Hampton Court early in October

1649 (*Queene Anna. at length wth a p^rspective; by van somer;* L. R. MS., f. 118) and sold to Jackson and others on 23 October 1651. Probably the *Queene Ann at Length. by vansomer*, valued at £20, which was declared by Thomas Beauchamp in his possession at the Restoration (H. of L. MSS.). It is impossible accurately to disentangle the portraits of the queen with attributions to Van Somer in later records but no. 106 can be traced successively at Whitehall (?), Windsor and Kensington.

Literature: Vertue, *Notebooks*, vol. II, p. 29; Walpole, *Anecdotes*, vol. I, p. 210; Law, 1881, 1898 (764); Collins Baker, *Lely*, vol. I, pp. 30, 32, vol. II, p. 108, *Hampton Court*, p. 152.

Painted 1617–18, and perhaps at one time hanging at Hampton Court (see above) as a pendant to no. 104. The background, which does not appear to be by Van Somer, was frequently said (*e.g.*, by Vertue, Walpole and Law, *loc. cit.*) to represent Inigo Jones's design for the restoration of the West End of St. Paul's Cathedral, although this was not carried out until the reign of Charles I, and even (*Kensington*, 1818 (262)) as 'a View of the Palace at Theobalds'. It is an entirely fanciful concoction, very close in style to the extravaganzas of Vredeman de Vries; its insertion is an early instance of a practice which was very popular with patrons at the Stuart court and which later brought Hendrick van Steenwyck into collaboration with Mytens and, abortively, with Van Dyck (Whinney and Millar, p. 69, n. 2). The head is painted on an inset piece of canvas of 21×16 in.; the continuation of the join in the canvas to the top of the picture may mark the division between the work of Van Somer and his collaborator. The portrait seems to have been a popular image of the Queen. In versions, reductions and copies she is set against a much simpler background (*e.g.*, no. 111 below and at Euston and Grimsthorpe), but in a copy at Drumlanrig she rests her hand on a Mannerist fountain. A derivation in reverse at Gripsholm is dated 1618.

107. WILLIAM HERBERT, THIRD EARL OF PEMBROKE (1590–1630)

Windsor Castle (1107). 52×39¼ in., 132,1×99,7 cm.; there is a later addition of 1½ in. at the top of the canvas.

Signed and dated: *A^o 1617 | van somer f.*

Three-quarter-length, wearing the ribbon of the Garter; from his waist is suspended the key, and he holds the white staff of office as Lord Chamberlain.

Presumably painted for James I; the inventory of Oatlands, 7 October 1617, includes: *The Lo: Chamberlaine Pembrooks picture* (Glynde MSS.): on 13 September 1649 the Trustees for Sale valued at £6 *The Lord Wm Earle of Pembroock, Chamberlaine. by Van Somer* among the pictures in the King's Gallery at Oatlands (Corsham MS., f. 10); sold to Captain Stone and others on 23 October 1651. Declared by John Stone to the House of Lords Committee, 17 May 1660 (H. of L. MSS.), and thereafter at Whitehall, St. James's and Windsor.

Literature: Vertue, *Notebooks*, vol. IV, p. 108; Walpole, *Visits*, p. 15, *Anecdotes*, vol. I, p. 209; O. Millar, 'A Little-known Portrait by Paul van Somer', *Burl. Mag.*, vol. XCII (1950), p. 294; Waterhouse, *Painting in Britain*, p. 34.

Another portrait of Pembroke by Van Somer was engraved by Simon van de Passe with the date 1617 (A. M. Hind, *Engraving in England in the Sixteenth and Seventeenth Centuries*, vol. II (1955), p. 265). Charles I also owned his portrait by Mytens (see p. 84).

A prominent figure at the early Stuart court, Pembroke became Lord Chamberlain in 1615, Lord Steward in 1626 and bore the crown at Charles I's Coronation; he was the elder of Shakespeare's 'Incomparable pair of Brethren' to whom the Frist Folio was dedicated, the friend and patron of Donne, Jonson, Massinger and Inigo Jones, and a prominent member of the 'Whitehall group' of collectors (see also no. 314).

Attributed to Paul van Somer

108. NICHOLAS TOOLEY (d. 1623). *Identity uncertain.*

Hampton Court (703). Panel: 37½×41⅞ in., 95,3×106,4 cm.; there are apparently additions of *c.* 4¾ in. on the left, and *c.* 5¼ in. on the right; the original panel was thus *c.* 37½×32 in.

Half-length, seated in a chair with a pike (?) in his left hand.

Probably to be identified with a portrait in Charles II's collection to which no artist's name is given: *Captaine   sitting in a Chayre* (Charles II, *Hampton Court* (169), measurements given as 44×33 in.). This may have been the portrait (*Captaine Touly done by Van. Somer*) valued by the Trustees for Sale at £5 among the pictures in the King's Galleries at Oatlands on 13 September 1649 (Corsham MS., f. 10), and sold to Captain Stone and others on 23 October 1651; it was reported to the House of Lords Committee on 17 May 1660 by J. Stone (H. of L. MSS.) and thus presumably came back into the royal collection. No. 108 is not, however, identifiable in royal inventories between a reference in an early eighteenth century inventory of pictures at Windsor (B. M., Books c. 119 h. 3), where it appears (252) in the Prince's Dressing Room (*An old Man half Length with a Pike in his hand*), and its record in the *V.R. inv.* on 7 March 1863.

Literature: Law, 1881, 1898 (794); Collins Baker, *Hampton Court*, p. 168.

No. 108 is in so damaged a condition that any attribution must be considered tentative. It was clearly painted *c.* 1620 and would not be inconsistent with Van Somer's style if it can be linked with the references above. If it is the portrait recorded at Oatlands in the time of Charles I it would presumably have been painted for James I. It is possibly relevant that Van Somer's portrait of 'Captaine Touly' appears as no. 49 in the Trustees' valuation and that his *Earl of Pembroke* (no. 107) was no. 43; and that £5 (*c.v.*, no. 107) would be the Trustees' usual valuation for a portrait by Van Somer of these proportions. 'Captaine Touly' is perhaps to be identified with Nicholas Tooley alias Wilkinson (*d.* 1623) who was from before 4 May 1605 a member of the King's company of actors at the Globe under Richard Burbage, with whom he was closely associated for many years; he acted in plays by Webster and Ben Jonson. A smaller portrait of the same sitter, very close to no. 108 but turned to the right, was sold at Sotheby's, 21 December 1960 (224).

109. PORTRAIT OF A MAN, *possibly* A FRENCH AMBASSADOR TO JAMES I

Hampton Court (1333). 49¼×43¾ in., 125,1×111,1 cm.

Three-quarter-length, standing by a table on which rests his hat, with his right hand on a stick (see below) and his left on his hip, and wearing a gold chain round his neck.

In September 1649 the Trustees for Sale valued at £10 at Somerset House: *An Embassad^r of ffrance by van somer* (Corsham MS., f. 51) which had presumably been painted for James I; this was reserved from sale for Oliver Cromwell's use (H. of L. MSS.) and is probably to be identified in Charles II's collection in the Queen's Gallery at Hampton Court: *Monsr Soubise – At Length* (Charles II, *Hampton Court* (8), measurements given as 82×50 in., hanging next to no.

112); this is recorded in the royal collection until the time of George I, when it hung at St. James's (B. M., Stowe MS. 567, f. 75 v.). Probably thereafter cut down (see below); recorded at Buckingham House in 1819 (858, with an attribution to Mor); later at St. James's (*V.R. inv.*).

Literature: Law, 1907 (359); Collins Baker, *Hampton Court*, p. 168.

The canvas has clearly been cut down: the sitter's right hand originally rested on a stick, which has been partly painted out and which seems to imply a full-length design. The portrait seems almost certainly to be by Van Somer and it is reasonable therefore to connect it with the portrait in Charles I's collection. If it is also the portrait in Charles II's collection, the identity may by then have been confused. Benjamin de Rohan, Baron de Soubise (1585–1642), was a prominent Huguenot who came on a mission to James I on behalf of the Huguenots in the summer of 1622, about six months after the death of Van Somer; he was in England on a number of occasions and died in London.

After Paul van Somer

110. JAMES I

Holyroodhouse. Panel: 25½ × 18¼ in., 64,8 × 46,4 cm.

Head and shoulders wearing the ribbon of the Garter.

Perhaps to be identified with a portrait in Charles II's collection: *King James – To the Waste* (*Hampton Court* (140), measurements given as 26 × 20 in.) and in James II's collection (B. M., Harl. MS. 1890, f. 78, Bathoe, *James II* (939)); it can probably be traced at Kensington early in the eighteenth century (B. M. Stowe MS. 567, f. 16 v., as *Vansomer;* Vertue inv., *Kensington*, f. 5, as *Corn: Jonson or Vansomer*); at Kensington in 1818 (335), moved to Hampton Court, 15 December 1835 and to Holyrood in 1864. Either of two portraits of James I in Charles I's collection may be identical with no. 110: a portrait valued by the Trustees for Sale at Hampton Court at £4 (L. R. MS., f. 121) and another in the same palace valued at ten shillings (*ibid.*, f. 122); both were sold to Emmanuel De Critz and others on 18 November 1651 (S.P. 29/447, 24, 1). *A peice of King James* was recovered on 6 August 1661 (Col. Hawley, f. 6).

Probably a contemporary reduction of one of the slightly later (*c.* 1620?) derivations from Van Somer's original of 1618 (no. 103) which seem to take into account the changes in the King's appearance. The type is very close to that engraved by R. White (1696) as after Cornelius Johnson.

111. ANNE OF DENMARK

Holyroodhouse. 94¼ × 58 in., 239,4 × 147,3 cm.; there are additions of *c.* 9 in. at the bottom and 6⅜ in. on the left.

Full-length standing with a feather fan in her right hand and resting her left hand on a table.

Queen Anne's inventory includes two full-lengths of Anne of Denmark, with attributions to Van Somer (Queen Anne, *St. James's* (49) and *Somerset House* (19)), which do not seem to be identical with the two originals by Van Somer that are still in the royal collection. No. 111 was hanging in the Queen's Audience Chamber at Windsor (Pyne, vol. I, plate (1818) opposite p. 92), and both can probably be traced thereafter at Hampton Court (265, 518); apparently sent to Holyrood in 1864.

An exact copy of the figure of the Queen from no. 106; the architectural fantasy in no. 106 has been replaced by a hanging curtain and the marbled floor by an embroidered carpet. The curtain, carpet and table-cloth appear to be later and were perhaps added, or reworked, at the time (*c.* 1700?) when the additions were made.

Abraham van Blyenberch

fl. 1617–22. Recorded at Antwerp in 1622, probably soon after his departure from London, where he had been living in the parish of St. Martin-in-the-Fields, 1619-21, had worked on designs for tapestries woven at Mortlake, and had painted a number of portraits at court, including the 3rd Earl of Pembroke (1617), the Earl of Ancrum (1618), Ben Jonson and Charles I when Prince of Wales. Charles I owned, in addition to this last portrait (probably to be identified with National Portrait Gallery no. 1112), *Jacob. & Esau done by Blenberch*, valued at £6 by the Trustees for Sale among the pictures at Oatlands in September 1649 (Corsham MS., f. 10) and sold to Thomas Beauchamp and others on 20 September 1650.

Attributed to Abraham van Blyenberch

112. DIEGO SARMIENTO DE ACUÑA, COUNT GONDOMAR (1567–1626) (*Plate* 46)

Hampton Court (551). 77 × 51 in., 196 × 130 cm.

Inscribed later: *J. Gusman.*

Full-length, standing by a table on which rests his hat, with his left hand on his sword and wearing the order of Calatrava.

Presumably painted for James I. *A Picture of Gondomore. done by Blenberg* was valued at £7 by the Trustees for Sale among the pictures in the King's Galleries at Oatlands on 13 September 1649 (Corsham MS., f. 10), was sold to Captain John Stone and others on 23 October 1651, and was declared by Stone to the House of Lords Committee on 14 May 1660 (H. of L. MSS.); placed in the Queen's Gallery at Hampton Court (Charles II, *Hampton Court* (9), measurements given as 85 × 50 in.). In the eighteenth century (when it presumably received its misleading inscription) it hung over a door in the Prince of Wales's rooms at Hampton Court (Vertue inv., *Hampton Court*, f. 13) and was thereafter often confused with one of its companions there (Hampton Court no. 593). The width of both pictures was enlarged to *c.* 63 in. in order that they should fit their allotted spaces (and see no. 126).

Literature: Granger, vol. II p. 223; Waagen (1854), vol. II, p. 368; Law, 1881, 1898 (377); Collins Baker *Hampton Court*, p. 9.

Probably painted in London in 1622, perhaps on the eve of his departure from England in May of that year. It is very close to the portrait engraved by Simon van der Passe with the date 1622 (A. M. Hind, *Engraving in England in the Sixteenth and Seventeenth Centuries*, part II (1955), p. 257, pl. 153). The canvas appears to be worn and the style is not entirely consistent with the little that is known of Blyenberch's work, but the portrait is probably the one that was in Charles I's collection under his name.

Another portrait of Gondomar, sold at Sotheby's, 18 December 1957 (124), and now in the Ministry of Foreign Affairs in Madrid, is very close to Willem van der Passe's engraving (dated 1622; A. M. Hind, *op. cit.*, p. 289, pl. 177); it was stated, almost certainly wrongly, to have belonged to Charles I. James I or Anne of Denmark appear to have owned an earlier portrait of Gondomar: *A picture of the Count of Gondom^r ambassador for Spaine* was among the pictures recorded at Oatlands in October 1616 and October 1617 (Glynde MSS.).

Ambassador from Philip III and Philip IV to James I, 1613–18 and 1620–22, and a diplomat of marked ability and infinite subtlety, who exercised great influence on James I and brought about the negotiations for a marriage between the Prince of Wales and the Spanish Infanta.

Jacob van Doort

d. 1629. Portrait painter in miniature and in large; thought to be of Dutch origin and to be the son of Pieter, and brother of Abraham, van der Doort. Possibly born in Hamburg, he was established there by 1621, but travelled extensively; he worked in Denmark, Gottorp, Stockholm and Brunswick and in 1624 came to London.

Attributed to Jacob van Doort

113. CHARLES I (*Plate* 60)

St. James's Palace. $86\frac{1}{4} \times 53\frac{3}{4}$ in., 219,1 × 137 cm.

Full-length, standing in an interior, wearing the Garter and the ribbon of the Order, with his right hand on a stick, beside a table on which rests his hat.

Formerly at Cobham Hall and perhaps the *King Charles y^e first* recorded (80) in the Wardrobe of Pictures at Cobham in an inventory of the possessions of the last Duke of Lennox and Richmond, taken in 1672 after his death (*Archaeologia Cantiana*, vol. XVII (1887), p. 405); presumably passed with Cobham and its contents from the Duke's sister, Lady Katherine O'Brien, to her granddaughter the 1st Countess of Darnley; Earl of Darnley sales, Christie's, 1 May 1925 (54; as by Mytens), and Sotheby's, 23 July 1957 (368), when it was purchased by Her Majesty the Queen for the royal collection. Later at Windsor (3076).

Literature: *Archaeologia Cantiana*, vol. XI (1877), p. LXXXII; F. G. Stephens, 'On the Pictures at Cobham Hall', *ibid.*, pp. 175, 180 (as by Mytens); O. Millar, 'Some Painters and Charles I', *Burl. Mag.*, vol. CIV (1962), pp. 325–6.

Probably painted just before the King's accession on 27 March 1625; his costume is almost identical in Mytens's portraits of him (dated 1624) at Copenhagen (461) and in the National Gallery of Canada (768), and in so formal a portrait the regalia would almost certainly have been introduced if Charles had already succeeded to the Crown. It is possible that no. 113 is the portrait of Charles I recorded in the collection of the Duchess of Buckingham at York House in 1635: *Abra: Dorts Bro: A Picture of King Charles at length* (R. Davies, 'An Inventory . . .', *Burl. Mag.*, vol. X (1907), p. 380). This could have passed to the Duchess's daughter (no. 159) and thus gone to Cobham (see above). In character no. 113 is not incompatible with what is known of the style of Jacob van Doort. The portrait could have been the outcome of letters from Christian IV of July and August 1624, recommending Van Doort to the notice of James I (O. Millar, *loc. cit.*) and could have been given by James I or Charles I to the 1st Duke of Buckingham or his Duchess. A drawing formerly at Weimar (*Fig.* 15) seems to be a preparatory study for this portrait.

Daniel Mytens

c. 1590–1647. Born in Delft. Mytens entered the Guild of St. Luke at The Hague in 1610 and was married there in 1612. By August 1618 he was in England, had worked for the Earl of Arundel and was anxious to 'fynde occasion to drawe the Princes highnes picteure'. On 19 July 1624 James I gave him a grant of £25 and an annual pension for life of £50 'in consideracon of the good service donne unto us'. Soon after his accession Charles I appointed Mytens 'one of our picture-drawers of our Chamber in ordinarie' for life; Charles had earlier secured his denization and a house in

St. Martin's Lane for which he paid rates until 1633–4. From 1620 to 1634 there is a continuous series of payments to Mytens for pictures painted for the Crown. They include a series of official royal portraits, primarily for presentation to friends at home or for despatch to relatives and rulers abroad; posthumous likenesses of the King's Scottish forebears; and 'a coppy of Titian's great Venus'. In addition to the portraits still in the royal collection Charles I owned portraits by Mytens of James IV, *done after an Auncient water cullored peece*, Henry, Prince of Wales (after Isaac Oliver), the Duke of Buckingham, the 3rd Earl of Pembroke and the Earl of Nottingham. Of these the last four were recovered at the Restoration, but were later dispersed: *Buckingham*, which is now at Euston Hall, was probably given by Charles II to Barbara Villiers, *Pembroke* was reported missing by Thomas Coke in his notes to Queen Anne's inventory, *Prince Henry* was given to Henry Addington in 1804 and is still in Lord Sidmouth's possession, and *Nottingham* was among the naval portraits presented to Greenwich Hospital by George IV. It is perhaps significant that Charles I does not seem to have retained any of Mytens's official portraits of himself or his Queen (see no. 119).

114. PORTRAIT OF THE ARTIST (*Plate* 53)

Hampton Court (106). Panel: $26\frac{7}{8} \times 23\frac{1}{8}$ in., 68,3 × 58,8 cm.

Head and shoulders in black.

Presumably painted for Charles I (the CR brand is on the back), and placed by him *above the doore* in *the little roome Betwene the kings Withdrawing roome . . . and the longe gallorie* at Whitehall near *Selfportraits* by Rubens and Van Dyck: *the Picture of Mitins done by himself to the Should^{rs} In a black Ebbone frame* (Van der Doort p. 38); valued at £6 by the Trustees for Sale (L. R. MS., f. 164) and sold to Hunt and Bass on 1 March 1653. Recovered at the Restoration (Col. Hawley, ff. 12, 29 v.) and thereafter at Whitehall, Kensington and Buckingham House.

Literature: Vertue, *Notebooks*, vol. II, p. 146, vol. IV, p. 159; Walpole *Anecdotes* vol. I, p. 216; Waagen (1854), vol. II, p. 357; Law, 1881, 1898 (770); Collins Baker, *Lely*, vol. I, p. 49, vol. II, p. 110, *Hampton Court*, p. 108; R. A., *King's Pictures* (43).

Probably painted *c.* 1630, towards the end of Mytens's career in Charles I's service. At some point in the eighteenth century the panel seems to have been extended: in the Dressing Room at Buckingham House (George III, *Buck. Ho.*, f. 52; *Queen's House*, 1819 (672)) and later at Hampton Court (*e.g.*, *V.R. inv.*, 9 February 1867, and Law, 1898, p. 266) the measurements appear as *c.* 30 × 23 in. At Buckingham House the portrait was attributed to Van Dyck and at Hampton Court, for a short period, to Van der Helst. Walpole (notes to Bathoe, *James II*, 2 June 1763) saw it at Kensington and described it as 'damaged'. The background may have become worn and there is an apparent *pentimento* between hair and collar, but Walpole may have been misled by the portrait's freedom and spontaneity. A drawing by Aart Schouman (1787) records a *Self-portrait* of 1625 in which Mytens seems to be slightly younger (A. Bredius and E. W. Moes, 'De Schildersfamilie Mytens, II', *Oud-Holland*, vol. XXV (1907), p. 82; the source of this drawing may have been a *Self-portrait* now in the Muzeul Brukenthal at Sibiu (781)).

115. MARGARET TUDOR, QUEEN OF SCOTLAND

Holyroodhouse. 94 × $55\frac{5}{8}$ in., 238,8 × 141,3 cm.; there are later additions of 2 in. at the top and *c.* 4 in. at the bottom.

Inscribed on the contemporary *cartellino*: *Margarita, vxor. Jacobi quarti. | Regis Scotorum, filia Henrici | Septimi Anglorum*

Regis. | *Ætatis suæ 26.* (The last line is in a smaller and paler script).

Full-length standing in front of a balcony, beyond which is a landscape with a river, with a monkey seated on her arm.

Presumably painted for Charles I; hung near Mytens's posthumous portraits of James IV and Mary, Queen of Scots (no. 116), in the Bear Gallery at Whitehall: *. . . the Said Kinge James the ffourth his Queene . . . done after an Auncient peece . . .* (*Van der Doort* p. 4); valued at £20 by the Trustees for Sale (L. R. MS., f. 8 v.) and sold to Margaret Thomson on 8 November 1650. Apparently recovered at the Restoration, but not recorded until 1687, when it was among pictures at Somerset House in Catherine of Braganza's custody (Harl. MS. 1890, f. 71; Bathoe, *James II* (737)); thereafter at Hampton Court (519) and St. James's.

Literature: Vertue *Notebooks*, vol. II, p. 67, vol. IV, p. 74 (omitting the age from his transcription of the *cartellino*); Granger, vol. I, p. 102; Waagen (1838), vol. II, p. 117 (doubting the current attribution to Holbein); Law, 1881, 1898 (558).

Mytens's source was presumably the portrait, now lost, of Queen Margaret *Painted . . . in a Black habbitt with yellow sleeves wth a litle Monkey houlding uppo her hands . . .*, among the *Nyne old heades* at Whitehall in the time of Charles I (*Van der Doort*, p. 28). Copies exist of no. 115, *e.g.*, Christie's, 19 February 1954 (116), and, half-length, at The Queen's College, Oxford.

116. MARY, QUEEN OF SCOTS

Holyroodhouse. 84⅛ × 49½ in., 213,7 × 64,8 cm.

Inscribed on the contemporary *cartellino*: MARIA | DG | SCOTIÆ PIISSIMA REGINA | FRANCIÆ DOTARIA | ANNO | ÆTATIS REGNIQ. | 38 | 1580. A section of the original inscription, above the date, has been painted out.

Full-length standing, resting her left hand on a table and holding a rosary in her right.

On 10 July 1627 a warrant was issued for payment to Mytens of £100 for three pictures, which included portraits of James IV and *Mary the last Queen of Scotland* (Charlotte Stopes in *Burl. Mag.*, vol. XVII (1910), p. 161); hung in the Bear Gallery at Whitehall, next to Mytens's two other posthumous royal portraits (see no. 115; *Van der Doort*, p. 5); valued at £20 by the Trustees for Sale (L. R. MS., f. 8) and sold to Ralph Grynder and others on 23 October 1651 (S.P. 29/447, 24, 1), but soon afterwards seen by Richard Symonds (B. M., Egerton MS., 1636, f. 95 v.) with Knightley: 'at length of the Qu: of Scots. bella femina'. Recovered at the Restoration and thereafter at Whitehall, Windsor, St. James's (where it was engraved by John Faber jun.), Hampton Court (667) and St. James's.

Literature: Vertue, *Notebooks*, vol. I, pp. 65–6, 74, vol. IV, pp. 67, 70–1; Walpole, *Visits*, p. 15, *Anecdotes*, vol. I, p. 162 n; Law, 1881, 1898 (560); New Gallery, *The Royal House of Stuart*, 1889 (37); Sir L. Cust, *Notes on the Authentic Portraits of Mary Queen of Scots* (1903), pp. 64–91.

Mytens may have used as a prototype a version of the 'Sheffield' portrait of the Queen in captivity by Peter Oudry (1578: examples in the Scottish National Portrait Gallery (1073), Hatfield and Hardwick). Mytens reversed the Oudry type, but the stance, costume and accessories are close to this source; the source itself may not have been *ad vivum*, but based in turn on a miniature by Nicholas Hilliard (E. Auerbach, *Nicholas Hilliard* (1961), pp. 76–7, 294). Charles I owned a number of portraits of his grandmother: among them a full-length *Brought from Scotland*, given to the King and hung in the Tennis Court Chamber at Whitehall (*Van der Doort*, p. 1), is probably the portrait in the National Portrait Gallery (429). No. 116 was attributed to 'Gennet' in the early eighteenth, and to Zucchero in the nineteenth, century. Vertue (*op. cit*) made a copy of it (1720 ?), discussed the in-

scriptions and seems to indicate that the canvas had been damaged in the interval between his sights of it. Versions of it are in the Seaforth collection (formerly at Brahan Castle) and at Euston, probably painted for the Earl of Arlington's portrait gallery. It is not always possible to determine whether later derivations of the design come from Mytens or from his source.

117. CHARLES I WHEN PRINCE OF WALES (*Plate* 47)

Hampton Court (1243). 80⅜ × 51 in., 204,2 × 130 cm.; the canvas may have been slightly stretched in lining and *c.* 1¾ in. of the original painted surface have been turned over down the right side.

Dated: ANNO. 1623. There are possible traces of a signature between the hat and the Prince's arm.

Full-length, standing by a table, wearing the Garter and the ribbon of the Order, in front of a balcony, beyond which is seen a view of the Thames and the Palace of Westminster.

Formerly in the Sneyd collection at Keele Hall; sold at Christie's, 27 June 1924 (97), as a portrait by Van Somer of Henry, Prince of Wales, and purchased by Her Majesty Queen Mary for the royal collection; later at Windsor (2855).

Literature: Collins Baker, *Windsor*, p. 242; R. A., *King's Pictures* (20); Waterhouse, *Painting in Britain*, p. 36.

Probably painted soon after the Prince's return from Spain. Charles had taken leave of his father on 17 February 1623 and was welcomed back in London on 3 October. On a warrant of 9 October £30 was paid to Mytens for *a picture of the Prince his Highness drawne at length and delivered to Don Carlos de Colona, the Ambassador from the King of Spaine* (Charlotte Stopes in *Burl. Mag.*, vol. XVII (1910), p. 161). In a copy at Alloa House the architecture and landscape in the background are replaced by a hanging curtain. Mytens also painted, probably in 1623, a full-length of the Prince, now at Parham Park (see *The Stuart Period* (*Connoisseur*, 1957), pl. 25) of a different design. No. 117 is perhaps more likely to represent the type destined for despatch to Spain.

118. CHARLES I (*Plate* 48)

Windsor Castle (3086). 86¼ × 59¾ in., 219,1 × 152 cm.

Inscribed, signed and dated: *Carolus. Dei. G.* | *Magnæ. Britaniæ. Franciæ* | *et. Hiberniæ. Rex.* | *fidei. Defensor &c* | *Ætatis: Suæ. 28.* | *anno. 1628.* | *ad vivum. dep.* | *D Mytens. p. Regius* | *1628.*

Full-length standing, wearing the ribbon of the Garter, his right hand on a stick, his left on a hip.

Believed to have been in the collection of William, 1st Earl of Craven (1606–97), and to have been given to him by Elizabeth, Queen of Bohemia, or bequeathed to him by Prince Rupert, who had inherited many of his mother's possessions; passed by descent to Cornelia, Countess of Craven, by whom it was bequeathed to Her Majesty The Queen in 1961.

Literature: R. A., *British Portraits*, 1956–7 (57).

An important version, presumably painted from a sitting, of probably the earliest of Mytens's standard types of the King after his accession. A variant in Turin (*Fig.* VIII), with a perspective painted by Steenwyck in 1626, is signed and dated 1627 and was probably painted for the Queen's sister, the Duchess of Savoy. A variant at Hatfield is presumably the portrait for which Mytens was paid £40 on 20 April 1629 and which had been delivered to the Earl of Salisbury on 19 February 1629. On 16 May 1628 Mytens was paid £40 for a 'great' picture of the King, possibly no. 118, which had been sent to the Countess of Nassau on 22 April 1628 (Miss C. C. Stopes, 'Daniel Mytens in England', *Burl. Mag.*, vol. XVII (1910), p. 162). A good version is at Milton. A copy is at Gorhambury. The head from this type was engraved by W. J. Delff with a companion plate of Henrietta Maria after Mytens. Certain payments to Mytens for royal portraits state that he had painted them at Greenwich. The background in no. 118 may be an impression of the river and the opposite bank taken from the Queen's House. The balustrade behind the King may therefore be intended for the balustrade on the north terrace of the house, though it is not exactly in the form in which it was finally constructed. See no. 130.

119. CHARLES I AND HENRIETTA MARIA (*Plate* 58)

Buckingham Palace. 37½ × 68¾ in., 95,3 × 175 cm.

Double half-length, under a hanging red curtain, holding between them a wreath of laurel.

On 21 March 1634 an order was issued for payment to Mytens for a number of portraits painted for the Crown, including *one picture of the King and Queen's Majesty, both half-way in one piece, for the cabinet at Denmark-house* (F. Devon, *Issues of the Exchequer . . . during the Reign of King James I* (1836), p. 358); the canvas was apparently taken down soon after it was placed (see below) and presumably put in store. It does not appear in the documents dealing with the Sale, but reappears after the Restoration (Charles II, *Hampton Court* (160): *King Charles. 1st & his Queene wth a lawrell betweene them*, with no artist's name); thereafter at Somerset House (1714 inv. (9), *after Vandyke . . . a Chimney piece*), at Kensington and Buckingham House (as by Van Dyck) and at Hampton Court, where (*e.g.*, 1835 inv. (504)) the attribution was changed to 'C. Janssen'. Later placed at Buckingham Palace (198) over a door in the Large (Blue) Drawing Room (*Buckingham Palace*, 1841, p. 97, 1885, p. 5).

Literature: Walpole, *Anecdotes*, vol. I, p. 321; Cust, *Van Dyck*, p. 265; R. W. Goulding, *Catalogue of the Pictures belonging to . . . the Duke of Portland . . .* (1936), p. 98; Waterhouse, *Painting in Britain*, pp. 37–8; O. Millar, 'Some Painters and Charles I, *Burl. Mag.*, vol. CIV (1962), pp. 326–9.

Presumably painted *c.* 1630–2: a drawing by Peter Oliver of the head of the King from no. 119 is at Windsor (*Fig.* 8) and is signed and dated 163– (A. P. Oppé, *English Drawings . . . at Windsor Castle* (1950), 469). The figure of the Queen has been amended and reinterpreted in Van Dyckian terms, but the original form of Mytens's composition can be seen in the copy at Welbeck (*Fig.* 12). Myten's original design for her figure, which exactly corresponds with the copy at Welbeck, can be seen clearly in X-ray and, in outline, with the naked eye to the right of the superimposed figure. With the possible exception of the head, this second image of the Queen does not seem to be by Van Dyck himself, but to be based on Van Dyck's portrait of her (no. 147). That portrait in turn is very close to the figure of the Queen in the double portrait by Van Dyck in the Archbishop's Palace at Kremsier (*Fig.* 14; see Glück, 374, for the secondary version at Euston Hall) which was also probably painted in 1632 as a reinterpretation in more sophisticated terms of Mytens's prototype, and replaced it at Somerset House (*Van der Doort*, pp. 105, 106). Mytens had presumably produced the design to fill a particular space in the interior decoration of Somerset (formerly Denmark) House. His presentation of Henrietta Maria may have been displeasing to the King who could take the opportunity of having it altered on the strength of Van Dyck's new portrait. The compromise perhaps then proved unsatisfactory and Van Dyck was commissioned to paint as a substitute his own version of the design, into which he brought back the Queen's left hand with the olive branch, missing

in no. 119 in its amended state, and introduced the regalia. The X-ray of no. 119 also seemed to show an extension of the curtain down behind the figure of the Queen; any amendment of such a passage was probably carried out by Mytens (see O. Millar, *loc. cit.*).

120. CHARLES I AND HENRIETTA MARIA DEPARTING FOR THE CHASE (*Plate* 59)

Hampton Court (1235). 111 × 160¾ in., 282 × 377,3 cm.

The King and Queen, hand-in-hand on a terrace, surrounded by dogs and attended by Jeffery Hudson, await their horses which are brought up by a negro page.

For some years in the hands of the painter Thomas Murray (1663–1734) and recorded by Vertue (1723?) in the possession of the Earl of Dunmore; it hung later at Holyroodhouse, in apartments occupied by the Dunmore family (T. Pennant, *A Tour in Scotland, 1772*, pt. II (1776), pp. 244–5; *Historical Description* (1819, 1821), pp. 99–100) and at Dunmore Park (Waagen (1857), pp. 454–5). Purchased by Queen Victoria at the sale of the Earl of Dunmore's pictures at Christie's, 17 March 1894 (49), and hung at Buckingham Palace (1909, p. 77 (70), 1920, p. 15; P.R.O., L. C. 1/605, II, 38, 40).

Literature: Vertue, *Notebooks* vol. I, pp. 117, 161, vol. IV, p. 69, vol. V, p. 78; Walpole, *Anecdotes*, vol. I, pp. 216–7; Collins Baker, *Lely*, vol. I, p. 47, vol. II, p. 110.

The composition probably dates from *c.* 1630–2. Vertue stated that this version ('. . . big as the life hand in hand. walking. hyde Park . . .') was very much damaged, but that Murray had 'repair'd it the best he coud'. He also mentioned versions at Holland House ('large but indifferent') and in the possession of Richard Arundell. He described the latter in detail; it later passed to the 2nd Viscount Galway and is now at Serlby Hall. It shows slight variations from no. 120. Another version is at Knowsley Hall (G. Scharf, *A . . . Catalogue of the . . . Pictures at Knowsley Hall* (1875), 255). The variant at Grimsthorpe (H. A. Tipping and C. Hussey, *English Homes*, Period IV, vol. II (1928), p. 311), also seen by Vertue, is a re-working of the design in Van Dyckian terms, including the figure of Prince Charles from no. 150. In the present condition of no. 120 it is impossible to assess its relationship to the Knowsley and Galway versions, but the figures seem to be by Mytens himself; there may be *pentimenti* in the hair on the King's right shoulder and in the head of the further of the dogs held by Hudson. Mytens can hardly have executed unaided so large a composition thrice over. It was his most ambitious royal group and its iconography was taken up by Van Dyck and treated in more sophisticated terms in his *Le Roi à la Chasse* (*Fig.* VII). A reduced copy of the design is at Drumlanrig and a variant on the same small scale is in the possession of Mr. John Marnan (exh. Arts Council, *British Life*, 1953 (100)). A reduced version, containing only the three principal figures, is in the collection of the Prince de Ligne at Belœil. The principal elements in the design appear in the background of an engraving (*Fig.* 5) of Henrietta Maria on horseback by Daret. For Jeffery Hudson see no. 125.

121. ELIZABETH, QUEEN OF BOHEMIA (*Plate* 49)

St. James's Palace. 77¼ × 45 in., 196,2 × 114,3 cm.; additions, made probably in the eighteenth and nineteenth centuries, were removed in 1958.

Full-length standing by a table, on which she rests her left hand, holding a feather fan.

Painted for Charles I: *The Queene of Bohemiagh. by Mytens* was valued at £20 by the Trustees for Sale among the pictures in the Cross

Gallery at Somerset House (Corsham MS., f. 55) and sold to Edmund Harrison on 23 October 1651 (S.P. 29/447, 24, 1); on a visit to Harrison on 30 December 1652 Richard Symonds records '4 Large pieces at length done by Vandyke . after old pictures . . . ye Qu: of Bohemia . . . 30 li a piece' (B. M., Egerton MS. 1636, f. 90 v.). Presumably recovered at the Restoration; thereafter at Somerset House, St. James's and Windsor (449).

Literature: Vertue, *Notebooks,* vol. IV, p. 75.

Symonds's attribution to Van Dyck was understandable: Van Dyck had contributed to the gallery of family portraits at Somerset House a number of portraits of which two (see nos. 141 and 142), were posthumous. The portrait of the Queen of Bohemia is, however, certainly *ad vivum* and by Mytens and was probably painted in Holland in 1626–7: on 10 August 1626 Mytens was granted a pass to travel in the Low Countries for six months and he may have been back in London by 7 March 1627. He again went to the Low Countries in the autumn of 1630. The portrait has been attributed to Van Somer and Honthorst and was engraved by Vertue as after Honthorst when it was at St. James's.

122. CHRISTIAN, DUKE OF BRUNSWICK AND LÜNEBURG (1599–1626) (*Plate* 56)

Windsor Castle (3014). $86\frac{5}{8} \times 54\frac{7}{8}$ in., $220 \times 139,3$; the additions, made probably in the eighteenth century, were later removed, but in the upper right corner is a rectangle of later canvas, $11\frac{1}{4} \times 8\frac{1}{2}$ in.

Inscribed on the contemporary, but badly worn, *cartellino:* *Christianus D[ei] grat[ia] Dux | [Bru]ns . . [wic] . censis et Luneburgensis | Ætatis su[æ] anº 1624.* Underneath the *cartellino* are traces of a signature; it cannot now be deciphered, but was read by Vertue in August 1735 (*Notebooks,* vol. IV, p. 74) as: *D Mitens fe | anº 1624.*

Full-length standing, partly in armour, in a landscape, wearing the ribbon of the Garter and with his truncated left arm tucked into a sash embroidered with intertwined B's.

Presumably painted for James I or for Charles I when Prince of Wales; hung in the Bear Gallery at Whitehall: *Done by Daniell Mitins . . . the duke of Bromswick als. called Busshopp of Harborstatt . . .* (*Van der Doort,* p. 3); valued at £20 by the Trustees for Sale (L. R. MS., f. 8 v.), sold to Edmund Harrison on 23 October 1651 (S.P. 29/447, 24, 1) and declared by him to the House of Lords Committee, 19 May 1660 (H. of L. MSS.). Hung thereafter at Hampton Court (457) and St. James's; sent to Carlton House 11 July 1816 at the Regent's commands to be considered for the Ante-Room, but sent back 18 July (Jutsham, *Receipts,* f. 4); sent to Windsor from Buckingham Palace, 1 April 1938.

Literature: Walpole, *Anecdotes,* vol. I, p. 216; Law, 1881, 1898 (330); R. A., *King's Pictures* (17); Whinney and Millar, p. 63.

The Duke left London on New Year's Day 1625 at the end of a week's visit, when he received 'entertainment . . . every way complete; very good and gracious words from the king, with the honour of the Garter [31 December 1624], and a pension of £2000 a year' (*The Court and Times of James I,* ed. R. F. Williams (1848), vol. II, pp. 488–9). The portrait shows signs of having been painted with extreme rapidity, but must have been completed after the Duke's departure. For a period during the nineteenth century and more recently it was attributed to Honthorst (*V.R. inv.,* 13 November 1871). A version of the head and shoulders is at Hardwick Hall. A small copy is in the Lothian collection. The portrait was engraved by Robert van Voerst, as was no. 126, for Van Dyck's *Iconography* with the inscription *Ant. van Dijck pinxit;* it is possible that grisailles were made from the portraits by Van Dyck during his residence in London (M.

Mauquoy-Hendrickx, *L'Iconographie d'Antoine van Dyck* (Brussels, 1956) no. 186).

Younger son of Henry Julius, Duke of Brunswick, and of Elizabeth, sister of Anne of Denmark; 'Administrator' of the secularized bishopric of Halberstadt; a champion of the Queen of Bohemia, he raised an army for the Protestant cause in the Thirty Years War, when he served in conjunction with Mansfeld and was wounded at Fleurus on 29 August 1622; a few days later his arm was amputated with full military honours. The defeat of the 'Mad Halberstädter' at Stadtlohn on 6 August 1623 was a disaster for the King of Bohemia's cause.

123. GEORGE VILLIERS, FIRST DUKE OF BUCKINGHAM (1592–1628) (*Plate* 51)

Hampton Court (589). Panel: $30\frac{5}{8} \times 24\frac{1}{2}$ in., $77,8 \times 62,2$ cm.

Head and shoulders in armour, wearing the ribbon of the Garter.

In the collection of George IV; thereafter at Hampton Court and Windsor (2958).

Literature: Law, 1881, 1898 (388); Collins Baker, *Lely,* vol. II, p. 110, *Hampton Court,* p. 109, *Windsor,* p. 243.

Recorded at Carlton House, 1816 (303) in store, as *A head of a nobleman, in armour, with a blue sash, and the George* in the *Style of Cornˢ Jansen.* The sitter had been identified by Collins Baker (*op. cit.*) as Frederick V, King of Bohemia, but a version of the portrait, with variations in costume, is in the Earl of Jersey's collection and is inscribed GEORGIVS VILLIERS. | MARCHIO BVCOVINGAN. Buckingham, who had received the Garter in 1616, was made a Marquis on 1 January 1618 and became a Duke on 18 May 1623, during his absence in Spain. The portrait was probably painted *c.* 1620–2. The nineteenth-century attributions to Johnson and Miereveld were corrected by Collins Baker.

The favourite of James I and Charles I and a lavish collector of works of art, he nevertheless did much, during and after his meteoric rise to power, to widen the rift between King and Parliament by his wayward and impetuous policy at home and abroad.

124. JAMES HAMILTON, SECOND MARQUIS OF HAMILTON (1589–1625)

Windsor Castle (2967). $87\frac{1}{8} \times 53\frac{1}{2}$ in., $221,3 \times 136$ cm.; probably slightly stretched in lining. At the top is a very early addition of between $3\frac{1}{4}$ and 4 in.

Inscribed on the contemporary, but damaged, *cartellino:* *Jacobus Marchis Hamiltoniæ | Ætatis suæ . 44 Anº Dni: 1622.*

Full-length standing, holding his hat and the white staff of the Lord Steward of the Household, wearing the ribbon of the Garter, with a view across a terrace to a landscape with horses and riders.

Probably painted for Charles I and recorded in his collection, *c.* 1624 (Sainsbury, p. 355); after his accession placed in the Bear Gallery at Whitehall (*Van der Doort,* p. 7); valued at £20 by the Trustees for Sale (L. R. MS., f. 8) and sold to Ralph Grynder and others on 23 October 1651 (S.P. 29/447, 24, 1). Probably returned at the Restoration, though there is no account of its recovery; at Hampton Court in 1688 (B. M., Harl. MS. 1890, f. 81; Bathoe, *James II* (1046)); moved from Hampton Court (41) to Windsor, 10 April 1933.

Literature: Vertue, *Notebooks,* vol. II, p. 67, vol. IV, pp. 74, 75, suggesting Mytens in face of the current attribution to Van Somer; Walpole, *Anecdotes,* vol. I, p. 210; Pyne, vol. II, p. 40, where it is seen in the position it had occupied for over a hundred years

(Queen Anne, *Hampton Court* (2)); Waagen (1854), vol. II, p. 355; Law, 1881, 1898 (44); Collins Baker, *Lely*, vol. I, pp. 44, 48, vol. II, p. 109, *Hampton Court*, p. 108, *Windsor*, p. 243; R. A., *King's Pictures* (16).

The facts on the *cartellino* cannot be reconciled. Hamilton never reached the age of 44, and, although he received the Garter in February 1622/3, he was not installed until 22 April 1623 and was not appointed Lord Steward until 28 February 1624; the portrait should probably be dated 1624. The original of the design is probably the portrait formerly at Hamilton Palace and bought back for the Hamilton collection at Lennoxlove when it appeared at Christie's in Viscount Furness's sale at Christie's, 28 March 1947 (41). No. 124 is certainly original, but in its present condition its relation to the Hamilton version is difficult to assess. A good version is at Hopetoun; in the copies at Knole (dated 1622) and Cowdray Park (ex-Lady Sinclair Haddington) the age has been omitted from the *cartellino*; another copy is in the Scottish National Portrait Gallery (1056) and reduced copies exist, *e.g.*, of the head only in the Lothian collection (where there is also a small copy of the whole), at Ham House and Bolton Abbey. In the Hamilton collection are a small copy of no. 124 and a small copy of the head. There are considerable variations in the landscapes and distant figures in the different versions. *The Marquesse Hambleton at length* by Mytens in the Duke of Buckingham's collection in 1635 (*Burl. Mag.*, vol. X (1907), p. 379) may have been a portrait of the 3rd Marquis.

'A goodly, proper and graceful gentleman, and generally esteemed', who filled a number of offices in the service of James I, including that of Lord High Commissioner to the Scottish Parliament.

125. JEFFERY HUDSON (1619–82) (*Plate* 50)

Hampton Court (892). 84¾ × 59 in., 215,3 × 150 cm.; there is an addition or replacement of *c.* 4¾ in. at the bottom of the canvas.[1]

Inscribed on the contemporary, but damaged, *cartellino*: *Godfridus Hudson. na[nus]* / *[Æt]atis 18. A . . . 1650 (sic)*.

Full-length, standing in a landscape with his hat on the ground beside him.

Painted for Charles I: a warrant was signed on 24 June 1630 to pay the artist £40 for the *picture of Jeoffry in a wood, sent to St. James's* (Charlotte Stopes in *Burl. Mag.*, vol. XVII (1910), p. 162); soon after placed in the Bear Gallery at Whitehall (*Van der Doort*, p. 7); valued at £10 by the Trustees for Sale (L. R. MS., f. 8) and sold to Ralph Grynder and others on 23 October 1651 (S.P. 29/447, 24, 1). Recovered at the Restoration (Col. Hawley, f. 5) and thereafter hung at Hampton Court, St. James's (Walpole, *Vivists*, p. 15) and Kensington.

Literature: Walpole, *Anecdotes*, vol. I, p. 216; Law, 1881, 1898 (798); Collins Baker, *Lely*, vol. II, p. 110, *Hampton Court*, p. 108; E. Cammaerts in *Burl. Mag.*, vol. LXXXV (1944), p. 304.

Mytens did not paint the landscape; in Charles I's catalogue it is said to be by *Corragio John*. This is a possible corruption of Alexander Keirincx, who was in the King's service in London during the 1630's, or, more improbably, of Cornelius Johnson, to whom the portrait was attributed by Thomas Coke in his annotations to Queen Anne's inventory, possibly as a result of the corruption which was printed later by Bathoe (*Charles I*, p. 90). There are indications of alterations by Mytens or his collaborator down the left side of the figure; the cloak and the left leg seem originally to have been placed further to the right.

---

1. The measurements are given by Van der Doort as 88 × 62 in., and at that time the canvas was without a frame.

Son of a butcher at Oakham and introduced at the age of nine to the Duchess of Buckingham; she released him from a pie at a dinner given to Charles I and Henrietta Maria, who took him into her service; an adventurous career included a period of enslavement by Barbary pirates. When he was thirty he attained the height of forty-two or forty-five inches.

126. ERNST VON MANSFELD (1585–1626)

Windsor Castle (2536). 77½ × 65¼ in., 197 × 166 cm.; the width was enlarged, presumably early in the eighteenth century, from 50½ in.

Inscribed on the contemporary *cartellino*: *Ernestus Princeps et Comes Mansfeldiæ* / *Marchio Castelnovi & Boutigliere* / *Baron . . . Heldrungen, Generalis* / *&c Ætatis. 48. 1624.*

Full-length standing in armour, wearing a richly embroidered sash and holding a baton, beside a table on which rests his helmet.

Possibly the portrait (*Mitens. Count Mansfelt at length*) in the Duke of Buckingham's collection at York House in 1635 (*Burl. Mag.*, vol. X (1907), p. 379). Hung in the time of Charles I in the Bear Gallery at Whitehall (*Van der Doort*, p. 2, measurements given as 88×54 in.); valued at £20 by the Trustees for Sale (L. R. MS., f. 8) and sold to Emmanuel De Critz and others on 18 November 1651 (S.P. 29/447, 24, 1). Recovered at the Restoration (Col. Hawley, f. 77 v.) and thereafter at Whitehall, Windsor, Somerset House, St. James's and Hampton Court (590).

Literature: Vertue, *Notebooks*, vol. II, p. 146, vol. IV, p. 74; Law, 1881, 1898 (405); Collins Baker, *Windsor*, p. 245; Whinney and Millar, p. 63.

Presumably painted during Mansfeld's visits to London in 1624; he was given a cordial reception by James I and Prince Charles when he was in London 14–25 April 1624: 'the king praised him and the prince desired his portrait' (*Cal. S.P. Ven., 1623–5*, p. 304). He returned in the autumn and again on 4 November to take command of the expedition, which sailed from Dover on 31 January 1625, planned to recover the Palatinate. The red cloth on the table seems to have been overpainted at the time the additions were made, probably when it was hung, with other portraits (to some of which similar additions were made) over the doors in the Prince of Wales's rooms at Hampton Court (Vertue inv., *Hampton Court*, f. 13). Engraved by Robert van Voerst (see also no. 122) for Van Dyck's *Iconography*, with the inscription *Ant. van Dijck pinxit*, which may mean that Van Dyck produced a grisaille of it during his residence in London (Marie Mauquoy-Hendrickx, *L'Iconographie d'Antoine Van Dyck* (Brussels, 1956), no. 187). A copy of the head is in the Lothian collection.

Illegitimate son of Peter von Mansfeld, governor of Luxembourg; a professional soldier and mercenary leader who maintained an army in the Protestant service in the Thirty Years War until his defeat by Wallenstein in 1626 at the Bridge of Dessau.

Attributed to Daniel Mytens

127. EDWARD LA ZOUCHE, ELEVENTH BARON ZOUCHE OF HARRINGWORTH (*c.* 1556–1625)

Hampton Court (307). 86¾ × 52¼ in., 220,3 × 133 cm.

Full-length seated, with his right hand on a stick, beside a table on which rests his hat.

Probably acquired by Frederick, Prince of Wales; seen by Horace Walpole at Kew (1761): 'a good whole length of an old Man sitting, rich habit; I think by Mytens' (*Visits*, p. 39); described by Sir William Chambers (*Plans . . . of Kew* (1763), p. 17) as a portrait of Lord Burghley; removed to Buckingham House (1801?), by which time it had acquired an attribution to 'Zuccaro' (George III, *Removals*, f. 17; *Queen's House*, 1819 (747)); sent to Hampton Court, 2 May 1833.

Literature: Waagen (1854), vol. II, p. 362; Law, 1881, 1898 (336); Collins Baker, *Hampton Court*, p. 109.

The attribution to Mytens, repeated by Collins Baker from nineteenth-century authorities, is an intelligent one, and the portrait may be by or after Mytens, *c.* 1618; in presentation and tonality it is very close to Mytens's earliest English portraits, but these qualities could also be found in the other painters who were working in the Anglo-Netherlandish style of which Mytens was the most important and familiar exponent.

'A grave and wise counsellor', a passionate horticulturist and the friend of Ben Jonson; was among the peers who tried Mary, Queen of Scots, and thereafter President of Wales (1602), Lord Warden of the Cinque Ports (1615) and one of the first members (1620) of the New England council.

128. PORTRAIT OF A YOUTH

Holyroodhouse. Panel: $27\frac{1}{4} \times 19\frac{7}{8}$ in., $69,2 \times 50,5$ cm.

Head and shoulders in dark brown doublet and a ruff.

Recorded at Kensington in 1818 (115: *Portrait of Prince Henry. C. Janssen*) and moved to Hampton Court (269) on 1 November 1833. conceivably to be identified at Kensington in the reign of George II (Vertue inv., *Kensington*, f. 24: *A boy's head with a ruff & black habit*) and thus perhaps in James II's collection (B. M., Harl. MS. 1890, f. 59; Bathoe, *James II* (417): *A Boyes head with a Ruffe*).

The portrait does not represent Henry, Prince of Wales. It was probably painted *c.* 1618 and the sitter does not appear to be wearing the ribbon of the Garter. The panel is very worn and there is little of the original quality left in the head, but it is close to Mytens's earliest English portraits, such as his *3rd Earl of Southampton* (1618?) at Althorp or *Duke of Buckingham* (no. 123). The sitter was presumably a member of the court of James I.

Studio of Daniel Mytens

129. LUDOVICK STUART, SECOND DUKE OF LENNOX AND DUKE OF RICHMOND (1574–1624)

Windsor Castle (2974). $85\frac{3}{4} \times 54\frac{1}{8}$ in., $218 \times 137,5$ cm.; probably slightly enlarged in lining; there is a very early addition of *c.* $2\frac{1}{4}$ in. on the right.

Inscribed: LVDOVICVS STVART DVX / RICHMONDIÆ ET LENOXIÆ / 1623. ÆTATIS. LIX.

Full-length standing, wearing the Garter and the ribbon of the Order and holding his white staff of office as Lord Steward, beside a table on which rests a ducal coronet.

Presumably painted for James I; later in the Bear Gallery at Whitehall: *Done by Daniell Mitins . . . at Length. In a tawnie sute . . .* (*Van der Doort*, p. 6); valued at £20 by the Trustees for Sale (L. R. MS., f. 8), sold to Ralph Grynder and others on 23 October 1651 (S.P. 29/447, 24, 1), but soon afterwards apparently seen by Richard Symonds (B. M., Egerton MS. 1636, f. 95 v) with Knightley: '. . . at length . . . Duke of. Lenox'. Recovered at the Restoration (Col. Hawley, f. 5 v) and thereafter at Hampton Court, Somerset House, Windsor, Kensington, Buckingham House, Hampton Court (333) and St. James's.

Literature: Vertue, *Notebooks*, vol. II, p. 28; Law, 1881, 1898 (155); Collins Baker, *Lely*, vol. II, p. 110, *Windsor*, p. 242.

The portrait was presumably painted in Mytens's studio, but does not seem to be of autograph quality. It is slicker and less sensitive than the version in the Earl of Radnor's collection (Countess of Radnor and W. B. Smith, *Catalogue of the Pictures in the Collection of the Earl of Radnor* (1909), vol. I, pp. 24–6). It may have been designed to celebrate Lennox's elevation to the Dukedom of Richmond on 17 May 1623; the coronet, which covers the addition to the canvas (see above) is not entirely identical in handling with the rest of the canvas. In the Radnor version Richmond stands in front of a table on which is a plain black hat and there is a landscape background, as there is also in the version at Arundel. The proclamation of Richmond's dignities was taken up by his widow in her portraits by Van Dyck (of which the presumed original belonged to Charles I, hung as the pendant to the present portrait in the Bear Gallery and is known by versions at Drayton, Longleat, Drumlanrig etc.) and Cornelius Johnson (1635, formerly at Bramshill). The version at Petworth (98) of no. 129 is painted in Van Dyckian terms and may indeed be by Van Dyck. A copy of the head and shoulders, in black, is at Ham House.

Cousin of James VI, for a time heir to the throne of Scotland, and in favour at court from boyhood; in Scotland, and in England after the Union of the Crowns, he was closely associated with the King and his family and filled a number of high offices, including that of Lord Steward (1615).

After Daniel Mytens

130. CHARLES I

St. James's Palace. $30\frac{1}{8} \times 25\frac{1}{4}$ in., $77 \times 64,1$ cm.

Head and shoulders in a red doublet and ruff, wearing the ribbon of the Garter.

Presented to George IV, when Prince of Wales, by Sir William Scott, later Lord Stowell; received from him at Carlton House in March 1812 (Jutsham, *R/D*, f. 189) and catalogued (*Carlton House*, 1816 (375)) as *after Vandyck*.

Formerly attributed to Cornelius Johnson (*V.R. inv.*, St. James's, p. 19); though suggestive of Johnson in style and presentation, the canvas seems to be a slightly later derivation of a standard portrait by Mytens, possibly of the same type as no. 118. A better version of no. 130 is at Berkeley Castle.

131. GEORGE VILLIERS, FIRST DUKE OF BUCKINGHAM (1592–1628)

St. James's Palace. $30\frac{1}{2} \times 25\frac{1}{4}$ in., $77,5 \times 64,1$ cm.

Head and shoulders in the robes of the Garter.

Presented to George IV, when Prince of Wales, by Sir William Scott, later Lord Stowell; received from him at Carlton House in March 1812 (Jutsham, *R/D*, f. 189) and catalogued (*Carlton House*, 1816 (377)) as *A half length of a nobleman in his robes, and the collar and George*. Thereafter at Hampton Court (588) and Windsor (2929).

Literature: Law, 1881, 1898 (707); Collins Baker, *Windsor*, p. 244; C. R. Cammell, *The Great Duke of Buckingham* (1939), pp. 96, 374.

Formerly attributed to Cornelius Johnson, the canvas appears to be an early copy after Mytens, probably based on a full-length pattern; similar derivations exist, with variations in costume, *e.g.*, Christie's, 15 December 1944 (89), at Knole and at Cirencester (Earl Bathurst, *Catalogue of the Bathurst Collection* (1908), p. 30); the head is also close to the full-length in the National Maritime Museum.

See no. 123.

Cornelius Johnson

1593–1661. Born in London, of parents who had presumably fled to England from the religious persecutions in the Low Countries. On 5 December 1632 he was sworn in as 'his Majesty's servant in ye quality of Picture Drawer', and he was still among the King's 'servants in ordinary of the chamber' in 1641. He seems to have painted Charles I and Henrietta Maria *ad vivum* in 1633. In 1631 he had painted a full-length of the King almost indistinguishable from one of Mytens's official portraits. He painted for the King little full-lengths of Henrietta Maria and of Charles I, based on Van Dyck and Mytens and set in perspective fantasies by Gerrit Houckgeest and Steenwyck respectively. The *Charles I*, and its companion piece by Jan van Belcamp and Steenwyck, were recovered at the Restoration, but they seem to have been given away by Charles II and are now in Dresden. Johnson also painted miniatures of the King and Queen and small portraits of their three eldest children. These last are in the possession of Major the Hon. Henry Broughton. Johnson returned to Holland in 1643 and during the Interregnum painted portraits of some of the exiled Royalists (see O. Millar in *Burl. Mag.*, vol. CIV (1962), p. 330).

132. WILLIAM III AS A CHILD (*Plate* 97)

St. James's Palace. $64\frac{1}{4} \times 45\frac{3}{8}$ in. $163,2 \times 115,3$ cm; there is an early addition on the left of *c.* 2–3 in.

Full-length standing, wearing the ribbon of the Garter, by a table on which lies his plumed hat.

Stated (*V.R. inv.*, 1 March 1859) to have been purchased in Holland by Graves and acquired from him by Queen Victoria in 1858; later at Windsor (284).

Literature: Collins Baker, *Windsor*, p. 179; V. & A., *William and Mary and their Time*, 1950 (17); A. Staring, 'De Portretten van den Koning-Stadhouder', *Nederlandsch Kunsthistorisch Jaarboek*, vol. III (1950-51), pp. 163-4.

Johnson almost invariably signed his portraits and this may be a secondary version, probably executed in Johnson's studio and perhaps not entirely by the artist himself; a three-quarter-length original, signed and dated 1657, is at Knole. A signed and dated (1657) version of the head and shoulders belongs to Mrs. Hamilton-Browne and another, signed by Cornelius Johnson the younger and dated 1658, is at Eastnor Castle. There is a bust version in the National Gallery of Ireland and a half-length copy is in the National Portrait Gallery (272). Staring (*loc. cit.*) associates, not wholly convincingly, the commission to Cornelius Johnson with an order of September 1658 for payment of 250 florins to 'een schilder van Antwerpen, voor twee conterfeitsels van Zijne Hoogheid door dezen gemaakt en door Hare Koninklijke Hoogheid vereert aan Z. M. van Groot Britannien', but there is no trace in Charles II's collection of a portrait by Johnson of the young prince.

133. PORTRAIT OF A LADY

Holyroodhouse. Panel: $17\frac{1}{4} \times 13$ in., $43,8 \times 33$ cm.

Signed and dated: *CJ / 1624.*

Head and shoulders in a black and white dress, wearing an elaborate ear-ring, within a painted oval.

First recorded, as the Queen of Bohemia, in the reign of George II in the Queen's Dressing Room at Kensington (Vertue inv., *Kensington*, f. 26) as by *Corn. Jonson or Hontharst* and as the companion to no. 139; later at Hampton Court (312) and sent to Holyrood in 1864.

Literature: Walpole, *Anecdotes*, vol. I, p. 213, n. by Dallaway.

The composition is entirely typical of Johnson's portraits in England at this date; there are other instances of his use of this small scale, between his life-size portraits and his miniatures, though it is possible that the present portrait is a reduction of a larger image.

Attributed to Cornelius Johnson

134. PORTRAIT OF A YOUTH

Hampton Court (1275). Panel: $21\frac{7}{8} \times 14\frac{5}{8}$ in., $55,6 \times 37,1$ cm.

Inscribed later: OSANT, ET CRAIGNANT, over a contemporary but painted out inscription: *Ozant et Craig . . .*

Head and shoulders, wearing a red sash and a gorget.

Probably among the early portraits, formerly in the collection of Lady Capel, acquired at Kew. Probably later at Hampton Court (Mrs. Jameson (649)); recorded at Frogmore in 1871 (*V.R. inv.*).

Literature: Collins Baker, *Hampton Court*, p. 53.

Probably painted in England *c.* 1618 by a painter working in the Anglo-Netherlandish manner; it is very close in style and presentation to the earliest extant portraits by Cornelius Johnson (see Whinney and Millar, p. 65). It is possible that the background has been at least partly overpainted.

After Cornelius Johnson

135. PORTRAIT OF A MAN

Hampton Court (586). $31 \times 25\frac{1}{8}$ in., $78,7 \times 63,8$ cm.

Head and shoulders in black with a broad lace collar.

Recorded at Kensington in 1818 (85) as a portrait of a man by *Cor. Jansen*; removed on 1 November 1833 to Hampton Court, where it was identified as 'Lord Falkland'.

Literature: Law, 1881, 1898 (768); Collins Baker, *Hampton Court*, p. 165.

The portrait represents neither the great Lord Falkland nor his father, Sir Henry Cary, 1st Viscount (*d.* 1633); it is a copy of a portrait by Johnson of *c.* 1635–40.

Artists Unknown : Early Stuart Portraits

136. CHARLES I

Windsor Castle (2722). Panel (oval, with straight sides): $37\frac{3}{4} \times 29\frac{1}{4}$ in., $96 \times 74,3$ cm.

Head and shoulders, in a falling lace collar and the ribbon of the Garter, within a wreath of flowers.

Bequeathed, with its companion (no. 137), to George IV by Sir Ralph James Woodford (1784–1828) who had inherited it as having belonged to Ralph Brideoake, Bishop of Chichester (Will, Sutton 683); received at Carlton House (641) on 10 October 1828 (Jutsham, *Receipts*, f. 264), sent down to Royal Lodge on 13 October, but returned to London to be cleaned by Seguier; thereafter at Buckingham Palace (620) and St. James's.

Literature: Collins Baker, *Windsor*, p. 128.

When they were acquired by George IV the portraits were attributed to Cornelius Johnson. The practice of enclosing portraits or subject-pieces within wreaths of flowers originated in Antwerp with such painters as Daniel Seghers (1590–1661), whose works were popular in England during his lifetime. Nos. 136 and 137 were probably painted in Flanders *c.* 1650 (although a well-known poem by Andrew Marvell may be an indication that portraits were also painted in England in 'a Prospect of Flowers'), and portraits and flowers seem to be by the same hand. The source for the heads may have been portraits of *c.* 1632–5 by Cornelius Johnson, though they approximate to Van Dyckian prototypes. A different portrait of Charles I within a wreath, attributed to Verbruggen and of finer quality, was sold at Christie's, 25 July 1952 (102).

137. HENRIETTA MARIA

Windsor Castle (2723). Panel (oval, with straight sides): 37¼×29 in., 95×73,7 cm.

Head and shoulders, within a wreath of flowers.

See no. 136, with which it arrived at Carlton House (642); later hung at Buckingham Palace (621) and St. James's.

Literature: Collins Baker, *Windsor*, p. 128.

The portrait of the Queen is not unlike the type engraved after Van Dyck, in a floral wreath, by Jonas Suyderhoef.

138. THE FAMILY OF THE DUKE OF BUCKINGHAM (*Plate* 52)

Hampton Court (241). 63¼×97½ in., 160,9×278 cm.: there is an addition at the bottom of 2¼–3½ in.; the canvas may have been slightly enlarged at the top and reduced at the sides.

George Villiers, 1st Duke of Buckingham (1592–1628) is seated, holding the hand of his Duchess (*d.* 1649); in front are their two eldest children, Lady Mary Villiers (1622–85), and George, later 2nd Duke of Buckingham (1628–87), with an attendant; on the extreme left is seated the Duke's sister, Susan, Countess of Denbigh (*d. c.* 1655), and on his left his widowed mother, Mary Beaumont, Countess of Buckingham (1570–1632), accompanied by her younger sons, John, Viscount Purbeck (1591?–1658), and Christopher, 1st Earl of Anglesey (*d.* 1630), who rests his hand on a ledge, carved with the Duke's arms and the anchor of Lord High Admiral and supporting a carved lion; behind is an interior decorated with carved herms of mythological figures (Jupiter and Mercury are recognisable) and a portrait of the Duke's father, Sir George Villiers (*d.* 1606).

It is difficult to disentangle in early sources the references to this canvas and those to Honthorst's groups containing Buckingham and his family; possibly to be identified in Queen Anne's inventory (*Hampton Court*, store (85): *Hunthorst. The Duke and Dutchess of Buckingham & family a large Piece*, described at Somerset House in 1714 as *a very large piece*) and perhaps at the Earl of Oxford's lodgings at St. James's, January 1715: (4) *The Duke of Buckinghams family by Hunthurst* (H. M. C., *Cowper MSS.*, vol. III (1899), p. 112); but not identifiable with certainty before it appears at Carlton House (1816 (448): *Portraits of the family of*, measurements given as 63×98 in.). The 1816 label is on the back.

Literature: Waagen (1854), vol. II, p. 360; Law, 1881, 1898 (58); Collins Baker, *Hampton Court* pp. 78–9, repeating the traditional attribution to Honthorst; Collins Baker, *Lely*, vol. 1, pp. 57–8; C. R. Cammell, *The Great Duke of Buckingham* (1939), p. 381; R. Edwards, *Early Conversation Pieces* (1954), pp. 27–8, 157–8.

Painted in 1628. Vertue (1735 ?: *Notebooks*, vol. IV, pp. 71–2) noted a version of the design in Lambeth Palace, belonging to a Mr. Churchill; it was stated to have been left to him by an uncle who lived in Buckinghamshire and had bought the picture in Holland, whither it may have been transported at the dispersal of Buckingham's collection. Vertue's Mr. Churchill was probably William Churchill, to

whom in his Will of 27 April 1710 (Smith 106) Admiral George Churchill left 'the picture of the Duke of Buckingham's Family.' From Vertue's rough drawing it appears to have been identical in design with no. 138. Vertue gives its measurements (presumably wrongly) as 66×180 in. and also states that 'this picture represents in small life. figures about. 2. feet hi.' The picture seen by Vertue may have been the one now in the royal collection, which would invalidate the references given above from the time of Queen Anne and George I. The canvas is not in a satisfactory condition: it has been rubbed and, in some areas, heavily repainted; very little survives of the original handling of the heads of the Duke and his son; the sweep of curtain in the centre of the composition is almost certainly an addition; and the carved lion had been painted out and was not revealed until 1956. The authorship of the group must, therefore, remain obscure. The best preserved heads (those of the Duke's sister, daughter and mother) are very close to Cornelius Johnson, though the canvas as a whole now lacks his delicacy of touch and colour. At this date it would have been an unusually ambitious composition for Johnson. It is conceivable that it may have some connection with Sir Balthasar Gerbier (1591–1667), who was primarily occupied with the formation of Buckingham's collections, but was an amateur portrait painter in the Duke's service; full-lengths, formerly at Newnham Paddox (sold at Christie's, 1 July 1938 (49, 50, 52, 97)), which included the Earl of Denbigh and Buckingham's mother, were traditionally ascribed to Gerbier and seem to stand in rather the same relationship as no. 138 to Johnson. The portrait of Sir George Villiers in the background is reminiscent of one at Patshull (C. R. Cammell, *op. cit.*, p. 36).

The Duke married in 1620 Lady Catherine Manners, daughter of the 6th Earl of Rutland; in 1635, seven years after the Duke's assassination, she married the 2nd Earl of Antrim. The Duke's mother was created Countess of Buckingham for life in 1618; his sister had married, *c.* 1607, William Feilding, later 1st Earl of Denbigh, and was Lady of the Bedchamber to Henrietta Maria. Lord Purbeck was appointed (1616) Groom of the Bedchamber and Master of the Robes to the Prince of Wales and was the innocent party in a famous scandal; Lord Anglesey also held various offices at court. For the Duke see no. 123; for his children see nos. 153 and 159.

139. HENRY DE VERE, EIGHTEENTH EARL OF OXFORD (1593–1625)

Holyroodhouse. Copper: 17×12⅞ in., 43,2×32,7 cm.
Head and shoulders in a slashed doublet and ruff, within a painted oval.

First recorded, as the King of Bohemia, in the reign of George II in the Queen's Dressing Room at Kensington (Vertue inv., *Kensington*, f. 26) as by *Corn: Jonson or Honthorst* and as the companion to no. 133; they can be seen hanging together in Pyne, vol. II, *Kensington*, p. 63; later at Hampton Court (310) and sent to Holyrood in 1864.

Literature: Walpole, *Anecdotes*, vol. I, p. 213, n. by Dallaway; R. W. Goulding, *Catalogue of the Pictures belonging to . . . the Duke of Portland . . .* (1936), p. 369.

The portrait is not in fact a companion to no. 133, which is on panel and shows a different form of painted oval. A later copy on the same scale in the Scottish National Portrait Gallery (314) was also thought to represent the King of Bohemia and has been attributed to Mytens and to Cornelius Johnson; a version in the National Portrait Gallery (950) is associated with the studio of Miereveld. The source of these small portraits was probably a life-size portrait painted in England *c.* 1623–5; full-lengths, one formerly in the collection of the Marquess of Ailesbury and now in that of Mr. H. B. Binney (in which the head is very close to the present portrait), and another at Ombersley Court, are probably connected with Mytens.

Hereditary Lord Great Chamberlain of England and Esquire to Charles I when Duke of York. He served as a Captain in Sir Horatio Vere's regiment in Bohemia, went in 1624 to Holland as Colonel of a regiment of volunteers in the service of the Elector Palatine and died of wounds received at the siege of Breda.

140. PORTRAIT OF A MAN

Hampton Court (32). $27\frac{1}{4} \times 20\frac{1}{8}$ in., $69,2 \times 51,1$ cm.

Head and shoulders in a painted oval.

Recorded at Kensington in 1818 (15: *A Mans head. Dobson*).

Literature: Law, 1881, 1898 (370).

Apparently a copy of a portrait painted, almost certainly in England, but not by Dobson, *c.* 1645; the original may have been close in style to Isaac Fuller.

Sir Anthony van Dyck

1599–1641. By 1620, when he was still working in his native Antwerp in the studio of Rubens, Van Dyck had attracted the attention of English connoisseurs and diplomats. Charles I had bought before his accession one of Van Dyck's early studies, *an old mans heade without a frame with gray haire & beard . . . Being uppon a strayning frame* (*Van der Doort*, p. 58), and by 25 November 1620 Van Dyck was in London in the service of James I; he was apparently given an annual pension of £100 and a grant of £100 'for speciall service by him pformed for his Matie'. Van Dyck may have entered James I's service through the mediations of the Earl of Arundel and it was the Earl who secured for him a pass on 28 February 1621 for eight months' travelling; by staying in Italy until 1627, and remaining at Antwerp for another five years, Van Dyck seems to have caused offence at the English court. After his return to Antwerp from Italy, however, he resumed his contacts with the King's circle: portraits of Nicholas Lanier (?Glück, 349), which was done 'Beyond ye Seas', and of Henri Liberti (presumably the original of which Glück, 330, is a copy), painted in Antwerp, were in the King's collection; Charles commissioned (and bought in March 1630) *one picture of the Storie of Reynaldo & Armida* (Baltimore Museum of Art; Glück, 265);[1] and on the eve of Van Dyck's return to London the Earl of Portland presented to the King and Queen a *Mystic Marriage of St. Catherine* (see no 162). On his arrival in London (probably in March 1632) Van Dyck was warmly welcomed by the King and thereafter there are records of payments, and arrears of payments, of large sums for portraits of the King and his family (some of them for presentation at home or despatch abroad) and for such miscellaneous tasks as repairing and replacing the King's Titians. Van Dyck was knighted on 5 July 1632 and awarded an annual pension of £200. He lodged with Edward Norgate until he was established in a house at Blackfriars. He received a grant of denization in March 1638. He was out of England for some months in 1634–5 and again at the end

of his life, but he died in London and was buried in St. Paul's Cathedral.

In addition to earlier works cited above and to those still in the royal collection, Charles I owned the following: a Self-portrait *to the Should^rs with his left hand at his breast In an Ovall carved wodden frame* (*Van der Doort*, p. 38) which was recovered at the Restoration (*e.g.*, B.M., Harl. MS., 1890, f. 49; Bathoe, *James II* (124)), but is not recorded in the royal collection after 1688; the equestrian portrait of Charles I in the National Gallery (1172); the double-portrait now in Kremsier of the King and Queen (see no. 119); a copy of a portrait of the Queen in blue which Charles gave to the Earl of Pembroke in exchange for a Self-portrait of Pordenone (*Van der Doort*, p. 45); a full-length of the Queen (see nos. 145 and 167); a full-length of Marie de Medici, valued at £30 by the Trustees for Sale among the portraits in the Cross Gallery at Somerset House (Corsham MS., f. 55); and a half-length of the same person *Sitting in a Chare In a black habbitt houlding in her right hand a handfull of roases* (*Van der Doort*, p. 26); the *modello* for the Procession of the King and the Knights of the Garter, now at Belvoir Castle (see O. Millar, 'Charles I, Honthorst and Van Dyck', *Burl. Mag.*, vol. XCVI (1954), pp. 36–42); the double-portrait in the Louvre (1969) of Prince Charles Louis and Prince Rupert (Glück, 441); versions of the portrait of the Cardinal-Infant Ferdinand in the Prado (Glück, 423), of the official portrait of the Archduchess Isabella (*e.g.*, Glück, 299; *Van der Doort*, p. 194), and apparently of the portraits of Prince Thomas of Savoy (see no. 184) and Count Hendrick van den Bergh (see no. 178); full-lengths of Gaston, Duke of Orléans (see R. A., *Flemish Art*, 1953–4 (143)), his wife (presumably the portrait now in the Uffizi; Glück, 430), and her sister, Henrietta of Lorraine (now in the Iveagh Bequest, Kenwood (47); Glück, 431); a full-length of Frances, Duchess of Richmond (see no. 129); a portrait of a lady (*Van der Doort*, p. 197), conceivably Lady Carlisle; and *Our Ladie with Christ where manie Angells are a dauncing* (*ibid.*, p. 177), presumably a version of the picture now in the Hermitage, Leningrad (Glück, 261). *The great peece of Vandyke beinge. verry Curiouslij done*, valued by the Trustees for Sale at £60 (L. R. MS., f. 8 v.), cannot be identified with certainty.

The late Prince and Princess of Orange by Van Dyck is recorded at Whitehall, probably in the King's Great Bedchamber, in the reign of James II (B. M., Harl. MS. 1890, f. 72; Bathoe, *James II* (750)), and the same inventory included *A Ladyes Picture to the waste in a blew Garment* (*ibid.*, f. 56 v.; Bathoe (344)). Among the pictures bought by Charles II from Frizell in 1662 was *One sea peece of Vandyke* (B. M., MS. 23199, f. 28), which appears in store at Whitehall in the King's inventory (Charles II, *Whitehall* (637): *Vandyke. A Sea Peice with a great Rocke & some fisher men upon the Shoare*, measurements given as 46×36 in.). At Whitehall in the time of James II was *A Picture of a large Reddish Spanell by Van Dyck* (B. M., Harl. MS. 1890, f. 58; Bathoe, *James II* (382)), which was later at Kensington but is no longer in the royal collection.

141. JAMES I (*Plate* 54)

Windsor Castle (212). $94 \times 58\frac{1}{4}$ in., 239×148 cm.; there are later additions of *c.* $5\frac{1}{2}$ in. at the top, *c.* 8 in. on the right and 4 in. at the bottom.

Inscribed: IACOBVS:D:G:MAG:/ BR:FRA:ET:HI: REX./ A^O 1617

Full-length standing, wearing the ribbon of the Garter and resting his left hand on his sword, beside a table on which are the crown, sceptre and orb.

Painted for Charles I; valued at £30 by the Trustees for Sale among

---

1. This was probably *A Story out of Aryostrio done by Van dyke*, valued at £80 by the Trustees for Sale (Corsham MS., f. 52).

the pictures in the Cross Gallery at Somerset House: *King James. at Leng Coppie after van somer by vandyke* (Corsham MS., f. 55) and sold to Edmund Harrison on 23 October 1651 (S.P. 29/447, 24, 1); seen by Richards Symonds with Harrison on 30 December 1652 among '4 Large pieces at length done by Vandyke. after old pictures' (B. M., Egerton MS. 1636, f. 90 v.). It is difficult to disentangle, in the later inventories etc., the references to full-length portraits of James I (see nos. 103 and 104), but no. 141 was probably at Kensington in the middle of the eighteenth century (Vertue inv. *Kensington*, f. 22), had probably earlier been at Whitehall (B. M., Harl. MS. 1890, f. 50 v.; Bathoe, *James II* (163) as by Van Somer), and Somerset House and Windsor, and was moved to Windsor from Buckingham House (777) by order of George IV in 1821.

Literature: G. Bickham, *Deliciae Britannicae* ... (1742), p. 13; Vertue, *Notebooks*, vol. IV, p. 65; Walpole, *Anecdotes*, vol. I, pp. 179, 320 n.; Smith, 248; Law, *Van Dyck*, pp. 81–3; Cust, *Van Dyck*, pp. 23, 262; Collins Baker, *Windsor*, p. 300; R. A., *King's Pictures* (21).

There have been understandable confusions over the source used by Van Dyck. Walpole thought it had been a miniature by Isaac Oliver and the portrait was engraved by John Smith (1721) and John Faber the younger as by Van Dyck *ab Originali minuta fact: per Fra: Hilyard Aᵒ. Dⁱ. 1617* (it was also engraved by Vertue and Picart). The portrait is in fact a reinterpretation by Van Dyck of Van Somer's original full-length of 1618 (no. 103). He carefully copied the head from Van Somer's prototype, treated the regalia with more freedom, and wrought a most significant transformation in the King's appearance. His use of the date 1617 is inexplicable. He had presumably seen the King in London in the winter of 1620–1, but on that visit would, if commissioned to paint him, presumably have received a sitting from James. The portrait was almost certainly painted for Charles I, during Van Dyck's second visit to London, to form part of the royal family portrait gallery in the Cross Gallery at Somerset House for which he also produced six *ad vivum* portraits (see nos. 145 and 169) and no. 142; and see no. 121. In addition to no. 172 there are copies at, for example, Alloa, Helmingham and Narford and copies on a reduced scale also exist. The pattern was used in the series of royal portraits in tapestry at Houghton (see no. 105).

142. HENRY, PRINCE OF WALES (*Plate* 57)

Windsor Castle (2599). 84¾ × 47¼ in., 215,2 × 120 cm. At one time enlarged to *c*. 94 × 55 in. The additions are now mainly turned over: *c*. 6 in. on the left, *c*. 4–5 in. on the right, 5¾ in. at the bottom, and *c*. 6½ in. at the top. The original surface was probably *c*. 81¾ × 45½ in.

Full-length, standing in a suit of Greenwich armour, wearing the chain of the Garter, holding a baton in his right hand and with his plumed helmet beside him.

In a *Memoire pour Sa Magᵗⁱᵉ Le Roy* (1638?) of pictures painted by Van Dyck for the royal family, and for which payment was due, occurs *Le Prince Henry* at £50; it was marked by the King as one of the pictures which the Queen was to value and pay for (P. R. O., S.P. 16/406, 4; Hookham Carpenter, pp. 66–8). The portrait was thus almost certainly painted for Somerset House and it was valued at £30 by the Trustees for Sale among the pictures in the Cross Gallery there: *Prince Henry at Length. by vandyke* (Corsham MS., f. 55), and sold to Edmund Harrison on 23 October 1651 (S.P. 29/447, 24, 1); seen by Richard Symonds with Harrison on 30 December 1652 among '4 Large pieces at length done by Vandyke. after old pictures' (B. M., Egerton MS. 1636, f. 90 v.). Presumably recovered at the Restoration, but not recorded until the reign of Queen Anne, once more in the Cross Gallery at Somerset House (Queen Anne, *Somerset House* (20)); thereafter at Hampton Court (454) and St. James's; from 1816–22 temporarily at Carlton House (44), where it was reframed and reduced (probably to its present size and probably by Simpson under the eye of Lawrence) to hang in

the South Ante-room (Pyne, vol. III, p. 44 and pl.; Jutsham, *Receipts*, f. 4, R/D ff. 240, 252, *Deliveries*, f. 29).

Literature: Walpole, *Anecdotes*, vol. I, p. 320 n., *Visits*, p. 80 (on both occasions supporting the traditional attribution to Van Dyck in face of more recent ones to Van Somer or Mytens); Smith, 249; Cust, *Van Dyck*, pp. 23, 263; Collins Baker, *Windsor*, p. 247; E. Cammaerts in *Burl. Mag.*, vol. LXXXV (1944), p. 304; Tower of London, *Exhibition of Armour made ... at Greenwich*, 1951 (23, 79); R. A., *British Portraits*, 1956–7 (525).

The confusions about the authorship of the portrait are dispelled by the earliest references to it. It was painted by Van Dyck for Charles I during his second visit to London, presumably to form part of the royal family portrait gallery in the Cross Gallery at Somerset House (see also nos. 121, 141, 145 and 169). For Prince Henry's countenance Van Dyck used a miniature by Isaac Oliver in the collection of Charles I (*Fig.* 9); he dressed him in a famous armour for field and tilt (*Fig.* 10), made at Greenwich by William Pickering *c*. 1610 and decorated with the emblems of the Union of the Crowns; and stood him in a pattern that he evolved during his English period for the King (Glück, 390) and that served such other sitters as the Earl of Kinnoull (Glück, 462) and Lord Spencer of Wormleighton (Althorp). Mytens had earlier based on the same miniature a smaller portrait of Prince Henry for Charles I's Breakfast Chamber at Whitehall (see above p. 84). In a portrait (*c*. 1616) of Charles I when Prince of Wales, of which there is a version in the Marquess of Lothian's collection, the same armour may be represented. The later addition at the bottom covers part of the right foot: for its probable original appearance see the comparable passage in the portrait of the King (Glück, 390). The figure seems to be wholly by Van Dyck, but the curtain, cloth and plumes in the background were probably painted by an assistant and may have been partly overpainted later. A late copy of the portrait, sold from the collection of Lord Brocket at Sotheby's, 16 July 1952 (95), may record the appearance of the original when it was extended at the sides.

143. CHARLES I WITH M. DE ST. ANTOINE (*Plate* 65)

Buckingham Palace. 145 × 106¼ in., 368,4 × 269,9 cm.

Dated *1633*.

The King, wearing armour with the ribbon of the Garter and holding a baton, rides on a white horse through a triumphal arch, at the foot of which is a shield bearing the royal arms and surmounted by a crown; M. de St. Antoine is in attendance, carrying the King's helmet.

Painted for the Gallery at St. James's: *... the kings Maᵗⁱᵉ in Armoure upon a white Horse ... in a great large Carved frame By Sʳ Anthony Vandike* (Van der Doort, p. 226). Valued at £150 by the Trustees for Sale (L. R. MS., f. 167 v.) and sold to Pope on 22 December 1652; reported on 12 May 1660 to the House of Lords Committee by Geldorp as having 'stoud at Sᵗ Jaemes in the gallery' and as being in the hands of Remigius van Leemput (H. of L. MSS.), who was stated to have bought the picture, taken it to Antwerp, failed to sell it for the price he demanded and returned with it to England, 'where the Times being turn'd ... he had the Picture taken from him by due course of Law' (*Essay towards an English School* in English edition of De Piles's *Art of Painting* (1706), p. 458). After the Restoration placed at Hampton Court in 'Paradise' (Charles II, *Hampton Court* (80)); later hung, probably by William III and Mary II, in the Gallery (37) at Kensington (*Kensington*, 1697, f. 190; and see no. 150); thereafter at Buckingham House, in the Japan Room with no. 150, and Windsor (39: Pyne, vol. I, pp. 91–2 and pl.).

Literature: Vertue, vol. II, p. 88, vol. III, pp. 51, 129, vol. V, pp. 25, 51–2; Walpole, *Anecdotes*, vol. I, pp. 320–1, *Visits*, p. 78; Smith, 207, *Supplement*, 22, 23; Waagen (1838), vol. I, p. 171, (1854), vol. II, p. 429; Law, *Van Dyck*, pp. 47–52; Cust, *Van Dyck*, pp. 102–3, 263; Schaeffer, 306; Sir L. Cust, 'The Equestrian Portraits of Charles I by Van Dyck', *Burl. Mag.*, vol. XVIII (1911), pp. 202–9; Glück, 372, and 'Van Dyck's Equestrian Portraits of Charles I', *Burl. Mag.*, vol. LXX (1937), pp. 211–7; Collins Baker, *Windsor*, p. 78; R. A., *King's Pictures* (96); Whinney and Millar, p. 72.

Probably specially designed to hang at the end of the Gallery at St. James's, where it made a considerable impression: 'a un des bouts de cette gallerie . . . il y a un portrait du Roy . . . armé, a cheval, de la main de Monsieur le Chevallier Vandheich. Et a n'en mentir point, son pinceau en conservant la Majesté de ce Grand Monarque, la tellement animee par son industrie, que si les yeux pouvoyent estre creus tous seuls, ils souttiendroient hardiment qu'il vit dans ce portrait, tant l'aparance en est sensible' (P. de la Serre, *Histoire de l'Entree de la Reyne Mère . . ., dans la Grande-Bretagne* (1639); Marie de Medici had entered London on 10 November 1638 and was lodged at St. James's). Van Dyck had already used this equestrian pattern, with modifications and against different backgrounds, for Cornelis de Wael (Musée Royal des Beaux-Arts, Antwerp (892)) and for Antonio Giulio Brignole Sale (Glück, 200) in Genoa, and was to do so again in 1634 for the Marquis of Moncada (Louvre (1971); Glück, 420). It was used, presumably by a follower of Van Dyck in Genoa, for a portrait of Philip IV of Spain (Galleria Balbi di Piovera, exh. *Pittura del Seicento e Settecento in Liguria*, Genoa, 1947 (8)). It had originally been evolved by Rubens for the Duke of Lerma and had become common property in the Flemish studios. Its sumptuous adaptation for Charles I was perhaps not unrelated to the small equestrian portraits of Roman Emperors by Giulio Romano which hung, with Titian's *Emperors*, in the same Gallery at St. James's. See above pp. 17–18. A drawing in the British Museum (*Fig.* 19) is probably Van Dyck's first suggestion for the whole composition; it includes all its main elements. A rapid sketch of the rider and the archway is in Berlin (E. Bock and J. Rosenberg, *Die Niederländischen Meister* (1930), vol. I, p. 126 (4069). Preliminary studies of the horse (*Figs.* 21, 22) are also in the British Museum (A. M. Hind, *Catalogue of Drawings by Dutch and Flemish Artists . . .*, vol. II (1923), p. 65, nos. 46, 47, 48), but drawings of the horse at Windsor (L. van Puyvelde, *The Flemish Drawings . . . at Windsor Castle* (1942), 219) and formerly in the collection of J. G. Lousada (ed. Sir M. Conway, *Catalogue of Flemish and Belgian Art*, R. A., 1927 (586)) were drawn after the composition and not by Van Dyck. The canvas appears to be entirely by Van Dyck, and there seem to be slight alterations to the outlines of the curtain on the right and of the King's thigh.

Many copies exist (some of which lack the figure of St. Antoine or are otherwise simplified) and some were painted in the King's lifetime. The one formerly at Hamilton Palace (sold 17 June 1882 (32)), and apparently without the archway and St. Antoine, was probably *One peice of the kinge on horsebacke, a coppy after Sr Anthony: done by Rameye* (i.e. Van Leemput, see above), no. 292 in an inventory of the Hamilton collection (Hamilton MSS.) probably drawn up in the 1640's. The copy at Lamport Hall was secured for Sir Justinian Isham by Maurice Wace, who wrote to his patron on 24 May 1655, '. . . the King's Picture on horsebake is vallued at a great price 250 pounds, which once might have been bought for 80 pounds. Soe if you desire to have a good coppy thereof it will cost you 50 pounds . . .' (MS. at Lamport). The reduced copy at Petworth (124) was seen by Richard Symonds at Northumberland House on 27 December 1652 (B. M. Egerton MS. 1636, f. 92), and described in an inventory of Northumberland House, 30 June 1671, as *The King on Horse back, on a White Horse the face not finished by*

Van Dyke (MS. at Alnwick).[1] Other copies are nos. 173 and 174 below and at Warwick Castle, Corsham Court (121), Apsley House (1498), Thoresby Hall, Highclere Castle, Newbattle Abbey, Penshurst and (formerly) at Naworth Castle, Osterley and Stapleford Park (now in a private collection in New York); the copy in the Middle Temple, wrongly attributed to Lely, was acquired in November 1684. A simplified copy is at Dyrham. Many small copies and derivations exist (*e.g.*, at Claydon and Compton Wynyates). A small early copy against a landscape background in the Prado (1484; Schaeffer, 363) could again be by such a painter as Van Leemput. Small versions in a sketch-like style (*e.g.*, Christie's, 23 July 1954 (121)) seem to be based on, rather than preparatory for, the finished picture; the small eighteenth-century copy at Norton Conyers may be by Gainsborough. Among Charles Beale's drawings in the British Museum is a drawing of St. Antoine's head (B. M. G.g. 4. W. 5–73). The pattern was adapted on a small scale for different sitters, *e.g.*, William III, the 2nd Duke of Hamilton (*c.* 1650) at Newbattle Abbey, the 3rd Earl Rivers (*c.* 1685) in the Ancaster collection, the 2nd Duke of Montagu at Blenheim and an unknown sitter (*c.* 1710) at Buckingham Palace. Copies by Charles Jervas were recorded in his sale, 11 March 1740, and Vertue saw (*Notebooks*, vol. II, p. 88, vol. III, p. 51) a copy being made by Jeremiah Davison. The portrait seems to have been the source of a half-length etching made for Jean Meyssens (M. Mauquoy-Hendricx, *L'Iconographie d'Antoine Van Dyck* (Brussels, 1956), no. 119). Before 1658 Pierre Lombart had adapted Van Dyck's design to an equestrian engraving of Cromwell (*Fig.* 32), but the plate, after passing through the famous 'Headless' state, was later reworked with the heads of Charles I and Cromwell (F. O'Donoghue, *Catalogue of Engraved British Portraits . . .*, vol. I (1908), pp. 526–7; G. S. Layard, *The Headless Horseman* (1922)). No. 143 was engraved by Baron (1741).

Pierre Antoine Bourdin, Seigneur de St. Antoine, 'accounted the best master' in the art of horsemanship, had been sent by Henri IV of France, as 'ung escuier choisy de ma main' to James I in 1603 with a present of six horses 'des mieux dressez, fort richement enharnachez' for Henry, Prince of Wales; he remained in the service of the Prince, and later of Charles I, as riding-master and equerry. In the eighteenth-century (*e.g.*, Vertue, *Notebooks*, vol. V, pp. 51–2) the equerry in no. 145 was wrongly described as the Duc d'Epernon. The order which he is wearing appears to be either that of Saint-Lazare and Notre-Dame-du-Mont-Carmel or, less likely, of Saint-Michel.

144. CHARLES I ON HORSEBACK (*Plate* 64)
Windsor Castle (3037). 38 × 34 in., 96,5 × 61 cm.

The King, wearing armour and the Order of the Garter and holding a baton, rides out of a wood on a dun horse, followed by an equerry carrying his helmet. On a tablet hanging from the tree is inscribed: CAROLVS / REX MAGN[Æ] / BRITANNI[Æ].

Painted for the King and placed in the Chair Room at Whitehall: *the King. upon a Dunn horse one following his Matie carrying his head peece . . . 3 f 1 × 2 f 10 . . . Done by Sr Anthony Vandike being the first moddell of ye king in greate on horseback wch is at this time in the Princes Gallory at*

1. Sir Charles Lyttelton wrote to Lord Hatton, 7 March 1692: 'I have a very good copy, wch you may remember to have seen upon my staires, of Ch: ye 1st upon ye white hors. Y^e originall is Vandike and ye copy Remee. If I had y^r hall or a good staire case to put it, I shd not be tempted to sell it . . . 50 li will be ye lowest price of it' (*Correspondence of the Family of Hatton*, ed. E. M. Thompson, vol. II, *Camden Soc.*, N.S., vol. XXIII (1878), p. 172).

Hampton Court (*Van der Doort*, p. 62); possibly *King Charles. on Horsback. by van dyke*, valued at Hampton Court at £40 by the Trustees for Sale (L. R. MS., f. 124) and sold to John Boulton on 22 November 1649 (S.P. 29/447, 24, 1). After the Restoration its history is difficult to disentangle. *The King on horseback upon A dunn horse done by Vandicke* seems to be among the pictures recovered then (Col. Hawley, f. 65) and may have been the picture reported on 13 February 1661 to be among some of the late King's goods concealed in Cripplegate and Bishopsgate (*Cal. S.P.Dom.* (*1660–1*), p. 510). In James II's inventory are two relevant entries: 359 (*By Vandyck. King Charles the first. upon a Dunn horse* (B. M., Harl. MS., 1890, f. 57 v.; Bathoe, *James II* (359), Walpole note 'at Kensington') and 1076 (*Vandyck. King Charles the First, on a dun horse* (*ibid.*, f. 82 v.; p. 91, with inserted note 'at Hampton Court'). The latter, as among the pictures that had not belonged to Charles II, may have been *The late kings pict upon the Dunne horse* in the Duke of York's collection at Whitehall in 1674 (Bodl. Lib. MS. 891, f. 16 v.). Thereafter at Hampton Court, Windsor and Buckingham Palace (145). Between the reigns of Anne and George III(?), and probably in the reign of William III, there was at Kensington *King Charles the first upon a dun Horse, small figure*, described as after Van Dyck (Vertue inv., *Kensington*, f. 9) and stated by Walpole (1763) to be by Dobson after Van Dyck (notes in Bathoe, *James II*).

Literature: Bellori, *Le Vite de' Pittori* . . . (Rome, 1672), p. 260; Smith, 243; Waagen (1854), vol. II, p. 3, 457–8; Law, *Van Dyck*, pp. 99–100; Cust, *Van Dyck*, pp. 104, 263; Schaeffer, 340; Sir L. Cust, 'The Equestrian Portraits of Charles I by Van Dyck', *Burl. Mag.*, vol. XVIII (1911), pp. 202–9; Glück, pp. 560–1 and 'Van Dyck's Equestrian Portraits of Charles I', *Burl. Mag.*, vol. LXX (1937), pp. 211–7; R. W. Goulding, *Catalogue of the Pictures . . . belonging to . . . the Duke of Portland* (1936), 97; R. A., *King's Pictures* (32); *Van Dyck Tentoonstelling*, Antwerp, 1949 (53); R. A., *Flemish Art*, 1953–4 (407); H. Vey, 'Anton van Dycks Ölskizzen', *Musées Royaux des Beaux-Arts, Brussels, Bulletin*, vols. 2–3 (1956), pp. 198–9.

Painted, probably *c.* 1635–6, as a complete *modello* for the great equestrian portrait, now in the National Gallery (1172; *Fig.* 13), which was valued at £200 by the Trustees for Sale (Corsham MS., f. 52) and sold to Sir Balthasar Gerbier on 21 June 1650 (S.P. 29/447, 24, 1). In Van Dyck's original drawing in the British Museum (*Fig.* 20; A. M. Hind, *Catalogue of Drawings by Dutch and Flemish Artists . . .*, vol. II (1923), p. 65, no. 49) the King's head comes much closer to the top of the composition, and Van Dyck extended the canvas at the top by *c.* 4¾ in. The enlarged space round the King, and a subtle ennobling of his appearance, are the principal developments between *modello* and finished design. Apart from its brilliant quality and the statement in the King's catalogue, its position as a *modello* is confirmed by the alterations made by Van Dyck to the position of the King's right arm and shoulder and to the insignia of the Garter: the ribbon of the Order is still visible as well as the chain worn by the King in the final composition. According to Bellori (*loc. cit.*) Van Dyck deliberately painted Charles *à cavallo ad imitatione di Carlo Quinto espresso da Titiano, seguitato dietro da uno de' suoi gentil-huomini, che porta l'elmo*. Van Dyck's design is a reinterpretation of Titian's famous equestrian portrait of Charles V in the Prado; contemporary reinterpretations of the same source by Rubens were the portraits of Philip IV and the Cardinal-Infant Ferdinand, also in the Prado (R. Oldenbourg, *K.d.K.*, 446, 377; an equestrian portrait of the Cardinal-Infant in the Louvre (1954, attributed to Van Thulden) is directly based on Van Dyck's final composition). It is conceivable that Van Dyck had also been influenced by earlier English engraved equestrian portraits such as Thomas Cockson's plate of the 2nd Earl of Essex (*Fig.* 4; A. M. Hind, *Engraving in England in the Sixteenth and Seventeenth Centuries*, part I (1952), pp. 245–6). Numerous copies exist of no. 144, some of which seem to have been painted in the eighteenth century, *e.g.*, formerly in the Ashburnham collection, sold at

Sotheby's, 15 July 1953 (157), at Warwick Castle, Belvoir Castle (two), Corsham Court (122), at Abercairny House, Audley End, Welbeck (97), Chirk Castle, in the Christ Church Museum, Ipswich (perhaps the best) in the Evelyn and Clarendon collections, and formerly with Goudstikker, Amsterdam. A probably eighteenth-century copy was sold at Sotheby's, 15 November 1961 (5). Certain copies have been attributed, probably wrongly, to Gainsborough (*e.g.*, in Sir Charles Wakefield's collection, and *cf.*, *Burl. Mag.*, vol. XI (1907), pp. 96–9; *Emporium*, Nov.–Dec. 1947, p. 132), who took over Van Dyck's design for his portrait of Lt. General Philip Honywood (E. K. Waterhouse, *Gainsborough* (1958), pl. 83). The pattern was adapted for other sitters, such as Charles II and George III (Windsor Castle).

145. CHARLES I (*Plate* 71)

Windsor Castle (213). 97¾×60½ in., 248,3×31,8 cm.

Signed: *Antoo van dyck Eques Fecit* and dated *1636* under the initials *CR* below a crown.

Full-length, standing in robes of state with the collar of the Garter, beside a ledge on which are the crown and orb.

Painted for the King (the CR brand on the back is still visible from the front of the canvas), possibly to form part of the royal family portrait gallery in the Cross Gallery at Somerset House, where the Trustees for Sale valued *King. Charles at Length by vandyke* with its companion, *Quene Mary at Length by vandyke*, at £60 (Corsham MS., f. 55). They were sold to Colonel Webb, 29 October 1649, but seem to have been secured by Henry Browne, Keeper of Somerset House, who reported to the Committee of the House of Lords (presumably in May 1660) that many of the royal goods he had acquired 'he was forct to put of, for the buying of both their Ma^ts pictures done by Sr Anthony Van Dike' (H. of L. MSS.). Perhaps to be identified with *One picture of ye Late King done by Vandike*, delivered from the Jewel House (presumably in 1661; Col. Hawley, f. 7). Thereafter in store at Whitehall (Charles II, *Whitehall* (466)) and later placed over the mantelpiece in the Drawing Room at Hampton Court (*e.g.*, Queen Anne, *Hampton Court* (12); Vertue inv., *Hampton Court*, f. 2, '. . . in a carved & wainscot frame'). On approval at Carlton House, 18–20 July 1816 (Jutsham, *Receipts*, f. 4).

Literature: Celia Fiennes, *Journeys*, p. 354; Vertue, *Notebooks*, vol. IV, pp. 73, 74; Walpole, *Anecdotes*, vol. I, p. 320; Smith, 210; Law, *Van Dyck*, pp. 85–6; Cust, *Van Dyck*, pp. 105, 263; Schaeffer, 339; Glück, 382; Collins Baker, *Windsor*, p. 75; R. A., *King's Pictures* (45); Waterhouse, *Painting in Britain*, pp. 37, 48; R. A., *Flemish Art*, 1953–4 (131); Whinney and Millar, p. 71.

The head of the King is very close to the full-length by Van Dyck in armour in the Hermitage (Glück, 390) which, with its companion piece of the Queen (Glück, 391), was painted for Lord Wharton at the Queen's expense (P. R. O., S.P. 16/406, 4; Hookham Carpenter, p. 68); they bear the early inscription *about 1638*. No. 145 may partly have been conceived as an official state portrait. It certainly influenced the design of no. 335, for example, and it was much copied. Copies are at Lambeth Palace, Petworth (507), Jesus College, Oxford (bequeathed by Sir Leoline Jenkins in 1685), Woburn, Castle Ashby, Drayton (stated to be by Leonard Knyff), Narford, Goodwood, the Apothecaries' Hall, Gray's Inn and in the Swinburne collection; and reductions (*e.g.*, in the Wallace Collection (112), at Longleat and Brodie Castle) are also common. It is sometimes accompanied by a portrait or variant of the type of no. 167; the pendant (952) to the copy of no. 145 in the Scottish National Portrait Gallery (951) shows the Queen in state robes and the original pendant (see above) may have been of this type. A pair of this type is at Capesthorne. A very good pair of the King and Queen (*Fig.* 24) in robes, each bearing their monogram, dates (1637 on the Queen, possibly 1636 on the King) and the signature of the painter, is at Sanssouci; this could be the pair sent by the sitters to the Prince of Orange in 1638. A pair of copies was sold at Christie's, 28 February 1947 (87). The type was engraved by J. Simon and John Smith and, from a small version stated to have belonged to Charles I and James II, by Strange in 1770. Vertue (*op. cit.*, vol. IV, p. 74) was making a drawing from the head when Frederick, Prince of Wales, 'spoke to me in commendation of the work, – I was upon'. There is a *pentimento* in the mouldings at the foot of the column, which were originally slightly higher, and the crown seems likewise to have been slightly lowered. The type of the King's head is close to a three-quarter-length-design of which a version, probably not autograph, was formerly at Longford Castle (Glück, 370). See no. 175.

146. CHARLES I IN THREE POSITIONS (*Plate* 70)

Windsor Castle (29). $33\frac{1}{4} \times 39\frac{1}{4}$ in., $84,5 \times 99,7$ cm.

Head and shoulders, seen from three different points of view. The King wears the ribbon, and on the right the star, of the Garter.

Despatched by the King soon after 17 March 1636 to Gian Lorenzo Bernini in Rome to assist in the making of a marble bust; remained in Rome, where it was seen by Richard Symonds exhibited 'wth divers choice paintings' in the portico of La Rotonda on the 'Painters feast' of St. Joseph on 19 March (1650?): 'Among ye rest that of Vandykes the K. of Engl: in a little square frame the king drawne 3 times [Symonds adds a hurried sketch] All in 3 severall Coloured Satans shewing hands' (B. M., Add. MS. 17919, f. 41); seen by Baldinucci (*op. cit.*, p. 88) in the possession of Bernini's sons; the Duke of Shrewsbury saw on 6 February 1702 'the 3 heads of Ch: 1st done by Vandyke at Berninis which are excellent' (A Journal by his Grace Charles Duke of Shrewsbury . . ., MS. at Boughton, f. 149). Secured in 1802 from the Palazzo Bernini by Irvine on behalf of Buchanan and Arthur Champernowne (W. Buchanan, *Memoirs of Painting* (1824), vol. I, pp. 183–4, vol. II, pp. 110–1, 127), and put up for sale by Buchanan, anon. sale Christie's, 12 May 1804 (9), bought in (by Stewart). Apparently bought from Champernowne by Walsh Porter, whose son, after his death, wrote to the Prince of Wales on 21 December 1809 that the picture, 'lately in his collection intended for your Royal Highness, has been sold [presumably to William Wells of Redleaf] . . . I have since found a Catalogue wherein that picture is expressly designated as for your Royal Highness' (W. R. A., Geo. 31540–1); it is clear from a letter of Lord Yarmouth of 14 January 1812 (*ibid.*, 26902–3) that the Prince thought, probably wrongly, that he had actually paid for the picture. Eventually bought by George IV in 1822 from Wells for one thousand guineas (*Carleton Palace* (548)).

Literature: 'Diary of Nicholas Stone, Junior', ed. W. L. Spiers, *Walpole Soc.*, vol. VII (1910), pp. 170–1; Bellori, *Le Vite de' Pittori* . . . (Rome, 1672), p. 260; F. Baldinucci, *Vita di Bernini* (Florence, 1682), ed. S. S. Ludovici (Milan, 1948), pp. 88–9; Vertue, *Notebooks*, vol. I, p. 27, vol. IV, p. 36; Walpole, *Anecdotes*, vol. I, pp. 270–1; Smith, 212, *Supplement*, 26; Waagen (1838), vol. I, p. 172, (1854), vol. II, p. 428; Law, *Van Dyck*, pp. 61–4; Cust, *Van Dyck*, pp. 106–7, 264; Schaeffer, 345; Sir L. Cust, 'The Triple Portrait of Charles I by Van Dyck', *Burl. Mag.*, vol. XIV (1909), pp. 337–40; Sir E. Maclagan, 'Sculpture by Bernini in England', *Burl. Mag.* vol. XL (1922), pp. 56–63; Glück, 389; G. Albion, *Charles I and the Court of Rome* (1935), pp. 397–401; Collins Baker, *Windsor*, pp. 76–7; R. A., *King's Pictures* (30); Waterhouse, *Painting in Britain*, p. 49; R. A., *Flemish Art*, 1953–4 (138); R. Wittkower, *Gian Lorenzo Bernini* (1955), pp. 16–17, 200–1 (39); Whinney and Millar, pp. 6, 73, 121.

Probably begun in the second half of 1635. In his letter to Lorenzo Bernini of 17 March 1636 the King expressed the hope that Bernini would execute 'il Nostro Ritratto in Marmo, sopra quello che in un Quadro vi manderemo subito';[1] the

---

1. D. Bernini, *Vita del Cavalier . . . Bernino* (Rome, 1713), pp. 64-7; S. Fraschetti, *Il Bernini* (Milan, 1900), pp. 110-11. It has been suggested by Mr. C. F. Bell that the Marquis de Cugnac, a Huguenot refugee in London, whose wife was in the Queen's service, may have been the 'Milord Conik' or 'Monsieur Cognac' who is said to have taken the painting to Rome.

---

portrait was once stated to have been taken to Rome by Thomas Baker (R. Wittkower, *op. cit.*, p. 201) and to have impressed the sculptor with 'something of funest and unhappy, which the Countenance of that Excellent Prince foreboded' (J. Evelyn, *Numismata* (1697), p. 335). The bust was to be a papal present to Henrietta Maria and its creation had been specially arranged by Urban VIII at a time when hopes were entertained in Rome that the King might lead England back into the Roman Catholic fold. Urban's agent in London, Gregorio Panzani, had reported on 13 June 1635 the King's satisfaction with the papal permission granted to Bernini. The bust was executed in the summer of 1636 and sent from Rome, under the personal supervision of Cardinal Francesco Barberini, in April 1637. It was presented to the King and Queen at Oatlands on 17 July, was enthusiastically received by them and their court and universally admired 'nott only for the exquisiteness of the worke but the likenesse and nere resemblance it had to the King countenaunce' (see nos. 148 and 149). Bernini was rewarded in 1638 with a diamond ring, valued at £800. The bust was destroyed in the fire at Whitehall Palace in 1698, but its appearance can be realised from a marble bust at Windsor (*Fig.* 27; possibly made by Thomas Adye on the basis of a cast of the original belonging to Francis Bird), from an engraving by Robert van Voerst (?) (Sir L. Cust, 'The Triple Portrait . . .') and from drawings by Jonathan Richardson (R. Wittkower, *op. cit.*, p. 201).

The heads in no. 146 are drawn and modelled with a care and restraint unusual in Van Dyck. In the placing of the King's hands and in his decision to make a complete picture (Bernini would technically have required only the King's head) out of this unusual commission, Van Dyck had presumably been influenced by Lotto's *Portrait of a Man in Three Positions* in the Kunsthistorisches Museum, Vienna (B. Berenson, *Lorenzo Lotto* (1956), pl. 235) which was in Charles I's collection with an attribution to Titian (*Van der Doort, p.* 20). Philippe de Champaigne's triple portrait of Cardinal Richelieu in the National Gallery (798; M. Davies, *French School*, N. G. (1957), pp. 25–6) was probably painted to assist Bernini or a sculptor in his circle, or possibly Francesco Mochi, in a bust (1640–1) of the Cardinal (R. Wittkower, *op. cit.*, pp. 202–3 (42)). For the sculptor John Michael Rysbrack, Kneller painted the head of the 2nd Earl of Nottingham in three positions (National Portrait Gallery 3910) which closely follow Van Dyck in disposition. There is a direct reminiscence of the triple portrait of the King in a canvas at Ashburnham Place, showing in three positions a head based on a portrait by Hanneman which either represents a member of the Ashburnham family or the 8th Earl of Derby. The copies of no. 146 are uniformly unimportant, and were presumably based on early copies made in Rome. A copy by Michael Wright (presumably painted in Rome) appeared in an auction at Charing Cross in 1691; the 3rd Earl of Leicester bought a copy on 25 September 1690 from 'Mr Smith's Auction' (MS. at Penshurst); and the copy in the Ashmolean Museum (419) was given to Oxford University by Elias Ashmole (*d.* 1692). An early copy is at Sledmere; a copy at Weston is attributed to Maratta. Poor copies are at Swynnerton, in the Lothian collection, in the Prado (1500), in the V. & A. (598–1882) and in the collections of Lord Willoughby de Broke and, formerly, at Wroxton Abbey and in the collection of Rear-Admiral Sir Arthur Bromley; and others were recorded in the eighteenth century by Vertue (*op. cit.*, vol. IV, p. 148) and Granger (vol. II, p. 238, n.) and at the Duke of Chandos's sale, 6 May 1747, 3rd day (147). A copy of the profile head is at Noseley. An enamel of the profile head, signed and dated (1699) by Charles Boit, and a miniature copy of the whole, attributed to

Cosway, are at Windsor (2624); an enamel of the frontal head by Bone, painted in 1833, is at Buckingham Palace. Van Dyck used the central head for a portrait of the King in armour of which the finest version is at Arundel Castle (Glück, 392).

147. HENRIETTA MARIA (Plate 67)

Windsor Castle (23). 42¾ × 33⅞ in., 108,6 × 86 cm.; made out in lining, originally *c.* 42 × 33 in.

Half-length, standing by a table and resting her hand on two roses by her crown; above is inscribed her monogram HMR under a crown.

Painted for Charles I, probably in 1632: on 8 August a warrant was issued for payments to Van Dyck that included £20 for a portrait of *our royall Consort* (Hookham Carpenter, p. 71). Placed in the King's Bedchamber at Whitehall (*Van der Doort*, p. 35); possibly to be identified with *The Queenes picture by vandyke* valued by the Trustees for Sale at £30 (L. R. MS., f. 124) and sold to John Embree on 21 May 1650 (S.P. 29/447, 24, 1). At the Restoration it was returned to the King's Bedchamber; thereafter at Windsor.

Literature: Vertue, *Notebooks*, vol. II, p. 29, vol. IV, p. 119; Walpole, *Anecdotes*, vol. I, p. 321; Smith, *Supplement*, 31; Waagen (1854), vol. II, p. 427; Law, *Van Dyck*, pp. 25–8; Cust, *Van Dyck*, pp. 107, 265; Schaeffer, 333; Glück, 376; Collins Baker, *Windsor*, p. 79; R. A., *Flemish Art*, 1953–4 (224).

Perhaps the first single portrait of the Queen painted by Van Dyck after his arrival in London. The type is almost identical with the figure of the Queen in the double portrait at Kremsier (*Fig.* 14; see no. 119), from which John Hoskins in 1632 painted a miniature, now in the Rijksmuseum, Amsterdam (2842), of her head; variations (mainly in the curtain and accessories, the placing of the right hand, the little ornament in her hair and the form of the left sleeve) from these two sources seem to be combined in the more important versions of no. 147, *i.e.*, in the Loyd collection at Lockinge, at Alnwick (probably to be identified in the Northumberland collection in 1671) and at Cowdray Park. Other copies (*i.e.* at Deene Park, Burghley, Welbeck, Castle Grant and Hutton-in-the-Forest) are unimportant. A full-length extension is at Goodwood. A miniature copy of the head of this type is at Burghley. The curtain originally projected more to the left and seems to have been altered by Van Dyck to its present form, and there are signs of alterations down the shadowed area of the Queen's left sleeve. No. 147 was probably the source of the portrait of the Queen in the series of royal portraits in tapestry at Houghton (see no. 105), and the type comes close to that engraved by J. Suyderhoef.

148. HENRIETTA MARIA (Plate 68)

Windsor Castle (32). 31 × 25⅞ in., 78,7 × 65,7 cm.; stretched in lining and originally *c.* 29¼ × 24 in.

Head and shoulders to the front, wearing a richly jewelled chain and cross.

Painted, probably in 1639, for the Queen for despatch with no. 149 to Bernini in Rome. There are no references to the two portraits in the documents concerning Charles I's collection, its dispersal or its recovery. Probably in James II's collection at Whitehall (B. M., Harl. MS. 1890, f. 56 v.; Bathoe, *James II* (343): *Vandike. Queene Mothers picture to the waste in white Sattin*) and thereafter at Kensington. Both portraits were temporarily at Carlton House, probably in the Rose Satin Drawing Room, and were sent on 23 September 1816 to be varnished by Simpson under Lawrence's surveillance (Jutsham, *R/D*, f. 252); the frontal portrait is probably *A half Length Portrait of Henrietta Maria . . . by Vandyke* that had been sent to Simpson on 27 August 1810 to be cleaned (*ibid*, f. 70), but had been reported by him in 1811 to be in very bad condition (W. R. A., Geo. 26892).

Literature: F. Baldinucci, *Vita di Bernini* (Florence, 1682), ed. S. S. Ludovici (Milan, 1948), pp. 88–9; Vertue, *Notebooks*, vol. IV, p. 65; Pyne, vol. III, *Carlton House*, p. 33; Smith 217; Waagen (1838), vol. I, p. 172, (1854) vol. II, p. 428; Law, *Van Dyck*, pp. 65–6; Cust, *Van Dyck*, pp. 108–9, 266; Schaeffer, 354; Glück, 386; Collins Baker, *Windsor*, p. 81; R. A., *King's Pictures* (35); R. Wittkower, *Gian Lorenzo Bernini* (1955), p. 201.

The Queen had been so delighted with Bernini's bust of her husband (see no. 146) that she determined upon a companion bust of herself. The preparatory portraits were being painted in August 1638 and the frontal portrait may have been painted in 1637 (see below), but not until June 1639 did the Queen write to Bernini of her desire to have a bust of herself 'tirée sur les portraiets que vous fournir[a le] sieur Conneo' (MS. in Roy. Lib.).[1] In his *Memoire* (1638?) of pictures painted for the Crown (P. R. O., S.P.16/406, 4; Hookham Carpenter, pp. 66–8) Van Dyck asked for payment of £15 for two portraits of the Queen *pour M̄ons Barnino*. Three portraits were probably completed, but were never apparently sent to Rome: presumably because of 'le turbolenze, che poco dipoi insorsero in quel regno' (Baldinucci, *op. cit.*, p. 89), though Bernini had apparently flatly refused to do another bust on the basis of a painting even 'if thaire were best picture done by the hand of Raphyell' ('Diary of Nicholas Stone', ed. W. L. Spiers, *Walpole Soc.* vol. VII (1919), pp. 170–1). It is possible that the two portraits were never delivered to the Queen. The frontal portrait has been severely rubbed; the outline of the head has been altered thereby and in early copies (*e.g.*, at Ham House and at Sotheby's, 5 March 1958 (187)), the Queen's *coiffure* projects more at the sides; the copy at Ham, which probably appears (no. 170) in an inventory of Ham of 1679, bears the Queen's monogram under a crown and the date 1637. At some period no. 148 seems to have been used as the door in a piece of furniture; a lock of a fairly early date has been sunk into the stretcher just above the Queen's left shoulder.

149. HENRIETTA MARIA (Plate 69)

Windsor Castle (27). 28¼ × 22¼ in., 71,8 × 56,5 cm.

Head and shoulders in profile to the left.

See no. 148. Recorded in James II's collection at Whitehall (B. M., Harl. MS. 1890, f. 59 v.; Bathoe, *James II* (441): *Vandike. Queene Mother to the waste. a side face*). Thereafter at Kensington, and described there by Horace Walpole in 1763 as 'fine all but the hand' (notes to Bathoe, *James II*); taken to Carlton House (see no. 148) on 7 August 1812 (Jutsham, *R/D*, ff. 215, 252).

Literature: Vertue, *Notebooks*, vol. IV, p. 65; Smith, 218; Waagen (1838), vol. I, p. 172, (1854), vol. II, p. 427; Law, *Van Dyck*, p. 67; Schaeffer, 354; Glück, 387; Collins Baker, *Windsor*, p. 80; R. A., *King's Pictures* (37), *Flemish Art*, 1953–4 (154); Whinney and Millar, p. 72.

See no. 148. At some period after 1763 (see above) the Queen's right arm and hand, holding her scarf, were painted out. They are visible under infra-red light and their position can be seen in copies, *i.e.*, at Merton College, Oxford (*Fig.* 30). The other profile (*Fig.* 29; Glück, 387) was formerly at Hamilton Palace. Its present whereabouts are unknown. It measured 23 × 17¾ in. and may have been cut down. It can probably be identified in inventories of the Hamilton collection in the 1640's (*e.g.*, *The Queens face by Vādyke* and . . . *the queene to the waste syde faced of S* *r* *Anthonye Vandyke*) with a copy of the frontal portrait (Hamilton MSS.). Van Dyck thus seems to have completed the set of portraits of the Queen for

1. The letter was sent to England with no. 146, and Buchanan (*Memoirs of Painting* (1824), vol. I, p. 184, vol. II, pp. 127–8) describes its partial mutilation; this can be made good by a comparison with the Italian text of the letter printed by Baldinucci (*op. cit.*, p. 89).

Bernini, but the Queen may have presented one of them to the Duke or Duchess of Hamilton when it became clear that the bust would not be made. A copy of Glück, 387, is in the National Maritime Museum.

150. CHARLES I AND HENRIETTA MARIA WITH THEIR TWO ELDEST CHILDREN, PRINCE CHARLES (LATER CHARLES II) AND PRINCESS MARY (Plate 66)

Buckingham Palace. 146 × 108 in., 370,8 × 274,3 cm. The canvas has been made out all round, presumably to make it a pendant to no. 143. The original canvas measures $117\frac{1}{2} \times 98$ in., which includes additions made by Van Dyck of *c*. $12\frac{1}{2}$ in. at the top and $8\frac{1}{2}$ in. on the right.

Full-length group with a distant view of the Thames at Westminster: the King seated by a table, on which are the crown, sceptre and orb, wearing the ribbon and star of the Garter and with the little Prince at his knee; the Queen holding the Princess in her arms; and two Italian greyhounds at their feet.

Painted for Charles I: on 8 August 1632 a warrant was issued for payments to Van Dyck that included £100 for *One greate peece of o*^r *royall selfe, Consort and children* (Hookham Carpenter, p. 71). Placed in (presumably at one end of) the King's Long Gallery 'towards the Orchard' at Whitehall: *. . . whereby in a lanskipp Westminster painted and One* (sic) *of the Queenes litle doggs by. In a Carved Some part Guilded frame . . .*, measurements given as 116 × 96 in. (*Van der Doort*, p. 42); valued at £150 by the Trustees for Sale (Corsham MS., f. 44), sold to Emmanuel De Critz and others on 23 October 1651 (S.P. 29/447, 24, 1), recovered at the Restoration (Col. Hawley, f. 33), and hung once more at the end of the Long Matted Gallery at Whitehall (Charles II, *Whitehall* (1)), where Pepys saw on 26 April 1667 a young man 'most finely' making a copy in 'Indian inke'. Later hung, probably by William III and Mary II, in the Gallery at Kensington (*Kensington*, 1697, f. 189; and see H. M. C., *Cowper MSS.*, vol. III (1889), p. 187) to balance no. 143. Later at Buckingham House, in the Japan Room with no. 143, and Windsor (20: Pyne, vol. I, pp. 90–1 and plate).

Literature: Vertue, vol. II, pp. 88, 89, vol. IV, pp. 162–3, vol. V, p. 135; Walpole, *Anecdotes*, vol. I, p. 321, *Visits*, p. 78; Smith, 224; Waagen (1838), vol. I, p. 173, (1854), vol. II, p. 426; Law, *Van Dyck*, pp. 5–10; Cust, *Van Dyck*, pp. 99–100, 264–5, and 'The Great Piece, by Sir Anthony Van Dyck', *Burl. Mag.*, vol. XII (1908), pp. 235–7, 282–9; Schaeffer, 302; Glück, 371; Collins Baker, *Windsor*, pp. 82–3; R. A., *Flemish Art*, 1953–4 (160); Whinney and Millar, pp. 67, 71.

The group was painted very soon after Van Dyck's arrival in London and is thus the first of the great series of commissions carried out for the royal family. His preparatory chalk drawing of the King (Fig. 16; Antwerp and Rotterdam, *Antoon Van Dyck, Tekeningen en Olieverfschetsen*, 1960 (92)) probably records Charles's first sitting to his new painter. A chalk drawing of the Queen and Princess Mary in the British Museum (A. M. Hind, *Catalogue of Drawings by Dutch and Flemish Artists . . .*, vol. II (1923), p. 65, no. 45) is perhaps an early drawing after the finished painting; the sketch in the Museum Boymans, Rotterdam (129), is a much later (probably nineteenth-century) record of the composition. By 1676 the condition of the 'Great Piece' was unsatisfactory, apparently owing to Van Dyck's negligence in the priming; it was described as primed 'wth tobacco pipe clay' and 'now allmost all pilled of' (Charles Hatton to Lord Hatton, 23 September 1676, *Correspondence of the Family of Hatton*, ed. E. M. Thompson, vol. I, *Camden Soc.*, NS. vol. XXII (1878), pp. 139–40). Waagen (*op. cit.*) refers more specifically to its deterioration. The canvas has been so rubbed and is so darkened that the original tonality, the topographical details in the background and the impression created by the design

before it was enlarged can be more fully realised in early copies, of which the most important are at Goodwood (from the Orléans collection), the Royal Hospital, Chelsea (acquired between 1699 and 1702 at a cost of £47. 5s., including the frame, from Henry Ireton), and in the Devonshire collection. A copy was valued at £30 by the Trustees for Sale among the pictures at Hampton Court early in October 1649; on 19 August 1647 an order had been issued, by virtue of a Parliamentary ordinance of 21 September 1643, for payment of £50 to Remigius van Leemput for a copy 'according to ye Coppie of ye Great Peice at Whitehall', apparently painted on the Earl of Pembroke's instructions and on the King's behalf (B. M., Add. MS. 32476, f. 28). This may have been the copy recorded in the Queen's Gallery at Hampton Court after the Restoration (Charles II, *Hampton Court* (17), measurements given as 56 × 48 in.). A large copy was sold at Christie's, 29 October 1941 (424); another belongs to Lady Biddulph. Reduced copies are not uncommon (*e.g.*, at Raby Castle, Serlby Hall, in the collection of Sir V. Warrender and in the Stevens Memorial Library, North Andover, Mass.) and a small copy at Woburn is probably by Van Leemput. Copies also exist of the two halves of the composition, perhaps cut from complete copies (*e.g.*, of both in the Strickland collection (formerly at Howsham), of the male half in the Lothian collection and at Blickling and Northwick Park and of the female at Chequers); there is a copy of the figure of Prince Charles at Althorp, he appears in the composite royal group at Grimsthorpe Castle (see no. 120) and in no. 197 and is the source (with a figure from no. 151) of a Van Dyckian pastiche at Boughton. The 'Great Piece' was treated in the same way by engravers: the whole composition was engraved by Bernard Baron (1741), whose drawing of the King's head is in the Sutherland collection (vol. II, 291–366) in the Ashmolean Museum; there is an earlier anonymous mezzotint of the figures alone; the male half of the design was engraved in mezzotint by A. Browne and Prince Charles, with variations, by Blooteling and Vaillant; and the Queen and the children were adapted to an engraving by Robert Strange (1784). The figure of the King was probably the source of the engraving by Jonas Suyderhoef, whose preliminary drawing may also be that in the Sutherland collection (vol. I, 341–452). It is also the source of the portrait of Charles I in the series of royal portraits at Houghton (see no. 105). The portrait of the Queen seems to have been the source of a full-length standing portrait of which there are versions in the Poldi-Pezzoli collection, Milan, and at Upton House. The influence of the design is felt particularly strongly in Cornelius Johnson's group of the Capel family, *c*. 1640 (Whinney and Millar, pl. 17).

151. THE THREE ELDEST CHILDREN OF CHARLES I (Plates 73, 75, 78)

Windsor Castle (37). $52\frac{1}{2} \times 59\frac{3}{4}$ in., 133,4 × 151,8 cm.; stretched in lining.

Inscribed: REGIS MAGNÆ BRITANIÆ/PROLES/PRINCEPS CAROLVS NATVS 29 MAY 1630./IACOBVS DVX EBORACENCIS NATVS 14 OCT: 1633/ET FILIA PRINCEPS MARIA NATA 4 NO: 1631 and signed and dated . . . PER AN VAN DYCK EQ./ANNO 1635.

Full-length standing group with two King Charles spaniels: Prince Charles (later Charles II) and James, Duke of York (later James II) hold hands beside their sister Mary.

Probably painted for Henrietta Maria and hung in Somerset House; valued by the Trustees for Sale among the pictures at Somerset House at £60 (Corsham MS., f. 44: *The late Kings 3 Children. in one peece, by Vandyke*) and sold to Col. Webb on 25 October 1649; offered in 1654 to M. de Bordeaux, agent for Cardinal Mazarin, but rejected as too expensive (Comte de Cosnac, *Les Richesses du Palais Mazarin* (Paris, 1884), p. 228); passed into the hands of Peter Lely and declared by him to the House of Lords Committee, 18 May 1660 (H. of L. MSS.). Henrietta Maria seems understandably to have been very fond of the picture and at her death in 1669 it was hanging in her Presence Chamber at Colombes (P. R. O., S.P. 78/128, f. 209 v. . . . *To be sent hither*); brought back to Whitehall and thereafter at Kensington and Buckingham House (see no. 153).

Literature: Vertue, *Notebooks*, vol. II, p. 99; Walpole, *Anecdotes*, vol. I., p. 321, *Visits*, p. 78; Smith, 211, *Supplement*, 25; Waagen (1838), vol. I, pp. 171–2, (1854), vol. II, p. 429; Law, *Van Dyck*, pp. 33–6; Cust, *Van Dyck*, pp. 110–1, 266; Schaeffer, 337; Glück, 379; Collins Baker, *Windsor*, pp. 84–5; R. A., *King's Pictures* (34), *Flemish Art*, 1953–4 (156); Whinney and Millar, p. 73.

Earlier in 1635 Van Dyck had painted a group of the Queen's eldest children (*Fig.* 17) which she had sent to her sister, Christina, Duchess of Savoy, in exchange for portraits of the Duchess's children. The Queen wrote to her sister, apparently in July 1635, that the despatch of the portraits had been delayed because 'ma fille n'a jamais voulu avoir la pasiance de les leser achever', and the group was apparently sent to Turin in the late autumn (H. Ferrero, *Lettres de Henriette-Marie de France à sa soeur Christina Duchesse de Savoie* (Turin, 1881), pp. 40, 43). On 29 November 1635, however, Benoît Cize, the Savoy minister in London, reported to the Duke of Savoy that the King was 'faché contre le paintre Vandec por ne leur avoir mis leur Tablié comme on accoustume aux petit enfans' (Mazzo-Lettere Ministri Inghilterra, Archivio di Stato, Turin). He was presumably distressed that Prince Charles had been painted wearing his infant's 'coats', and it may partly have been to placate him that Van Dyck painted the second and more adult group, presumably between the end of November 1635 and 25 March 1636. It was a very popular design and copies are numerous. The best are at Euston Hall, Breamore, Wilton, Kingston Lacy, Grimsthorpe Castle, Boughton, Stourhead, Longleat, Goodwood, Penn House, Lacock Abbey, Burton Constable, in the Bute collection, formerly at Hinchingbrooke (sold at Sotheby's, 4 December 1957 (170)), in the Metropolitan Museum (25.110.48) and at Dresden (1033). Small copies and reductions also exist, *e.g.*, in the Louvre (1968), with the Ministry of Works, and in the Clarendon collection; the last, stated to have belonged to Charles I, may be identical with *the Kings 3 Children* valued at £10 by the Trustees for Sale among the pictures at Somerset House (Corsham MS., f. 49) and sold to Hunt on 14 May 1650. A version seems to have been in James II's possession at St. Germains at his death (inv. of 20 July 1703, attached to his Will). Among Charles Beale's drawings (*c.* 1675–80) in the British Museum are six studies (G.g.4.W.5–108 to 112) of the heads and hands, and a study of the Duke of York is in the Rothschild collection. The design was engraved by J. C. Le Blon, Richard Purcell and Robert Strange. A water-colour copy is at Buckingham Palace. A miniature copy is in the Buccleuch collection; another (1729) by Bernard Lens is at Chatsworth and Lens adapted the design to a group (1720) of the Marlborough children at Althorp. The heads of the two boys were copied in the borders of the tapestries at Houghton (see no. 105). One of the dogs is used in a Van Dyckian group at Deene Park. Van Dyck had to some extent anticipated the design in his group of three children in the Galleria Durazzo Pallavicini Giustiniani Negrotto, Genoa, painted when he was in Genoa (exh. Genoa, *100 Opere di Van Dyck*, 1955 (48)).

152. THE FIVE ELDEST CHILDREN OF CHARLES I (*Plates* 74, 76)

Windsor Castle (30). $64\frac{1}{4} \times 78\frac{1}{4}$ in., 163,2 × 198,8 cm.

Inscribed: REGIS MAGNÆ BRITANIÆ / PROLES / PRINCEPS CAROLVS NATVS 29 MAII 1630. / IACOBVS DVX EBORACENGIS NATVS 14 OCTOB: 1633 / PRINCEPS MARIA NATA 4 NOVEMB: 1631./PRINCEPS ELIZABETH NATA 28 DECEMB 1635/PRINCEPS ANNA NATA 17 MARTII 163$\frac{6}{7}$ and signed and dated *Antony van dyck Eques Fecit*, / *1637*.

Full-length standing group: Princess Mary and Prince James stand beside Prince Charles who rests his hand on a large mastiff; Princess Elizabeth supports the infant Princess Anne, watched by a small King Charles spaniel.

Painted for the King: in his *Memoire* (1638?) Van Dyck asked for payment of £200 (reduced by Charles to £100) for *Le Prince Carles avecq le ducq de Jarc Princesse Maria. Pse Elisabet Pr Anna* (P. R. O., S.P. 16/406, 4; Hookham Carpenter, pp. 66–8); placed, *in a blue and carved guilded frame, above the table in the King's Breakfast Chamber at Whitehall (Van der Doort*, p. 35); valued by the Trustees for Sale at £120 (L. R. MS., f. 124) and sold to Captain Geere on 14 May 1650 (S.P. 29/447, 24, 1); seen later by Richard Symonds in De Critz's house at Austin Friars (B. M., Egerton MS. 1636, f. 100), but bought on 17 May 1653 by Francis Trion, who hoped that he might lose it to Charles II and in whose possession Geldorp reported it on 12 May 1660 to the House of Lords Committee (*Cal. S.P.Dom.* (*1660–1*), p. 456; H. of L. MSS.); delivered at Whitehall, 6 August 1661 (Col. Hawley, f. 6). Possibly given by James II to his mistress, the Countess of Dorchester, who later married the 1st Earl of Portmore: on 6 February 1765 £525 was paid on behalf of George III to Mr *Pinchbeck for a Picture of Vandyke bought of Lord Portmore* (W. R. A., Geo. 17131). This was the 2nd Earl, son of the Countess. Placed at Buckingham House.

Literature: Vertue, *Notebooks*, vol. IV, p. 42; Walpole, *Anecdotes*, vol. I, p. 331 (n. by Dalloway); Granger, vol. II, p. 261; Pyne, vol. I, pp. 152–3; Smith, 208, *Supplement*, 24; Waagen (1838), vol. I, p. 171, (1854), vol. II, p. 428; Law, *Van Dyck*, pp. 55–8; Cust, *Van Dyck*, pp. 111–2, 266–7; Schaeffer, 344; Glück, 385; Collins Baker, *Windsor*, pp. 86–7; R. A., *King's Pictures* (101), *The Age of Charles II*, 1960–1 (6).

Van Dyck's rapid sketches in chalk (*Figs.* 26, 25) for the figures of Prince Charles and Prince James are respectively in the Royal Library (13018) and Christ Church, and his study in oils for the heads of the two younger Princesses is in the collection of Lord Chesham (Fig. 23, R. A., *Flemish Art*, 1953–4 (317)). There are alterations in no. 152 to the shape of the Duke of York's head and lace cap which Van Dyck seems to have had to enlarge. Copies of the group are numerous, *e.g.*, at Sanssouci and at Burghley, Hagley, Ugbrooke, Euston, Norton Conyers and Chequers; three-quarter-length reductions (*e.g.*, at Goodwood, Hardwick and in the National Portrait Gallery (267)) and small copies (*e.g.*, no. 176, at Syon, Sherborne Castle, Antony, Shrublands Park and, probably by Remigius van Leemput, at Woburn) are common. A miniature copy by Nicholas Dixon is at Welbeck (685). A copy of the figure of Princess Mary is at Penshurst and of the two youngest children at Highclere Castle. The design was engraved by Alexander Browne and Richard Cooper (1762) and reminiscences of it are to be found in English painting in the 1630's and 1640's: in Francis Cleyn's decorations in the North Drawing Room at Ham House, in Peter Lely's *Figures in a Landscape* (*c.* 1645–50) in the Lee collection (39), and in a group, formerly at Apethorpe, of the children of the 2nd Earl of Westmorland which is closely based on Van Dyck (*Victoria County History, Northamptonshire Families*, ed. O. Barron (1906), p. 102). The smaller of the dogs, which appears in another early subject-picture by Lely, is apparently identical with a dog in Cornelius Johnson's portrait (1631) of Charles I at Chatsworth.

153. GEORGE VILLIERS, SECOND DUKE OF BUCKINGHAM (1628–87), AND LORD FRANCIS VILLIERS (1629–48) (*Plate 77*)

Windsor Castle (25). 54×50¼ in., 137,2×127,7 cm.; there is an original addition at the bottom of *c*. 3 in.

Inscribed: GEORGIVS DVX BUCKINGHAMYE / CVM FRATRE FRANCISCO / 1635.

Two full-lengths, the Duke standing slightly in advance of his brother.

Painted for Charles I and hung in the Gallery at St. James's (*Van der Doort*, p. 226), near the portrait of their sister (no. 159); valued at £30 by the Trustees for Sale and sold to Kinnersley on 22 March 1650 (L. R. MS., f. 166); declared by Geldorp to the House of Lords Committee on 12 May 1660 to be in the possession of Mr. 'Vaeytchell' (presumably Vachell; H. of L. MSS.) and delivered at Whitehall, probably in 1661 (Col. Hawley, f. 16 v.). Thereafter at Windsor, Kensington and Buckingham House.

Literature: Vertue, *Notebooks*, vol. II, pp. 29, 98, vol. IV, p. 160; Walpole, *Anecdotes*, vol. I, p. 321; Smith, 219, *Supplement*, 37; Waagen (1854), vol. II, p. 427; Law, *Van Dyck*, pp. 37–40; Cust, *Van Dyck*, pp. 116, 270; Schaeffer, 338; Glück, 439; Collins Baker, *Windsor*, pp. 92–3; R. A., *King's Pictures* (38); Whinney and Millar, p. 70.

Van Dyck's original sketch in chalk for the figure of the younger boy is in the British Museum (*Fig.* 18; A. M. Hind, *Catalogue of Drawings by Dutch and Flemish Artists . . .*, vol. II (1923), p. 67, no. 56) and Van Dyck altered in painting the outline of his right hand and forearm which was originally at a sharper angle to the body. There are copies at Warwick Castle, Highclere Castle and Serlby, any of which could be the copy by Ranelagh Barret recorded by Vertue (*Notebooks*, vol. III, p. 112) in 1742; see also no. 191. Another copy was exh. in Paris, *Le Cabinet de l'Amateur*, 1956 (38). Later chalk drawings of the two heads are at Chatsworth. A copy of the elder boy is at Blenheim and another was sold at Christie's, 4 February 1927 (95). The group, which was engraved by McArdell in 1752, enjoyed a great vogue in the eighteenth century. Vertue much admired it and Walpole (*op. cit.*) said that 'nothing can exceed the nature, lustre, and delicacy of this sweet picture', which he regarded as 'one of the finest of this master' (notes to Bathoe, *James II*, part II, p. 50); it was, with no. 151, among the suitable pictures assembled by Zoffany in the interior of the Second Drawing Room or Warm Room at Buckingham House (see Pyne, vol. II, *Buckingham House*, pp. 15–18) in which he placed the Prince of Wales and Duke of York as children (Windsor Castle, no. 517); and its effect can be seen on the child portraiture of Reynolds, Gainsborough and Zoffany.[1]

The children of the murdered Duke of Buckingham were 'bred up by King Charles, with his own children, the same tutors and governors'; the young Duke and his brother served in the Civil War and Lord Francis was killed near Kingston. After the Restoration the Duke was one of the most brilliant and notorious members of the court of Charles II, satirised by Dryden as 'Zimri' and by Pope as a 'Lord of useless thousands'. See no. 138.

154. PORTRAIT OF A WOMAN, *formerly known as* LUCY PERCY, COUNTESS OF CARLISLE (*c.* 1600–1660) (*Plate* 80)

Windsor Castle (31). 82×46½ in.; 208,3×118,1 cm.; *c.* 1¾ in. are turned over at the bottom.

Inscribed later: LUCY. COUNTESS OF CARLISLE.

Full-length, standing in a wooded landscape and cooling her hand in the water that pours from a bowl held by a sculptured putto.

Possibly among the pictures, from the collection of Sir Daniel Arthur, which were seen on 3 February 1729 in the house of George Bagnall and included 'some other portraits' by Van Dyck (see no. 158). Acquired by Frederick, Prince of Wales, possibly before September 1747, when John Anderson's account for work on his pictures includes four guineas for cleaning and repairing *A Lady Whole Length by Vandike* (D. of Cornwall MSS., vol. XVII, f. 547); thereafter at Leicester House and Buckingham House.

Literature: Smith, *Supplement*, 45 (as the Duchess of Richmond); Waagen (1854), vol. II, p. 428; Law, *Van Dyck*, pp. 69–72; Cust, *Van Dyck*, pp. 121, 271; Schaeffer, 358; Glück, 471; Collins Baker, *Windsor*, pp. 88–9; R. A., *King's Pictures* (284).

The identity of the portrait has been questioned (*e.g.*, by Glück, *loc. cit.*), and the sitter seems to be younger than the other portraits of the Countess by Van Dyck, *i.e.*, a full-length (Glück, 447, is the most familiar version) and a half-length at Petworth (225) in which she is represented dipping her hand in water from an almost identical putto and urn. This may have caused the identification of no. 154 with the Countess. The costume and hair-style in no. 154 are, however, Flemish, and no. 154 was probably painted in Brussels in 1634–5, at the same period as no. 158. A small copy on panel, showing a little more background on the right, was (1946) in the collection of Mr. F. Harper. The motive of the hand held under the cooling water is a visual parallel to the lines, attributed to Thomas Randolph, 'On a maide of honour seene by a schollar in sommerset garden': 'When viewing curiously, away she slipt, And in a fount her whited hande she dipt.' The idea was taken up by Lely, and many of his portraits contain in the background such elaborate baroque statuary and water; no. 154 may have been the source of the design of a Lelyesque portrait (*c.* 1679) of Diana, Countess of Exeter, at Belvoir.

The Countess was daughter of the 9th Earl of Northumberland; she married in 1617 as his second wife James Hay, 1st Earl of Carlisle (*d.* 1636); a celebrated court beauty and a close friend of the Queen and of Strafford, she was a born intriguer who betrayed the Queen's trust to the King's opponents.

155. ZEGER VAN HONTSUM (*d.* 1643)

Buckingham Palace. 42¾×33¼ in., 108,6×84,5 cm.

Half-length in ecclesiastical robes, holding in his left hand a book and a black biretta.

Purchased by George III with the collection of Consul Smith in 1762 (Flemish and Dutch list, 13; measurements given as 36×33 in.), and placed in the Warm Room at Buckingham House; later in the Picture Gallery (120).

Literature: Smith, 239; Waagen (1854), vol. II, p. 4; Glück, 272.

In his Will (31 March 1642) Zeger van Hontsum left to his nephew his 'contrefeytsel gemaeckt van den schilder van Dyck' (J. Denucé, *The Antwerp Art Galleries . . .* (Antwerp, 1932), pp. 91–2). No. 155 was painted *c.* 1630 and was probably the source of the engraving by Adriaen Lommelin (M. Mauquoy-Hendrickx, *L'Iconographie d'Antoine Van Dyck* (Brussels, 1956), no. 109).

Canon and penitential of Antwerp Cathedral from 1619 until his death.

---

1. For example, Reynolds's *Jacob Bouverie* (E. K. Waterhouse, *Reynolds* (1941), pl. 42), and *John Darley* (?1776) in the Duncombe collection, Gainsborough's *Blue Boy* (E. K. Waterhouse, *Gainsborough* (1958), pl. 127), the Rev. M. W. Peters's *Lord Newbattle* (1778), and other portraits by Zoffany of the children of George III.

156. THOMAS KILLIGREW (1612–83) AND (?) WILLIAM, LORD CROFTS (c. 1611–1677) (Plate 79)

Windsor Castle (22). 52¼ × 56½ in., 132,7 × 143,5 cm.; slightly made out in lining.

Signed and dated: *A. van, Dyck, 1638.*

Seated, three-quarter-length, in conversation; Killigrew rests his head on his hand and holds a drawing of two female statues, while his companion holds a blank sheet of paper.

Stated to have been brought from Spain by Sir Daniel Arthur, a Jacobite exile; presumably among the pictures seen on 3 February 1729 by the Earl of Egmont in the house of George Bagnall, who had married Sir Daniel's widow (H. M. C., *Egmont MSS., Diary of the first Earl of Egmont,* vol. III (1923), p. 344) and who sold the picture to Frederick, Prince of Wales, in 1748 (Vertue, *Notebooks,* vol. V, pp. 79, 217); placed over the chimney in the Third Room at Leicester House.

Literature: Vertue, *Notebooks,* vol. I, p. 11, vol. IV, p. 125; Walpole, *Anecdotes,* vol. I, pp. 326–7; Smith, 214, *Supplement,* 36; Waagen (1838), vol. I, p. 172, (1854), vol. II, p. 427; Law, *Van Dyck,* pp. 77–80; Cust, *Van Dyck,* pp. 134–5, 276; Schaeffer, 350; Glück, 451; Collins Baker, *Windsor,* p. 91; R. A., *King's Pictures* (36); Waterhouse, *Painting in Britain,* p. 50; R. A., *Flemish Art,* 1953–4 (164); Whinney and Millar, p. 72.

Thomas Killigrew (for whom see also Glück, 396) is apparently in mourning for his wife, Cecilia Crofts, who had died on 1 January 1638. A wedding ring is bound by a black band around his wrist, the small gold and silver cross attached to his sleeve bears the intertwined initials ℭ, and the female statues in the drawing he holds seem to have some funereal significance; the larger of the two may be intended for his deceased wife, the child clasped at her side for her infant son Henry who had been born on 9 April 1637, and the other statue for Cecilia's sister Anne, Countess of Cleveland, who died on 16 January 1638. The identity of Killigrew's companion has never been satisfactorily established. Vertue stated (*op. cit.,* vol. IV, p. 125) that 'the other person is not known certainly', suspected he was Sir John Denham (1615–69), but later thought he was Thomas Carew (1594/5–1640). In Jervas's sale, 11 March 1740, 5th day (297), the sitter in his copy is called 'another Gentleman'.[1] Both Vertue and Walpole (*op. cit.*) associated the composition with Carew's song of *Iealousie* (sung in a masque at Whitehall in 1633) which Killigrew used in his *Cicilia and Clorinda* (1649–50; published 1664) 'because . . . 'twas writ at my request upon a dispute held betwixt Mistress *Cicilia Crofts* and my self, where he was present' (see Carew, *Poems,* ed. R. Dunlap (1949), pp. xliv–v, 244–5). Carew was a courtier and a friend of the Crofts and Killigrew families and had celebrated in verse (*ibid.,* pp. 79–80) the marriage that united them, but Killigrew's companion seems to be younger than Carew would have been in 1638. Nor is there any apparent reason why Carew should have been painted with Killigrew on this occasion. For a suggestion that Killigrew's companion is William Murray, Groom of the Bedchamber, see Cust, *op. cit.* A more plausible candidate is Killigrew's brother-in-law William, Lord Crofts, who had been brought up at court, was Master of the Horse to James, Duke of York, Captain of Henrietta Maria's Guards, and Gentleman of the Bedchamber to Charles II; the features of his effigy in his monument by Abraham Storey at Little Saxham Church are not irreconcilable with Van Dyck's profile. A double portrait, of which a version is at Wilton (Glück, 500), showing Cecilia Killigrew with a companion, thought to be the

Countess of Dalkeith but conceivably Killigrew's sister Anne, could possibly be a companion piece. In no. 156 there are slight alterations by Van Dyck to the shape of the collars of both sitters.

Thomas Killigrew, royalist, courtier, dramatist and wit, was a Page of Honour to Charles I and during the Commonwealth was Charles II's Resident in Venice. After the Restoration he was Groom of the Bedchamber and Master of the Revels and was granted a patent to build and manage the Theatre Royal, Drury Lane, whose actors were recognised as the King's servants.

157. MARGARET LEMON (Plate 81)

Hampton Court (73). 36¾ × 30⅝ in., 93,3 × 77,8 cm.

Half-length, clasping a cloak round her naked shoulders and bosom.

Probably acquired by Charles I: the Trustees for Sale valued at £20 Mrs Leamon – p^r Vandyke, among the pictures assembled at St. James's (L. R. MS., f. 164 v.); it was sold to the painter John Baptist Gaspars on 22 March 1650 (S.P. 29/447, 24, 1); recovered at the Restoration (Col. Hawley, f. 13) and placed in store at Whitehall (Charles II, *Whitehall* (533), measurements given as 40 × 31 in.); apparently taken to Kensington by William III and Mary II and hung in the Great Closet (*Kensington,* 1697, f. 192).

Literature: Walpole, *Anecdotes,* vol. I, pp. 333–4, *Visits,* p. 80; Smith 229, *Supplement,* 43; Waagen (1854), vol. II, p. 356; Law, 1881, 1898 (47), *Van Dyck,* pp. 97–8; Cust, *Van Dyck,* pp. 136, 277; Schaeffer, 420; Collins Baker, *Hampton Court,* p. 41; Glück, 492.

It is possible that no. 157 was acquired in an unfinished state, perhaps from the artist's studio after his death: among the pictures by Van Dyck, which M. de Bordeaux bought from painters in London in 1654 for Cardinal Mazarin, was *la teste de la maistresse de Van Dyck, qui n'est pas achevée.* The Cardinal did not, however, wish to retain them and in 1655 they seem to have been returned to the painters from whom M. de Bordeaux had bought them (Comte de Cosnac, *Les Richesses du Palais Mazarin* (Paris, 1884), pp. 231–6). An unfinished portrait might have been put in store (see above), and no. 157 seems to have been worked up, perhaps by Gaspars, at a very early date, possibly during the Interregnum. The modelling of the cloak appears to have been strengthened; the original dark brown background had been overpainted. This overpainting was removed in 1961, when X-ray revealed that the preparatory ground on the canvas was typical of Van Dyck. There are original *pentimenti* in the fingers. The portrait was presumably begun before Van Dyck's marriage (1639) to Lady Mary Ruthven. It was inspired by Titian's *Girl in a Fur Wrap* in the Kunsthistorisches Museum, Vienna (H. Tietze, *Titian* (1950), pl. 96), which was at that time hanging in the First Privy Lodging Room at Whitehall. A copy of no. 157 is at Newbattle Abbey.

Van Dyck's mistress in London: 'twas wondred by some that knew him thatt having bene in Italy he would keepe a M^rs of his in his howse M^ris Leman & suffer Porter to keep her company'; she is traditionally said to have attempted to damage Van Dyck's right hand in her fury at hearing of his marriage. See no. 166.

158. BEATRICE DE CUSANCE, PRINCESS OF CANTECROIX AND DUCHESS OF LORRAINE (1614–63) (Plate 72)

Windsor Castle (28). 82¼ × 47⅞ in., 209 × 121,6 cm.

Full-length, walking up a step and holding back a curtain with her right hand, while a small spaniel barks at her feet.

---

1. This copy could be the one now in the Union Club. In it the design is slightly extended to the right and the richer treatment of the sky may indicate that the sky in the original is worn. A reputed 'original sketch' by Van Dyck was sold at Christie's, 8–9 March 1782 (second day, 49).

Probably brought from Spain by Sir Daniel Arthur, a Jacobite exile; seen on 3 February 1729 by the Earl of Egmont in the house of George Bagnall, who had married Sir Daniel's widow (H. M. C., *Egmont MSS., Diary of the first Earl of Egmont*, vol. III (1923), p. 344) and who sold the picture to Frederick, Prince of Wales, in or before September 1747, when John Anderson's account for work on his pictures included four guineas for cleaning and repairing [*A Lady Whole Length by Vandike*] *Bought of Mr Bagnell* (D. of Cornwall MSS., vol. XVII, f. 547); in 1748 Benjamin Goodison was paid £10 for *A whole Length Picture frame carv'd & guilt in Oyl Gold wth a sanded ground ornamented wth Shells. to ye Picture of Mad^m Cantecroix* in the State (?) Room at Leicester House (W. R. A., Geo. 54560); later at Buckingham House.

Literature: Vertue, *Notebooks*, vol. I, p. 11, vol. V, p. 127, and B. M., MS. 19027, f. 20; Smith, 225, *Supplement*, 41; Waagen (1854), vol. II, p. 428; Law, *Van Dyck*, pp. 53–4; Cust, *Van Dyck*, pp. 92, 254; Schaeffer, 327; Glück, 427; Collins Baker, *Windsor*, p. 88; R. A., *King's Pictures* (280).

Painted in Brussels, probably early in 1635 at the time of her marriage to the Prince of Cantecroix. Anderson's attentions to the portrait (see above) may have been responsible for its worn condition, primarily in the blacks of the costume, and for the insertion of an area of later canvas at the bottom. *Pentimenti* reveal that the Princess was at first painted wearing the wired lace collar popular at the court of the Archduchess Isabella at Brussels (*e.g.*, Glück, 425, 430, 431); that the line of the present collar and of the Princess's back was originally further to the right; and that Van Dyck may originally have painted her head with a less bushy *coiffure*. An enlarged version at Warwick Castle probably gives an impression of the former appearance of the original. A version was on the art-market in Belgium in 1929. A grisaille of the design is in the Louvre (1982). A small copy was on the art-market in Berlin in 1912. The design was engraved by Pieter de Jode (M. Mauquoy-Hendrickx, *L'Iconographie d'Antoine Van Dyck*, (Brussels, 1956), no. 137). An oil sketch in the Muzeum Narodowe, Krakow, seems to repeat the design for a different sitter. In England Van Dyck adapted the design for the Countess of Carlisle (Glück, 447) and its appeal in the eighteenth century is perhaps suggested by Allan Ramsay's study of the pattern (National Gallery of Scotland, R.N. 2202).

Daughter of Claude-François de Cusance, baron of Belvoir in Franche-Comté; the 'Gentillesse de Cusance' and a celebrated beauty, she married (1635) Eugène-Léopold d'Oiselay, Prince of Cantecroix, and after his death (1637) she went through a form of marriage with her lover, Charles IV, Duke of Lorraine, a marriage that was solemnised on her death-bed.

159. LADY MARY VILLIERS, DUCHESS OF RICHMOND AND LENNOX (1622–85) (*Plate* 84)

Windsor Castle (21). 73½ × 54 in., 186,7 × 137,2 cm.; there is an addition of *c.* 2 in. at the right.

Seated full-length as St Agnes in a rocky cave, holding a palm branch in her left hand and resting her right hand on a lamb.

A portrait of the Duchess was painted for Charles I, probably in 1637, and hung near the portraits of her brothers (no. 153) in the Gallery at St. James's: *A Peece of the Dutchesse of Lenox before shee was married By Sr Anthony Vandike* (Van der Doort, p. 227). It does not appear in the documents relating to the dispersal and recovery of the collection, but may have passed into the collection of Sir Peter Lely: among the portraits by Van Dyck in Lely's sale, 18 April, 1682, was: 'The Dutchess of *Richmond*, a whole Length' (see *Burl. Mag.*, vol. LXXXIII (1943), p. 187) which was said to measure 85 × 52 in. and was sold for £61.[1] If it then passed into the royal

1. In an inventory of the Hamilton collection in 1704 is (236): *The Dutchess of Richmond by S^r. Peter Lilly after Vandike* (Hamilton MSS.).

collection the canvas may have been adapted to be set over the chimney in the King's Privy Chamber at Windsor, where it is recorded in the collection of James II (B. M., Harl. MS. 1890, f. 72; Bathoe, *James II* (742)).

Literature: Vertue, *Notebooks*, vol. IV, p. 119 (wrongly describing her as the Duchess of Portland); Smith, 231, *Supplement*, 44 (confused); Waagen (1838), vol. I, p. 172, (1854), vol. II, pp. 426–7; Law, *Van Dyck*, pp. 41–3; Cust, *Van Dyck*, pp. 117, 278; Schaeffer, 365; Glück, 489; Collins Baker, *Windsor*, p. 92; R. A., *King's Pictures* (39).

St. Agnes was the patroness of those about to be married and the portrait was probably painted on the eve of Lady Mary's marriage on 3 August 1637 to the Duke of Richmond. There is an alteration in her left shoulder and forearm which Van Dyck had at first painted further out. Engraved by G. Bockman. Copies are fairly numerous, *e.g.*, at Bowhill, probably a pendant to a portrait of the Duke (Glück, 488), Castle Howard, Lacock Abbey and with the Barber-Surgeons' Company, and, on a small scale, at Elmore Court; they probably indicate the original proportions of the canvas (see above). An enamel half-length copy (with variations) by Jean Petitot (1643) was in the Pierpont Morgan collection; reductions and variants are at Althorp, Knole and Penshurst and the design was the source for later derivations, *e.g.*, a portrait at Belvoir of Frances, Countess of Rutland (*c.* 1648), with her son posed like the Duchess's elder brother in no. 153, a Lelyesque portrait (*c.* 1665) of Lady Cardigan at Boughton, and Huysmans's portrait at Yester of the 2nd Marchioness of Tweeddale.

Only daughter of the murdered Duke of Buckingham and much beloved of the royal family. Her first marriage (1635) to Lord Herbert (*d.* 1636) took place in the Royal Closet at Whitehall and at her marriage to James Stuart, Duke of Richmond and Lennox (*d.* 1655), in the Archbishop's Chapel at Lambeth she was given away by the King. She was Lady of the Bedchamber to Catherine of Braganza. Her third marriage was to Col. Thomas Howard. See no. 138.

160. PORTRAIT OF A MAN (*Plate* 82)

Buckingham Palace. Panel: 48½ × 36½ in., 123,2 × 92,7 cm.

Three-quarter-length in black with a deep ruff, standing by a chair.

Acquired by Frederick, Prince of Wales, probably as by Rubens: possibly a *portrait of a Man over the Chimney drawing room* seen at Leicester House in July 1750 by Vertue (B. M., MS. 19027, f. 20) who noted 'fine portraits' there by Rubens and Van Dyck (*Notebooks*, vol. I, p. 11); John Anderson's account (September 1747) for work on the Prince's pictures includes two guineas for *Cleaning a Gent^m Half Length . . . by Rubens* (D. of Cornwall MSS., vol. XVII, f. 547); thereafter perhaps at Kensington and at Buckingham House (Geo. III, *Buck. Ho.*, in the Passage Room) and Windsor (162).

Literature: Smith, *Supplement*, 40 and 57; Waagen (1854), vol. II, p. 437; H. Rosenbaum, *Der junge Van Dyck* (Munich, 1928), p. 27; Collins Baker, *Windsor*, p. 93; R. A., *King's Pictures* (276).

Painted (*c.* 1618–20) towards the end of Van Dyck's first Flemish period and still to some extent influenced by Rubens. There are considerable *pentimenti* in the ruff (which originally rose less stiffly from the neck but stood up higher behind the head), in the hanging curtain, and in the outline of the sitter's left shoulder and arm which was at first nearer the body.

161. THE VIRGIN AND CHILD

Buckingham Palace. 46 × 38⅝ in., 116,8 × 98,1 cm.

The Infant Christ lying on the Virgin's lap.

First recorded in the collection of James II at Whitehall: *Vandike. A Madona as big as the life* (B. M., Harl. MS. 1890, f. 60 v.; Bathoe,

James II (464)); thereafter at Kensington, Buckingham House and Windsor.

Literature: Smith, 245, *Supplement*, 112; *Buckingham Palace*, 1852 (51); Waagen (1854), vol. II, p. 3; Law, *Van Dyck*, pp. 101–2; Cust, *Van Dyck*, p. 239; Schaeffer, 438; Glück, 225; R. A., *King's Pictures* (292).

Probably painted late (*c.* 1630–2) in the second Flemish period, or conceivably after Van Dyck's arrival in London. A number of copies exist, *e.g.*, in the Wallace Collection (123), at Ugbrooke and Charlecote, and in the collection of Lord Harrington. Others were on the art markets in Brussels (1927), Detroit (1928) and London; yet others were formerly in the Hope, Oxenden and Hoschek (Prague) collections and at Stowe. A slightly later copy was sold at Sotheby's, 30 March 1960 (13). And see no. 189. Engraved by Hendrik Snyers as a *Rest on the Flight*; a landscape background with St. Joseph and the ass are inserted in the preparatory grisaille (*Fig.* 28) which is probably by Van Dyck (H. Vey, 'Anton van Dycks Ölskizzen', Musées Royaux des Beaux-Arts, Brussels, *Bulletin*, 2–3 (1956), p. 186; Antwerp and Rotterdam, *Anton van Dyck, Tekeningen en Olieverfschetsen*, 1960 (124A)). Van Dyck's debt to Titian in this type of composition is clearly demonstrated in the Chatsworth Sketch-Book.

162. THE MYSTIC MARRIAGE OF ST. CATHERINE (*Plate* 86)

Buckingham Palace. 49¾ × 47 in., 126,4 × 119,4 cm.

Signed: *A VAN DYCK*.

The Infant Christ, seated on the Virgin's lap, is about to place a ring on the hand of St. Catherine who holds her martyr's palm and broken wheel.

Acquired in 1802 from the de Bustancy family, Brussels, by the Chevalier de Burtin (*d.* 1818), who imported it into England, apparently with the intention of offering it to George IV; not apparently in the de Burtin sale at Christie's, 22 July 1820; bought for George IV by Sir Charles Long, and apparently received at Carlton House in September 1821 (Jutsham, *Receipts*, f. 150; *Carlton House*, 1816, *Addn.* (587)); hung in the Blue Velvet Room at Carlton House and later in the Picture Gallery at Buckingham Palace (155).

Literature: F.-X. de Burtin, *Traité Théorique et Pratique des Connaissances . . .*, vol. II (Brussels, 1808), pp. 187–9; Smith, 234, *Supplement*, 107; *Buckingham Palace*, 1841 (169); Waagen (1854), vol. II, p. 3; Law, *Van Dyck*, pp. 103–4; Cust, *Van Dyck*, pp. 46, 239; Schaeffer, 77; Glück, 231; R. A., *King's Pictures* (290), *Flemish Art*, 1953–4 (451).

Painted *c.* 1630. It was a favourite subject with Van Dyck: in December 1631 Sir Balthazar Gerbier sent to the Earl of Portland, as a New Year's gift to Charles I and Henrietta Maria, 'une fort belle Notre Dame et Ste. Catharine faict de la main de Van Dyck', which he had bought from Salomon Nobliers and which had been placed by the Archduchess Isabella in the private chapel used by Queen Marie de Medici at the Court in Brussels, and it seems that a version of it had been sent to Holland (Hookham Carpenter, pp. 57–64). The Infant Christ and the Saint (recast as the Magdalen) are almost identical in a picture in the Rijksmuseum, Amsterdam (864; Glück, 150). The Child reappears in the *Madonna and Child with Two Donors* in the Louvre (1962; Glück, 245). A version can be seen in Willem van Haecht's *Interior of a Picture Gallery* in the Marquess of Bute's collection; copies and lesser versions are recorded. The design was engraved by Adriaen Lommelin. Van Dyck's debt to Titian in this type of composition can be seen on page after page of the 'Chatsworth' Sketch-Book.

163. THE INFANTS CHRIST AND ST. JOHN THE BAPTIST (*Plate* 85)

Buckingham Palace. 29¾ × 23⅞ in., 75,6 × 60,6 cm.

The Baptist kneels to be embraced by Christ; beside them are the usual attributes: the globe, lamb and the Baptist's cross with the motto.

Recorded in Charles II's collection in store at Whitehall: *Sʳ Anthony Vandyke. Our Saviorʳ & Sᵗ John naked, when young* (Charles II, *Whitehall* (618)); inscribed with the number (331) under which it appears in James II's inventory. Later at Kensington and Windsor (570).

Literature: Smith, 247; Nottingham University Art Gallery, *Paintings and Drawings by Van Dyck*, 1960 (10).

A late work, perhaps painted in England. It is possible that this is the version engraved by Aernout de Jode in London in September 1666, when it belonged to Lely, with a dedication to the artist; the subject was not among the pictures by Van Dyck that were sold with Lely's collection after his death. In certain small details the engraving is closer to the version at Lamport; this was bought from Maurice Wase by Sir Justinian Isham in 1655, probably for £24, as an original by Van Dyck ('. . . it is a pretty thing, but hath been much spoiled, though indifferently repaired'; MS. at Lamport; *Country Life*, vol. CXII (1952), pp. 1024–5, vol. CXIII (1953), pp. 1802–3). Lesser copies (*e.g.*, Christie's, 10 October 1958 (56)) and variations exist. In a version sold at Christie's, 24 April 1959 (142), the design was surrounded with a wreath of flowers. The subject may have been suggested to Van Dyck by the composition of the two Infants embracing which belonged to Charles I with an attribution to Parmigianino.

164. CHRIST HEALING THE PARALYTIC (*Plate* 87)

Buckingham Palace. 47½ × 58⅝ in., 120,7 × 149 cm.

A group of five half-length figures: Christ, accompanied by St. John (?), addressing the man sick of the palsy (Matthew IX. 2–8).

In the collection of Martin Robyn, sold in Brussels, 22 May 1758 (1), as by Rubens; Verhulst, sold in Brussels, 16 August 1779 (77); François Pauwels, sold in Brussels, 22 August 1803 (98); de Marneffe; Smeth van Alphen, sold in Amsterdam, 1–2 August 1810 (30); brought to England by Lafontaine and sold in his collection, Christie's, June 1811 (51), although it is stated already to have been bought by George IV for 3000 guineas; placed in the Audience Room at Carlton House (1816 (50)) and later in the Picture Gallery at Buckingham Palace (146).

Literature: Smith, 235; Waagen (1854), vol. II, p. 3; Law, *Van Dyck*, pp. 105–6; Cust, *Van Dyck*, pp. 46, 237; Schaeffer, 46; Glück, 64.

Painted in Antwerp *c.* 1619, when the young painter was closely associated with Rubens, whose influence is deeply felt in the scale, form, types and handling of the design. The canvas lacks in part the brilliance that is usual with Van Dyck at this period, but there are *pentimenti* which probably give it pride of place among the other versions of the design: the outline of the wall and the Apostle's cloak on the right were originally nearer to the left and are now painted over the sky and the landscape. A chalk study for the paralytic is in the collection of Dr. and Mrs. F. Springell (Antwerp and Rotterdam, *Anton van Dyck, Tekeningen en Olieverfschetsen*, 1960 (17)). A version with variations is at Schleisheim; other versions are in the Musée du Chanoine Puissant, Mons and in the possession of Mme. Laurens, Sablé sur Sarthe; a canvas containing copies of some of the heads in the design was with Paltzer, Cologne. It has been suggested (see Glück, *loc. cit.*) that the composition may have been intended to form part of a series of pictures of the life of Christ; the composition is related to the central part of a drawing by Van Dyck in the Albertina (*Fig.* 33) of the same period as no. 164 but of a more elaborate design (exh. Antwerp and Rotterdam (18)). The design was engraved by P. de Jode.

165. ST. MARTIN DIVIDING HIS CLOAK
(*Plates* 61–3)

Windsor Castle (154). 101½ × 95½ in., 257,8 × 242,6 cm. There is an original addition on the right of 15 in.; at the top 6¼ in. is visible of a later addition of *c.* 13½ in.

The Saint on horseback, accompanied by two armed riders, is in the act of dividing his cloak between two struggling beggars and an importunate woman with two children.

Probably presented by Van Dyck to Rubens: at Rubens's death 'Un *S. Martin* [du Chevalier *van Dyck*]' was no. 234 among the pictures in his house (J. Denucé, *The Antwerp Art-Galleries* ... (Antwerp, 1932), p. 66), stated to be *uppon cloth* (Sainsbury, p. 242). Probably acquired in Spain by Sir Daniel Arthur; seen on 3 February 1729 by the Earl of Egmont in the house of George Bagnall, who had married Sir Daniel's widow: *two large pieces of Rubens, one, the Legend of St. Martin cutting off a piece of his cloke to relieve the beggar ... several figures in it as big as the life* (H. M. C., *Egmont MSS., Diary of the first Earl of Egmont*, vol. III (1923), p. 344). Bought from Bagnall by Frederick, Prince of Wales, before September 1747, when John Anderson was paid £31. 10s for *Cleaning & makeing Out & Repairing yͤ Sͭ Martinⁿ;* on 28 October 1748 Paul Petit was paid £67. 16s for *a large picture frame richley Carved neatley repaired gilt In Burnish'd Gold to the picture of Sͭ Martin put up at Lester House*[1] (D. of Cornwall MSS., vol. XVII, ff. 530, 547). Later in the Drawing Room at Buckingham House (Pyne, vol. II, *Buckingham House*, p. 14), removed to the King's Closet at St. James's in 1824 and sent to Windsor on 10 September 1835.

Literature: Vertue, *Notebooks*, vol. I, p. 11, vol. V, pp. 78, 126; Walpole, *Anecdotes*, vol. I, p. 312, *Visits*, p. 79; Smith, *Rubens*, 822; Waagen (1838), vol. I, p. 174, (1854), vol. II, p. 435; M. Rooses, *L'Œuvre de P. P. Rubens*, vol. II (Antwerp, 1888), pp. 327–8 (as by Van Dyck); Law, *Van Dyck*, pp. 93–6; Cust, *Van Dyck*, pp. 32–3, 67; Schaeffer, 43; Glück, 25; Collins Baker, *Windsor*, p. 94; R. A., *King's Pictures* (282), *Flemish Art*, 1953–4 (142); H. Vey, *Van-Dyck-Studien* (Inaugural-Dissertation zur Erlangung des Doktorgrades ... Köln, 1955), pp. 61–77.

Painted *c.* 1620, and when Van Dyck was still much under the influence of Rubens; it is possible that it was painted as a present to Rubens at the time when Van Dyck was contemplating leaving Antwerp. He had earlier painted, probably for Ferdinand van Boisschot, Lord of Zaventem, a smaller version of the subject (*Fig.* 31), which is in the Church of St. Martin at Zaventem (see *Van Dyck Tentoonstelling*, Antwerp, 1949 (12)). The preparatory drawings for the horse, for the naked beggar and (two) for his companion are associated (with other comparative material) with this earlier version (H. Vey, *op. cit.*, p. 61). In this later version the design is treated on a more monumental scale and is given a new grandeur. Probably during the evolution of the design Van Dyck moved the architectural background over to the left and enlarged the canvas (see above) in order to incorporate the woman and children behind the beggars. In this process he may have reworked the area of sky around the woman and the beggar seen in profile. There are *pentimenti* in the drawing of the Saint's right hand and in his horse's left forefoot which was at first slightly lower. Vertue had already

1. This is almost certainly the frame which is now, apparently considerably altered, on the portrait at Buckingham Palace of a member of the Habsburg family on horseback after Rubens.

noticed the probable link between the beggar in profile and a figure in Raphael's Cartoon of *The Healing of the Lame Man.* The figure of the Saint may contain a reminiscence of a detail from Domenico delle Grecche's woodcut after Titian's *Crossing of the Red Sea* (H. Tietze, *Titian* (1950), pl. 321) of which Van Dyck made a rapid sketch in the 'Chatsworth' Sketch-Book (G. Adriani, *Anton Van Dyck Italienisches Skizzenbuch* (Vienna, 1940), pp. 48–9, pl. 41v–42). An oil sketch, wrongly attributed to Rubens and in the possession of Mme. L. Huguenin, Geneva (*Olieverfschetsen van Rubens*, Boymans Museum, Rotterdam, 1953 (3a, pl. 4)), may, however, indicate a prototype by Rubens for Van Dyck's design. The attribution of the Windsor canvas to Rubens, although Waagen (*loc. cit.*) had recognised Van Dyck's hand in the execution, persisted into the nineteenth century. Copies with variations are in Vienna, Sanssouci, in the Schönborn Collection at Pommersfelden and in the Vintners' Hall. A small copy is in Toledo, U.S.A., and another was on the art market in Amsterdam in 1952. A sketch of a variant was in the Holford collection (Glück, 26). A small copy of a variant design was sold at Christie's, 21 October 1949 (134). St. Martin's companions were used by Simon de Vos in a *Martyrdom* (signed and dated 1648), sold at Christie's, 27 January 1956 (58). A drawing after no. 165 by Géricault is in the Musées Royaux des Beaux-Arts in Brussels (482).

166. CUPID AND PSYCHE (*Plate* 88)

Buckingham Palace. 78½ × 75½ in., 199,4 × 191,8 cm.; there are early additions at the top (between 3¾ and 4¼ in.) and bottom (*c.* 2¼ in.).

Cupid discovers Psyche in the 'dull lethargy' of sleep that overcame her on yielding to the temptation to open the 'box of beauty' which Venus had asked her to bring back from Proserpine.

Painted presumably for Charles I and entered, probaby by Van der Doort himself, in the draft of the King's catalogue as in the King's Long Gallery at Whitehall (*Van der Doort*, p. 43; *bing onlij als it opan a straning fram* . . .; measurements given as 74 × 77 in.); valued at £110 by the Trustees for Sale among the pictures from Wimbledon House (L. R. MS., f. 140) and sold to Robert Houghton on 8 October 1651 (S.P. 29/447, 24, 1); suggested in 1654 as a possible purchase to Cardinal Mazarin by his agent M. de Bordeaux, but rejected as too expensive (Comte de Cosnac, *Les Richesses du Palais Mazarin* (1884), pp. 216, 218, 221, 223, 224, 225, 227, 244–5); later in the possession of Peter Lely, declared to the House of Lords Committee, 18 May 1660 (H. of L. MSS.), and delivered to Thomas Chiffinch on 3 August 1661 (Col. Hawley, f. 5 v). Thereafter at Whitehall (in Charles II's Bedchamber), Kensington, Hampton Court (206) and Windsor (3055).

Literature: Smith, 246; Waagen (1854), vol. II, p. 360; Law, 1881, 1898 (663); Cust, *Van Dyck*, pp. 112–3, 251; Schaeffer, 126; Collins Baker, *Hampton Court*, p. 40; Glück, 362; A. P. Oppé, 'Sir Anthony Van Dyck in England', *Burl. Mag.*, vol. LXXIX (1941), pp. 186–190; R. A., *King's Pictures* (293), *Flemish Art*, 1953–4 (282); Whinney and Millar, p. 74.

The picture's being inserted, apparently unframed, into the King's catalogue indicates that it was painted late in Van Dyck's years at the English court, possibly as late as 1639–40. The canvas is painted in a spontaneous and sketch-like style; there are slight alterations and modifications in many areas (*e.g.*, in the open box) and the background and foreground are so thin as to suggest that the picture was not finished. It is possible that the canvas was in some way connected with the plans for the decoration of the Queen's Cabinet at Greenwich with canvases by Rubens and Jordaens illustrating the story of Cupid and Psyche. The scheme was probably initiated in October 1639 (Sainsbury, pp. 211–34; R.–A. d'Hulst, *De Tekeningen van Jakob Jordaens* (Brussels, 1956), p. 130). The episode treated by Van Dyck figures in Jordaens's plans for the cycle on a canvas of almost the same proportions (D. Schlugheit, 'L'Abbé de Scaglia, Jordaens et "l'Histoire de Psyché" de Greenwich-House', *Revue Belge d'Archeologie et d'Histoire de l'Art*, vol. VII (1937), pp. 139–66). It is conceivable that *Cupid and Psyche* was *Une piece pour la Maison a Grunwitz* for which Van Dyck was claiming payment (£100) in his *Memoire* (1638?) of pictures painted for the Crown (P. R. O., S.P. 16/406, 4; Hookham Carpenter, pp. 66–8). On the other hand it may have been thought suitable as a subject to the festivities (April–May 1641) in connection with the marriage (which Van Dyck recorded in a double portrait) of Princess Mary to Prince William II of Orange. Van Dyck's rendering of a moment in the story of Cupid and Psyche is faithful to Apuleius (see A. P. Oppé, *loc. cit.*), but the interest in the story at the Caroline court is further illustrated by Shakerley Marmion's *Cupid and Psyche* (1637), presented to the King's nephew Prince Charles Louis on his visit to England in 1637. Symon Stone's bill, receipted 29 August 1661, for work for the Earl of Bath includes 'a Great peece Coppied after Sᵣ Anthony Vandike, wherein is Cupid & Cica' (B. M. Add. MS. 27872, f. 3); a copy, belonging to H. C. Erhardt, was sold at Christie's, 19 June 1931 (127), and another, from Grimsthorpe Castle (probably reduced), 9 April 1954 (47). The design was engraved in mezzotint by Bernard Lens in the same reduced format and with a more elaborate background. Psyche's features resemble those of Van Dyck's mistress, Margaret Lemon (*e.g.*, no. 157).

Studio of Sir Anthony van Dyck

167. HENRIETTA MARIA

Windsor Castle (35). 82½ × 52½ in., 209,6 × 133,4 cm.; *c.* 2 in. at the top, and 1¾ in. at the bottom, are turned over.

Full-length, standing in white satin with an elaborate jewelled chain and resting her right hand beside her crown and a glass bowl of roses.

Acquired, possibly from George Bagnall, by Frederick, Prince of Wales, perhaps before September 1747, when John Anderson's account for work on his pictures includes four guineas for cleaning and repairing *the Queen Mother*. *Vandike* (D. of Cornwall MSS., vol. XVII, f. 547). Thereafter at Leicester House and Buckingham House.

Literature: Vertue, *Notebooks*, vol. I, p. 11; Waagen (1854), vol. II, p. 429; Law, *Van Dyck*, pp. 59–60; Cust, *Van Dyck*, pp. 108, 265; Schaeffer, 457; Glück, 383; Collins Baker, *Windsor*, p. 95.

Probably the best version extant of a very popular composition, and in quality close to Van Dyck himself. It is possible that the companion piece to no. 145 (*q.v.*) at Somerset House was of this type, which should thus perhaps be dated 1636. Versions are at Althorp and Euston Hall (both bearing the date 1636 and the crowned monogram HMR), in the Clarendon collection (with the monogram), at Broadlands and at Castle Howard (with the monogram and the date 1634). An oval copy of the head and shoulders at Althorp and a pendant (probably based on Glück, 390) bear the date 1638. A miniature copy of the head is at Chatsworth and another, signed and dated (1639) by Jean Petitot, is at Welbeck (R. W. Goulding, 'The Welbeck Abbey Miniatures', *Walpole Soc.*, vol. IV (1916), p. 174). Jan van Belcamp painted in 1637 (see above p. 90) a small copy of this type, with a perspective background by Hendrick van Steenwyck, which is now in Dresden (1188). A comparison with the

versions and copies, where the Queen's *coiffure* is livelier and more broken, seems to indicate that at a later stage the outline of the Queen's head in the Windsor version was altered. The type was engraved by R. Peake. The design of the figure is repeated verbatim in the portrait of Penelope, Countess of Pembroke, at Wilton (Glück, 478).

168. HENRIETTA MARIA

St. James's Palace. 54 × 43¾ in., 137,2 × 111,1 cm.

Three-quarter-length standing, resting her right hand by her crown on a table and holding a rose at her waist with her left hand.

Sold in the Cholmeley Dering sale at Christie's, 7 June 1858 (78, as by 'Old Stone'; Christie's stencil is on the back); purchased by the Lord Chamberlain in December 1864.

Possibly painted in Van Dyck's studio and based on a portrait by Van Dyck of *c.* 1632; the quality of the head is good and there appear to be *pentimenti* in the right hand and wrist. The curtain appears to have been heavily overpainted. The pattern is presumably related to no. 147.

169. CHARLES II WHEN PRINCE OF WALES

Windsor Castle (33). 60½ × 51¾ in., 153,7 × 131,4 cm.; slightly stretched in lining; there is an original addition of 8¼ in. on the right.

Full-length standing in armour, with a pistol in his right hand and resting his left hand on a plumed helmet.

Apparently painted for Henrietta Maria: Van Dyck's *Memoire* (1638?) includes *Le Prince Carles en armes. pour Somerset*, for which payment of £40 was due from the Queen (P. R. O., S.P. 16/406, 4; Hookham Carpenter, pp. 66–8); valued at £25 by the Trustees for Sale among the pictures in the Cross Gallery at Somerset House (Corsham MS., f. 55) and sold to Colonel Webb on 29 October 1649; declared by John Cade to the House of Lords Committee on 18 May 1660 to be in his possession (H. of L. MSS.). At Henrietta Maria's death in 1669 it was apparently hanging in the Vestibule at Colombes: *The King in Armes with a Pistol in his hand, when he was Prince of Wales* (P. R. O., S.P. 78/128, f. 212 v.); recorded at Windsor, in the King's Great Bedchamber, where it had probably been placed by Charles himself, in James II's inventory (B. M., Harl. MS. 1890, f. 72; Bathoe, *James II* (753)).

Literature: Smith, 227; Waagen (1854), vol. II, pp. 428–9; Law, *Van Dyck*, pp. 73–5; Cust, *Van Dyck*, pp. 112, 267; Schaeffer, 348; Collins Baker, *Windsor*, p. 83.

The design presumably dates from 1637 or early in 1638. The Prince does not wear the insignia of the Garter (he was installed on 21 May 1638) and the portrait is so close in type to the figure of the Prince in no. 152 of 1637 as to suggest that it was dependent on the same sittings. It was painted for the royal family portrait gallery in the Cross Gallery at Somerset House and its unusual shape may have been dictated by its original position there, possibly over a door. The canvas has an impeccable provenance but, with the possible exception of the face, does not seem to have been painted by Van Dyck himself. There are, however, *pentimenti* in the outlines of the shoulders and upper left arm and in the shape of the head, and the fall of curtain nearest the Prince originally came lower. It is generally assumed that the version at Welbeck (98), which shows slight variations in the head and the background, may have been the earlier of the two; it is traditionally stated to have been presented by the sitter to the Marquess of Newcastle who was appointed his Governor on 15 May 1638 and his Gentleman of the Robes on 17 July 1641 (Glück, 388; R. W. Goulding, *Catalogue of the Pictures belonging to . . . the Duke of Portland . . .* (1936), pp. 37–8). Copies are fairly common: the version in the Prado (1499) is a respectable studio copy and may have been sent by Henrietta Maria in 1638 to her sister, the Queen of Spain (Sainsbury, pp. 353–4); other copies are at Althorp, Belvoir, Cirencester, Euston, Breamore (with landscape background), Lanhydrock, with Agnew's (1958) and formerly in the Smythe collection at Ashton Court. Miniature copies of the head by Jean Petitot, signed and dated 1638, are at Welbeck (R. W. Goulding, 'The Welbeck Abbey Miniatures', *Walpole Soc.*, vol. IV (1916), p. 174) and in the Dutch royal collection. The type was engraved by Pieter de Jode and Matthäus Merian with the addition of the Garter ribbon.

170. MARY, PRINCESS OF ORANGE

Windsor Castle (3082). $61\frac{1}{4} \times 43\frac{1}{4}$ in., $155,6 \times 109,9$ cm.

Full-length standing, with her left hand at her side.

Believed to have been in the collection of William, 1st Earl of Craven (1606–97), and to have been given to him by Elizabeth, Queen of Bohemia, or bequeathed to him by Prince Rupert, who had inherited many of his mother's possessions; passed by descent to Cornelia, Countess of Craven, by whom it was bequeathed to Her Majesty The Queen in 1961.

Literature: Cust, *Van Dyck*, p. 267.

A version, probably painted in Van Dyck's studio, of a type which Van Dyck presumably evolved soon after Princess Mary's marriage to William II of Orange in London. The Princess wears her wedding ring and the large diamond brooch given to her by her husband on 13 May 1641, the day after their wedding (R. van Luttervelt, 'Het portret van Willem II en Maria Stuart in het Rijksmuseum', *Oud-Holland*, vol. LXVIII (1953), pp. 159–69). Versions of the design were presumably being made in Van Dyck's studio in the summer of 1641 and no. 170 may have been painted for the Princess's aunt, the Queen of Bohemia. A better version is at Courteenhall and another, sold at Christie's, 4 May 1951 (58), belongs to the Ministry of Works.

171. SIR KENELM DIGBY (1603–65)

Windsor Castle (34). $60\frac{1}{2} \times 50\frac{1}{4}$ in., $153,7 \times 127,6$ cm.; there are early additions of *c*. $3\frac{1}{2}$ in. at the top and *c*. $3\frac{3}{4}$ in. on the right.

Three-quarter-length, seated beside a table on which stands an armillary sphere; in the middle of the sphere is an indecipherable inscription, perhaps intended for *Ponderibus librata suis*.[1]

Probably in Charles II's collection, but first recorded in James II's collection in the King's Withdrawing Room at Windsor (B. M., Harl. MS. 1890, f. 72; Bathoe, *James II* (745) as by *Vandyck*), where it was placed over a door, which may account for the enlargements; sent to Kensington in 1736 to hang in the Great Drawing Room (*Kensington*, Geo. II, f. 2); later at Buckingham House.

Literature: Vertue, *Notebooks*, vol. II, p. 29, vol. IV, p. 160; Walpole, *Anecdotes*, vol. I, p. 324; Smith, 220, *Supplement*, 38; Waagen (1854), vol. II, p. 428; Law, *Van Dyck*, pp. 11–18; Cust, *Van Dyck*, pp. 89, 274; Schaeffer, 309; Collins Baker, *Windsor*, p. 89.

Infra-red photographs reveal that no. 171 is a fragment cut from a version of the group, painted by Van Dyck in 1632, of Sir Kenelm, his wife (see no. 179) and their two eldest sons (Bellori, *Le Vite de' Pittori*... (Rome, 1672), p. 260); the outline of Lady Digby's right shoulder can be seen with the naked eye. There are copies of the group at Sherborne Castle and Welbeck (374: Glück, 398, and R. W. Goulding, *Catalogue of*

the Pictures belonging to ... the Duke of Portland ... (1936), pp. 148–9); miniature copies of the group by Peter Oliver are in the Nationalmuseum at Stockholm (969, *Fig.* 36) and (dated 1632 and in the form of a diptych) at Sherborne Castle (B.F.A.C., *Exhibition of Portrait Miniatures* (1889), pl. VII). Vertue refers (*Notebooks*, vol. III, p. 131) to a copy by Ranelagh Barret. It is hard to assess no. 171, which has probably been fairly severely rubbed, but it is of better quality than the other extant versions of the group (it is at least a good studio copy) and the group from which it was cut may have been the original and thus possibly *a rare originall picture of Sir Kenelme Digby and his lady Venetia, in one piece, by the hand of Sir Anthony van Dyke*, which Aubrey noted at Gayhurst (*Brief Lives*, ed. A. Clark (1898), vol. I, p. 232). The cutting and the slight additions were made at a very early date, probably to fit the space in which the picture was first put up at Windsor. The armillary sphere is of considerable significance and in the portrait of Sir Kenelm 'in habito di filosofo', in mourning for his wife (*e.g.*, Glück, 449), the sphere is shattered, and according to Bellori (*loc. cit.*) was to be accompanied by the motto *Si fractus illabatur orbis intrepidum* [for *impavidum*] *ferient ruinae*. Engraved by Houbraken.

'A person very eminent and notorious throughout the whole course of his life', who indulged in science, letters, diplomacy and a naval command. As Henrietta Maria's agent in Rome (1645–7) he gave information to Bellori about Van Dyck who had been bound to him by 'una vicendevole collegatione di genio, e di benevolenza' and had painted religious pictures as well as family portraits for him.

After Sir Anthony van Dyck

172. JAMES I

St. James's Palace. $94\frac{3}{4} \times 61\frac{3}{4}$ in., $240,7 \times 156,8$ cm.; there is an addition of *c*. 7 in. at the top. The head, painted on a canvas of *c*. 30×25 in., has been inserted into the larger canvas.

Inscribed: JACOBVS D G MAG / [BR] FRA [ET HI] REX[1]

It is impossible to disentangle the references in the early inventories to nos. 141 and 172. No. 172 was certainly at Windsor in the eighteenth century: an inventory of the pictures at Windsor *c*. 1790 mentions in the Queen's Presence Chamber a full-length of James I in which 'the head ... was painted by Van Somer, and made into a whole length by Vandyck'. No. 172 may be the full-length recorded in store (4) at Windsor in the time of Queen Anne (Queen Anne, *Windsor*); and was certainly brought from Windsor in 1821 to replace no. 141 at Buckingham House. No. 172 may thus be the version recorded by Pyne at Windsor (vol. 1, p. 91 and plate).

Apparently a good early version of no. 141. The make-up of the canvas is puzzling. The quality of the piece that contains the head seems less good than the remainder of the design, but both seem closely dependent in type on no. 141; it is curious that a copy of no. 141 should have been composed in this way.

173. CHARLES I WITH M. DE ST. ANTOINE

Hampton Court (87). $138\frac{1}{2} \times 101\frac{1}{2}$ in., 353×258 cm.; stretched in lining.

It is impossible accurately to disentangle the references in the earlier inventories to the equestrian portraits of Charles I, but no. 173 seems first to appear at St. James's House in the reign of Queen Anne (Queen Anne, *St. James's* (54), with note by Thomas Coke: *Qre if not a Copy after*; B. M., Stowe MS. 567, f. 75).

---

1. This is inscribed above the sphere in Peter Oliver's copies in miniature of Van Dyck's original (see above).

1. This is now very obscure and has been made up from the inscription in no. 141.

Literature: Waagen (1838), vol. II, p. 118; Law, 1881, 1898 (85); Collins Baker, *Hampton Court*, p. 40.

A good early copy of no. 143.

174. CHARLES I WITH M. DE ST. ANTOINE

Holyroodhouse. 123×85¾ in., 312,5×218 cm.

Traditionally stated to have been given by Charles II to James Graham, 2nd Marquess of Montrose (1631?–1669); sold at Christie's, 21 June 1946 (136); presented to His Majesty King George VI by the 6th Duke of Montrose in July 1946.

A later seventeenth-century, simplified, copy of no. 143.

175. CHARLES I

St. James's Palace. 94×58¾ in., 238,8×149,2 cm.

A copy, painted in December 1864 by J. B. Williamson after no. 145, for the set of royal portraits at St. James's.

176. THE FIVE CHILDREN OF CHARLES I

Holyroodhouse. 19×22 in., 48,2×55,9 cm.

Among the portraits, formerly in the collection of Lady Capel, whose seal is on the front of the canvas, acquired at Kew; later at St. James's and Hampton Court (639).

A reduced, probably late seventeenth-century, copy of no. 152; the inscriptions identifying the sitters are repeated from the original.

177. KATHERINE HOWARD, LADY D'AUBIGNY (d. 1650)

Windsor Castle (2591). 41⅞×33¾ in., 106,4×85,7 cm.

Half-length, standing in a white dress with her hands at her waist.

Perhaps acquired by Frederick, Prince of Wales, but first recorded in the Warm Room at Buckingham House (Geo. III, *Buck. Ho.*) as a portrait of Henrietta Maria; later at St. James's Palace.

An early copy of Van Dyck's portrait, of which the original is probably the double portrait in the Hermitage (Glück, 499) in which Lady d'Aubigny appears with Frances Stuart, Countess of Portland (?). It is possible that the present canvas was cut from a copy of the double portrait and the eyes re-painted to face the spectator. Another copy of this single figure is at Kedleston and another, formerly in the Clarendon collection and with a landscape background as in the original, was sold at Christie's, 10 December 1954 (137). The type was engraved by Arnold de Jode and Adrien Lommelin (M. Mauquoy-Hendrickx, *L'Iconographie d'Antoine Van Dyck* (Brussels, 1956), nos. 97, 110). See also no. 220.

Daughter of the 2nd Earl of Suffolk, she married secretly in 1638 George Stuart, Seigneur d'Aubigny, who was killed at Edgehill in 1642; in or just before 1649 she married Sir James Levingston, later Earl of Newburgh.

178. COUNT HENDRICK VAN DEN BERGH (c. 1575–1641)

Windsor Castle (19). 42½×35 in., 108×83,8 cm.

Half-length, within a painted oval, in armour and holding a baton in his left hand.

Acquired by George IV, probably before 29 November 1810, when *A half Length Portrait a General Officer – supposed Vandyke* was delivered to Simpson to be cleaned (Jutsham, *R/D*, f. 78); later at Carlton House (1816 (298)).

Literature: Waagen (1854), vol. II, p. 426; Law, *Van Dyck*, pp. 29–30; Cust, *Van Dyck*, pp. 74, 253; Schaeffer, 469; Collins Baker, *Windsor*, p. 98.

A poor copy, simplified and with variations, of the portrait in the Prado (1486; Glück, 318). The original was painted, presumably in Brussels or Antwerp, c. 1630, belonged to Charles I (*Van der Doort*, p. 2), was valued at £26 by the Trustees for Sale (L.R. MS., f. 166) and sold to John Baptist Gaspars on 2 April 1650 (S.P. 29/447, 24, 1).

Soldier in the Spanish service in the Low Countries; served with Spinola at the Siege of Breda, in 1629 succeeded him in command of the Spanish forces in the Netherlands, but later defected to the Prince of Orange.

179. VENETIA STANLEY, LADY DIGBY (1600–33)

Windsor Castle (24). 84¾×62⅞ in., 215,3×158,4 cm.; there is an original addition on the right of 10 in.

Full-length, seated in a landscape as Prudence (see below).

Recorded in the collection of James II (B. M., Harl. MS. 1890, f. 72 v.; Bathoe, *James II* (771)), but noted by John Aubrey in the previous reign (c. 1679/80): 'Her picture drawn by Sir Anthony Vandyke hangs in the queene's draweing-room, at Windsor-castle, over the chimney' (*Brief Lives*, ed. A. Clark (1898), vol. I, p. 232; Pyne, vol. I, pp. 106, 111–2).

Literature: Bellori, *Le Vite de' Pittori...* (Rome, 1672), p. 261; Vertue, *Notebooks*, vol. II, pp. 29, 98, vol. IV, p. 119; Walpole, *Anecdotes*, vol. I, pp. 323–4; Hazlitt, 'The Pictures at Windsor Castle' (1823), *Works*, ed. A. R. Waller and A. Glover, vol. IX (1903), p. 38; Smith, 221, *Supplement*, 39; Waagen (1854), vol. II, p. 427; Law, *Van Dyck*, pp. 19–24; Cust, *Van Dyck*, pp. 89, 274; Schaeffer, 311; Gluck, 399; Collins Baker, *Windsor*, p. 90; R. A., *King's Pictures* (33).

Sir Kenelm Digby (no. 171) was passionately devoted to his wife and shattered by her premature death on 1 May 1633. He caused her to be painted by Van Dyck on her death-bed 'the second day after she was dead' (V. Gabrieli, *Sir Kenelm Digby* (Rome, 1957), pp. 246, 248) and it may have been as a further posthumous tribute to her and as a vindication of her reputation that he conceived the idea, which he described in detail to Bellori (*op. cit.*), of a portrait of his wife: 'on a large canvas . . . as Prudence, sitting in a white dress with a coloured wrap and a jewelled girdle. Under her hand are two white doves, and her other arm is encircled by a serpent. Under her feet is a plinth to which are bound, in the guise of slaves, Deceit with two faces; Anger with furious countenance; meagre Envy with her snaky locks; Profane Love, with eyes bound, wings clipped, arrows scattered and torch extinguished; with other naked figures the size of life. Above is a glory of singing Angels, three of them holding the palm and the wreath above the head of Prudence as a symbol of her victory and triumph over the vices; and the epigram, taken from Juvenal, NULLUM NUMEN ABEST SI SIT PRUDENTIA'. Sir Kenelm Digby's memory may not have been wholly accurate and there are discrepancies between Bellori's description and the present version of the design. Bellori adds that Van Dyck was so pleased with the composition that he also painted a small version, and that both were taken to France in the Civil War; Cardinal Mazarin's inventory (1661) contained (1235) a small version *faict par Vandeck* and stated to measure 36×29 in. (Comte de Cosnac, *Les Richesses du Palais Mazarin* (Paris, 1884), pp. 337–8). Despite Hazlitt's praise[1] (*loc. cit.*) no. 179 does

---

[1] 'You are introduced into the presence of a beautiful woman of quality of a former age, and it would be next to impossible to perform an unbecoming action with that portrait hanging in the room. It has an air of nobility about it; a spirit of humanity within it . . .'

not seem to be by Van Dyck himself, but to be a contemporary copy, probably executed in Van Dyck's studio. A better version in the Palazzo Reale, Milan, has more at top and bottom and may show the original design which may in the case of no. 179 have been mutilated in the time of Charles II when it was set into its place at Windsor (see above); another version is at Bosworth Hall. A very good small version (*Fig.* 35)[1] inscribed *Omne Numen adest*, may be the reduced version that was taken to France (see above); it was seen by Vertue (*Notebooks*, vol. III, p. 141, vol. IV, p. 179, vol. V, p. 43) and Walpole (*loc. cit.*) in the collection of Thomas Walker and later of Mr. Skinner; it was later in the Hervey collection at Rolls Park, Essex. A small copy, with variations, is in the van Berg collection, New York (*The van Berg Collection of Paintings* (N. Y., 1947), pp. 24–5; *Van Dyck Tentoonstelling*, Antwerp, 1949 (67)). Copies by Jervas of the head and of the figure on a reduced scale are recorded in his sale, 11–20 March 1739 (90, 273); and in a half-length copy at Bisterne Lady Digby's two sons are incorporated from Van Dyck's family group (see no. 171).

Daughter of Sir Edward Stanley; a celebrated, but in her youth most imprudent, beauty, of 'a most lovely and sweet-turn'd face' and 'a most beautifull desireable creature'. She married Sir Kenelm Digby (probably in 1626) secretly and against his mother's wishes, but was a devoted and loyal wife.

180. FRANCES CRANFIELD, COUNTESS OF DORSET (*d.* 1687)

Windsor Castle (38). 74½×54⅞ in., 189,2×139,4 cm.; there is a later addition at the right of 2¾ in.

Full-length, walking in a landscape.

First recorded in James II's inventory (*... at length a Copy after Vandike*) over the chimney in the King's Presence Chamber at Windsor (B. M., Harl. MS. 1890, f. 72; Bathoe, *James II* (740)).

Literature: Cust, *Van Dyck*, pp. 125, 274; Schaeffer, 409; Collins Baker, *Windsor*, p. 96.

An early copy of the original, painted *c.* 1637, which is at Knole (Glück, 469), where there is also another copy. There are also copies at Welbeck (403: R. W. Goulding, *Catalogue of the Pictures belonging to ... the Duke of Portland* ... (1936), pp. 160–1), Compton Place, Lullingstone Castle, and elsewhere, and miniature copies attributed to Peter Oliver in the Hamilton and Buccleuch collections. The pattern is one that was exploited for other sitters by Van Dyck's followers and particularly interested Lely; the background is almost identical in Van Dyck's portrait of Lady Dorset's niece Anne, Countess of Clanbrassil, in the Frick collection, New York. Between the reigns of James II and Queen Anne there are references to another copy after Van Dyck of the Countess of Dorset, apparently a half-length, in the royal collection (B.M., Harl. MS. 1890, f. 55 v.; Bathoe, *James II* (304); Queen Anne, *Windsor*, store (59)).

Sister and heiress of Lionel Cranfield, 3rd Earl of Middlesex; she married in 1637 Richard Sackville, later 5th Earl of Dorset.

181. THE CARDINAL-INFANT FERDINAND OF AUSTRIA (1609–41)

Buckingham Palace. 41×32¼ in., 104,1×81,9 cm.

Half-length in a richly laced military dress, holding a baton in his right hand.

1. It was put up at Christie's, 29 June 1962 (69).

Purchased by Queen Victoria at the sale of King Louis Philippe's Spanish pictures at Christie's, 6–7 May 1853 (420), and placed in the Spanish Room at Buckingham Palace (666).

Formerly attributed to Gaspar de Craeyer, no. 181 is an early derivation, of poor quality and with slight variations, from Van Dyck's portrait of the Infant, painted in Brussels in 1635, of which the original is in the Prado (1480; Glück, 423), but of which a number of copies and variants exist. The type was engraved for the *Iconography* by Pieter de Jode (M. Mauquoy-Hendrickx, *L'Iconographie d'Antoine Van Dyck* (Brussels, 1956), no. 138).

Younger brother of Philip IV, King of Spain, and Governor of the Spanish Netherlands; in Van Dyck's portrait he is wearing the costume in which he made his triumphal entry into Brussels on 17 April 1635 after his victory over the Protestant forces at the battle of Nördlingen in 1634.

182. JAN VAN MALDEREN (MALDERUS) (1562–1633)

Buckingham Palace. Panel: 21⅞×18½ in., 55,6×47 cm.

Head and shoulders wearing a biretta.

Purchased by George III with the collection of Consul Smith in 1762 (Flemish and Dutch list, 22, as *Portrait of Tassis Bp of Antwerp Engraven*) and thereafter at Windsor and in the Picture Gallery at Buckingham Palace (175, as by Rubens).

Literature: Smith, 226; Waagen (1854), vol. II, pp. 2–3; Schaeffer, p. 505.

An early copy from the three-quarter-length, painted by Van Dyck in Antwerp *c.* 1626–7, of which the most familiar (but probably not the best) version is in the Musée Royal des Beaux-Arts, Antwerp (402; Glück, 298); a copy by Erasmus Quellin is recorded in his possession in 1678 (J. Denucé, *The Antwerp Art-Galleries* ... (Antwerp, 1932), p. 283) and the type was engraved by Hollar (1645) and Adriaen Lommelin (M. Mauquoy-Hendrickx, *L'Iconographie d'Antoine Van Dyck* (Brussels, 1956), nos. 133, 178) as after Van Dyck.

Bishop of Antwerp from 1611 until his death.

183. MARGARET OF LORRAINE, DUCHESS OF ORLÉANS (1615–72)

Hampton Court (423). Panel: 15⅝×11¾ in., 39,7×29,8 cm.

Full-length standing, holding flowers in her right hand at her waist.

Purchased by George III with the collection of Consul Smith in 1762 (Flemish and Dutch list, 15); later at Kensington.

Literature: Law, 1881, 1898 (730), confusing it with no. 158; Collins Baker, *Hampton Court*, p. 164.

A contemporary sketch-like copy on a small scale of the portrait in the Uffizi (777; Glück, 430), which was painted in Brussels in 1634; other small copies exist and the type was the source of Schelte a Bolswert's engraving (M. Mauquoy-Hendrickx, *L'Iconographie d'Antoine Van Dyck* (Brussels, 1956), no. 23).

Daughter of Francis II, Duke of Lorraine, she married Gaston, Duke of Orléans, in 1632.

184. PRINCE THOMAS OF SAVOY-CARIGNAN (1596–1656)

Windsor Castle (26). 46¼×38¼ in., 117,5×97,2 cm.; probably slightly reduced; the painted surface is turned over all round.

Three-quarter-length in armour, wearing the Order of the Annonciade, holding a baton in his right hand and resting his left on his helmet.

Acquired by Frederick, Prince of Wales, and seen by Walpole in the Drawing Room at Kew in September 1761 (*Visits*, p. 39; '... very fine; especially in the left hand'); perhaps the *Gent^m Half Length* by Van Dyck which was cleaned for the Prince by John Anderson in or before September 1747 (D. of Cornwall MSS., vol. XVII, f. 547; but see also no. 188); later described (Geo. III, *Kew*) as a portrait of the King of Bohemia.

Literature: Smith, 213; Waagen (1854), vol. II, p. 427; Law, *Van Dyck*, pp. 31–2; Cust, *Van Dyck*, pp. 91, 259; Collins Baker, *Windsor*, p. 97.

A contemporary copy of good quality, particularly in the head, of the portrait in Berlin, which was painted by Van Dyck in Flanders in 1634 and belonged to Charles I (Glück, 422; see *ibid.*, 421, for Van Dyck's receipt, dated 3 January 1635, for payments for portraits of the Prince). In October 1649 the Trustees for Sale valued at £15 at Hampton Court *Prince Thomas. by vandyke* (L. R. MS., f. 121 v.) which was sold to Turbridge on 14 May 1650; the canvas in Berlin has the form of *cartellino* that was painted on portraits in Charles I's collection. The design was engraved by Paul Pontius (M. Mauquoy-Hendrickx, *L'Iconographie d'Antoine Van Dyck* (Brussels, 1956), no. 163.

Son of Charles Emmanuel I, Duke of Savoy; General in command of the Spanish forces in the Low Countries.

185. CHARLES, MARQUIS DE LA VIEUVILLE (c. 1582–1653)

Windsor Castle (11). 82¼ × 45⅛ in., 209 × 114,6 cm.

Full-length standing, holding his gloves in his left hand and wearing the ribbon of the Order of the St. Esprit and the star of the Order on his cloak.

Received at Carlton House from Colnaghi on 23 May 1814: ... *Marchal Biron – from the Gallery of M. Zolozam – by Crayers pupil of Rubins. – whole Length* (Jutsham, *R/D*, f. 309); placed in store at Carlton House (the 1816 label (246) is still on the back); later at Hampton Court.

Probably a contemporary copy of a portrait painted by Van Dyck (1634–5?) during the Marquis's exile in Brussels. A better, but not original, version was formerly at Stowe and was sold at Christie's, 18 June 1954 (33).

Grand Fauconnier and (1623) Surintendant des Finances; intrigued against Richelieu and was disgraced in 1632; he was, however, reinstated as Surintendant by Cardinal Mazarin.

186. ENGLEBERT TAIE, BARON VAN WEMMEL (d. 1638)

Hampton Court (1309). 25½ × 20¼ in., 64,8 × 51,4 cm.

Head and shoulders in black, wearing a ruff and a gold chain.

Possibly purchased by George III with the collection of Consul Smith in 1762: no. 14 in the Flemish and Dutch list under Van Dyck's name is *a Portrait ½ length with a ruff* (the measurements are given as 28 × 23 in., but the canvas may since have been cut down) and the frame is of the type usually associated with Smith; recorded in the reign of George III at Kensington (*e.g.*, *Kensington*, 1818 (252) as *in the manner of Vandyke*); later at St. James's.

Literature: Law, 1908 (642); Collins Baker, *Hampton Court*, p. 164.

A fairly early copy of the portrait in Dresden (1037; Glück, 295), painted *c.* 1630 during Van Dyck's second Flemish period and of the type engraved by Cornelis Galle (M. Mauquoy-Hendrickx, *L'Iconographie d'Antoine Van Dyck* (Brussels, 1956), no. 128).

Burgomaster of Brussels 1620, 1626–7, and member of the States of Brabant.

187. PORTRAIT OF A MAN

Hampton Court (later no. 906). 27⅞ × 23¼ in., 70,8 × 59,1 cm.; there appear to be additions of *c.* 3¼ in. at the top and 2 in. at the bottom.

Head and shoulders, nearly in profile, in a painted oval.

Probably acquired by George III, but conceivably by Frederick Prince of Wales: John Anderson's account (September 1747) included *Lineing Clean: & Repairing ... a Mans Head Vandike* (D. of Cornwall MSS., vol. XVII, f. 547); thereafter at Windsor (818).

Probably a contemporary copy of a portrait painted *c.* 1630 during Van Dyck's second Flemish period, when he painted a number of sitters in this particular format.

188. PORTRAIT OF A MAN

Windsor Castle (40). 48 × 36½ in., 122 × 92,7 cm.

Three-quarter-length, clasping the hilt of his sword in his left hand, with his gloved right hand at his side.

Probably acquired by Frederick, Prince of Wales, and perhaps the *Gent^m Half Length* by Van Dyck which was cleaned in or before September 1747 (D. of Cornwall MSS., vol. XVII, f. 547; but see no. 184); hanging at Buckingham House in the Passage Room (Geo. III, *Buck. Ho.*) and later at St. James's.

Literature: Waagen (1854), vol. II, p. 429; Law, *Van Dyck*, p. 45; Cust, *Van Dyck*, pp. 80, 260; Schaeffer, 271; Glück, 273; Collins Baker, *Windsor*, p. 99.

Apparently a copy, of poor quality, of a portrait painted by Van Dyck in Antwerp *c.* 1630. The sitter's identity has not been satisfactorily established. Waagen (*loc. cit.*) corrected the earlier identification with Jan Snellinx (1549–1638) and it was later suggested (*e.g.*, by Glück, *loc. cit.*) that it was a portrait of Peter Snayers (1592–1667), the Flemish painter of battle pieces who painted an elaborate record of the campaigns of the Habsburg Archdukes; the sitter bears a resemblance to Van Dyck's engraved (by Andries Stock) portrait of Snayers (M. Mauquoy-Hendrickx, *L'Iconographie d'Antoine Van Dyck* (Brussels, 1956), no. 98). See Glück (*loc. cit.*) for the use by Van Dyck of the same design for another patron.

189. THE VIRGIN AND CHILD

Hampton Court (766). 47½ × 37½ in., 120,7 × 95,3 cm.

Apparently recorded at St. James's, probably in the reign of George I: *La Vierge offrant le Teton a L'Enfant Jesus Copié apres Vandyke* (B. M., Stowe MS. 567, f. 73 v.); thereafter at Kensington, Buckingham House, Hampton Court (766) and St. James's.

Literature: Law, 1881, 1898 (431).

A bad later copy of no. 161, with variations in the background: there is a curtain on the left and, apparently, a view through a window on the right.

After Sir Anthony van Dyck (? by Nathaniel Dance)

190. SAMSON AND DELILAH

Hampton Court (952). 47 × 79 in., 119,3 × 200,7 cm.

Recorded in the collection of George III in the Octagon near the Library at Buckingham House (Geo. III, *Buck. Ho.*); later at Windsor.

Literature: Law, 1881, 1898 (387); Collins Baker, *Hampton Court*, p. 164.

A copy, stated in Francis Legge's catalogue (1813) of pictures at Windsor to be *Copied from Vandyck by Dance*, of the design, of which the original, painted in Antwerp *c.* 1628–30, is in the Kunsthistorisches Museum, Vienna (1043; Glück, 262). Possibly acquired by George III from Nathaniel Dance.

After Sir Anthony van Dyck
by William Hanneman

191. GEORGE VILLIERS, SECOND DUKE OF BUCKINGHAM, AND LORD FRANCIS VILLIERS

60 × 50⅝ in., 152,4 × 128,6 cm.

Inscribed and signed and dated: GEORGE DUKE *of* BUCK-INGHAM | *and* FRANCIS *his Brother, painted by Van Dyk.* 1635. | *Copy'd by William Hunneman,* 1783.

Possibly painted for George III; recorded at Kensington in 1818 (269): later at Hampton Court (245). Lent to the Ministry of Works in 1929.

Literature: Waagen (1864), vol. II, p. 360; Law, 1881, 1898 (453).

A competent copy of no. 153.

After Sir Anthony van Dyck
(? by William Hanneman)

192. THE VIRGIN AND CHILD

Hampton Court (765). 58 × 42 in., 147,3 × 106,7 cm.

The Virgin stands, three-quarter-length, looking upwards and supporting the Infant Christ on a stone ledge.

Probably acquired in the reign of George III, but not certainly recorded in the royal collection before 1872 (*V.R. inv.*); later at St. James's.

Literature: Law, 1881, 1898 (451).

Apparently an eighteenth-century copy of a design produced by Van Dyck in Antwerp *c.* 1630, of which the best version (and possibly the source of this copy) is at Dulwich (90; Glück, 234–5). On the back of the original canvas is inscribed *Mr Honeyman* | [*?at the*] *acedemy* and it is possible that the copy is by William Hanneman (see no. 191); he may have been identical with a Christopher Wilhelm Hanniman who was admitted in 1773, at the age of eighteen, into the Royal Academy schools, where he gained a silver medal in 1776.[1] Another inscription on the back, which reads *L drawing Room*, may refer to the house of a previous owner.

School of Sir Anthony van Dyck

193. CHARLES CAVENDISH, VISCOUNT MANSFIELD (*d.* 1659), and HENRY CAVENDISH, SECOND DUKE OF NEWCASTLE (1631–91)

Hampton Court (909). 52½ × 52¾ in., 133,4 × 134 cm.

Double three-quarter-length. Lord Mansfield rests his left hand on his sword and his brother, standing in profile with one leg raised on a step, looks over his left shoulder.

Possibly acquired by Frederick, Prince of Wales: John Anderson's account of September 1747 includes sixteen guineas for *two Heads Dobson* sold to the Prince (D. of Cornwall MSS., vol. XVII, f. 548 v.); recorded at Kensington in 1818 (270) as by Hanneman.

1. Mr. Sidney Hutchison most kindly looked for, and sent me, this reference.

Literature: Vertue, in B. M. MS. 19027, f. 21; Law, 1881, 1898 (351); Collins Baker, *Hampton Court*, p. 159.

Painted *c.* 1645–50 and formerly attributed to Dobson (*V.R. inv.*) and to Weesop (Collins Baker, *loc. cit.*); a better version is at Welbeck (R. W. Goulding, *Catalogue of the Pictures belonging to . . . the Duke of Portland . . .* (1936), pp. 161–2). The design is based very closely on Van Dyck's portrait of two young men in the National Gallery (3605).

Two of the sons of William Cavendish, 1st Duke of Newcastle; served under their father in the Civil War, left England with him after his defeat at Marston Moor in 1644, but soon returned to England. Henry Cavendish succeeded his father in 1676 and was Gentleman of the Robes to Charles II, 1660–2.

194. JOHN TUFTON, SECOND EARL OF THANET (1608–64), AND MARGARET SACK-VILLE, HIS WIFE (1614–76) (*Plate* 83)

Buckingham Palace. 49⅞ × 58 in., 126,7 × 132,1 cm. The canvas may have been very slightly reduced all round.

Double three-quarter-length portrait, seated together in a rocky landscape.

Recorded by Mrs. Jameson (623) at Hampton Court in 1842 as a *Self-portrait* of William Dobson with his wife (later inv. no. 870); later placed over one of the doors in the Blue Drawing Room at Buckingham Palace.

Literature: Waagen (1854), vol. II, p. 410; Law, 1881, 1898 (376); Collins Baker, *Lely*, vol. I, p. 95; E. Cammaerts, 'William Dobson's Self-Portraits', *Connoisseur*, vol. CIII (1939), pp. 244–7; *ibid.*, vol. CV (1940), p. 27; R. A., *King's Pictures* (31).

Painted, not later than *c.* 1645, by a close imitator, presumably a pupil, of Van Dyck and in a vigorous, rather coarsened derivation of his style. A version was at Burley-on-the-Hill (P. Finch, *History of Burley-on-the-Hill* (1901), vol. II, p.38); another, stated to be signed and dated (1644) by Dobson, was formerly at Bill Hill, near Wokingham. Another was sold at Sotheby's, 12 March 1958 (147); another, from the collection of the Earl of Thanet, seems to have been sold at Christie's, 17 March 1888 (72), and a copy is at Appleby Castle. Copies of the figure of the Earl, apparently cut from copies of the whole composition, are at Drumlanrig Castle and in the collection of Mme. Mayer-Warnant in Brussels; and copies of the two heads also exist, *e.g.*, in miniature of the Earl in the collection of M. Albert Warnant, and a bad copy of the Countess, sold at Christie's, 17 October 1952 (143). A drawing, attributed to Hanneman, and thought to be connected with his group of the Huyghens family in the Mauritshuis (241), contains a study for a husband and wife that is very suggestive of this composition.

The Earl of Thanet was in arms for the King in Sussex early in the Civil War, but took the Oath to Parliament on 22 April 1645; he had married in 1629 Margaret, daughter of the 3rd Earl of Dorset.

Manner of Sir Anthony van Dyck

195. HEAD OF A YOUNG MAN

Buckingham Palace. 19¾ × 16⅛ in., 50,2 × 41 cm.; there are later additions of 3⅜ in. on the right and 3¾ in. on the bottom.

In profile to the right, with his right hand raised to his neck.

Purchased by the Prince Consort in 1841 as by Van Dyck (MS. in Surveyor's Office, List of Pictures presented to or purchased by His Royal Highness Prince Albert (42): *Study of a Head of St John*); later at Osborne.

No. 195 seems to be a skilful later imitation of Van Dyck's style in his second Flemish period. The head, probably correctly identified in 1841 (see above) as a St. John, is very reminiscent of Van Dyck's studies for heads in his religious compositions, *e.g.*, a *St. George* (?), sold at Christie's, 18 June 1948 (32). The addition to the canvas, which includes the hand, is certainly later.

Adriaen van Stalbemt

1580–1662. Flemish landscape painter, working primarily in Antwerp; in the reign of Charles I he paid a visit to England. The King acquired from Keirincx four landscapes which appear to have been painted by Stalbemt or on the basis of drawings by him (*Van der Doort*, p. 160). In addition to nos. 196 and 197, the Trustees for Sale valued at £12 among the pictures at Oatlands on 13 September 1649 *A Landshape done Stalband* (Corsham MS., f. 11), sold to Wright for £12. 10s. on 21 May 1650, and at £2 among the pictures at Hampton Court in October 1649 *A landshape: done by stalband* (L. R. MS., f. 119), sold to Gaspars on 21 May 1650 (S.P. 29/447, 24, 1).

196. A VIEW OF GREENWICH

Buckingham Palace. 37½ × 65 in., 95,3 × 165,1 cm.

A view from the high ground on the south-east, looking down on the Tudor palace of Greenwich with the river and a distant impression of London; on the left, on the site of the later Observatory, is Duke Humphrey's Tower and in the foreground are shepherds with their flocks and two more courtly figures beside an artist who appears to be taking a 'prospect' of Greenwich.

Probably the picture valued at £8 by the Trustees for Sale at Oatlands on 13 September 1649: *A Landshape. of. Grenew^ch done by Stalband* (Corsham MS., f. 8), which was sold to James Guinion or Ginion on 7 May 1650 (S.P. 29/447, 24, 1). Recovered at the Restoration and placed in store at Whitehall (Charles II, *Whitehall* (630): *A Landship of Greenewich*, measurements given as 38 × 67 in.), but thereafter it is impossible to follow with certainty through the inventories and Stalbemt's name has not been associated with it since 1649. It may have been at Windsor in the time of Queen Anne (Queen Anne, *Windsor* (169): *A Landskip wth Building & figures one drawing after it*) and at Kensington in 1818 (279: *Landscape and figures*, measurements given as 37½ × 65 in.); recorded at Buckingham Palace (776) in 1876 (*V.R. inv.*).

Probably painted *c.* 1632-5, at the same period as no. 197. No. 196 is severely rubbed and much of the detail is now indistinguishable. But the 'prospect' seems to be an accurate account of the palace from a point near the present Vanbrugh's Castle; the Tudor palace and James I's wall enclosing the park are fairly clearly defined, but nothing can be seen, in the present condition of no. 196, of the progress being made on the Queen's House.

Adriaen van Stalbemt and Jan van Belcamp

197. A VIEW OF GREENWICH (*Plate* 89)

Kensington Palace. 32¼ × 42⅛ in., 82 × 107 cm.

Signed, very obscurely: *A v Stalb . . . / J v B . . .*

A view, from the hill on which the Observatory now stands, down to Greenwich and the river. The Tudor palace is clearly seen and the ground floor of the half-completed Queen's House astride the road outside the wall of the park. In the foreground are seen Charles I, Henrietta Maria and Prince Charles with attendant ladies and courtiers.

Presumably painted for Charles I: recorded (probably in 1639) in the King's First Privy Gallery at Greenwich: *don bij stalbant . . . a pitur auff a lantship Wrin grinwij pijntit and de king and qin and som nobelmen besijd dat* (Van der Doort, p. 195). Probably the picture valued at £5 by the Trustees for Sale *out of the Gallaries at Grenew^ch* (L. R. MS., f. 6 v.) and sold to Col. Webb on 25 October 1649. Recovered at the Restoration and placed in the King's Dressing Room at Hampton Court (Charles II, *Hampton Court* (38): *King Charles. I. with . . . severall Lords, & Ladys . . . a landskip of Greenwich . . .*, measurements given as 38 × 53 in.); later at Kensington, Carlton House, Buckingham Palace (161) and Windsor (2969).

Literature: Vertue, *Notebooks*, vol. IV, pp. 124, 176, vol. V, p. 22; Smith, 233, *Supplement*, 115; Waagen (1854), vol. II, p. 4; G. H. Chettle, *The Queen's House*, L. C. C., *Survey of London*, vol. XIV (1937), p. 30; Collins Baker, *Windsor*, p. 289; Whinney and Millar, p. 261; H. V. S. and M. S. Ogden, *English Taste in Landscape in the Seventeenth Century* (Ann Arbor, 1955), p. 59.

Presumably painted in, or very soon after, 1632. The figure of Prince Charles is taken direct from no. 150 and that of his mother is presumably derived from no. 147, both painted in that year. The landscape, and all the figures except for those in the clear light in the foreground, are presumably by Stalbemt and are close in style to no. 196. The Queen's House had been begun by Inigo Jones for Anne of Denmark in 1616. On her death in 1619 work was abandoned, not to be resumed until 1630 for Henrietta Maria. The house was probably finished in 1635. The figures in the foreground are presumed to be by Belcamp. Apart from the royal family only two can be identified with certainty. The figure in black, wearing the ribbon of the Garter, is Richard Weston, 1st Earl of Portland (1577–1635), Lord High Treasurer, 1628–33; the little figure seems dependent on Van Dyck's portrait of which the original is lost. The florid gentleman on the left, resting his left hand on a stick, is Endymion Porter (1587–1649), one of the King's most devoted courtiers and active in the formation of his collections. The elderly gentleman beside him, wearing the ribbon of the Garter, may be Philip Herbert, 4th Earl of Pembroke (see no. 314), or James Hay, Earl of Carlisle (*d.* 1636), a prominent courtier, whose wife, the famous Lucy Percy (see no. 154), could be the darker of the two ladies climbing the slope behind the Queen. If the measurements given in Charles II's inventory (see above) are correct, no. 197 must have been considerably reduced. The area to the left of the old tear in the canvas on the left is a later addition to make good damages to the original canvas. While the picture was at Carlton House, George Simpson's account for work on the Prince Regent's pictures in 1811 included twelve guineas for 'Restoring the Originality. Cleaning & [?uniting] w^t the Original an addition to a Picture a View of Greenwich Park w^t the Portraits of Ch^s 1st & Queen . . .' (W. R. A., Geo. 27830).

Jan van Belcamp

d.c. 1652. Probably of Dutch origin, but recorded in London in 1624-5. He seems to have specialised in making copies and was associated with Abraham van der Doort in keeping the King's pictures: in 1641 he was, apparently in succession to Van der Doort, Keeper of the Pictures 'on the King's side', and he was stated by Richard Symonds to have been responsible for producing copies of the King's pictures when they were required (*Van der Doort*, p. xvi; B. M., Egerton MS. 1636, f. 100 v.). Charles I owned a little full-length of Henrietta by Belcamp after Van Dyck and a full-length of Prince Charles in 'coats' with a dish of fruit (*Van der Doort*, pp. 68, 181). On 11 November 1647 Charles I wrote to Colonel Whaly for the return of a copy by Belcamp of a portrait of Princess Mary (*Reliquiæ Sacræ Carolinæ* (The

Hague, 1650), pp. 206–7). A copy by Belcamp of a portrait of the Princess was declared by Thomas Beauchamp to the House of Lords Committee and valued at £10 (H. of L. MSS.); this may have been the full-length, valued at £10 by the Trustees in a valuation (L. R. MS., f. 67) stated in the Sebright MS. to be of goods in the Armoury at St. James's, and sold to De Critz and others. *A large picture of a Stagg* by Belcamp was recorded in the King's Guard-Chamber at Whitehall in the reign of James II (B. M., Harl. MS. 1890, f. 62 v.; Bathoe, *James II* (534)), but is not recorded in the royal collection after 1714.

198. EDWARD III

Windsor Castle (282). 79½ × 50⅞ in., 202 × 129,2 cm.; there are additions on the left of *c.* 3½ in., on the right of *c.* 3 in. and of *c.* 2½ in. at the bottom to make good a damaged area.

Full-length standing in armour, holding a spear in his left hand and wearing the Garter, within a niche decorated with small statues of mediaeval warriors under little Gothic canopies.

Presumably painted, with no. 199, for Charles I; probably the portraits valued together at £25 by the Trustees for Sale at Hampton Court in October 1649 (*King Edward yᵉ 3ᵈ at length . . . Edward yᵉ Black Prince*; L. R. MS., f. 122), sold to Edmund Harrison and others on 23 October 1651 (S.P. 29/447, 24, 1); and seen with Harrison by Richard Symonds in 1652 (B. M., Egerton MS. 1636, f. 91). They were recovered at the Restoration (Col. Hawley, f. 7) and placed in the Queen's Gallery at Hampton Court (Charles II, *Hampton Court* (2, 27), measurements of no. 198 given as 86 × 45 in.); later at St. James's.

Literature: (for the pair) Walpole, *Anecdotes*, vol. II, p. 8; Collins Baker, *Windsor*, p. 16.

The portraits of the two principal figures in the foundation of the Order of the Garter were presumably painted in the 1630's. With Van Dyck's sketch of Charles I in procession with the Knights of the Garter, and the larger scheme of which that was to be a part (and with which nos. 198 and 199 may have been connected), they are among the earliest indications of an interest in recording on so large a scale the history and ceremonial of the Order; in this they anticipate the work done by Verrio and Benjamin West for Charles II and George III. They are also among the earliest examples of historical and ancestral portraits, for which there was an increasing vogue later in the century. They are reasonably accurate evocations of the general outlines of late fourteenth-century armour, but are very inaccurate in detail: for no. 199 Belcamp does not seem to have examined the Black Prince's tomb in Canterbury Cathedral. Charles I also owned *One Picture of Edward yᵉ 3ᵈ at length. wᵗʰ a greene Curtaine before it*, valued in the Garter Room at Windsor on 14–15 September 1649 at £4 by the Trustees for Sale (Corsham MS., f. 33), which was at one stage reserved from the sale of the King's goods (H. of L. MSS.).

199. EDWARD, PRINCE OF WALES, 'THE BLACK PRINCE' *(Plate 55)*

Windsor Castle (283). 80½ × 51¼ in., 204,5 × 130,2 cm.; at the top *c.* 1¾ in. is turned over and there are additions on each side of *c.* 3¼ in.: in Charles II's inventory (see no. 198) the measurements are given as 85 × 45 in.

Full-length standing in armour, wearing the Garter and a gipon on which his arms are woven, and holding a spear in his right hand, within a niche decorated with small statues of mediaeval warriors under little Gothic canopies.

See no. 198.

The canvas is badly damaged at the bottom; it is this area

that has been renewed in the companion piece. The Prince's sword seems to be of seventeenth-century make. A variant, possibly also by Belcamp, is at Lyme Park.

200. EDWARD IV

Windsor Castle (2535). 104 × 72 in., 264,2 × 182,9 cm.; the canvas has been enlarged on all sides and was originally *c.* 88 × 50 in.,

Full-length standing in profile to the left, in a fur-lined gown, with the regalia on a table behind him.

Presumably painted for Charles I and probably the portrait valued at £15 by the Trustees for Sale: *King Edward yᵉ 4ᵗʰ at Length* (L. R. MS., f. 67; this section of the MS. is stated in the Sebright MS. to cover the Armoury at St. James's). Apparently not sold, and recorded in the Queen's Gallery at Hampton Court in the reign of Charles II (Charles II, *Hampton Court* (25): *Belchamp. (a side face) in a gowne loyn'd with Furre . . .*, measurements given as 88 × 50 in.); later at St. James's, Buckingham House and Hampton Court (523).

Literature: Vertue, *Notebooks*, vol. I, p. 54; Walpole, *Anecdotes*, vol. I, p. 46, vol. II, p. 8, *Visits*, pp. 59–60; Law, 1881, 1898 (776); Collins Baker, *Windsor*, p. 17.

Probably painted *c.* 1635.

201. LOUIS XIII

Windsor Castle (2534). 79½ × 48¼ in., 202 × 122,6 cm.

Inscribed, probably slightly later: *Lewis yᵉ 13ᵗʰ*

Full-length standing, wearing the ribbon of the St. Esprit and resting his right hand on a stick; beside him is a table and a dog.

Probably painted for Charles I (see below) and perhaps to be identified with the portrait (*yᵉ King of france at Length lewis yᵉ 13ᵗʰ*) valued by the Trustees for Sale at £15 (L. R. MS., f. 67; the Sebright MS. states that the valuation in which this appears was of objects in the Armoury at St. James's); this was reserved for the use of Oliver Cromwell (H. of L. MSS.) and is probably to be identified with the portrait in the Queen's Gallery at Hampton Court after the Restoration (Charles II, *Hampton Court* (18): *Belchamp Lewis 13 of France in a red habit, with a dog by him At Length*, measurements given as 86 × 54 in.); remained at Hampton Court (581); taken to Windsor in July 1901.

Literature: Walpole, *Anecdotes*, vol. II, pp. 8–9; Law, 1881, 1898 (407); Collins Baker, *Windsor*, p. 17.

On 13 January 1636 a warrant was issued to pay £300 to Belcamp for his services and expenses on a visit to France undertaken at Charles I's commands in order to paint for the King portraits of Louis XIII and his Queen (*Cal. S.P.Dom.* (1635–6), p. 159). No. 201 may be the portrait of Louis XIII painted on that occasion. It seems likely that Belcamp copied existing portraits and did not have a sitting from the French King. Versions of the portraits which Belcamp may have copied are in the Devonshire collection (attributed to Ferdinand Elle) and there the figure of Louis XIII is identical in design with no. 201; the dog, however, stands on the other side of the King. Other versions of the portrait of the King are at Holdenby and (at half-length) at Danny. If the measurements in Charles II's inventory were correctly recorded, no. 201 must have been cut down, presumably when it was set over the chimney in the Prince of Wales's Presence Chamber at Hampton Court in the eighteenth century.

Jan van Belcamp (after Paul van Somer)

202. ANNE OF DENMARK

Holyroodhouse. 94¼ × 55 in., 239,4 × 139,7 cm.; enlarged at the top and bottom and on the right; originally 82½ × 50 in.

Full-length standing, apparently in an interior, in hunting costume with two Italian greyhounds.

Probably the portrait of *Queene. Ann at Length wth 2 little doggs* valued in the Armoury at St. James's by the Trustees for Sale at £10 (L. R. MS., f. 67; Sebright MS., f. 251). In Charles II's collection: *Coppied by Belchamp . . . (Hampton Court* (16), measurements given as 83 × 50 in.); thereafter at Hampton Court (459); sent to Holyrood in 1881.

Literature: Vertue, *Notebooks*, vol. II, p. 67; Walpole, *Anecdotes*, vol. I, p. 210; Law, 1881, 1898 (273).

An adaptation, probably painted by Belcamp for Charles I in the 1630's, of Van Somer's portrait of 1617 (no. 105); a similar derivation, but including a third greyhound and part of Oatlands House in the background, is at Kinnaird Castle.

William Dobson

1611–46. Perhaps apprenticed to Robert Peake and at one time associated with Francis Cleyn, he was influenced by Van Dyck and by the great collections assembled by Charles I, particularly by the King's Venetian pictures. He is stated to have been a Groom of the Privy Chamber and Serjeant-Painter to Charles I, and during the Civil War he painted at the royalist headquarters in Oxford portraits of the King, his two eldest sons, his nephews and many of his officers. He had returned to London by 5 August 1646 and is said to have died in poverty.

203. CHARLES I

Windsor Castle (512). 30¼ × 25 in., 76,8 × 63,5 cm.; there is an addition at the bottom of 3½ in.

Head and shoulders in armour, wearing the ribbon of the Garter.

Probably begun for the King, but not apparently recorded until after the Restoration in store at Hampton Court (Charles II, *Hampton Court* (202): *Dobson King Charles the 1ˢᵗ unfinisht*, measurements given as 32 × 29 in.); later at St. James's and Kensington (note in Geo. III, *Kensington: Vandyke*); sent to Carlton House on 7 August 1812 (Jutsham, *R/D*, f. 215; *Carlton House*, 1816 (384) . . . *called Vandyck*; there is a fragment of the 1816 label on the frame).

Although it has recently been described as a copy after Van Dyck by 'Stone' (*e.g.*, *V.R. inv.*, 14 June 1878) the identification with Dobson's unfinished portrait in Charles II's possession seems certain. The head, though very worn, is certainly by Dobson, and so is the area immediately around it. The head (though perhaps not the hair) had presumably been finished by Dobson at Oxford, possibly on a slightly larger canvas. The King's headquarters had been at Oxford from 29 October 1642, but the portrait was presumably unfinished when the King left the City on 27 April 1646 and its earlier progress may have been interrupted by the King's campaigns. Dobson presumably laid out the design, which agrees with his normal presentation on this scale (*e.g.*, the portraits at Patshull of Prince Rupert and Prince Maurice; O. Millar, *William Dobson*, Tate Gallery, 1951 (17, 9, pl. III)). It is possible that the portrait was finished, perhaps by Jonathan Richardson (see no. 205), in the reign of Queen Anne: in her inventory (*St. James's House* (27)) it is no longer described as unfinished. The portrait seems to have been the source of a Civil War type: a copy at Badminton, with variations and in a painted oval, possibly gives an idea of Dobson's original intentions; and the portrait may have been the basis of copies on a small scale, *e.g.*, in the National Gallery of Ireland (251) and at Belton. The latter has an apparently seventeenth-century attribution on the back to Joan Carlile and is very close to the original (M. Toynbee and Sir G. Isham, 'Joan Carlile (1606?–1679) – An Identification', *Burl. Mag.*, vol. XCVI (1954), p. 277, fig. 5). A half-length drawing of the King, formerly in the collection of Sir John Ramsden, signed (by Alexander Marshall?) and dated 1651, seems also to be derived from Dobson.

204. CHARLES II WHEN PRINCE OF WALES (*Plate* 95)

Windsor Castle (3083). 48⅛ × 39 in., 122,2 × 99,1 cm.

Inscribed: *CP* (below a crown) *Æ. | 14 | 1644.*

Three-quarter-length in a richly gilded suit of armour and wearing the chain of the Garter, resting his right hand on his helmet and his left on a baton; a cavalry action in the background.

Believed to have been in the collection of William, 1st Earl of Craven (1606–97), and to have been given to him by Elizabeth, Queen of Bohemia, or bequeathed to him by Prince Rupert, who had inherited many of his mother's possessions. In the Great Gallery at Coombe Abbey in 1814 (J. Britton, *The Beauties of England and Wales*, vol. XV, pt. II, p. 53). Passed by descent to Cornelia, Countess of Craven, by whom it was bequeathed to Her Majesty The Queen in 1961.

Literature: Collins Baker, *Lely*, vol. I, p. 99, vol. II, p. 116; R. A., *Kings & Queens*, 1953 (171).

Painted at Oxford, probably slightly later than the portrait by Dobson in the Scottish National Portrait Gallery (1244), in which the Prince wears the cuirass from the same suit of armour (which survives in the Tower of London). A contemporary version, probably a copy, is at Wentworth Woodhouse.

205. JAMES II WHEN DUKE OF YORK (*Plate* 96)

Windsor Castle (290). 37½ × 31½ in., 95,3 × 80 cm.; originally 29¾ × 25½ in.

Half-length with his right hand on his hip, holding in his left the ribbon of the Garter.

Probably begun for Charles I, but not apparently recorded until after the Restoration in store at Hampton Court (Charles II, *Hampton Court* (203): *Dobson The Duke of Yorke unfinisht*); later at Kensington and St. James's.

Literature: Collins Baker, *Windsor*, p. 69; R. A., *King's Pictures* (29); O. Millar, *William Dobson*, Tate Gallery, 1951 (5).

Presumably painted at Oxford. Probably begun *c.* 1644–5 as a head and shoulders, but left unfinished when the City surrendered to the Parliamentarians in June 1646 and the Duke fell into their hands. The head and the area around it are wholly by Dobson (the hair may not be quite finished) and the indication of the collar below the jaw seems to be original. There is no indication of Dobson's further intentions; he presumably planned a head and shoulders portrait, perhaps within a painted oval (see O. Millar, *op. cit.* (15, 16, 17, and 20, pls. II, III)), and probably indicated the colour of the costume. The canvas was enlarged and the portrait worked up by Jonathan Richardson, probably in the reign of Queen Anne (Queen Anne, *Kensington*, store (194) . . . *not finishd*, but, in Thomas Coke's slightly later notes, in the Lanthorn Room as *bigger then ¾*; B. M., Stowe MS. 587, f. 15: *La Tête par Dobson La Draperie par Richard*). As it stands the handling of the costume is entirely typical of Richardson and he knew enough of the portrait styles of the previous century to evolve the design, which attempts an elegance foreign to Dobson. He may also have designed the background, but the relation between the figure and the background is typical of Dobson and the background is probably fundamentally Dobson's.

Style of William Dobson

206. PORTRAIT OF A MAN *called* ABRAHAM VAN DER DOORT (*d.* 1640)

St. James's Palace. 23½ × 18¾ in., 59,7 × 47,6 cm.

Head and shoulders in a loose black cloak.

Formerly in the collection of the Marquess of Townshend and sold at Sotheby's, 21 February 1911 (22); purchased later by J. D. Milner, presented by him in December 1919 to Her Majesty Queen Mary and added by her to the royal collection; later at Windsor (2829).

Literature: O. Millar, 'Abraham van der Doort's Catalogue', *Walpole Soc.*, vol. XXXVII (1960), p. xvi.

Formerly described as a portrait of Inigo Jones. The more recent identification with Abraham van der Doort and the attribution to William Dobson were presumably based on a likeness to the portrait, attributed to Dobson and now in the Hermitage, Leningrad, (there is a copy in the National Portrait Gallery (1569)), which was purchased by Sir Robert Walpole from Jonathan Richardson and was recorded by Vertue (*Notebooks*, vol. II, p. 77) as 'Ab. Vander Dort ... his head ... painted by Dobson'. The likeness is certainly close, but there is probably an inherent danger in the tempting identification of these harassed, hirsute faces with such sitters as Jones and Van der Doort. The present canvas is rubbed, but is suggestive of Dobson. If the attribution of this portrait and that in Leningrad to Dobson is correct, they would be his earliest surviving works and would support the theory that he had privileged access to the King's collection through its Surveyor.

Medallist of Dutch origin, perhaps in the service of the Emperor Rudolph II in Prague; sent to England, probably in 1609, he entered the service of Henry, Prince of Wales, as Keeper of his Cabinet; he continued in the service of Charles I in the same post and as Master Embosser and Maker of Medals and Provider of Patterns for the coinage. As Surveyor of the King's Pictures he compiled the famous catalogue of part of the King's collections.

Robert Walker

d. 1658. As a portrait painter was deeply influenced by Van Dyck, but was particularly associated with the parliamentarians and painted, at least until 1655, portraits of Cromwell and his fellow-officers; he copied pictures from Charles I's collection and bought pictures when the collection was dispersed.

207. PORTRAIT OF THE ARTIST (*Plate* 94)

Hampton Court (587). 30½ × 25¼ in., 77,5 × 64,1 cm.

Head and shoulders, almost in profile, looking over his shoulder and holding a drawing in his right hand.

Recorded at Carlton House in 1816 (371), in store (*A half length of an artist, with a drawing in his hand. believe. Hanneman*) and perhaps acquired by George IV in or before 1806; but Frederick, Prince of Wales, had acquired before July 1750 *Walker the painter his head by himself done* (Vertue, B. M. MS. 19027, ff. 21, 24), which may have been the portrait of *Walker the painter – as the print is*, seen by Vertue (*Notebooks*, vol. V, p. 20) at a sale in May 1743, and which may thereafter have hung at Kensington, where it was suggested as a portrait of Milton (*e.g.*, Falkner, p. 376; Pyne, vol. II, *Kensington*, p. 62).

Literature: Walpole, *Anecdotes*, vol. II, p. 73; Law, 1881, 1898 (365); Collins Baker, *Hampton Court*, p. 159.

Probably painted *c.* 1645; versions are in the National Portrait Gallery (753) and Belvoir Castle (exh. Worcester, *Paintings from 1642 to 1651*, 1951 (52)) and the type (probably no. 207) was engraved in London by Pierre Lombart. In a more elaborate variant in the Ashmolean Museum (464; Waterhouse, *Painting in Britain*, pl. 50) the artist points to a statue of Mercury.

Edward Bower

d. 1667. Perhaps a native of the West Country, where he seems for a time to have had a local practice as a portrait painter, but he was apparently 'servant to Anthony Vandike' and for much of his career he was working in London; Master of the Painter-Stainers Company in 1661–2 and among those appointed to ride in attendance on Charles II when he came to the City soon after the Restoration.

208. CHARLES I AT HIS TRIAL (*Plate* 91)

St. James's Palace. 51⅝ × 38⅞ in., 131,1 × 98,7 cm.

Signed and dated: *Edw. Bower. | att Temple Barr. | fecit. 1648.*

Three-quarter-length, seated in black, wearing the ribbon and star of the Garter and holding a paper in his right hand.

Formerly in the collection of the Earls of Winchilsea and Nottingham, sold at Christie's, 9 May 1947 (49, as Van Dyck) and again 6 April 1951 (135), when it was purchased by Her Majesty Queen Elizabeth The Queen Mother.

Literature: E. K. Waterhouse, 'Edward Bower, Painter of King Charles I at his Trial', *Burl. Mag.*, vol. XCI (1949), pp. 18–21; *Paintings from 1642 to 1651*, Worcester, 1951 (1); R. A., *Kings and Queens*, 1953 (134); Whinney and Millar, p. 80; D. Piper, *The English Face* (1957), p. 102, pls. 42, 43.

From a comparison with the two other signed and dated versions, at Belvoir and Antony (Waterhouse, *loc. cit.*), it is probable that Bower made drawings in Westminster Hall, where the King appeared on trial for his life before the High Court of Justice on 20, 22, 23 and 27 January 1649, and worked up his portraits from them in his studio at Temple Bar. The changes in the three versions in the position of the King's hands, in his glance and in the way in which he clasps his stick and paper, are presumably the result of careful observation of the King's movements and gestures during the trial. The version at Antony is traditionally stated to have been painted for John Carew, who was one of the King's judges and signed his death-warrant, and the commission to Bower may originally have sprung from some of the King's opponents. The subject probably became popular in royalist households: when the 2nd Earl of Ailesbury waited on James II after his abortive flight from London he found him 'sitting in a great chair, his hat on, and his beard being much grown, and resembled the picture of his royal father at the pretended High Court of Justice' (*Memoirs*, ed. W. E. Buckley, Roxburghe Club (1890), vol. I, p. 209). Copies and variants are at Burton Agnes, Badminton, Ombersley Court (extended to a full-length), Danny, Pendarves, Pencarrow, in the collections of Lord Newton and Mr. F. N. Holland-Griffith-Carpenter, in the Scottish National Portrait Gallery (815), at All Souls (eng. by John Faber the elder, 1713; Mrs. R. L. Poole, *Catalogue of Portraits ...*, vol. II (1925), pp. 183–4)) and in the University of St. Andrews. A reduced copy of the composition was painted by Goddard Dunning in 1677 and the type was the basis of a drawing by Jonathan Richardson in the Sutherland collection (vol. II, 1–68) in the Ashmolean Museum.

At the trial of the King, John Bradshaw, the President of the Court, ordered a chair, covered with crimson velvet, to be placed for the King in front of his judges; the silver head of the King's cane fell off when he touched the arm of John Cook who was reading the charge against him.

Adriaen Hanneman

c. 1601–71. Born and probably trained in The Hague, he was in London from 1626 until c. 1637; he was presumably associated with Mytens, but he was deeply influenced by Van Dyck and perhaps also by the Venetian pictures in Charles I's collection. After his return to The Hague his Van Dyckian style and his associations with the English court made him understandably popular with the House of Orange and, later, with the exiled Stuarts and their followers. By 1645 he was working for Prince Frederick Henry and Amalia van Solms and in 1646 he painted their daughter-in-law, Princess Mary, who patronised him continuously. In their exile Hanneman painted Charles II and Henry, Duke of Gloucester, and Charles II owned a portrait of the Duke of Monmouth (Charles II, *Whitehall* (546), in store, measurements given as 35 × 26 in.) which may have been the portrait of the Duke, *Hanniman . . . when he was young*, in James II's collection (B. M., Harl. MS. 1890, f. 60 v.; Bathoe, *James II* (443)).

209. WILLIAM III (*Plate* 98)

St. James's Palace (24). 51¾ × 41½ in., 130,8 × 105,4 cm.

Signed and dated: *Anᵒ 1664. | Adr. Hanneman. F.*

Three-quarter-length in armour, wearing the chain of the Garter and holding a baton in his right hand beside his helmet and gauntlet.

Painted for the English court (and see no. 210) and placed with other family portraits in Charles II's Bedchamber at Whitehall (Charles II, *Whitehall* (244)); later at Windsor.

Literature: M. Toynbee, 'Adriaen Hanneman and the English Court in Exile', *Burl. Mag.*, vol. XCII (1950), p. 76, fig. 17; V. & A., *William and Mary and their Time*, 1950 (10); A. Staring, 'De Portretten van den Koning-Stadhouder', *Nederlandsch Kunsthistorisch Jaarboek*, vol. III (1950-1), p. 172, pl. 13.

On 26 June 1664 Hanneman was paid 500 gulden for two identical portraits (see no. 210) of the Prince of Orange 'tot de knie toe', which were to be sent to England for the Queen Mother, Henrietta Maria, and Anne Hyde, Duchess of York (Archief Nassausche Domeinen, Ordonnantieboek, 1658–67, Inv. no. 739, f. 187 v.).[1] The commission may have been given by the Prince's grandmother, Amalia van Solms, who, in her correspondence with Constantijn Huygens, reported (17 January 1664) that Hanneman had begun the portraits, and described (15 May) the difficulties encountered in 'faire asseoir un enfant qui n'a gueres d'arrest, outre qu'on a affaire à un peintre qui est lent et plein d'autres ouvrages'. On 27 June she announced the despatch of the portraits and asked Huygens to present them to the royal ladies. Huygens reported the great success of the portraits and the Queen's resolve to persuade Charles II to sit for a double portrait with herself which could be sent in return for them (*De Briefwisseling van Constantijn Huygens*, ed. J. A. Worp, vol. 32, part VI (1917), pp. 33, 64, 75, 87)[2]

1. This reference was discovered by Miss J. Wittenaar and kindly communicated to me by Mr. Th. H. Lunsingh Scheurleer.
2. I am very grateful to Mr. A. Staring for sending me these references.

210. WILLIAM III

Kensington Palace. 74 × 40¾ in., 188 × 103,5 cm.; there is an addition at the bottom of 24½ in.

Signed and dated: *Anᵒ, 1664 | Adr. Hanneman F.*

Painted, with no. 209, for the English court; recorded over a door in the Princess's Dressing Room at Windsor (Queen Anne, *Windsor* (216): . . . in *Armour at length when young*); later at Buckingham House and at Hampton Court (252). Both versions of the portrait were for a time during the eighteenth century thought to represent Charles II as a boy, and no. 210 was identified slightly later as the Duke of Monmouth.

Literature: Law, 1881, 1898 (571); Collins Baker, *Hampton Court*, p. 70.

See no. 209. This was possibly the version painted for the Duchess of York. It appears to be the first version and to be richer in quality; there are also *pentimenti* in the drawing of the stone carving below the ledge on which the helmet rests. The addition, clumsily extending the portrait to a full-length, was probably made c. 1700, and the bottom of the original canvas seems to have been overpainted at the same time.

211. MARY, PRINCESS OF ORANGE

St. James's Palace. 47 × 38¼ in., 119,4 × 97,2 cm.

Three-quarter-length, standing in a feathered cloak, holding a switch (?) and wearing an elaborately feathered and jewelled turban.

Probably the portrait recorded in Charles II's Bedchamber at Whitehall: *The Princess of Orange in a feather Mantle of severall collours at Halfe Length* (Charles II, *Whitehall* (242), measurements given as 46 × 38 in.); no artist is mentioned, but in James II's inventory it appears as by Hanneman (B. M., Harl. MS. 1890, f. 48; Bathoe, *James II* (94)). Among James II's pictures at St. James's, however (*ibid.*, f. 86; *ibid.* (1231)) was: *Princesse Royall at halfe length with a feather mantle*; and it was probably for this picture that Mary of Modena, on 25 January 1688, ordered a 'straining frame' (Bodl., Rawlinson MS. C.987, f. 89: 'for the princesse Royalls picture in A feather Mantle'). Thereafter it is probable that the references in the inventories to nos. 211 and 212 have been confused; no. 211 was probably at Kensington in the time of George III and was at Hampton Court (929) until 1924.

Literature: Law, 1881, 1898 (777); M. Toynbee, 'Adriaen Hanneman and the English Court in Exile', *Burl. Mag.*, vol. XCII (1950), pp. 74-5.

Perhaps painted to record the Princess's appearance at an entertainment in The Hague early in 1655, 'very well dressed, like an Amazon'. The portrait is worn and has been overpainted and it is hard to tell whether it is an original by Hannemann or a contemporary copy. The Princess was painted in the same costume by Hanneman, apparently for her son, in the posthumous portrait, now in the Mauritshuis (429), for which he was paid on 28 June 1664: 'het conterfeitsel van Hare Koninklijke Hoogheid Hooglofffelijker memorie met een tulband met pluimen op het hoofd . . .'

212. MARY, PRINCESS OF ORANGE

Windsor Castle (2490). 54½ × 39¾ in., 138,4 × 101 cm.; enlarged at top and bottom and on the right to hang as a pair with no. 286; the original canvas is c. 47 × 37 in.

Signed and dated: *Anᵒ, 1660 | Adr: Hanneman. F*

Three-quarter-length standing, holding a chain of pearls in her left hand.

Perhaps painted for the Princess's mother: *The Princesse Royall to the halfe by Honjman* was hanging, *fixt over the Chimney*, in the Queen's Presence Chamber at Colombes in 1669 (P. R. O., S.P. 78/128, f. 209 v.); probably the portrait at St. James's in James II's collection (B. M., Harl. MS. 1890, f. 86; Bathoe, *James II* (1230)). Hanging in the reign of Queen Anne in the Queen's Dressing Room at St. James's (Queen Anne, *St. James's House* (17)), apparently already as a pair with no. 286; they were seen hanging over the doors in the King's Closet at St. James's by Vertue (1735) and Walpole (1758); moved to Windsor in 1901.

Literature: Vertue, *Notebooks*, vol. IV, p. 75; Walpole, *Visits*, p. 15; Collins Baker, *Windsor*, p. 151; M. Toynbee, 'Some early Portraits of Princess Mary . . .', *Burl. Mag.*, vol. LXXXII (1943), pp. 101–3, 'Adriaen Hanneman and the English Court in Exile', *ibid*, vol. XCII (1950), p. 75, 'An Additional Note', *ibid.*, vol. XCIII (1951), p. 329.

Presumably painted in The Hague; the Princess arrived in London on 25 September 1660 and died there three months later. The portrait was engraved by William Faithorne. It was perhaps the last portrait of the Princess painted from life by Hanneman, but the head is close to the portrait of 1659 in the Scottish National Portrait Gallery (1308), which is in turn close to a variant three-quarter-length of which versions are in the collection of the Earl of Clarendon (signed) and at Holkham. The copy of no. 212 formerly at Haigh Hall is now at Montacute; other copies also exist, *e.g.*, at Ampleforth (formerly at Deramore).

213. WILLIAM HAMILTON, EARL OF LANARK AND SECOND DUKE OF HAMILTON (1616–51)

Kensington Palace. 52¾ × 41½ in., 134 × 105,4 cm.

Signed and dated: *An⁰, 1650 | Adr: Hanneman: F.*

Three-quarter-length, wearing the ribbon of the Garter and the star embroidered on his cloak.

Recorded in store at Whitehall in Charles II's collection: *Hanneman. William Duke Hamilton at halfe length* (Charles II, *Whitehall* (467)); thereafter at Windsor (60).

Literature: Vertue, *Notebooks*, vol. I, p. 78, vol. II, p. 29, vol. IV, p. 119; Walpole, *Anecdotes*, vol. II, p. 18; Collins Baker, *Lely*, vol. I, pp. 88–9; M. Toynbee, 'Adriaen Hanneman and the English Court in Exile', *Burl. Mag.*, vol. XCII (1950), p. 79; exh., *Paintings from 1642 to 1651*, Worcester, 1951 (23).

Painted in The Hague after Hamilton's nomination as Knight of the Garter on 12 January 1650 and before his departure for Scotland with Charles II in June; possibly given to the King before the Restoration. The portrait seems to have become popular; copies are at Longleat, Brodick Castle, Kinnaird Castle and in the National Portrait Gallery (2120). The two versions in the Hamilton collection appear in an inventory of the Earl of Arran's pictures, 12 August 1695 (Hamilton MS.); the complete version is attributed to Hanneman, the head and shoulders copy to the elder Jervas. The design is based on a portrait of Charles I by Van Dyck (Glück, 378), of which the original may then have been in The Hague.

Younger son of the sitter in no. 124; with his elder brother, the 1st Duke, pursued a tortuous course during the Civil War, but was a loyal supporter of the Covenant; a Privy Councillor to Charles II in exile, he was killed in the King's army at the Battle of Worcester.

214. PETER OLIVER (*c.* 1594–1648) (*Plate* 93)

Hampton Court (104). 30 × 22 in., 76,2 × 55,9 cm.

Head and shoulders in a black cloak.

Probably acquired by Charles II from Peter Oliver's widow soon after the Restoration (Col. Hawley, f. 31: *A picture of peter Oliver by yᵉ Life*); hung at Whitehall between the Green Room and the Closet (Charles II, *Whitehall* (271): *Peter Oliver by the life*, measure-

ments given as 44 × 25 in.); thereafter at Kensington and Buckingham House, apparently at one time as by Van Dyck.

Literature: Vertue, *Notebooks*, vol. IV, p. 159; Walpole, *Anecdotes*, vol. I, p. 223, pl. opp. p. 221, *Visits*, p. 80; Law, 1881, 1898 (766); Collins Baker, *Lely*, vol. I, p. 87, *Hampton Court*, p. 70; R. A., *King's Pictures* (41); Whinney and Millar, p. 76.

Probably painted *c.* 1632–5. Although Hanneman's name was apparently not attached to the portrait until the time of Vertue, it clearly belongs to a small group of portraits which are Hanneman's earliest surviving works, painted while he was in London. A portrait at Warwick Castle, signed and dated (1632?; Whinney and Millar, *op. cit.*, pl. 19b), is very close in style to no. 214 and another of the same type, a portrait of an elderly man, is in the Mountbatten collection. The sitters in this group probably represent Hanneman's countrymen and fellow-artists in London. The engraving reproduced by Walpole (see above) indicates that the portrait has been cut. Vertue (*Notebooks*, vol. V, p. 61) refers to a portrait of Mrs. Oliver which may have been a pendant.

Miniature painter who was trained by his father, Isaac, and succeeded to his position at court; painted royal portraits and executed for Charles I copies in miniature of some of the King's finest Renaissance paintings. Charles II was stated to have secured from his widow a number of her husband's works; at least twenty-two miniatures by Peter Oliver are recorded in Charles II's inventory.

Charles Wautier

fl. 1652–60. Flemish painter, perhaps a pupil of Rubens.

Attributed to Charles Wautier

215. JAMES II WHEN DUKE OF YORK (*Plate* 92)

St. James's Palace. 48¾ × 36½ in., 123,8 × 92,7 cm.

Three-quarter-length standing, holding a baton in his right hand and wearing the ribbon of the Garter over armour and a buff doublet.

Purchased by Her Majesty The Queen for the royal collection in 1960 from Mr. D. Baskett of Colnaghi's.

Literature: R. A., *The Age of Charles II*, 1960–1 (42).

No. 215 seems to be the portrait on which Pieter de Jode based the engraving which gives C. Wautier as the painter.[1] It was presumably painted during the time spent by the Duke in Flanders from 1656 to the Restoration. It shows him as a soldier, when he was serving with the Spanish forces in the Netherlands; he and his brother Henry, Duke of Gloucester, won golden opinions for their conduct at the battle of the Dunes on 3 June 1658.

Remigius (Remy or Remee) van Leemput

d. 1675. Probably of Flemish, though possibly of French, origin, and established in London by October 1635. He painted portraits, under the influence of Van Dyck, and had a considerable reputation as a copyist, especially after Van Dyck. Small copies by him after Titian and Honthorst are recorded at Kensington in the time of Queen Anne (Queen Anne, *Kensington*, store (46, 47)).

1. I am very grateful to Mr. David Piper for drawing my attention to this print. No. 215 agrees exactly in style with a portrait by Wautier, stated to be of the Comte de Roeulx, exh. Bruges, *La Toison d'Or*, 1962 (223).

216. HENRY VII, ELIZABETH OF YORK, HENRY VIII AND JANE SEYMOUR (*Plate 26*)

Hampton Court (308). 35 × 38⅞ in., 88,9 × 98,7 cm.

Inscribed, signed and dated: PROTOTYPVM IVSTÆ MAGNITVDINIS IPSO OPERE TECTORIO / FECIT HOLBENIVS IVBENTE HENRICO VIII. / ECTYPVM A REMIGIO VAN LEEMPVT BREVIORI TABELLA / DESCRIBI VOLVIT CAROLVS II. M.B. F.E.H.R. / Aº DNI. MDCLXVII.

In a richly decorated Renaissance interior, in which is inscribed the date *AN. Ďoi. 1537*, the two sovereigns stand divided from their consorts by a sarcophagus, on which Henry VII leans with his left arm and on which is inscribed:

SI IVVAT HEROVM CLARAS VIDISSE FIGVRAS,
    SPECTA HAS, MAIORES NVLLA TABELLA TVLIT.
CERTAMEN MAGNVM, LIS, QVÆSTIO MAGNA PATERNE,
    FILIVS AN VINCAT. VICIT. VTERQVE QVIDEM.
ISTE SVOS HOSTES, PATRIÆQVE INCENDIA SÆPE
    SVSTVLIT, ET PACEM CIVIBVS VSQVE DEDIT.

FILIVS AD MAIORA QVIDEM PROGNATVS AB ARIS
    SVBMOVET INDIGNOSI SVBSTITVITQVE PROBOS.
CERTÆ, VIRTVTI, PAPARVM AVDACIA CESSIT,
    HENRICO OCTAVO SCEPTRA GERENTE MANV
REDDITA RELIGIO EST, ISTO REGNANTE DEIQVE
    DOGMATA CEPERVNT ESSE IN HONORE SVO.

Painted for Charles II and recorded in the reign of James II at Whitehall (B. M., Harl. MS. 1890, f. 57; Bathoe, *James II* (355): *King Henry the Eighth, being a Copy after the peice upon the Wall in the Privy Chamber by Remy*); thereafter at Kensington.

Literature: B. Buckeridge in an *Essay towards an English School* in English edition of De Piles's *Art of Painting* (1706), pp. 435, 458; Vertue, *Notebooks*, vol. I, pp. 55–6, vol. IV, p. 65; Walpole, *Anecdotes*, vol. I, pp. 81–2; Waagen (1854), vol. II, p. 413; R. N. Wornum, *Some Account of the Life and Works of Hans Holbein* (1867), pp. 303–8; Law, 1881, 1898 (601); Ganz, *KdK*, 179; A. B. Chamberlain, *Hans Holbein the Younger* (1913), vol. II, pp. 94–7; Collins Baker, *Hampton Court*, pp. 87–8; Schmid, *Tafelband* (1945), p. 34 (102), Textband (1948), vol. II, pp. 373–4; R. A., *Works by Holbein and other Masters*, 1950–1 (204); Waterhouse, *Painting in Britain*, p. 8; Ganz, *Holbein*, p. 289 (179).

Copied for Charles II, apparently (according to Buckeridge) for £150, from the life-size composition, painted by Holbein for Henry VIII in 1537 on the wall of the Privy Chamber in Whitehall. According to Charles Patin, writing in October 1671, 'Dans l'anti-chambre du Roy, il y a sur le pignon de la croisée de la main d'Holbein, le portrait d'Henry VIII. & des Princes ces enfans, dont le Roy a fait tirer une excellente copie, pour en étendre la posterité, s'il faut ainsi dire, & n'abandonner pas une si belle chose à la fortune des tems' (*Relations Historiques et Curieuses de Voyages . . .* (Paris, 1674), p. 170). The wall-painting was destroyed in the fire at Whitehall Palace on 4 January 1698, when 'endeavours were us'd to remove that part of the Wall on which these Pictures were painted, but all prov'd ineffectual.' Holbein's original cartoon (*Fig. II*) for the left half of the composition is in the National Portrait Gallery (4027); in the final composition, according to Leemput's record of it, Holbein slightly altered the position of the figure of Henry VIII (as well as modifying the tilt of Henry VII's head) creating thereby the source from which the familiar full-length portraits of Henry VIII were produced by Holbein's pupils and followers (*e.g.*, nos. 34–8). The background in no. 216 is derived in part from an engraving of 1481 designed by Bramante. In 1669 Leemput painted, probably for the Seymour family, a variant which is at Petworth (347; C. H. Collins Baker, *Catalogue of the*

Petworth Collection . . . (1920), p. 72). This shows a little more round the edges of the composition, and incorporates in the foreground the figure of Edward VI, based on the version at Petworth (370) of no. 44; the royal and Seymour arms replace the verses on the sarcophagus. According to Vertue (*op. cit.*, vol. I, p. 56) Leemput made life-size copies after Holbein of Henry VIII and Jane Seymour and it is possible that the copies at Drayton House of Henry VII and Henry VIII, from the wall-painting or the cartoon, which are stated to be by Belcamp, are in fact by Leemput. Vertue's detailed water-colour after Leemput, signed and dated 1737, is in the Royal Library (A. P. Oppé, *English Drawings . . . at Windsor Castle* (1950), p. 98 (625)) and was the source of his engraving.

217. HENRY HYDE, SECOND EARL OF CLARENDON (1638–1709), **WHEN VISCOUNT CORNBURY, WITH HIS FIRST WIFE, THEODOSIA CAPEL** (1640–62)

Hampton Court (608). Panel: 14½ × 18⅝ in., 36,8 × 47,3 cm.

Double three-quarter-length, seated in front of an elaborately carved fountain.

Recorded in Queen Anne's inventory in store at Kensington (50) and slightly later in the Lanthorn Room: *Old Remy – Earl of Clarendon & his first Lady Small Life Copy after Sʳ Peter Lely*; from the time of George III, however, attributed to Russell.

Literature: Law, 1881, 1898 (188); Collins Baker, *Hampton Court*, p. 132.

A copy, possibly painted for Queen Anne, who was Lord Cornbury's niece, of the double portrait by Lely, painted in 1661. The signed original belongs to the Earl of Clarendon (Beckett, *Lely*, no. 122).

Lord Cornbury was Private Secretary and Chamberlain to Catherine of Braganza and a supporter of his brother-in-law, James II. He married his first wife, daughter of Lord Capel, in January 1661.

Attributed to Remigius van Leemput

218–30. PORTRAITS OF LADIES, after VAN DYCK, LELY and SAMUEL COOPER

In Queen Anne's inventory the set appears (*Windsor* (192–205)) in the Bathing Room at Windsor with nos. 232 and 233 as *14 . . . Ladies heads Copys by Remy*. By the reign of George III, when they had been hung with Lely's *Beauties* (see nos. 257–66) in the Room of Beauties or Queen's Old State Bedchamber, they were attributed to Theodore Russell (1624–88) (*e.g.*, Pote, 1768, p. 6; Pyne, vol. I, p. 129). He was stated to have studied under Cornelius Johnson, who was his uncle, and with Van Dyck. Very few documented works by Theodore Russell or Roussel survive, but signed and dated portraits of 1644 are on the scale of life and are close in style to the work of his uncle. The persistent tradition that he specialised in small copies after Van Dyck, such as nos. 219, 220, 223, 224 and 228, goes back to the time of George Vertue (*e.g.*, *Notebooks*, vol. I, p. 79; vol. II, p. 12), whose source was Russell's son, Anthony, but has not so far been supported by contemporary evidence. Such copies, often framed in small versions of fine contemporary frames, were obviously much in demand and a number of painters must have produced them; even within the best set of all, at Woburn Abbey, several hands seem to have been at work. The portraits recorded in Queen Anne's Bathing Room perhaps indicate a late instance of the hanging of such little pictures so as to form an intimate cabinet of portraits of relations, or, in this instance, of famous women.

The present set falls into three groups of clearly defined scales The two smaller groups, particularly nos. 223–6, are very close indeed in quality to nos. 217 and 231 and there seems no reason to doubt the early attribution to Leemput. The five larger panels, nos. 218–22, are on the scale usually associated with Russell, but could equally well be by Leemput. The set was probably acquired by Queen Anne or in the previous reign. The panels bear on the back seventeenth-century labels with numbers that probably relate to their previous ownership (and see no. 234). The identities of the sitters cannot be established in every case and have caused confusion in the past.

Literature: (for the set). Walpole, *Anecdotes*, vol. I, p. 215; Law, 1881, 1898 (189, 193); Collins Baker, *Hampton Court*, pp. 130–3.

218. BARBARA VILLIERS, DUCHESS OF CLEVELAND (1641–1709)

Hampton Court (175). Panel: $15\frac{1}{2} \times 12\frac{1}{2}$ in., $39,4 \times 31,8$ cm.

Head and shoulders, leaning her head on her right hand.

Copied from a full-length by Lely, of which the most familiar (but not the best) version was given to the 1st Earl of Sandwich before 10 July 1664 and was formerly at Hinchingbrooke (Beckett, *Lely*, pl. 90).

See no. 257.

219. FRANCES STUART, COUNTESS OF PORTLAND (1617–94)

Hampton Court (183). Panel: $15\frac{1}{2} \times 12\frac{1}{2}$ in., $39,4 \times 31,8$ cm.

Head and shoulders, glancing to the right.

Copied from a double portrait by Van Dyck, of which the original is in the Hermitage (Glück, 499) and in which she appears with Lady d'Aubigny, no. 220.

Daughter of the 3rd Duke of Lennox; at her marriage (1632) to Jerome Weston, 2nd Earl of Portland, the King himself gave her to her bridegroom.

220. KATHERINE HOWARD, LADY D'AUBIGNY (d. 1650)

Hampton Court (186). Panel: $15\frac{1}{2} \times 12\frac{1}{2}$ in., $39,4 \times 31,8$ cm.

Head and shoulders, looking to the left.

Copied from a double portrait by Van Dyck, of which the original is in the Hermitage (Glück, 499) and in which she appears with Lady Portland, no. 219. See also no. 177.

221. JANE NEEDHAM, MRS. MYDDELTON (1645–92)

Hampton Court (173). Panel: $15\frac{1}{2} \times 12\frac{1}{2}$ in., $39,4 \times 31,8$ cm.

Head and shoulders in a red cloak.

Copied from a portrait by Lely of which there is a version at Althorp.

See no. 266.

222. PORTRAIT OF A LADY

Hampton Court (184). Panel: $15\frac{1}{2} \times 12\frac{1}{2}$ in., $39,4 \times 31,8$ cm.

Head and shoulders in an elaborate head-dress of pearls.

Probably copied from a portrait painted by Van Dyck *c.* 1640.

223. DIANA RUSSELL, COUNTESS OF BRADFORD (1624–95)

Hampton Court (176). Panel: $10\frac{3}{8} \times 12\frac{5}{8}$ in., $26,4 \times 32,1$ cm.

Head and shoulders, holding her sleeve in her right hand.

Presumably copied from a portrait by Van Dyck.

Daughter of the 4th Earl of Bradford; married (1642) Francis Newport, later Viscount Newport and Earl of Bradford.

224. ANNE VILLIERS, COUNTESS OF MORTON (d. 1654) (*Plate* 128)

Hampton Court (174). Panel: $10\frac{1}{4} \times 12\frac{1}{2}$ in., $26 \times 31,8$ cm.

Head and shoulders in a fur wrap with a vase of flowers behind her.

Presumably copied from a portrait by Van Dyck, of which there is a version at Dalmahoy.

Daughter of Sir Edward Villiers and sister of no. 226; married (1627) Robert Douglas, 8th Earl of Morton; governess to Henrietta, youngest daughter of Charles I, with whom she escaped to France in disguise in 1646.

225. PENELOPE NAUNTON, COUNTESS OF PEMBROKE (1620–?47)

Hampton Court (172). Panel: $10\frac{1}{4} \times 12\frac{1}{2}$ in., $26 \times 31,8$.

Head and shoulders, holding her scarf in her right hand.

Possibly copied after Van Dyck, but more likely after an early portrait by Lely.

Daughter of Sir Robert Naunton; married (1639) as his first wife, Philip Herbert, 5th Earl of Pembroke.

226. BARBARA VILLIERS, COUNTESS OF SUFFOLK (1622–81)

Hampton Court (187). Panel: $10\frac{1}{4} \times 12\frac{1}{2}$ in., $26 \times 31,8$ cm.

Head and shoulders.

Copied from a portrait by Lely (*c.* 1665) of which a version was sold at Christie's, 13 December 1957 (15).

Daughter of Sir Edward Villiers and sister of Lady Morton, no. 224; married (1651) as his second wife, James Howard, 3rd Earl of Suffolk, Groom of the Stole to Catherine of Braganza.

227. FRANCES STUART, DUCHESS OF RICHMOND (1647–1702)

Hampton Court (179). Panel: $9\frac{1}{4} \times 7$ in., $23,5 \times 17,8$ cm.

Head and shoulders.

Copied from Samuel Cooper's unfinished miniature (*c.* 1665) at Windsor.

See no. 258.

228. ANNE CARR, COUNTESS OF BEDFORD (1615–84)

Hampton Court (177). Panel: $9\frac{1}{2} \times 7$ in., $24,1 \times 17,8$ cm.

Head and shoulders.

Copied from the portrait by Van Dyck at Petworth (218; C. H. Collins Baker, *Catalogue of the Petworth Collection . . .* (1920), p. 28).

Daughter of James I's favourite, the Earl of Somerset, and of his notorious Countess; married (1637) William Russell, 5th Earl and later 1st Duke of Bedford.

229. ELIZABETH WRIOTHESLEY, COUNTESS OF NORTHUMBERLAND (1646–90). *Identity uncertain.*

Hampton Court (185). Panel: 9¼ × 7 in., 23,5 × 17,8 cm.

Probably copied from a portrait by Lely (*c.* 1665).

See no. 261.

230. HENRIETTA BOYLE, COUNTESS OF ROCHESTER (1646–87). *Identity uncertain.*

Hampton Court (178). Panel: 9⅛ × 7 in., 23,2 × 17,8 cm.

Head and shoulders.

Copied from a portrait by Lely (*c.* 1668) of which there is a version at Chatsworth.

See no. 262.

231. DOROTHY SIDNEY, COUNTESS OF SUNDERLAND (1617–84)

Hampton Court (605). Copper: 15¾ × 12⅞ in., 40 × 32,7 cm.

Inscribed: *Sacharissa*

Half-length, resting her left hand on a carved vase.

Recorded at Hampton Court in the reign of George III (Geo. III, *Hampton Court*) and attributed to Russell.

Literature: Law, 1881, 1898 (187); Collins Baker, *Hampton Court*, p. 130.

A copy, close in style and scale to Leemput, of the portrait by Van Dyck of which the best version is at Petworth (305; C. H. Collins Baker, *Catalogue of the Petworth Collection . . .* (1920)), p. 31).

Daughter of the 2nd Earl of Leicester and celebrated as Waller's 'Saccharissa', she married the 2nd Earl of Sunderland in 1639.

Manner of Remigius van Leemput

232. CHARLES II

Holyroodhouse. Panel: 21½ × 15⅞ in., 54,6 × 40,3 cm.

Full-length seated, wearing the robes of the Garter.

Nos. 232 and 233 are recorded in the Bathing Room at Windsor in the time of Queen Anne (Queen Anne, *Windsor* (190, 191), next to nos. 218–30, but without attributions); later at Hampton Court (607).

A reduced copy, in the manner of Leemput though attributed to Russell from the middle of the eighteenth century, of a portrait of Charles II of *c.* 1665, of which there are versions at Gorhambury, Longleat and Tyninghame, and which was engraved by Hermann Quiter as after Lely.

233. JAMES II WHEN DUKE OF YORK

Holyroodhouse. Panel: 21⅝ × 15⅞ in., 54,9 × 40,3 cm.

Full-length standing, wearing the robes of the Garter; behind are the fluke of an anchor and ships at sea.

See no. 232; later at Hampton Court (604).

Companion piece to no. 232, and likewise attributed to Russell from the middle of the eighteenth century. No. 233 is a reduced copy of a design evolved by Lely *c.* 1665 and used by him, with slight variations, for the 1st Duke of Albemarle, the 1st Duke of Ormond, the Earl of Arlington and the 3rd Duke of Richmond. The last, in the North Carolina Museum of Art (96), comes closest to no. 233, of which no life-size version is known.

234. PORTRAIT OF A WOMAN

Hampton Court (338). Panel: 15½ × 12⅜ in., 39,4 × 31,4 cm.

Head and shoulders in a painted oval wearing costume of *c.* 1535 and on her breast a badge decorated with a relief of Leda and the Swan (?).

On the back is a seventeenth-century label bearing a number (40) of the type that occurs on the backs of nos. 218–30, so no. 234 may therefore have come from the same source and made up, with nos. 218–30, the fourteen pictures recorded in Queen Anne's inventory (see above). Probably to be identified with a portrait recorded early in the nineteenth century at Hampton Court (Pyne, vol. II, *Hampton Court*, pp. 62–3; inv. of 1835 (352), measurements given as 15¼ × 12 in.), where it was said to be of Anne Boleyn and ascribed to Holbein; at Hampton Court in 1858 (*V.R. inv.*) as a portrait of an unknown lady.

Literature: Law, 1881, 1898 (604); Collins Baker, *Hampton Court*, pp. 51–2.

A version of a portrait apparently once thought to represent Anne Boleyn. On the basis of a version at Warwick Castle, which has a companion portrait of Anne Boleyn, the type was later associated with her elder sister Mary. Another version is at Longford Castle. There does not, however, appear to be any contemporary evidence for this, and no. 234 was certainly painted in the seventeenth century. It is very close in style to Leemput.

Sir Peter Lely

1618–80. Born at Soest in Westphalia, where his father's regiment was stationed, and recorded in De Grebber's studio in Haarlem in 1637; in 1647 Lely painted the semi-captive Charles I and the younger royal children for the Earl of Northumberland; during the Interregnum he may have been in touch with the exiled court and after the Restoration, he was appointed (1661) Principal Painter and awarded an annual pension of £200 'as formerly to Sr Vandyke'. He painted a number of portraits of Charles II and Catherine of Braganza, but seems to have been particularly patronised by the Duke and Duchess of York. Most of the pictures that Lely painted for the Crown are still in the royal collection, but James II seems also to have owned two portraits by Lely of Princess Anne (B. M. Harl. MS. 1890, ff. 82, 85 v.; Bathoe, *James II* (1075, 1187)); one of these was apparently an unfinished half-length, was in store at Windsor in Queen Anne's time (Queen Anne, *Windsor*, store (51)), but is not recorded after 1714. The Duke of Buckingham was stated to have removed at the Revolution a portrait painted by Lely for Charles II which was at Whitehall in the reign of James II, described as: *By Danckers* [and] *Sr Peter Lely. Being the Slideing Peice before Madam Gwynn's Picture naked with a Cupid* (B. M., Harl. MS. 1890, f. 55 v.; Bathoe, *James II* (305)).

235. PORTRAIT OF THE ARTIST

Hampton Court (882). 30¼ × 25⅜ in., 76,8 × 64,5 cm.

Head and shoulders.

Probably purchased by George IV; recorded at Carlton House in 1816 (368) in store: *A head of a gentleman* (the 1816 label is on the back).

Literature: Law, 1881, 1898 (852); Collins Baker, *Lely*, vol. II, p. 127, *Hampton Court*, p. 93.

The condition of the head is not satisfactory, but the portrait may be autograph. The head is very close in type to the self-portrait with Hugh May (*c.* 1675) at Audley End, in which

Lely seems slightly older. *Sᴿ Peter Lilly by himself* [*his head*] was recorded by Vertue in the collection of Frederick, Prince of Wales, in 1750 (B. M., MS. 19027, f. 20v.). On the back of no. 235 is an obscure inscription in chalk (? *Little Drawing Room . . . PW*) and it is possible that it is the portrait that belonged to the Prince.

236. CHARLES II

Windsor Castle (137). 48⅛ × 39 in., 122,2 × 99,1 cm.

Three-quarter-length standing in armour, wearing the chain of the Garter, holding a baton in his right hand and resting his left hand on a helmet below the crown and sceptre.

The reference to an unfinished portrait of Charles II in James II's collection probably refers to no. 237, and there is no certain record of no. 236 before the nineteenth century (*V.R. inv.*, 1869).

Literature: Collins Baker, *Windsor*, p. 319.

The canvas seem originally to have been left unfinished. The King's face (and perhaps his collar) appears to be by Lely, *c.* 1665–70, of a type that was much repeated, principally in portraits of the King in Garter robes (*e.g.*, full-lengths at Boughton and Helmingham, three-quarter-lengths at Ugbrooke and in the possession of the Earl of Jersey, and a good head and shoulders, reduced from a full-length, at Althorp).

The composition was probably completed later, possibly in Lely's studio; this particular Van Dyckian pattern was also used for a head by Lely (*c.* 1660) of John Stone. At a still later period the canvas was enlarged to a full-length, but the additions were removed in 1955. A variant is at Stanford Park. A portrait at Ragley, close to no. 236, is presumably the half-length of Charles II bought by George IV in 1806 from Alexander Anderson, but sent to Lord Hertford on 29 May 1810 (W. R. A., Geo. 26835–7; Jutsham, *R/D*, f. 60). On a visit to Lely's studio on 18 June 1662, Pepys saw a portrait of the King 'that is not finished'.

237. CHARLES II

Windsor Castle (214). 94 × 57¾ in., 238,8 × 146,7 cm.; originally *c.* 49 × 39½ in. (see below).

Full-length standing in Garter robes, with his plumed hat on a table beside him.

Perhaps (but see also no. 236) *A head of King Charles the second, not finished*, which was in store at Whitehall, with no artist's name attached to it, in the reign of James II (B. M., Harl. MS. 1890, f. 59 v.; Bathoe, *James II* (439)). Presumably the portrait placed in the Queen's Gallery at Kensington in the set of royal full-lengths (Vertue inv., *Kensington*, f. 22; Bickham (p. 13) describes it as 'the Face by Sir *Peter Lely*, the posture by another Hand').

Literature: Pyne, vol. I, pp. 170, 172 (seen in plate of the room); Collins Baker, *Windsor*, p. 221.

The face and surrounding hair appear to be by Lely, *c.* 1672, but to have been left unfinished on a three-quarter-length canvas which was presumably worked up and enlarged, conceivably by Gaspars, at the end of the seventeenth, or early in the eighteenth, century. The head is of the type that was used by Lely for the full-length of the King, seated in Garter robes, of which many versions exist and of which the original is at Euston (see R. A., *Kings and Queens*, 1953 (173) and pls. 44, 47 in the illustrated souvenir). It is remarkable that Charles II seems to have owned no finished portrait of himself by Lely; in Lely's studio at his death there were seventeen copies of his portraits of the King. See no. 271.

238. CATHERINE OF BRAGANZA (*Plate* 99)

Windsor Castle (3067). 49¼ × 40⅜ in., 125 × 102,6 cm.

Three-quarter-length seated, with her hands in her lap.

Recorded in the reign of Queen Anne over a door in the Queen's Dressing Room at Windsor: *Queen Dowager at* ½ *length* (Queen Anne, *Windsor* (77)); later at Hampton Court (182) and St. James's.

Literature: Collins Baker, *Lely*, vol. II, p. 127.

Probably painted *c.* 1663–5, and perhaps for the Queen herself. Early copies, probably painted in Lely's studio, are at Brocklesby Park, in the collection of Mr. R. B. Beckett (Beckett, *Lely*, no. 69), and at Bramshill (sold at Christie's, 11 July 1958 (166)); copies of a reduced size are at Althorp, Parham Park, Hardwick and one was sold at Christie's, 7 March 1958 (41); and in a portrait of the Queen at Gripsholm the same head is incorporated into a more Van Dyckian design. A portrait of the Queen was among the unfinished half-lengths by Lely in James II's collection (B. M., Harl. MS. 1890, f. 85v.; Bathoe, *James II* (1191)).

239. JAMES II WHEN DUKE OF YORK

Buckingham Palace. 50 × 40¼ in., 127 × 102,2 cm.

Three-quarter-length standing in armour, with a baton in his right hand and resting his left hand on his helmet.

See nos. 240 and 274 for the impossibility of disentangling in the earlier inventories the references to portraits by Lely of the Duke of York and his first Duchess. No. 239 is probably *The King's head only dead coloured* among the unfinished portraits by Lely in James II's collection (see nos. 240 and 245). At some period it was hung as a pendant to no. 275; the pair may have been those hanging in the reign of George II on the Pictured Staircase at Kensington (see no. 274); they were later in the King's Closet at Windsor (Pyne, vol. I, pp. 135–6, 147).

The face, the first indications of the hair on the brow, and possibly the left hand, are apparently by Lely, *c.* 1663–5; if the portrait can be identified with the unfinished portrait in James's collection (see above), the composition was presumably completed towards the end of the seventeenth century, and apparently to a Van Dyckian design (the pattern is usually associated with Sir Edmund Verney (Glück, 448)) and not on a basis indicated by Lely himself. A contemporary version of the head was sold at Sotheby's, 17 February 1960 (169).

240. JAMES II WHEN DUKE OF YORK (*Plate* 100)

St. James's Palace. 49⅞ × 40½ in., 126,7 × 102,9 cm.

Three-quarter-length, standing in armour, wearing the ribbon of the Garter and holding a baton in his right hand.

Three unfinished portraits of James II by Lely are recorded in his collection, all at St. James's Palace: *The King at halfe length, The King in Armour at halfe length*, and *The Kings head onely dead coloured* (B. M., Harl. MS. 1890, f. 85 v.; Bathoe, *James II* (1185, 1190, 1192)); no. 240 is probably the first or second of the three. It is impossible in the later inventories to disentangle the references to Lely's portraits of the Duke and his first Duchess which came to be hung together. In Queen Anne's collection a pair hung in the Queen's Green Closet, and later in the Queen's Bedchamber, at St. James's House (Queen Anne, *St. James's* (29, 30)) and another, in which apparently both portraits were unfinished, was in store at Windsor (*ibid.*, *Windsor*, store (48, 49)). No. 240 was later hanging with no. 274 in the Dressing Room at Buckingham House and the portrait of the Duchess, presumably with its companion, was taken to St. James's on 2 February 1834.

Literature: Walpole, *Visits*, p. 79; Beckett, *Lely*, no. 263.

The portrait is almost certainly one of the unfinished portraits in the King's collection; the head, hair and cravat are by Lely (*c.* 1665) and the rest of the design was probably completed, presumably on indications left by Lely, at a slightly later period. There is a *pentimento* in the baton which was originally held more upright. A portrait of the Duke was hanging with the portraits of his flag-officers by Lely (see nos. 252 and 254) in the Great Chamber at Culford Hall in 1671 (Bodl. MS. 891, f. 22). Sixteen copies of Lely's portraits of the Duke were in his studio at his death. The head in no. 240 appears to be of the same type as the portrait by Green-hill at Dulwich (416).

241. JAMES II WHEN DUKE OF YORK

Windsor Castle (215). 94 × 58¼ in., 238,8 × 132,7 cm. The original was *c.* 81½ × 50½ in., but there are early additions of 4 in. on the right, 4 in. at the top and 9 in. at the bottom. There are further later additions of 2¼ in. on both sides.

Full-length in robes of state, wearing the collar of the Garter and standing by a richly stuffed chair on which is his coronet.

First recorded in store (5) at Windsor in Queen Anne's inventory: *Lelley A whole length of Kᵍ James the Second in Parliamᵗ Robes*; later in the set of royal full-lengths in the Queen's Gallery at Kensington.

Literature: Collins Baker, *Windsor*, p. 222.

Probably painted *c.* 1665–70. The head seems to be entirely by Lely and there are alterations in the drawing of the draperies in the left arm. The robes may be by Lely, but studio assistance is obvious in the background. It became an extremely popular design and was perhaps to some extent an official likeness of the Duke. The design was engraved by R. White. Full-length copies are, for example, at Narford, Pet-worth, Longleat, Burton Agnes and Ingatestone; and see nos. 272 and 273. Three-quarter-length copies are at Brocklesby, Syon and Burton Constable; a head and shoulders copy is at Bisham Abbey. In Lely's studio at his death there were six whole-length copies of the Duke of York.

242. ANNE HYDE, DUCHESS OF YORK (*Plate 101*)

Kensington Palace. 49½ × 40½ in., 125,7 × 102,9 cm.

Three-quarter-length, seated and holding in her right hand a tress of hair.

See no. 240 for the impossibility of disentangling in the early inventories the portraits by Lely of James II when Duke of York and his first Duchess. The present portrait may have been the only version recorded in James II's collection, hanging in the King's Closet at Windsor: *Sir Peter Lilly The first Dutchess of Yorke* (B. M., Harl. MS. 1890, f. 82; Bathoe, *James II* (1071)). It is probably the version recorded thereafter at Windsor until 28 April 1832; later at Hampton Court (1236).

Literature: Collins Baker, *Hampton Court*, p. 94; R. A., *The Age of Charles II*, 1960–1 (31).

Apparently the finest, and probably the earliest, version of this pattern (*c.* 1662), which would probably confirm its identification with the one that belonged to James II. It does not seem to have been paired off at any period with a portrait of her husband. Copies are common, *e.g.*, in the collection of Lord Clifford and Sotheby's, 5 March 1958 (182); and see nos. 274 and 275.

243. ANNE HYDE, DUCHESS OF YORK

Hampton Court (180). 81 × 51 in., 205,7 × 129,5 cm. About 2 in. have been turned over at the top and the canvas seems to have been slightly stretched at the bottom; at a later period the lower corners have been repaired and replaced by triangular insertions of new canvas: 11½ × 12 in. on the left, 11 × 11 in. on the right.

Full-length seated, holding in her right hand a tress of her hair that hangs loosely about her.

Apparently first recorded by Celia Fiennes, probably in its present position, at Hampton Court *c.* 1701–3 (*Journeys*, p. 355), and definitely there later in the reign of Queen Anne (Queen Anne, *Hampton Court* (15): *In the great Bed Chamber . . . over the Chimney*).

Literature: Vertue, *Notebooks*, vol. II, p. 67; Law, 1881, 1898 (190); Collins Baker, *Lely*, vol. II, p. 125, *Hampton Court*, p. 89; Beckett, *Lely*, no. 574.

Pepys saw in Lely's studio, on 18 June 1662, 'the Duchess of York, her whole body, sitting in state in a chair, in white satin'; but no. 243 was probably painted a few years later, though probably not as late as 1666, when, on 24 March, the Duke of York took Pepys into his lodgings 'into a chamber where the Duchesse was sitting to have her picture drawn by Lilly, who was there at work.' On the second occasion Pepys thought the portrait was not a good likeness. No. 243 may have been painted later than the three-quarter-length version of this design (no. 242). The Duchess regularly patronised Lely and there were ten copies of his portraits of her in his studio at his death. See no. 276.

244. MARY OF MODENA WHEN DUCHESS OF YORK

Hampton Court (484). 83½ × 53¼ in., 212,1 × 135,3 cm.

Full-length, standing on a step and resting her right hand on a richly carved vase in which is an orange tree.

Owing to the confusion (see below) between this portrait and no. 281, it is difficult to provide an accurate history of no. 244 before its appearance at Hampton Court in the nineteenth century.

Literature: Law, 1881, 1898 (65); Collins Baker, *Hampton Court*, p. 85 (both as Kneller).

The canvas appears to be entirely by Lely, probably *c.* 1677, except for the flowers which may have been painted by a specialist in the studio; the design is repeated for Lady Cornwallis at Audley End and, with variations, for the Duchesses of Norfolk (1677) and Cleveland. The identity is not entirely certain, but a royal ducal coronet is worked into the decoration of the carved vase. On the back of the canvas is an (early?) eighteenth century inscription: *N 29/ Dutches of Richmond / Dining Room . . .* The portrait of the Duchess of Richmond (no. 281), which is close in design, used to be known as 'Mary of Modena' so it is probable that the early references to a portrait of the Duchess of Richmond in the royal collection should be associated with no. 244.

245. MARY OF MODENA WHEN DUCHESS OF YORK

St. James's Palace. 50⅛ × 40½ in., 127,3 × 102,9 cm.

Three-quarter-length seated, resting her right hand on the head of a lamb.

Probably the portrait, *By Lilly, unfinished The Queene at halfe length*, recorded at St. James's Palace in James II's collection (B. M., Harl. MS. 1890 f. 85 v.; Bathoe, *James II* (1186)). Possibly at Kensington in the reign of George II, but owing to the confusion in earlier inventories between the Duke of York's two Duchesses and between his elder daughter and his second wife, and because of the identification of no. 245 in the nineteenth century with Nell Gwyn, its later movements are obscure; at Hampton Court (190).

Literature: Law, 1881, 1898 (196); Collins Baker, *Hampton Court*, p. 93.

The head appears to be by Lely, *c.* 1675–80, but the rest of the design is by an inferior hand, presumably on indications left by Lely. The landscape, however, seems to be by Lely or at least to be part of the original design. A miniature copy of the head, stated to be by Richard Gibson, is at Welbeck (R. A., *The Age of Charles II*, 1960–1 (683)).

246. PRINCESS ISABELLA (*Plate* 117)

Hampton Court (748). 36×31½ in., 91,4×80 cm.

Full-length, seated almost naked in a landscape, clasping a lamb.

First recorded in store at Kensington in the reign of Queen Anne: *Sʳ P. Lelly The Lady Issabella when a Child with a Lamb* (Queen Anne, *Kensington*, store (38); sent to Hampton Court in 1833.

Literature: Law, 1881, 1898 (501); Collins Baker, *Hampton Court*, p. 92; Beckett, *Lely*, no. 259.

Presumably painted in 1677; the Princess was born on 28 August 1676. There are *pentimenti* in the draperies and the canvas has been reduced; its original appearance can be seen in the mezzotint by Alexander Browne (*Fig.* 38). Copies are at Drayton, Berkeley Castle and formerly at Bramshill. The latter, sold at Sotheby's, 16 July 1952 (71), could have been the copy painted for Lely's executors by Frederick Sonnius (B. M., Add. MS. 16174, f. 10). The derivations of the design for the use of other sitters, such as a child at Deene and Jocelyn Sidney at Penshurst, may be based on the mezzotint.

247. HENRY, DUKE OF GLOUCESTER (*Plate* 104)

Hampton Court (1203). 59×51¼ in., 149,9×130,2 cm.

Full-length standing in a landscape, plucking a bunch of grapes from a pile of fruit beside him.

Possibly the portrait of *The Duke of Glocester in Sky colour'd Coates*, hanging at Colombes at the time of Henrietta Maria's death in 1669 (P. R. O., S.P. 78/128, f. 212 v.). Recorded in the King's Presence Chamber, apparently over a door, at Windsor in the reign of James II (B. M., Harl. MS. 1890, f. 72; Bathoe, *James II* (739); later inv. no. 46).

Literature: Vertue, *Notebooks*, vol. IV, p. 119; Miss M. Toynbee, 'The Early Work of Sir Peter Lely', *Burl. Mag.*, vol. LXXXVI–VII (1945), pp. 125–7, vol. LXXXVIII (1946), pp. 75–6.

Presumably painted at Syon House in 1647 when the Duke, with his sister Elizabeth and the Duke of York, were in the care of the Earl of Northumberland. The other portraits of the royal family, painted for Northumberland at that time (see Whinney and Millar, pp. 170–1), remained in Northumberland's possession, but it is possible that the Earl presented this portrait of the little Duke to Henrietta Maria or Charles II after the Restoration.

248. HENRY, DUKE OF GLOUCESTER

Hampton Court (1454). 50¼×40¼ in., 127,6×102,9 cm. Apparently originally conceived by Lely on a canvas 31½×28¾ in., but enlarged by him to 43×36¼ in.; at a later (but still early) date enlarged to its present size by another hand.

Three-quarter-length, walking in a landscape as a shepherd, with a crook over his shoulder and followed by a setting spaniel.

Probably the portrait by Lely of the Duke recorded in James II's collection at Windsor, in the Princess's Dressing Room, among the pictures which had not belonged to Charles II (B. M., Harl. MS. 1890, f. 83; Bathoe, *James II* (1109)); possibly therefore the *Duke of Glocester in a guylt frame* recorded in James's collection in Whitehall in 1674 (Bodl. MS. 891, f. 16 v.). Apparently thereafter at St. James's, Buckingham House, Kensington and St. James's.

Literature: Collins Baker, *Hampton Court*, p. 80, as by Huysmans.

Probably painted at Penshurst, where the Duke and his sister Elizabeth were in the care of the Earl and Countess of Leicester from June 1649 until August 1650. The Arcadian mood in which the portrait is conceived seems to have been reserved by Lely for the children of the Sidney and Percy families. The dog, moreover, appears in comparable portraits of the same date of Henry Sidney (Waterhouse, *Painting in Britain*, pl. 55) and the 11th Earl of Northumberland at Petworth (293), and probably belonged to the Leicesters. The dog was presumably added to the design by Lely when he enlarged his original composition; this enlargement seems to have been done almost immediately, but there are indications that the smaller original canvas was, if only for a very short time, nailed on a stretcher.

249. MARY II WHEN PRINCESS (*Plate* 103)

Kensington Palace. 48½×38½ in., 123,2×97,8 cm.; there is a very early addition at the bottom of *c.* 4½ in.

Walking in a landscape as Diana, wearing the crescent moon on her brow, drawing her bow and followed by a greyhound.

Almost certainly to be identified with *The Lady Mary when young wᵗʰ a bow and Arrow ½ length* which hung in the Queen's Dining Room at Windsor in the reign of Queen Anne (Queen Anne, *Windsor* (76); Lely's name is presumably meant to cover nos. 75–6 in this inventory); described in the same room by Vertue as *A little Diana Princess Mary* (Vertue inv., *Windsor*, f. 5)[1]; later at Hampton Court (171) and Windsor (3071).

Literature: Law, 1881, 1898 (186); Collins Baker, *Lely*, vol. I, pp. 167–8, vol. II, p. 126, *Hampton Court*, pp. 88–9; R. A., *British Art*, 1934 (128), *Commemorative Catalogue*, 1935 (39), *King's Pictures* (40); Beckett, *Lely*, no. 270.

Painted *c.* 1672. From the time of Law (*loc. cit.*) the portrait has been identified with Jane Kellaway on the basis of Alexander Browne's mezzotint, but the engraving, although of the same design, shows a different sitter. The portrait bears a very close resemblance to other early portraits of Princess Mary and its identification with her when it was in her sister's collection (and for many years thereafter) is conclusive. A copy was formerly at Oxonhoath and another is at Pencarrow; another was sold at Christie's, 30 May 1958 (144).

250. MARY II WHEN PRINCESS OF ORANGE (*Plate* 105)

Kensington Palace. 49¾×40½ in., 126,4×102,9 cm.

Three-quarter-length, seated in front of an elaborately carved vase of flowers.

Presumably painted for James II or William III and perhaps the portrait in the Queen's Green Closet, and later in the Queen's Bedchamber, in St. James's House in the reign of Queen Anne: *Lelly Mary Princess of Orange ½ length* (Queen Anne, *St. James's* (31)). Thereafter at Kensington (?), Windsor, Hampton Court (871) and St. James's Palace, but for a long time wrongly identified as Mary of Modena and thought to be the portrait of her by Verelst which is really no. 293.

Literature: R. A., *The Age of Charles II*, 1960–1 (377).

Probably painted in the autumn of 1677 at the time of her marriage to Prince William of Orange. The prince landed in England on 9 October, the wedding took place on 4 November and the Princess departed with her husband on 19 November. A good version of the portrait of William, presumably painted by Lely at the same time, is at Syon House; both portraits became popular and a number of variants and

---

1. Lely's name is attached to the portrait in the list of pictures at Windsor given to Thomas Hearne (*Remarks and Collections*, vol. xi, ed. Rev. H. E. Salter, *Oxford Hist. Soc.*, vol. LXXII (1922), p. 199 (1733)).

versions exist. One pair of copies was given by the sitters to Cornelis van Eck, Professor of Law at Utrecht (see V. & A., *William and Mary and their Time*, 1950 (29–31)) and a pair of small copies by Caspar or Constantin Netscher are in the Musée de Mayence (P. Bautier, 'Le Portrait de Marie Stuart au Musée de Bruxelles', *Musées Royaux des Beaux-Arts, Brussels, Bulletin* (June, 1956), pp. 70–4). In no. 250 there are traces of alterations by Lely to the drapery over the bosom. The pattern, with the variations in the accessories that appear in the variant portraits of the Princess, was also used by Lely for the Countess of Abingdon (Beckett, *Lely*, no. 2) and the Countess of Dalhousie at Colstoun. The head is used in a portrait of the Princess of a different design at Dunrobin Castle. The design was also used by painters in Lely's circle for other sitters, *e.g.*, Mrs. Fox, sold at Christie's, 18 March 1960 (19), which bore an early inscription attributing it to Riley. James II owned four unfinished half-length portraits by Lely of the Princess and one of the Prince (B. M., Harl. MS. 1890, f. 85 v.; Bathoe, *James II* (1188, 1189, 1193–5)). It was probably in connection with an earlier portrait that the Princess had written to Frances Apsley: . . . 'I am in great haste to be drest for Mr. Liley will be here at ten of the cloke'.

251. QUEEN ANNE WHEN A CHILD (*Plate* 118)

Hampton Court (778). 49¾ × 40⅛ in., 126,4 × 102 cm.

Full-length seated, wearing a feathered cap and holding a great tit on the end of a string.

First recorded in the Prince's Bedchamber at Kensington in the reign of Queen Anne: *Queen Ann wⁿ Child at length this Picture was bought by yᵉ Prince*, *i.e.* by Prince George of Denmark, presumably at some date after his marriage to the Queen in 1683 (Queen Anne, *Kensington* (185); later note by Thomas Coke: . . . *wᵗʰ a Bird in a String*). Sent to Hampton Court in 1838. During the later eighteenth and nineteenth centuries the sitter was thought to be the Duke (Henry?) of Gloucester.

Literature: Law, 1881, 1898 (515); Collins Baker, *Hampton Court*, p. 92; Beckett, *Lely*, no. 13.

Probably painted *c.* 1667–8. The bird, which is apparently painted over the curtain, may have been put in by one of Lely's assistants. The pattern was used by an imitator for a portrait of a boy sold at Christie's, 26 February 1960 (19).

252. PRINCE RUPERT (*Plate* 120)

Windsor Castle (55). 48¼ × 39⅝ in., 122,6 × 100,1 cm.

Inscribed slightly later: *Prince Rupert*

Three-quarter-length, standing in a breastplate and buff doublet, holding his baton in his left hand and resting his right hand near his helmet and gauntlet.

Part of the set of thirteen portraits, painted for the Duke of York, of the Duke's flag-officers in the battle of Lowestoft; eight of the portraits, including *prince Rupert*, were hanging in the Great Chamber at Culford Hall in October 1671 (Bodl. MS. 891, f. 22) and in James II's collection the set was apparently in store at St. James's (B. M., Harl. MS. 1890, f. 85 v.; Bathoe, *James II* (1198–1210)). In the reign of Queen Anne the portraits hung at Windsor in the King's Eating Room below Stairs (Queen Anne, *Windsor* (175–87)) and they remained at Windsor until, with the exception of nos. 252 and 254, they were presented by George IV in 1824 to Greenwich Hospital. They were now in the National Maritime Museum.

Literature: Waagen (1854), vol. II, p. 430; Collins Baker, *Lely*, vol. I, pp. 12, 165, 169–71, vol. II, p. 126, *Windsor*, p. 221; Beckett, *Lely*, no. 450; Waterhouse, *Painting in Britain*, pp. 66–7; Whinney and Millar, p. 174 (these references are mainly to the series).

On 18 April 1666 Pepys visited Lely's studio, where he 'saw the heads, some finished, and all begun, of the Flaggmen in the late great fight with the Duke of Yorke against the Dutch. The Duke of Yorke hath them done to hang in his chamber, and very finely they are done indeed. Here is the Prince's . . .' In the victory off Lowestoft on 3 June 1665 Rupert had been in command of the White and Vice-Admiral of the Fleet under the command of his cousin James. Although the heads of the 'Flaggmen' are among Lely's finest portraits the remainder of the designs seem to have been painted by his assistants. In no. 252 this is certainly the case. There is indeed a slight, but obvious, hiatus between the body and the head. The head is a sensitive *ad vivum* portrait and seems to have been used by Lely and his studio in full-length (*e.g.*, at Euston), and perhaps in three-quarter-length (*e.g.*, in the Uffizi), portraits of the Prince (see A. M. Crinò and O. Millar in *Burl. Mag.*, vol. C (1958), p. 129). See also no. 277.

253. ELEANOR NEEDHAM, LADY BYRON (1627–64) (*Plate* 102)

Hampton Court (170). 62¾ × 52¼ in., 156,8 × 132,7 cm.

Nearly full-length seated, as St. Catherine; resting her left hand on the wheel, holding a martyr's branch of palm and looking up at two flying putti, one of whom holds a crown of bay leaves over her head.

Recorded in Charles II's collection in store at Whitehall: *Lilly The Lady Byron with Sᵗ Katherines wheele* (Charles II, *Whitehall* (495), measurements given as 65 × 50 in.). Possibly, through a confusion, the portrait by Lely of *The Dutchesse of York in the manner of St. Catherine*, recorded in James II's collection at Windsor, apparently in Mr. Chiffinch's lodgings (B. M., Harl. MS. 1890, f. 75; Bathoe, *James II* (864)), and described in a slightly later variant of the MS. as *Lady Bellasis in the manner of Sᵗ Catharine. Lelly*; neither entry can be attached to a portrait in earlier or later sources. No. 253 hung over the chimney in the Queen's Waiting Room at Windsor, with Lely's *Beauties* (see nos. 257–66), in the time of Queen Anne: *Sʳ Peter Lely My Lady de Byron over the Chimʸ at whole length. a Sᵗ Kath.* (Queen Anne, *Windsor* (61), with note by Thomas Coke: *Qʳᵉ if not Housman*).

Literature: Vertue, *Notebooks*, vol. IV, p. 119; Walpole, *Anecdotes*, vol. II, p. 122; Law, 1881, 1898 (185); Collins Baker, *Lely*, vol. II, p. 125, *Hampton Court*, p. 88; R. A., *King's Pictures* (99); Beckett, *Lely*, no. 60.

The two confusions that have developed over no. 253 can be traced back to the early references to it, but the reference in Charles II's inventory settles the identity of the sitter and confirms the attribution to Lely. Thomas Coke's suggestion that Huysmans may have painted the portrait was taken up by, for example, Vertue and Walpole (*loc. cit.*). But it seems that the confused early references only concern *one* portrait. Probably painted, or begun, just before Lady Byron's death on 26 January 1664. There is perhaps studio work in draperies and accessories, but the head is of fine quality; there are alterations in the painting of the scarf and cloak over the edge of the chemise. It is one of Lely's most ambitious designs of *c.* 1663–4. A good, but not autograph, version at Tabley House probably belonged to the Byron family; lesser versions and variants are, for example, at Sledmere, Chatsworth (as 'Lady Anson') and Drumlanrig (as Lady Bellasis). A copy of the head was sold at Sotheby's, 15 November 1961 (3). *The Lady Biron* appears among the whole-length copies in Lely's studio at his death.

Daughter of Robert Needham, Viscount Kilmorey; married (1644) as his second wife, John, 1st. Baron Byron of Rochdale (*d.* 1652), the royalist commander and Governor of James II when Duke of York. She was reputed to have been one of Charles II's mistresses while he was in exile.

254. SIR JOHN LAWSON (d. 1665)

Buckingham Palace. 50¼×40¼ in., 127,6×102,2 cm.

Inscribed later: SIR JOHN LAWSON. LELY.

Three-quarter-length with a naval engagement in the background, standing in a breastplate and buff doublet, leaning on a cannon and holding a baton in his right hand.

Part of the set of portraits painted for the Duke of York (see no. 252), but retained, apparently by accident, when the portraits were presented to Greenwich Hospital by George IV in 1824; later at Hampton Court (1052).

Literature: Law, 1881, 1898 (7); see no. 252 for references to the series.

The portrait is entirely consistent with no. 252 and with the other portraits of the Duke of York's 'Flaggmen' that are now in the National Maritime Museum: the head is certainly by Lely, but the rest of the composition almost certainly by an assistant. Lawson was, however, mortally wounded in the battle that was stated by Pepys to have been commemorated by Lely's portraits for the Duke of York. If Lawson's portrait was painted *ad vivum* after the battle it must have been while Lawson was suffering from the wound of which he eventually died on 25 June 1665. The portrait of Lawson was among those recorded at Culford Hall in October 1671 (see no. 240), but was not one of the 'heads, some finished, and all begun', that Pepys saw in Lely's studio on 18 April 1666. It is possible, therefore, that after Lawson's death, and perhaps even after Pepys's visit to Lely, the Duke decided to add his portrait to the set and commissioned a posthumous portrait from Lely. The copy that presumably went to Greenwich in 1824 with the other 'Flaggmen' is first recorded in the Solebay Room at Hampton Court in the reign of George III and must thereafter have been changed with the original; another copy is at Avebury Manor.

A distinguished naval officer, with anabaptist and republican opinions, who had held commands at sea for the parliament since 1642, but supported the Restoration and won the favour of Charles II and the Duke of York.

255. HENRY CAVENDISH, EARL OF OGLE (1663–80)

Hampton Court (864). 49¾×40½ in., 126,4×102,9 cm.

Standing, in semi-classical costume, pointing across his body with his right hand.
Apparently first recorded at Hampton Court in 1849 as a portrait of William III by Kneller; later at St. James's, Kensington and (?) York House.

Literature: Law, 1881, 1898 (16); R. W. Goulding, *Catalogue of the Pictures . . . at Welbeck Abbey . . .* (1936), nos. 171–2, 542–3.

This and its companion (no. 256) seem to be the best versions of the pair of portraits that are probably referred to in the payment by the Duchess of Newcastle, Lord Ogle's mother, of £100 on 6 March 1680 'for Lord and Lady Ogle's pictures by Sir Peater Lilly'. The portraits had presumably been painted to celebrate their marriage on 27 March 1679 and were completed before Lord Ogle's death on 1 November 1680. They are thus among Lely's last works and there is probably studio assistance in the execution. The two pairs of copies at Welbeck (see A. S. Turberville, *A History of Welbeck Abbey and its Owners* (1938), vol. I, pp. 216, 218; and Beckett, *Lely*, nos. 399, 493) are of less good quality and are associated with the copies by Mary Beale recorded in her husband's notebook; the references are obscure, but seem to indicate that in 1681 she painted one, and possibly a second, pair of copies and a reduced copy of the portrait of

Lord Ogle. An old copy belongs to the Earl of Scarbrough.

Son and heir of Henry Cavendish, 2nd Duke of Newcastle, but died before his father: 'the saddest creature . . . as ugly as anything young can be'.

256. LADY ELIZABETH PERCY, COUNTESS OF OGLE (1667–1722)

Hampton Court (1239). 50×40¼ in., 127×102,2 cm.

Three-quarter-length, seated and pointing with her left hand; behind is a parrot perched in an orange tree.

Perhaps the portrait recorded in the Dining Room in Buckingham House in 1819 (740: *Portrait of a Lady. Wissing,* measurements given as 50×40 in.) and later at Kensington and St. James's.

Literature: Collins Baker, *Hampton Court,* p. 93.

See no. 255. Perhaps of slightly better quality than the companion portrait and certainly painted in Lely's studio; a good version is at Bolton Hall. The head is repeated in a portrait of a different design, probably from Lely's studio, at Albury Park. The design was engraved by Jan van der Vaart with a landscape background. A drawing after the composition is in the National Portrait Gallery (1753), and a copy in pastel is at Chirk Castle.

Daughter of the 11th (and last) Earl of Northumberland (the sitter in no. 261 was her mother) and one of the greatest heiresses in Europe; after Lord Ogle's death she was married to Thomas Thynne, who was murdered in 1682; later in the year she married, as his first wife, Charles Seymour, 6th Duke of Somerset. She was chief mourner at the funerals of Mary II and Queen Anne and was Groom of the Stole, 1711–14.

257–66. THE WINDSOR BEAUTIES

The series was painted for Anne Hyde, Duchess of York (see no. 243). In the *Memoirs* of the Chevalier de Gramont it is stated that 'the Duchess of York wished to have the portraits of the most beautiful women at Court. Lely painted them, devoted all his powers to the task and could not have worked on more lovely subjects.' The set was probably painted *c.* 1662–5. On 21 August 1668 Pepys 'did first see the Duke of York's room of pictures of some Maids of Honour, done by Lilly: good, but not like.' In an inventory of the Duke of York's possessions, drawn up on 1 June 1674, the portraits appear in the White Room at Whitehall: 'Hunge wth white sarsanett, and over it blew Mohair with silk fringe, . . . Madam Grammonds gone for fframe, six narrow long pictures [by Schiavone] under the great ones' (Bodl. MS. 891, f. 7 v.). Of the eleven portraits listed, ten can be identified with the Windsor Beauties and the remaining portrait, described as *Lady Fran Hyde,* was probably a portrait of the Duchess's sister Frances. They were taken to Windsor, presumably by James II, and hung in the Princess's Dressing Room (B. M., Harl. MS., 1890, f. 83; Bathoe, *James II* (1111–1120)). With them (*ibid.,* 1121) was a portrait by Lely of the King's sister Henrietta, Duchess of Orléans.[1] In the reign of Queen Anne they were in the Queen's Waiting, or Private Eating, Room (Queen Anne, *Windsor* (61–71)) and were joined by portraits of the same date and type (nos. 253, 326–8). The augmented series hung later in the Queen's State Bedchamber, or Beauty Room (Pyne, vol. I, pp. 116–29), where they were harshly criticised by Hazlitt: 'a set of kept-mistresses, painted, tawdry, showing off their theatrical or meretricious airs and graces, without one touch of real elegance or refinement, or one spark of sentiment to touch the heart.' They were at Hampton Court by June 1835.

1. This could perhaps have been the portrait now at Goodwood (Beckett, *Lely,* pl. 77).

Although the Windsor Beauties have always represented the most familiar and vulnerable aspect of Lely's achievement, he seems to have served his patroness well according to his own lights and, with the exception of no. 263, the portraits are wholly by his hand. The landscape backgrounds are particularly good. Vertue refers (*Notebooks*, vol. I, pp. 72–3) to copies of some of the Windsor Beauties in the collection of Thomas Wright and (*ibid.*, vol. III, p. 129) to copies of several of them by Jeremiah Davison. Eight of the portraits were engraved in mezzotint by James MacArdell and Thomas Watson (1778–9).

Literature: (for the set) Vertue, *Notebooks*, vol. II, p. 29; Walpole, *Anecdotes*, vol. II, pp. 93, 95 (n. by Dallaway); Hazlitt, 'The Pictures at Windsor Castle' (1823), *Works*, ed. A. R. Waller and A. Glover, vol. IX (1903), pp. 38–9; Mrs. Jameson, *Memoirs of the Beauties of the Court of Charles II* . . . (2nd ed., 1838); Waagen (1838), vol. II, p. 118, (1854), vol. II, p. 360; Chaloner Smith, pp. 868, 882, 1551–2; Collins Baker, *Lely*, vol. I, pp. 165–8, *Lely and Kneller* (1922), pp. 30–1; Waterhouse, *Painting in Britain*, p. 67; Whinney and Millar, pp. 173–4; A. M. Crinò and O. Millar, 'Sir Peter Lely and the Grand Duke of Tuscany', *Burl. Mag.*, vol. C (1958), pp. 127–9.

257. BARBARA VILLIERS, DUCHESS OF CLEVELAND (c. 1641–1709) (*Plate* 109)

Hampton Court (199). 49×40 in., 124,5×101,6 cm.

Standing as Minerva in a stormy landscape, wearing a plumed helmet, holding a spear in her left hand and resting her right hand on a shield on which is carved a gorgon's head.

Literature: Law, 1881, 1898 (205); Collins Baker, *Lely*, vol. II, p. 126, *Hampton Court*, p. 91; Beckett, *Lely*, no. 105.

Probably painted *c.* 1665. Engraved by Thomas Watson. The *Duchesse of Cleaveland with a guylt frame*, perhaps a different picture, appears among the Duke of York's pictures in the Green Mohair Closet at Whitehall in 1674 (Bodl. MS. 891, f. 17).
Charles II owned a portrait of the Duchess: *Mʳ Lilly One Picture of Lady Castlemaines sitting at length* (Charles II, *Whitehall* (642), in store, measurements given as 73×50 in.).[1]

Daughter of William Villiers, 2nd Viscount Grandison; married (1659) Roger Palmer, later Earl of Castlemaine, but became the King's mistress at the Restoration. She seems to have borne him at least six children; she was created by him a Lady of the Bedchamber to Catherine of Braganza. She was on many occasions and in many guises painted by Lely, 'who used to say, that it was beyond the compass of art to give this lady her due, as to her sweetness and exquisite beauty'. At the time of his death Lely's studio contained thirteen copies and one original portrait of the Duchess.

258. FRANCES STUART, DUCHESS OF RICHMOND (1648–1702) (*Plate* 113)

Hampton Court (189). 49½×40¾ in., 125,7×103,5 cm.

Walking in a landscape with a bow in her left hand.

Literature: Law, 1881, 1898 (195); Collins Baker, *Lely*, vol. II, p. 125, *Hampton Court*, p. 89; Beckett, *Lely*, no. 433.

Probably one of the earliest in the series and painted not later than *c.* 1662; Lely's preparatory drawing (*Fig.* 37) for the right hand is on the same sheet as his studies for the hands in no. 259. A copy, possibly by Jeremiah Davison (see above) and described as the Countess of Northumberland, is at

1. This could be the full-length of the Duchess at Euston, or a version of that type (Beckett, *Lely*, no. 102).

Drumlanrig. An early copy was sold at Christie's, 18 February 1927 (153). Engraved by Thomas Watson. Lely used the design, with slight variations and possibly earlier, for Elizabeth de Grey, Lady Maynard.

Daughter of Walter Stuart of Blantyre, Maid of Honour and Lady of the Bedchamber to Catherine of Braganza, and one of the greatest beauties at the Restoration court; Charles II was passionately devoted to her and was infuriated by her clandestine marriage (1667), as his third wife, to Charles Stuart, 3rd Duke of Richmond.

259. MARY BAGOT, COUNTESS OF FALMOUTH AND DORSET (1645–79) (*Plate* 110)

Hampton Court (197). 48⅞×40 in., 124,1×101,6 cm.

Standing with a crook (?) in her left hand, leaning her right arm on a ledge.

Literature: Law, 1881, 1898 (203); Collins Baker, *Lely*, vol. II, p. 125, *Hampton Court*, pp. 90–1; Beckett, *Lely*, no. 167.

Lely's preparatory drawing (*Fig.* 37) for the hands is on the same sheet as the study for a hand in no. 258. Probably painted *c.* 1664–5; a copy, possibly by Jeremiah Davison (see above), is at Drumlanrig. Engraved by Thomas Watson, but as the Countess of Ossory; the identity of the portrait was confused in the nineteenth century. A copy, called Lady Denham, is at Chirk Castle.

Daughter of Hervey Bagot; married (1664) Charles Berkeley, Earl of Falmouth (killed at sea, 1665), and afterwards (1674) Charles Sackville, 6th Earl of Dorset.

260. ELIZABETH HAMILTON, COUNTESS OF GRAMONT (1641–1708) (*Plate* 108)

Hampton Court (201). 49¼×40 in., 125,1×101,6 cm.

Signed: *PL* in monogram.

Seated, apparently as St. Catherine, beside a column, holding a palm branch in her left hand.

Literature: Law, 1881, 1898 (207); Collins Baker, *Lely*, vol. II, p. 125, *Hampton Court*, p. 92; Beckett, *Lely*, no. 220; R. A., *King's Pictures* (44).

Probably painted *c.* 1663. According to De Gramont each portrait in the series of Beauties was a masterpiece and 'that of Miss Hamilton seemed the most finished. Lely avowed that he had taken great pleasure in it. The Duke of York delighted in looking at it and began to ogle the original once more.' There are possible indications that the head was at first painted a little higher on the canvas. Engraved by MacArdell. A copy, possibly by Jeremiah Davison (see above), is at Drumlanrig; another, from the collection of General W. C. Hadden, was on the art market in 1905; a copy from the collection of the Earl of Cork was on the art market in New York in 1935; and see no. 278.

Daughter of Sir George Hamilton and one of the greatest beauties at the Restoration court; her famous courtship by Philibert, Comte de Gramont, ended in their marriage (1663) and departure for France. Walpole, who was anxious in 1746 to secure copies of the set of Beauties 'even in Indian ink' (letter to George Montagu, 24 June 1746 (*Correspondence*, ed. W. S. Lewis, vol. IX (1941), pp. 34–5), had a particular obsession with portraits of the Countess and her family.

261. ELIZABETH WRIOTHESLEY, COUNTESS OF NORTHUMBERLAND (1646–90) (*Plate* 114)

Hampton Court (196). 49½×40¾ in., 125,7×103,5 cm.

Advancing in a landscape and pointing with her right hand to the distance.

Literature: Law, 1881, 1898 (202); Collins Baker, *Lely*, vol. II, p. 125; R. W. Goulding, 'Wriothesley Portraits', *Walpole Soc.*, vol. VIII (1920), pp. 89–90; Collins Baker, *Hampton Court*, p. 90; Beckett, *Lely*, no. 357.

Probably one of the latest in the series and not painted before 1665. Engraved by Thomas Watson. The design was repeated for portraits of, among others, Jane Seymour, Lady Clifford (by Lely himself) at Chatsworth; Lady Elizabeth Hastings; and an unknown woman at Crichel.

Daughter of Thomas Wriothesley, Earl of Southampton; married (1662) Joceline Percy, 11th Earl of Northumberland (d. 1670), and afterwards (1673), as his first wife, Ralph, 1st Duke of Montagu.

262. HENRIETTA BOYLE, COUNTESS OF ROCHESTER (1646–87) (*Plate* 115)

Hampton Court (191). 49 × 40 in., 124,5 × 101,6 cm.

Leaning against a carved ledge, plucking a rose with her right hand.

Literature: Law, 1881, 1898 (197); Collins Baker, *Lely*, vol. II, p. 125, *Hampton Court*, p. 89; Beckett, *Lely*, no. 440.

Painted *c.* 1665, or possibly slightly later. Engraved by MacArdell and Watson. The design was copied for a portrait of an unknown woman at Crichel and used for a portrait of a woman, wrongly called the Countess of Rochester, in the Minneapolis Institute of Arts.

Daughter of Richard Boyle, 1st Earl of Burlington; married (1665) Lawrence Hyde, 1st Earl of Rochester; Governess to Princess Anne in 1677 and 1682.

263. ANNE DIGBY, COUNTESS OF SUNDERLAND (*c.* 1646–1715) (*Plate* 116)

Hampton Court (200). 49¼ × 40¼ in., 125,1 × 102,2 cm.

Seated beside a richly carved gilt urn, leaning her left arm on a stone ledge.

Literature: Law, 1881, 1898 (206); Collins Baker, *Lely*, vol. II, p. 125, *Hampton Court*, pp. 91–2; Beckett, *Lely*, no. 520A.

Apparently a second version of the original portrait at Althorp which is inscribed slightly later with the date 1666; no. 263 was probably painted in Lely's studio, but does not seem to be by Lely himself. The design was also used for a portrait of the Duchess of Cleveland of which a studio copy was sold from Ashburnham Place by Sotheby's, 15 July 1953 (150).

Daughter of George Digby, 2nd Earl of Bristol; married (1665) Robert Spencer, 2nd Earl of Sunderland. Her husband assembled the fine collection of female portraits by Lely which is still at Althorp.

264. MARGARET BROOKE, LADY DENHAM (*c.* 1647–1667) (*Plate* 111).

Hampton Court (198). 49 × 39¾ in., 124,5 × 101 cm.

Seated, holding a basket of flowers on her lap.

Literature: Law, 1881, 1898 (204); Collins Baker, *Lely*, vol. II, p. 125, *Hampton Court*, p. 91; Beckett, *Lely*, no. 155.

Painted *c.* 1663–5. There is a copy at Ombersley Court.

Daughter of Sir William Brooke and sister of Lady Whitmore; married (1665) Sir John Denham but soon became known as the Duke of York's mistress.

265. FRANCES BROOKE, LADY WHITMORE (d. 1690) (*Plate* 112)

Hampton Court (195). 49 × 40 in., 124,5 × 101,6 cm.

Seated in a landscape, resting her left arm on a rocky ledge.

Literature: Law, 1881, 1898 (201); Collins Baker, *Lely*, vol. II, p. 125, *Hampton Court*, p. 90; Beckett, *Lely*, no. 564.

Probably painted *c.* 1665. The leaves over the dress in the lower right corner are an afterthought by Lely. A copy at Drumlanrig, possibly by Jeremiah Davison (see above), is called the Countess of Southesk, with whom the original was also confused by Mrs. Jameson (*op. cit.*, vol. II, pp. 77–85); other copies are at Chirk Castle and Plas Powr (as Lady Denham); another copy was sold at Sotheby's from Bramshill, 16 July 1952 (74). The design was used for portraits of the Countess of Southesk at Narford and Mrs. Middleton (?) at Althorp. Engraved by Thomas Watson.

Daughter and co-heir of Sir William Brooke, nephew of Henry, Lord Cobham; she married before May 1665 Sir Thomas Whitmore (d. 1682), and secondly Matthew Harvey (d. 1693).

266. JANE NEEDHAM, MRS. MYDDELTON (1646–92) (*Plate* 107)

Hampton Court (193). 48⅞ × 40 in., 124,1 × 101,6 cm.

Standing, clasping a cornucopia to her side.

Literature: Law, 1881, 1898 (199); Collins Baker, *Lely*, vol. II, p. 125, *Hampton Court*, pp. 89–90; Beckett, *Lely*, no. 341.

Painted *c.* 1663–5. Engraved by MacArdell. A copy is at Kingston Lacy; the head was used in a variant portrait of her, sold at Christie's, 29 January 1960 (17); and the design was copied for a portrait of an unknown woman at Crichel. *Mrs. Midlton with a guylt frame*, perhaps a different picture, appears among the Duke of York's pictures in the Green Mohair Closet at Whitehall in 1674 (Bodl. MS. 891, f. 17). Five copies of portraits of her were in Lely's studio at his death.

'That famous, & indeede incomparable beautifull Lady', daughter of Sir Robert Needham; married in 1660 Charles Myddelton of Ruabon; she was a skilful amateur painter.

267. PORTRAIT OF A LADY

Buckingham Palace. 36 × 28 in., 91,4 × 71,1 cm.

Half-length, seated in a landscape, resting her left hand on the carved edge of a fountain (see below).

First recorded at Buckingham Palace in 1841, set over one of the doors in the Yellow Drawing Room (*Buckingham Palace*, 1841, p. 96) as a portrait of Anne Hyde, Duchess of York, but possibly to be identified earlier in the royal collection: *A Portrait Sir P. Lely*, for example, was earlier at Kew (Geo. III, *Kew*), and Pyne records (vol. II, *Buckingham House*, p. 13) in the King's Dining Room 'some female portraits . . . by Sir Peter Lely . . . among which is a fine picture of Anne Hyde'.

Apparently an autograph portrait of *c.* 1658–60 of an unidentified sitter. The canvas was presumably originally of a normal three-quarter-length size and was cut down so that it should fit its present position. The sitter was probably to be seen holding in her right hand a shell in which fell a jet of water. Her right arm, however, and part of her sleeve, have been painted out, presumably when the canvas was reduced.

268. THE PENITENT MAGDALEN

Hampton Court (849). 72¾ × 62½ in., 184,8 × 158,8 cm.; enlarged at the top, bottom and on the right; the original area measures 64 × 56 in., including Lely's own addition of 11 in. on the left.

Full-length, seated in a cave and contemplating a skull and a crucifix.

Probably acquired by James II and recorded in his collection at St. James's: *Lilly. A Magdalen at length* (B. M., Harl. MS. 1890, f. 86; Bathoe, James II (1215)); later at Windsor: the additions to the canvas probably date from the time when it was set over a door in the Queen's Presence Chamber.

Literature: Vertue, *Notebooks* (?vol. I, p. 78 (as St. Catherine)), vol. IV, p. 119; Law, 1881, 1898 (781); Collins Baker, *Hampton Court*, p. 92.

A second version, possibly by Lely himself, of the picture at Kingston Lacy (Beckett, *Lely*, no. 592), painted *c.* 1650–5, probably for Sir Ralph Bankes. The version at Kingston Lacy preserves the original proportions of the design. The model seems to have been a member of Lely's circle during his earlier years in London. She re-appears, with only the most superficial change of mood, as Europa in the picture at Chatsworth (*ibid.*, no. 582) and as the pupil in Lord Dulverton's *Music Lesson* of 1654 (*ibid.*, no. 593). A drawing in the collection of the Earl of Jersey may be a preliminary *ad vivum* study used by Lely in compositions of this nature.

Sir Peter Lely and Benedetto Gennari

269. JAMES II, WHEN DUKE OF YORK, WITH ANNE HYDE AND THEIR TWO DAUGHTERS, PRINCESS MARY AND PRINCESS ANNE

Windsor Castle (2968). 66¼ × 76½ in., 168,3 × 194,3 cm.

Inscribed slightly later: DVKE AND DVTCHES OF / YORK WITH PRINCES / MAREY AND ANN.

Three-quarter-length group, the Duke and Duchess seated, the Duke leaning on a globe and accompanied by a setting spaniel (on whose collar is inscribed IACOBVS), the Duchess with her little daughters beside her, Princess Mary holding a wreath.

Formerly at Ditchley (seen there by Vertue, *loc. cit.*). Perhaps presented by the Duke to his niece Charlotte Fitzroy, Countess of Lichfield;[1] passed by descent to the Viscounts Dillon and sold at Sotheby's, 24 May 1933 (67); purchased by Her Majesty Queen Mary for the royal collection.

Literature: Vertue, *Notebooks*, vol. II, p. 65; Walpole, *Visits* (to Ditchley in 1760), p. 26 (... 'The Duke's head & one hand by Lely, good; all the rest by some wretched Scholar of his'); Lord Dillon, *Catalogue of the Paintings ... at Ditchley* (1908), no. 2; Collins Baker, *Lely*, vol. I, pp. 213–4, vol. II, p. 154, *Windsor*, p. 176; R. A., *King's Pictures* (105).

Benedetto Gennari's own account of the pictures painted by him in London, where he began painting in October 1674, includes (no. 62): *Finito un ritratto principiato da Lilli ritratto della prima moglie della duca di Yorck con due piccole sue figliuole cioe la Sr Principesse Maria, e Principess' Anna* (MS. B. 344 in Biblioteca Comunale dell'Archiginnasio, Bologna, f. 22)[2]. Lely had evolved the composition in a double portrait (*c.* 1663) of the Duke and Duchess of which the finest version is at Petworth (see R. A., *Kings and Queens*, 1953 (194) and pl. 50 in the illustrated souvenir) and this group was in turn related to the particularly sumptuous single portraits of the couple which Lely had painted, probably on the occasion of their

marriage, for the Duchess's father (now nos. 901 and 1179 in the Scottish National Portrait Gallery). Lely had presumably started (*c.* 1668–70) a version that would include the Duke's two daughters; they were fitted into the old design in a way reminiscent of the children in Lely's earlier group of the Carnarvon family (Beckett, *Lely*, no. 66). The figures and the curtain had probably only been blocked in by Lely when Gennari (probably *c.* 1680) was commissioned to finish the composition. The quality is consistently coarse throughout, the drawing is clumsy in detail and the confusion between the Duke's sash and Garter ribbon is perhaps a result of Gennari's inability to interpret what remained of Lely's intentions. The landscape, however, is of better quality and may have been finished before Lely abandoned the group.

After Sir Peter Lely

270. PORTRAIT OF THE ARTIST (?)

Hampton Court (972). 30 × 25¼ in., 76,2 × 64,1 cm.

Head and shoulders.

Probably purchased by George IV; recorded at Carlton House, 1816 (369) in store: *A head of a gentleman* (the 1816 label is on the back).

Literature: Law, 1881, 1898 (862); Collins Baker, *Lely*, vol. II, p. 127, *Hampton Court*, p. 166.

A copy of a portrait of *c.* 1665; it does not bear a very close resemblance to other self-portraits of Lely (*e.g.*, no. 235) but a better, though not autograph, version in the possession of Sir Danvers Osborn bears a later inscription: *Sir Peter Lely by Himself.*

271. CHARLES II

St. James's Palace. 94 × 58¼ in., 238,8 × 148 cm.

Recorded at St. James's in 1865 (*V.R. inv.*).

A nineteenth-century copy of no. 237.

272. JAMES II WHEN DUKE OF YORK

St. James's Palace. 94 × 58 in., 238,8 × 147,3 cm.

Recorded at St. James's in 1865 (*V.R. inv.*).

A nineteenth-century copy of no. 241.

273. JAMES II WHEN DUKE OF YORK

Holyroodhouse. 94 × 54¾ in., 238,8 × 139,1 cm.

Sold from the collection of Capt. Young at Christie's, 15 December 1882 (250; Christie's stencil is on the back); bought from Graves and sent to Holyrood in 1883 with no. 276 (P.R.O., L. C. 1/405).

An early copy of no. 241.

274. ANNE HYDE, DUCHESS OF YORK

St. James's Palace. 50⅛ × 40⅞ in., 127,3 × 103,8 cm.

Three-quarter-length, seated and holding in her right hand a tress of hair.

See no. 240 for the impossibility of disentangling the references in the earlier inventories to the portraits of James II and his first Duchess. At Kensington in the reign of George II one pair was in the Privy Chamber and another on the Pictured Staircase (Vertue inv., *Kensington*, ff. 1, 23); no. 274 and no. 240 may have been together in the Privy Chamber and certainly hung together later in the Dressing Room at Buckingham House.

A copy, probably painted in Lely's studio, and with changes in colour and other slight variations from no. 242.

---

1. It does not, however, appear in Thomas Hearne's account of the pictures at Ditchley in 1718, and he states emphatically that the Countess did not own a portrait of her uncle.

2. This MS. was kindly brought to my notice by Mr. Denis Mahon.

275. ANNE HYDE, DUCHESS OF YORK

Windsor Castle (2959). $49\frac{3}{4} \times 40\frac{1}{4}$ in., $126,4 \times 102,2$ cm.

See nos. 240 and 274. Possibly the version recorded in store at Kensington in the time of Queen Anne: *after Lelly Dutchess of York $\frac{1}{2}$ length* (Queen Anne, *Kensington*, store (26)); thereafter probably paired with no. 239 at Kensington (in the pair on the Pictured Staircase at Kensington the Duchess is stated to be a copy), Windsor and Buckingham Palace (794), but moved alone to Windsor on 15 April 1931.

Literature: Collins Baker, *Windsor*, p. 222.

A respectable early copy after no. 242.

276. ANNE HYDE, DUCHESS OF YORK

Holyroodhouse. $94\frac{1}{2} \times 53\frac{3}{4}$ in., 240×137 cm.; the canvas has apparently been enlarged all round and was originally *c.* 82×48 in.

First recorded in the reign of Queen Anne over the chimney in the Blue Room in St. James's House (Queen Anne, *St. James's* (15): *Lelly The Dutchess of York at length . . .*); thereafter probably in the set of royal portraits in the Queen's Gallery at Kensington (Vertue inv., *Kensington*, f. 22) and later at Windsor and St. James's.

An early copy of no. 243.

277. PRINCE RUPERT

Windsor Castle (2701). $13\frac{1}{2} \times 11\frac{1}{4}$ in., $34,3 \times 28,6$ cm.

Purchased by King Edward VII in 1909.

Literature: Collins Baker, *Windsor*, p. 225.

An unimportant copy from the type of which no. 252 is the original.

278. ELIZABETH HAMILTON, COUNTESS OF GRAMONT (1641–1708)

St. James's Palace. $49\frac{1}{2} \times 37\frac{1}{4}$ in., $125,7 \times 94,6$ cm.

Recorded in the Dining Room at Buckingham House in 1819 (743: *Portrait of a Lady in the Character of St Catherine. Sir P. Lely . . . Equal to many of the Works of Vandyke*); later at Kensington, St. James's and Windsor (2489).

Literature: Collins Baker, *Windsor*, p. 224.

An early copy of no. 260. There were two copies of Lely's portrait of the Countess in his studio at his death.

279. BAPTIST MAY (1629–98)

St. James's Palace. $48\frac{3}{4} \times 40\frac{1}{4}$ in., $123,8 \times 102,2$ cm.

Three-quarter-length, standing in a landscape with his left hand on his sword.

Stated to have been bought at the sale of Mr. Patterson of Cringleford, Norfolk, by C. R. Freeman of Park House, Norwich, and to have been sold by the executors of his daughter, Mrs. R. R. Wheeler of Frampton Cotterell, Gloucestershire; purchased from Leggatt's by King Edward VII in 1907. Formerly at Windsor (2623).

Literature: Collins Baker, *Lely*, vol. I, p. 176, vol. II, p. 129, *Windsor*, p. 223.

A good copy, probably painted in his studio, of the portrait by Lely (*c.* 1672; R. B. Beckett, *Lely*, no. 334) that has passed by descent from the sitter to Lord De Saumarez at Shrublands Park; other copies exist and a full-length variant is at Cirencester. The pattern was used by Lely and his assistants for a number of patrons and may have been evolved for a portrait of the 3rd Duke of Somerset (1671) at Badminton.

Keeper of the Privy Purse to Charles II (1665–85), Ranger of Windsor Great Park (1671–97) and one of Charles II's most intimate and discreditable courtiers.

280. SIR THEODORE TURQUET DE MAYERNE (1573–1655)

Hampton Court (264). $30\frac{1}{4} \times 25\frac{1}{4}$ in., $76,8 \times 64,1$ cm.

Head and shoulders, wearing a black cap.

Among the portraits, formerly in the collection of Lady Capel, acquired at Kew; a particularly good impression of Lady Capel's seal is on the front of the canvas; later at Kensington.

Literature: Law, 1881, 1898 (711).

Formerly thought to be a copy after Rubens, no. 280 is not connected with Rubens's portrait of Mayerne, of which the best version is in the North Carolina Museum of Art (128). It seems, however, to be a contemporary copy of a portrait by Lely of *c.* 1650; in style and presentation it is entirely consistent with Lely's style at that date.

A celebrated French physician who worked at Montpellier and Paris before coming in 1606 to England, where he was appointed Physician to Queen Anne of Denmark and, in 1611, first Physician to James I; he built up a large practice and later became Physician to Charles I and his Queen. He was also interested in the nature of artists' pigments; died in retirement at Chelsea.

281. FRANCES STUART, DUCHESS OF RICHMOND (1648–1702)

Windsor Castle (2498). $86\frac{1}{2} \times 50$ in., $219,7 \times 127$ cm.; 3 in. of the original canvas are turned over at the bottom.

Full-length standing, resting her left elbow on a carved stone ledge.

Perhaps the portrait recorded at St. James's in 1819 (1027): *Full length Portrait of a Lady. Sir G. Kneller*, measurements given as 89×50 in.; later at Buckingham Palace (1060) and St. James's.

Literature: Collins Baker, *Windsor*, p. 187.

Apparently a contemporary copy of a portrait of *c.* 1678–80. The design is engraved by A. Browne as after Lely, but neither no. 281 nor the other known versions are Lelyesque in quality. No. 281 and the better version at Goodwood are slightly suggestive of Kneller. There are versions at Budapest (1330) and (a copy) at Castle Howard. Copies of the head alone are at Goodwood and Holkham. No. 281 was formerly identified as Mary of Modena and it is therefore possible that the earlier references to this portrait and no. 244 have been confused. A comparison with the other versions indicates that no. 281 has been cut down at top and bottom and possibly on the right.

See no. 258.

282. EDWARD MONTAGU, FIRST EARL OF SANDWICH (1625–72)

Buckingham Palace. $50\frac{1}{8} \times 40\frac{3}{8}$ in., $127,3 \times 102,6$ cm.

Three-quarter-length standing in armour, wearing the chain of the Garter and resting his left hand on a cannon; in the background his flagship as Admiral of the Blue is engaged with a Dutch warship. The Earl's coronet in the background was added later.

First recorded, with an attribution to Dobson, in the reign of George III in the Solebay Room at Hampton Court; remained at Hampton Court (1063) until 1915.

Literature: Law, 1881, 1898 (11).

Probably painted towards the end of the seventeenth century. The head is based on a portrait by Lely of which a version, probably painted on the eve of the Restoration, is in the National Maritime Museum; a variant formerly at Hinchingbrooke and using the same head, is the portrait by Lely which Pepys saw in October 1661 and which Emmanuel De Critz copied for him. The Van Dyckian design probably derives ultimately from Van Dyck's *1st Duke of Hamilton* (Glück, 463).

Served on land and sea for the Parliament in the Civil War, but played an important part in restoring Charles II to the throne; conducted Catherine of Braganza to England (1661); killed at the Battle of Solebay. His portrait was among the 'Flaggmen' commissioned by the Duke of York (see no. 240).

283. PORTRAIT OF A LADY

St. James's Palace. 30¼ × 25¼ in., 76,8 × 64,1 cm.

Head and shoulders in a painted oval, wearing a chain of pearls over her shoulders.

Probably purchased by George IV; recorded at Carlton House in 1816 (300: *A head of a Lady*); later at Hampton Court (886).

Literature: Law, 1881, 1898 (54).

The sitter bears a very close resemblance to the Duchess of Portsmouth (see no. 292) and the portrait appears to be an early copy of a portrait of her by Lely of *c.* 1675.

284. PORTRAIT OF A LADY

Hampton Court (1237). 49½ × 41 in., 125,7 × 104,1 cm.

Three-quarter-length, seated in a landscape, resting her left arm on a ledge.

Possibly the picture recorded in the Duke of Cumberland's apartments in St. James's in 1819 (1058: *Portrait of a Lady. Sir P. Lely*); later at St. James's.

Literature: Collins Baker, *Hampton Court*, p. 94.

A copy, probably painted in Lely's studio, of a portrait of *c.* 1663–5.

John Michael Wright

1617–1700?. Born in London, but probably of Scots parents, and recorded in 1636 as an apprentice to George Jamesone in Edinburgh; spent a number of years in Italy and Flanders, where he may have made contact with the exiled court during the Interregnum. After the Restoration he painted portraits of Charles II, James II and Prince Rupert, but, although on occasion he styled himself 'Pictor Regius', he does not seem to have been officially attached to the royal service. He was a Roman Catholic and in 1686 went as chief steward to Lord Castlemaine on the embassy from James II to Innocent XI. Evelyn, in his account, probably expanded later, of a visit to Wright's studio on 3 October 1662, recorded among his works '. . . some pieces in White hall, as the roofe in his Majesties old Bedchamber, being *Astrea*, the St. *Catharine*, a Chimney piece in the *Queenes* Privy Chamber.' The first of these was in store at Windsor in the time of Queen Anne (Queen Anne, *Windsor*, store (76): *Wright An Oval Piece for a Sealing wth King Charles in it*), but is not recorded in the royal collection thereafter and is now in the Nottingham Art Gallery.

285. CHARLES II (*Plate 123*)

St. James's Palace. 111½ × 94¾ in., 283,2 × 225,4 cm.; the original canvas seems to have been cut all round and slightly stretched in lining.

Full-length seated under a canopy of state, embroidered with the royal arms and set in front of a (sixteenth-century?) tapestry apparently representing the Judgement of Solomon. The King is in Parliament robes over Garter costume; he wears St. Edward's Crown and holds the orb and the sceptre with cross, and on his left hand wears a ring.

Purchased for the royal collection from Graves in 1889 (P.R.O., L. C. 1/513, II, 5, 7).

Literature: New Gallery, *Royal House of Stuart*, 1889 (135); Collins Baker, *Lely*, vol. I, p. 190; Whinney and Millar, p. 186; R. A., *The Age of Charles II*, 1960 (39).

No. 285 was ascribed to Pieter Nason at the time of its purchase, and was first attributed to Wright by Collins Baker (*loc. cit.*). Its recent cleaning (1960) has confirmed his opinion beyond all doubt. Nothing appears to be known of the occasion for which the portrait was painted or of its original location. It must have been painted soon after the King's Coronation (23 April 1661) and is as much a demonstration of restored monarchy and an illustration of the revived royal ceremonial apparel, of the new Garter costume and of the new regalia, as a portrait of the King. The orb, St. Edward's Crown and the sceptre with cross appear to be fairly accurately rendered,[1] with slight variations in shape and ornamental detail and embellishment from their present form. The symbolism, and at this period the ceremonial significance, of the orb and the sceptre with cross were almost interchangeable; they represent the King's temporal power under the blessing of the Cross. The earlier regalia had been destroyed during the Interregnum and Sir Robert Vyner (the King's Goldsmith and a patron of Michael Wright) was commissioned to make the new regalia for the Coronation of Charles II at a cost of £31,978. 9s. 11d. The orb and sceptre with cross were entirely new, but for the new St. Edward's Crown the old Imperial Crown appears to have been repaired, renewed and embellished.[2] So elaborate a composition, and possible links with the exiled court during the Commonwealth, may have won for Wright the title of 'Pictor Regius' which he frequently used. He wrote on 27 July 1676 that 'the King will sit to my great picture for the Citty this next moneth' (W. J. Smith, 'Letters from Michael Wright', *Burl. Mag.*, vol. XCV (1953), p. 234), but no. 285 must be of an earlier date. It was probably a derivation of no. 285 which was set up in the Gallery of the Palazzo Doria-Pamphily in Rome at a 'mighty Entertainment' given to the great prelates of Rome by the Earl of Castlemaine on his Embassy from James II to Innocent XI. Wright described the decoration of the dining-room: '. . . in the middle of the side, opposite to the coming in, was plac'd a Cloth of State, Embroider'd with Gold, under which, was the King's Picture, as big as the Life, sitting Crown'd on his Throne, and clad, in his Regal Habit'. It is clearly seen in G. B. Lenardi's view of the table spread for the banquet (Michael Wright, *An Account of His Excellence Roger Earl of Castlemaine's Embassy* . . . (1688), pp. 54–6). This should presumably have been a portrait of James II, but was clearly so close to no. 285 as to suggest that if it was not a portrait of Charles II, a version of it had been adapted for the new King. See above p. 22.

286. PRINCESS HENRIETTA ANNE, LATER DUCHESS OF ORLÉANS

Windsor Castle (2488). 54½ × 37¾ in., 138,4 × 95,9 cm.; enlarged at top and bottom to hang as a pair with no. 212: the original canvas is *c.* 43½ × 35½ in.

Three-quarter-length, standing on a terrace and holding her veil in her right hand.

1. The best modern account of the regalia is to be found in Major-General H. D. W. Sitwell, *The Crown Jewels and other Regalia in the Tower of London* (1953); see particularly pp. 43–9.

2. See M. Holmes, 'New Light on St. Edward's Crown', *Archaeologia*, vol. XCVII (1959), pp. 213–23.

Possibly painted for Charles II, but first recorded at St. James's, in the Queen's Dressing Room, in the reign of Queen Anne: *Wright The Duches of Orleans ½ length over the door* (Queen Anne, *St. James's House* (18), apparently already as a pair to no. 212); seen hanging in the King's Closet at St. James's, as a pair to no. 212, by Vertue (1735) and Walpole (1758): moved to Windsor in 1901.

Literature: Vertue, *Notebooks*, vol. IV, p. 75; Walpole, *Visits*, p. 15; M. Toynbee, 'Adriaen Hanneman and the English Court in Exile', *Burl. Mag.*, vol. XCII (1950), pp. 76–9.

Presumably painted between the Princess's arrival in London, after the Restoration, on 2 November 1660, and her departure for France on 25 January 1661. The curtain behind the sitter seems to have been painted when the canvas was enlarged. The identities of the portrait and the artist had been lost for a long time, until Miss Toynbee (*loc. cit.*) suggested that the sitter was Princess Henrietta. The measurements of the original fit very closely a confusing entry in Charles II's inventory for a picture hanging in the King's Bedchamber at Whitehall: *Pim The Princess Henriette Maria. A halfe length* (Charles II, *Whitehall* (243), measurements given as 43 × 36 in.); the artist's name could conceivably be due to a misreading of a signature or monogram by Wright.

287. JAMES, DUKE OF CAMBRIDGE

Buckingham Palace. 59½ × 41¼ in., 151,1 × 104,8 cm. The canvas was considerably enlarged by the artist: 8¼ in. at the top, 7 in. on the right and 24¼ in. at the bottom.

Inscribed by the artist on the back: *James Duke of Cambridge. Son to his | Royall. Highness James Duke of Yorke | Brother to Charles the. 2ᵈ King of Great Brittai[n].*

Full-length standing, in the robes of the Garter and wearing the plumed hat of the Order, resting his right hand on a table beside his royal ducal coronet.

Perhaps painted for his grandmother, Queen Henrietta Maria: at her death in 1669 *The Duke of Cambridge in his Robes of Knight of the Garter* was hanging in the Vestibule at Colombes (P. R. O., S.P. 78/128, f. 212 v.). Soon after, both Wright's portraits of the Duke (see below) seem to have been in the Duke of York's possession (Bodl. MS. 891, f. 17, in the Green Mohair Closet at Whitehall (1674) and, f. 23, in the Duke's Bedchamber at Culford Hall in 1671), and after his accession they were at Windsor and St. James's (B. M., Harl. MS. 1890, ff. 74 v., 86; Bathoe, *James II* (835, 1236)). In the reign of Queen Anne no. 287 was over the chimney in the Queen's Dressing Room at St. James's House (Queen Anne, *St. James's* (16)); later at Kensington and Hampton Court, but placed before 1841 over one of the doors in the Green Drawing Room at Buckingham Palace (214).

Literature: Walpole, *Anecdotes*, vol. II, p. 123.

Presumably painted between 3 December 1666, when the Duke was nominated and invested as Knight of the Garter, and his death on 20 June 1667; an autograph version is at Belvoir. The second portrait by Wright (*Fig.* 45) was perhaps presented by James II to Sir Peter Apsley or to Lady Bathurst by Mary II and thus may be the portrait at Cirencester (R. A., *The Age of Charles II*, 1960–1 (25)); it was probably the *ad vivum* portrait from which Wright painted the more elaborate portrait, and seems, from Mary II's letter to Lady Bathurst (see no. 320), to have been the source from which Wissing was commissioned to paint a posthumous full-length.

288. JOHN LACY (*d.* 1681) (*Plate* 126)

Hampton Court (847). 92¼ × 68½ in., 234,3 × 173,4 cm.

Full-length standing, in three different parts (see below).

Painted for Charles II and hung at Windsor, apparently in the passage between the King's Eating Room and the King's Withdrawing Room: *Wright. A large peice being Lacy in three severall Postures* (B. M., Harl. MS. 1890, f. 73 v.; Bathoe, *James II* (804)).

Literature: Aubrey, *Brief Lives*, ed. A. Clark (1898), vol. II, p. 28; Anthony à Wood, *Athenæ Oxoniensis*, vol. II (1692), p. 380; G. Langbaine, *An Account of the English Dramatick Poets* (1691), p. 317; Vertue, *Notebooks*, vol. II, p. 66, vol. V, p. 51; Walpole, *Anecdotes*, vol. II, p. 123; Law, 1881, 1898 (369); Collins Baker, *Lely*, vol. II, p. 150, *Hampton Court*, p. 170; M. Summers, *The Restoration Theatre* (1934), pp. 287–8; City Museum and Art Gallery, Birmingham, *Painters and the Theatre*, 1949 (195); Waterhouse, *Painting in Britain*, p. 73.

Evelyn visited Wright on 3 October 1662; when, at a later date, he wrote up this event, he was able to expand his account of what he had seen: 'but his best in my opinion is *Lacy* the famous *Rossius* or Comedian, whom he has painted in three dresses, a Gallant, a Presbyterian Minister, and a *Scots* highlander in his plod: It is in his Majesties *Dining roome* at *Windsor*' (*Diary*, ed. E. S. de Beer (1955), vol. III, pp. 338–9).[1] The exact date of the portrait is difficult to determine. In 1862 a piece of canvas, alleged to be a later addition, was removed; it was said to have been inscribed with the parts in which the actor was painted and *Michael Wright Pinxt 1675* (Redgrave in *V.R. inv.*, April 1863, stating that this was not an original signature); this date is quoted by later writers such as Walpole (*loc. cit.*) and Pyne (vol. I, pp. 130–1). The composition probably dates from *c.* 1668–70 and certainly seems to have been in existence before 1675: on 22 April 1673 Wright signed a receipt for eight shillings paid to him by Sir Robert Shirley for a case 'to send the Lady Cleveland's and Lacy's pictures in' (H. M. C., *Hastings MSS.*, vol. I (1928), p. 403). Although its condition is far from satisfactory, the canvas painted for Charles II is entirely autograph and may have been the original of a popular design; as early as 1698 two large versions seem to have been in a sale of pictures in Edinburgh.[2] A small copy is in the Garrick Club (C. K. Adams, *A Catalogue of the Pictures in the Garrick Club* (1936), no. 122). A small version sold at Sotheby's, 18 May 1949 (147), from the collection of Lt.-Col. G. Bryant (*Country Life*, vol. CI (1947), p. 610), was stated to have been formerly at Ettington Park and may thus be the one sent down to Sir Robert Shirley in 1673 (R. A., *The Age of Charles II*, 1960–1 (164)). Vertue records a copy by Wright in the possession of the Duke of Norfolk and refers to 'several done at that time' and to a copy made by Ranelagh Barret for Lord Foley. The generally accepted identifications of Lacy's three roles in the portrait are Sauny in *Sauny the Scott: or, the Taming of the Shrew* (acted 1667), which was Lacy's adaptation from Shakespeare; Monsieur Device in the Duke of Newcastle's *The Country Captain* (1649); and Scruple in *The Cheats* (acted 1662) by John Wilson (but see Langbaine, *op. cit.*).

Actor and dramatist, recorded on the London stage as early as 1631, who served in the royalist army in the Civil War; as a comedian who excelled in 'humours' he was a special favourite with Charles II at the Theatre Royal.

Jacob Huysmans

c. 1633–1696. Born and trained in Antwerp, recorded by July 1662 in London, where he seems to have owed much of his immediate success at court to his Catholicism; he was particularly patronised by Catherine of Braganza and

1. Acceptance of the date given by Evelyn, unqualified by all his editors before Mr. de Beer, caused confusion, *e.g.*, to C. W. Cowper in 'The Triple-Portrait of John Lacy', *Publications of the Modern Language Association of America*, vol. XLVII (1932), pp. 759–65.

2. This reference was kindly given to me by Mr. Robin Hutchison.

'valu'd himself most upon' his portrait of her which 'did him great Service, so that he always boasted of that Performance, and call'd himself her Majesty's Painter. He carry'd the Compliment yet farther, for in all his Historical Pieces, for a *Madonna*, a *Venus*, or any suitable Figure, he always introduc'd something of her Resemblance. The most famous Piece of his Performance was over the *Altar* of that Queen's Chapel at *St. James's* . . .' Charles II owned: *M* *Husman. My Lady Falmouth halfe length* (Charles II, *Whitehall* (643), measurements given as 51 ×43) which is not recorded thereafter in the royal collection.

289. CATHERINE OF BRAGANZA (*Plate 124*)

Windsor Castle (2830). 85¼ × 58½ in., 216,5 × 148,6 cm.; enlarged on the left by Huysmans *c.* 6 in.

Full-length, dressed as a shepherdess and seated by a stream; resting her left hand on a sheep while a putto strews flowers on its back; in the foreground are a ram and a duck with ducklings and in the background more putti, sheep and flowers.

Painted for the Queen or her husband and placed in the Queen's Gallery at Hampton Court: *Huitzman. The Queene sitting in a Shepherdessess Laying her left hand on a Lambe* (Charles II, *Hampton Court* (12), measurements given as 90 × 60 in.); later at St. James's and Buckingham Palace (611).

Literature: Walpole, *Visits*, p. 16, *Anecdotes*, vol. II, p. 122; Collins Baker, *Lely*, vol. II, p. 154, *Windsor*, p. 174; R. A., *King's Pictures* (117); Waterhouse, *Painting in Britain*, p. 69; Whinney and Millar, p. 182.

On 26 August 1664 Pepys was taken to see 'some pictures at one Hiseman's, . . . a Dutchman, which is said to exceed Lilly . . . The Queene is drawne in one like a shepherdess, in the other like St. Katharin, most like and most admirably.' It has been suggested (*e.g.*, by Waterhouse, *op. cit.*) that the putto strewing flowers on the lamb (the Paschal lamb was used as an emblem of the Queen) may be an allusion to one of the Queen's unhappy pregnancies. The shepherdess's crook, which is now behind her, seems originally to have been supported in her right arm, and there also seem to be alterations to the draperies round the Queen's left shoulder and arm. As one of Huysmans's most important *ad vivum* portraits of his patroness it presumably served as the source for some of his smaller portraits of her; a version of the whole composition, with Windsor in the background, was in the collection of the Empress Frederick and is now at Schloss Friedrichshof. William Sherwin's engraving (1670) of the Duchess of Cleveland seems to imitate deliberately the design and iconography of no. 289.

290. CATHERINE OF BRAGANZA

St. James's Palace. 71¼ × 41¼ in., 182,2 × 106 cm.

Full-length, as St. Catherine, holding a branch of palm in her right hand and resting her left hand on the broken wheel, accompanied by the heads of three putti.

Possibly originally in the collection of Charles II. Formerly in the Geary collection at Oxonhoath and sold at Oxonhoath, 26–8 May 1952 (765); purchased by Her Majesty The Queen in 1955 for the royal collection.

Literature: R. A., *The Age of Charles II*, 1960–1 (35).

On Pepys's visit to Huysmans's studio on 26 August 1664 (see no. 289) he also saw 'The Queene . . . drawn . . . like St. Katharin.' The original of the design was probably the one recorded in Charles II's collection in store at Whitehall: *M* *Husman. The Queenes picture in manner of a St Katherine* (Charles II, *Whitehall* (639), measurements given as 75 × 41

in.) ; this does not reappear in later royal inventories and may have been given away by the Queen or her husband. No. 290 seems to be by Huysmans himself and may be the version from Charles II's collection, but another good version (*Fig. 34*), in the collection of Dr. Manoel Bento de Sousa, Quinta das Torres, Azeitão, Portugal, apparently agrees almost exactly with the measurements in Charles II's inventory, is stated to have been in Portugal since at least 1750, and may have been given by Queen Catherine to the Cremar or Van Zeller families. Copies are at Gorhambury, Ugbrooke, Castle Bromwich and Drumlanrig; a version from Seighford Hall was sold at Christie's, 12 February 1960 (15); and the design was engraved by R. Tompson (R. A., *Kings and Queens*, 1953 (190)).

The Queen had been born on the feast of St. Catherine; the figure of her patron saint is to be seen on the reverse of Roettier's portrait medal of the Queen in 1662 (*Medallic Illustrations . . .*, XLVII (1906)).

291. FRANCES STUART, DUCHESS OF RICHMOND (1647–1702) (*Plate 132*)

St. James's Palace. 50¼ × 41 in., 127,6 × 104,1 cm.

Three-quarter-length standing, wearing a man's buff doublet with a sword at her side and a baton in her right hand resting near a helmet.

Probably painted for Charles II and to be identified in his inventory: *M* *Stuart Halfe Length* (Charles II, *Whitehall* (644), in store and measurements given as 51 × 41 in.: the name of *M* *Husman* by the previous entry may be intended to apply equally to no. 644); thereafter at Kensington, St. James's, Buckingham House, St. James's, Buckingham Palace and Windsor (2930).

Literature: Walpole, *Visits*, pp. 15, 17, describing her as *Lady Fretcheville in Man's cloaths*; Collins Baker, *Lely*, vol. I, p. 210, vol. II, p. 154, *Windsor*, p. 175.

It was probably from a sitting to Huysmans or Cooper that Pepys (on 15 July 1664) saw the Duchess coming out of the Chair Room at Whitehall 'in a most lovely form, with her hair all about her eares, having her picture taking there'; and on a visit to Huysmans's studio on 26 August the portraits he saw included 'Mayds of Honour (particularly Mrs. Stewart's in a buff doublet like a soldier) as good pictures, I think, as ever I saw'. The practice of dressing up in male costume was popular at this time: '. . . one cannot possibly know a woman from a man . . . They do not weare any hood but only men's perwick hatts and coats'. The Duchess was painted in a similar costume by Samuel Cooper (Whinney and Millar, p. 95, pl. 24b).

See nos. 258 and 281.

Philippe Vignon

1638–1701. French portrait painter, the younger son of Claude Vignon; during the reign of Charles II came to London with his brother Claude François (1633–1703), who was primarily a decorative painter; a warrant was issued on 4 October 1669 to swear in both painters as limners in ordinary to the King (*Cal. S.P. Dom. (1668–9)*, p. 516).

292. LOUISE RENÉE DE PENANCOET D KÉROUALLE, DUCHESS OF PORTSMOUT AND AUBIGNY (1649–1734) (*Plate 106*)

St. James's Palace. 49¾ × 40¼ in., 126,4 × 102,2 cm.

Three-quarter-length, seated and displaying a wreath of flowers in her left hand.

Probably painted for Charles II; recorded in store at Whitehall in the reign of James II: *By Vignon The Dutches of Portsmouth at halfe length* (B. M., Harl. MS. 1890, f. 55 v.; Bathoe, *James II* (307)); thereafter at Kensington, Buckingham House (?), St. James's and Hampton Court (188).

Literature: Law, 1881, 1898 (194); Collins Baker, *Lely*, vol. II, p. 66, *Hampton Court*, p. 155.

The portrait, painted *c.* 1673, is certainly by the same hand as a female portrait, in the possession of Sir Campbell Stuart, signed *Vignon. f.*, and it can be safely identified with the entry in James II's catalogue. The portrait was sometimes attributed in the eighteenth and nineteenth centuries to Henri Gascars; the more recent attribution to Simon Verelst (*e.g.*, by Law and Collins Baker, *loc. cit.*) was due to a confusion between the references in James II's catalogue to portraits of the Duchess by Vignon and Verelst (see no. 294).

Daughter of the Sieur de Kéroualle, of a very old Breton family; appointed (1668) Maid of Honour to Henrietta, Duchess of Orléans, whom she accompanied to England in 1670; she was later sent back by Louis XIV to enthral Charles II and she became his mistress in 1671. She bore the King one son, Charles, Duke of Richmond, and was the heart of the French interest and a lavish exponent of French taste at the English court until her departure for France in 1688.

Simon Verelst

1644–1710. Dutch flower-painter, born in The Hague, who probably came to London in 1669; stated to have been inordinately vain of his ability, to have gained a considerable reputation by the realism of his pictures, and to have been persuaded, apparently by the Duchess of Portsmouth and the Duke of Buckingham, to paint portraits as well. His sitters seem to have been drawn only from the Court circle and included Charles II and Prince Rupert. James II also owned two pictures that appear no longer to be in the royal collection: *By Simon Verhelst. A Landskip with a small Venus naked under a tree* and *Velhelst. A peice of flowers* (B. M., Harl. MS. 1890, ff. 55 v., 69 v.; Bathoe, *James II* (312, 708)); and Queen Anne owned: *Verhelst. The late Dutchess of York at ½ length* (Queen Anne, *Windsor*, store (44)), also no longer in the collection.

293. MARY OF MODENA WHEN DUCHESS OF YORK (*Plate* 129)

Windsor Castle (3068). 50 × 40⅝ in., 127 × 102,6 cm.

Three-quarter-length, standing in a landscape, dressed in a richly embroidered male riding habit, holding a feathered and be-ribboned hat in her right hand and a hunting crop in her left.

Presumably painted for the Duchess or her husband and recorded in the King's Bedchamber at Whitehall in the reign of James II: *Verhelst. The Queene att halfe length* (B. M., Harl. MS. 1890, f. 83 v.; Bathoe, *James II* (1129)); described in Queen Anne's inventory (*Windsor*, store (98)) as: *Verhelst . . . at ½ length in her Riding habit.* Thereafter at Kensington, Hampton Court (918) and St. James's.

Literature: Law, 1881, 1898 (799, as Kneller?); Collins Baker, *Hampton Court*, p. 59 as 'French School'; R. A., *The Age of Charles II*, 1960–1 (403).

Painted *c.* 1675; in the collections of James II and Queen Anne it is recorded next to a companion portrait of James by Verelst . . . *at half length in the Robes*, which may be the portrait in the possession of Lord Bolton.

294. LOUISE RENÉE DE PENANCOET DE KÉROUALLE, DUCHESS OF PORTSMOUTH AND AUBIGNY (1649–1734)

Hampton Court (921). 49¾ × 40⅛ in., 126,4 × 102 cm.

Three-quarter-length seated, holding a rose in her lap and resting her left arm on a ledge.

Presumably painted for Charles II; recorded at Whitehall in James II's collection: *By Simon Verhelst. The Dutches of Portsmouth at halfe length Red Garment* (B. M., Harl. MS. 1890, f. 54 v.; Bathoe, *James II* (272)); later at Windsor, Buckingham House (?) and Kensington (?).

Literature: Law, 1881, 1898 (800); Collins Baker, *Hampton Court*, p. 168.

Probably painted *c.* 1670–2, at the time of the Duchess's establishment as Charles II's mistress; the identification of artist and sitter has been lost for many years owing to the confusion of the entries in the inventories that relate to portraits of the Duchess by Vignon (no. 292) and Verelst.

See no. 292.

295. A BUNCH OF GRAPES

Hampton Court (414). 18 × 14 in., 45,7 × 35,6 cm.; slightly stretched in lining.

A bunch of grapes with a Large White butterfly perched upon a leaf.

Presumably painted for Charles II; recorded at Whitehall in the reign of James II: *Verhelst. Two Bunches of Grapes with a white Butterfly* (B. M., Harl. MS. 1890, f. 57 v.; Bathoe, *James II* (361)); later at Windsor.

Literature: Walpole, *Visits*, p. 80; Law, 1881, 1898 (732); Collins Baker, *Hampton Court*, p. 155; R. A., *King's Pictures* (317).

Probably painted *c.* 1670–5, soon after Verelst's arrival in London.

Antonio Verrio

?1639–1707. Decorative painter, born in Lecce; trained in Naples and Paris, came to England *c.* 1672 and was almost immediately taken into royal service. His Catholicism and his baroque training were greatly in his favour; he was extensively employed by Charles II and James II at Windsor and Whitehall and was lavishly rewarded by them. He was, however, only employed by William III at the end of his reign, when he began the painted decoration of the new state apartments at Hampton Court, where he died, still in the service of the Crown. In 1685 he had succeeded to Lely's position as Principal Painter, but at the Revolution was replaced by Riley and Kneller. He was also a celebrated gardener and in the reign of James II he was Keeper of the Great and Privy Gardens in St. James's Park. In the Queen's Private Chapel at Windsor in the time of James II was: *Seign^r Vario . . . Our Saviour upon the Crosse* (B. M., Harl. MS. 1890, f. 75; Bathoe, *James II* (853)), which is not recorded in the royal collection after 1714.

296. CHARLES II (*Plate* 131)

Windsor Castle (1634). Oil on plaster, 36 × 27 in., 91,4 × 68,6 cm.

Head and shoulders in armour, within an oval formed by two palm branches; the head is painted as if on a sheet of paper.

Literature: Collins Baker, *Windsor*, p. 302.

A fragment preserved by Sir Jeffery Wyatville (see no. 336) and removed to his residence at Winchester Tower when so much of Verrio's painted decoration in the Castle was being swept away. It may have come from the ceiling of the King's Presence Chamber where 'The Ceiling is *Mercury* with a Portrait of King *Charles* II (an Original, and true likeness) shewing the Monarch to the four Quarters of the World, . . .' (J. Pote, *The History and Antiquities of Windsor Castle, . . .* (1749), p. 422); according to Pyne (vol. I, pp. 170–1), the portrait of the King was 'said to be the most perfect resemblance that is known of that "merry monarch" '. The ceiling of the King's Presence Chamber was probably painted in 1677–8 and Verrio's payment for work upon it appears in the accounts for the years 1675–8 (W. H. St. John Hope, *Windsor Castle* . . . (1913), vol. I, p. 317). The portrait of the King is very close to the head in Lely's slightly earlier portrait of which the best version is at Euston. The fragment containing Verrio's portrait of the King from the ceiling of the King's Drawing Room is at Packwood House (C. H. Collins Baker in the *Connoisseur*, vol. CXXXI (1953), p. 12).

297. THE SEA TRIUMPH OF CHARLES II (*Plate* 121)

St. James's Palace. $87\frac{1}{2} \times 90\frac{1}{4}$ in., 222,3 × 229,2 cm. There is a later addition of $6\frac{3}{4}$ in. at the top and the original canvas appears to have been cut at both sides.

Signed: *Antonius Verrio | Neapolitanus f.*

The King, wearing classical armour, is driven through the water by Neptune in a high, shell-backed chariot, accompanied by three female figures carrying crowns and embodying his three kingdoms; above his head Fame holds a scroll inscribed IMPERIVM OCEANO FAMAM QVI TERMINET ASTRIS and Time and a female figure hold above his head a wreath and a helmet respectively; in the sky Envy is struck by lightning and chased by putti with the attributes of Peace and Love, and two more putti carry the royal arms on a shield; below two dark-skinned (?American or West Indian) putti carry a map inscribed, over an apparently erased earlier inscription, PACATVMQVE REGET . . .[1] Beyond are Minerva and Venus (?) looking down on the British fleet at anchor with the royal standard flying on a warship.

Painted for Charles II and placed in the Second Privy Lodging Room at Whitehall: *By Seignior Vario. A Sea Triumph being a large peice with King Charles the Second in it* (B. M., Harl. MS. 1890, f. 47; Bathoe, *James II* (57)); later at Windsor, Buckingham Palace (995), St. James's and Hampton Court (1240).

Literature: Vertue, *Notebooks*, vol. II, pp. 29, 132; Walpole, *Anecdotes*, vol. II, pp. 117–18; Collins Baker, *Hampton Court*, p. 156; Whinney and Millar, p. 296; R. A., *Italian Art and Britain*, 1960 (28).

Probably correctly stated, *e.g.*, by Vertue (*op. cit.*, vol. II, p. 132) to have been the first work painted by Verrio for Charles II, presumably *c.* 1674. The subject may have been inspired to some extent by the signing, on 9 February 1674, of the Treaty of Westminster which brought to an end the Third Anglo-Dutch War and by which the Dutch ceded the honours of the flag to English ships in British waters. The iconography, however, is to some extent an elaboration in very conventional terms of Thomas Simon's design (1665) for Charles II's medal of the Dominion of the Sea. The portrait of the King does not seem to be *ad vivum* and was probably worked up by Verrio from a miniature by Samuel Cooper, from the same source as no. 301. It is conceivable that the design was painted as a trial piece, before Verrio had seen his new patron, to give him an idea of his abilities. The Fleet in the background may have been painted by another hand.

1. See no. 337, where the same motto seems to have been used by Kneller.

298. CHRIST HEALING THE SICK (*Plate* 122)

Buckingham Palace. $40\frac{3}{4} \times 80\frac{3}{4}$ in., 103,5 × 205,1 cm.

Signed: *Ant Verrio f:*

The episode of Christ healing the sick at Capernaum (Mark II. 1–12) is taking place in an elaborate columned hall, open to the sky and seen through openings flanked with twisted columns.

Presumably painted for Charles II; recorded at Windsor, probably in the King's Great Bedchamber, in the reign of James II: *Seignr Vario. Our Saviour cureing the lame and the blind* (B. M., Harl. MS. 1890, f. 72; Bathoe, *James II* (751)); later at Kensington and Hampton Court; recorded at Buckingham Palace (1066) in 1871 (*V.R. inv.*).

Literature: Vertue, *Notebooks*, vol. I, p. 73; Whinney and Millar, p. 299.

The preliminary *modello* for the painting on the north wall of the King's Chapel in the new State Apartments at Windsor. The payments for the work at Windsor between 1 October 1680 and 30 September 1682 included £1050 paid to Verrio 'for Painting and adorning of the Ceilings, Side Walls, End Walls, . . . in the King's Chappell . . .' (W. H. St. John Hope, *Windsor Castle* . . . (1913), vol. I, p. 322). The Chapel was demolished early in the nineteenth century, but can be seen in C. Wild's illustration to Pyne, vol. I, p. 179. The wall-painting seems to have been executed along the lines of the *modello*, but with modifications in detail. Verrio did not repeat on the wall the architectural base on which the painted structure is raised, or the steps in the foreground; in the Chapel his painted twisted columns rested on the choir-stalls. On the wall of the Chapel the top of the design was, of course, more closely integrated with the painting on the ceiling and coving. No. 298 seems to have been made by the artist into a finished picture and not left as the sketch for a fragment of a very elaborate decorative scheme. The two contemporary portraits in the opening on the right are of Verrio himself and Hugh May (1622–84), the architect with whom Verrio was associated at Windsor. In no. 298 the two portraits are much more carefully treated than the other heads and may be by a different hand; the head of May seems to have been based on the portrait by Lely at Audley End. The woman seated on the steps in the foreground and the group in the foreground on the right are painted over the steps. See no. 299.

After Antonio Verrio

299. CHRIST HEALING THE SICK

Hampton Court (688). $41\frac{1}{2} \times 83$ in., 105,4 × 210,8 cm.

Recorded at Hampton Court in 1869 (*V.R. inv.*).

Literature: Law, 1881, 1898 (458); Collins Baker, *Hampton Court*, p. 170.

A copy of no. 298, probably painted in England *c.* 1720.

Artists Unknown : Later Seventeenth-Century Portraits

300. A MEMORIAL PICTURE OF CHARLES I

St. James's Palace. $70\frac{1}{2} \times 99\frac{3}{4}$ in., 179,1 × 253,4 cm.

Full-length, kneeling in robes of state before an altar on which is placed an open Bible; at the foot of the altar is the Crown of Thorns resting on a cushion and the King looks up at a vision of a heavenly crown while he makes the gesture of spurning his earthly crown. In the background is a design, in an elaborately carved frame, showing, in the middle of a raging sea, an island on which grows a palm tree from which are suspended two weights.

Purchased by Sir J. C. Robinson at Foster's, 22 July 1891 (89) (P.R.O., L. C. 1/552, II, 79; 570, 93); bought for the royal collection in 1892.

No. 300 is a painted variant of a very popular design demonstrating Charles I's acceptance of the crown of martyrdom and his rejection of his earthly crown. The source of the design was William Marshall's famous plate, which may have been designed in part by the King himself, to the *Eikon Basilike* of 1649. Many of the elements in no. 300 have been taken over from the plate: the tempest raging round a rock and the weighted palm tree that symbolise the King's steadfast faith; the rejection of the earthly crown for the crown of thorns and an ultimate crown of glory; the figure in robes of state kneeling before an altar and the Bible in which he has placed his hope. Of Marshall's design many adaptations were made in England and abroad and after the Restoration it was taken over for stained glass, tapestry and paintings (see M. D. George, *English Political Caricature to 1792* (1959), pp. 34–6 (pl. 12)). No. 300 was certainly painted in the second half of the seventeenth century. On the back of the frame is a partly defaced label in French stating that the picture had formed part of the decoration of one of the salons in the hôtel on the Lange Vijverberg in The Hague occupied by the Colemborg family. This is no. 11 on the Lange Vijverberg. An illegible reference on the label to Nieuwenhuys having taken the picture to France presumably alludes to the dealer J. Nieuwenhuys who brought many pictures to England in the time of George IV.

301. CHARLES II

Windsor Castle (3084). 29 × 23½ in., 73,7 × 59,7 cm.

Head and shoulders in armour in a painted oval.

Inscribed: *C.2.R.* under a crown.

Possibly in the collection of William, 1st Earl of Craven (1606–97); passed by descent to Cornelia, Countess of Craven, by whom it was bequeathed to Her Majesty the Queen in 1961.

Based on a miniature (*c.* 1665–70) of the King by Samuel Cooper. The original of this type may be the unfinished head in the Chiddingstone Castle collection (National Portrait Gallery, *Some Portraits of Charles II*, 1960 (17)); a signed version in armour is at Welbeck (R. W. Goulding, 'The Welbeck Abbey Miniatures', *Walpole Soc.*, vol. IV (1916), p. 84); a large version is at Windsor, dated 1667; and the head is used in the large miniature of the King in the V. & A., signed by *WP* and dated 1676. See no. 297.

302. CHARLES II

Buckingham Palace. 51 × 42 in., 129,5 × 106,7 cm.

Three-quarter-length, standing in Garter robes with his crown beside him.

Presented to King George V, on the occasion of his marriage, by Captain V. Lovett Cameron, R.N.

Formerly said to be a portrait of James II, but the sitter appears to be Charles II, *c.* 1684–5; the portrait is of very poor quality and is perhaps a copy of a portrait by Simon Verelst or Antonio Verrio.

303. HENRY, DUKE OF GLOUCESTER

Windsor Castle (3085). 30 × 25 in., 76,2 × 68,5 cm.

Head and shoulders within a painted oval wearing a breastplate and scarlet sash over a buff doublet.

Stated to have been in the collection of William, 1st Earl of Craven (1606–97), and to have been given to him by Elizabeth, Queen of Bohemia, or bequeathed to him by Prince Rupert, who had inherited many of his mother's possessions; passed by descent to Cornelia, Countess of Craven, by whom it was bequeathed to Her Majesty The Queen in 1961.

Formerly attributed to Dahl. No. 303 seems a later copy of a portrait of the Duke which exists in two types. It is close in the head to a portrait in armour of which a version in the Groothuis in Bruges is said to have been painted in Bruges in 1657 by Johann Boeckhorst; others are in the National Portrait Gallery (1932) and the Devonshire collection. The costume of no. 303 is related to a variant design of which there are versions at Knole and Hagley.

304. HENRIETTA, DUCHESS OF ORLÉANS

Buckingham Palace. 68¼ × 41 in., 173,4 × 104,1 cm.; there is an early addition at the top of *c.* 5½ in.

Full-length, seated in a landscape as Minerva, wearing a plumed helmet, clasping a spear in her left hand and resting her right hand on a shield.

First recorded in the reign of Queen Anne over a door in the Princess's Dressing Room at Windsor (Queen Anne, *Windsor* (215): *Madam Dutchess of Orleans at length Sitting*), where the identity of the portrait was later lost; recorded at Kensington in 1818 (130) with an attribution to Michael Wright; sent to Hampton Court on 1 November 1833, but taken to Buckingham Palace (653) and placed by Queen Victoria with other Bourbon pieces in the suite prepared for Leopold I, King of the Belgians, in 1847.

Literature: Buckingham Palace, 1909, p. 15.

Probably painted *c.* 1665, and certainly in France, after the Princess's marriage to the Duke of Orléans in 1661. In style no. 304 is typical of portrait painting at the court of Louis XIV in the 1670's and could be tentatively attributed to Jean Nocret.

305. WILLIAM III WHEN PRINCE OF ORANGE

Hampton Court (353). 50¼ × 40 in., 127,6 × 101,6 cm; the canvas has been enlarged at the top by *c.* 4 in. and on the left by *c.* 7½ in., and was originally 45½ × 32½ in.

Three-quarter-length in 'coats', wearing the ribbon of the Garter and holding a baton in his right hand; on the canvas added later on the left a feathered hat rests on a table.

Probably the portrait recorded in store (96) at Windsor in the reign of Queen Anne (Queen Anne, *Windsor: King Cha yᵉ 2ᵈ wⁿ young at ½ length in yellow wᵗʰ a Trunchⁿ*; later placed over a door in the Queen's Bedchamber in her Garden House at Windsor); recorded at Hampton Court by Pyne (vol. II, p. 44, as a portrait of Charles II 'erroneously ascribed to Sir Godfrey Kneller'); later identified as James II when Duke of York and sent (1881) to St. James's.

Literature: Law, 1881, 1898 (568, as James II); Collins Baker, *Hampton Court*, p. 165 (as Henry, Duke of Gloucester).

Probably painted, according to the costume, *c.* 1658, but altered later. The sitter wears 'coats' and must, therefore, be very young; the ribbon of the Garter identifies him almost conclusively with William III who had been created Knight of the Garter in 1653 (*c.v.*, no. 132). His uncle Henry, Duke of Gloucester (see nos. 247 and 248), had been made a Knight in the same year, but was eleven years older than the Prince. The hat seems to be *c.* 1685–90 in style and the background of the original canvas seems to have been overpainted when the later additions were made to the canvas.

306. QUEEN ANNE WHEN PRINCESS

St. James's Palace. 31¾×25¼ in., 806,5×64,1 cm.

Half-length, fondling a little spaniel which jumps up at her.

Recorded in James II's collection at St. James's (B. M., Harl. MS. 1890, f. 86 v.; Bathoe, *James II* (1247): *Lady Anne with a little Dogg*); in the reign of Queen Anne it was recorded in store at Kensington (Queen Anne, *Kensington*, store (172)), with a slightly later note by Thomas Coke: *The Present Queen drawn in France when She was a Child . . .*; later at St. James's and Windsor (515).

Literature: Collins Baker, *Windsor*, p. 274 (as by Riley).

The Princess was in France for the sake of her health between July 1668 and July 1670. For much of the time she was in the care of her aunt the Duchess of Orléans and no. 306 was painted, presumably by a painter at the French court, during this period. It is completely French in style and was probably brought back with the Princess when she landed at Rye on 23 July 1670.

307. WALTER, COUNT LESLIE (1606–67)

Holyroodhouse. 68¼×47¼ in., 173,4×120 cm.; there are additions at the top of *c.* 6¾ in. and at the bottom of *c.* 7 in.; the original canvas was *c.* 54¾×47¼ in., including an enlargement on the right during painting of *c.* 12 in.

Three-quarter-length standing, wearing a fur-lined robe and the order of the Golden Fleece, resting his right hand on a table.

Recorded in store at Whitehall in the reign of Charles II (Charles II, *Whitehall* (609): *Count Lashley To yᵉ knees*, with the date *1666* and measurements given as 54×48 in.); possibly later at St. James's, as a portrait of Potemkin, the Russian Ambassador to Charles II (B. M., Stowe MSS. 567, f. 66 v.: *. . . en soutane Blanche et Robe de Pelice demie Figure*); later at Windsor (1076).

Probably painted in Austria in 1666 (see above) and presumably given to Charles II very soon after it was painted. The Count had received the Fleece in 1665. An early engraving of this type exists.

Scots soldier of fortune who rose to high rank in the Imperial service; he fought with distinction in the Thirty Years War and was prominent in the assassination of Wallenstein. In 1665 he went as Ambassador to the Turkish Porte.

308. THEODORE RANDUE (1643–1724)

Windsor Castle (840). 78¼×49¾ in., 198,8×126,4 cm.

Inscribed on a *cartellino:* Mʳ THEODORE RANDUE / KEEPER OF THEIR MAJESTYˢ / ROYAL PALLACE, IN WINDSOR / CASTLE IN Yᴱ REIGNS OF KING / CHARLES II. KING JAMES. & / KING WILLIAM. SEP. XIII. MDCC. / ALSO TO QUEEN ANN. / AND TO KING GEORGE:

Full-length standing, holding a bundle of keys in his left hand and with his right hand opening a door with an official key.

Recorded at Hampton Court in 1842 (Mrs. Jameson (571)) and at Windsor in 1878 (*V.R. inv.*).

The date on the *cartellino* could well be the date at which no. 308 was painted; the two last lines of the inscription are probably later additions. It is conceivable that there is an inaccurate reference to no. 308 in Bickham's description (pp. 174–5) of the Inner Court at Windsor: 'Over the Colonades is a Stone Gallery, and over the Door of the Entrance into it, on the Left, is a whole Length Portrait of the Donor of the Equestrian Statue, which stands in The Quadrangle . . . drawn in a modern Dress, by Sir *Godfrey Kneller*'. The donor of the statue was Tobias Rustat (*d.* 1687), but there is no evidence elsewhere of a portrait of him in the royal collection and the placing of the figure in no. 308 on a feigned ledge

could indicate that it was painted to be placed over a door and seen from below.

During his youth was in the service of the Duke of Gloucester in exile; in 1660 he was taken into the service of Charles II as Page of the Bedchamber and in 1673 he was appointed Keeper of the King's House and Privy Lodging at Windsor Castle.

309. PORTRAIT OF A MAN

Buckingham Palace. 30×24¾ in., 76,2×62,9 cm. The canvas was originally an oval, *c.* 24×19 in.

Head and shoulders, in a painted oval, in a loose cloak.

Recorded in the collection of George IV at Carlton House in 1816 (304: *A head of a nobleman;* the 1816 label is still on the back); at Buckingham Palace in 1876 (*V.R. inv.*, no. 1114).

No. 309 has been extensively overpainted, apparently at the time when the canvas was enlarged (see above). It appears to have been fundamentally a portrait of *c.* 1660, possibly by Gerard Soest.

310. PORTRAIT OF A MAN WITH A SECRETARY

Windsor Castle (1598). 35¾×49½ in., 90,8×125,7 cm.

The older man is seated at a table with a paper in his right hand, apparently dictating to a younger man; on the table are an ink-well shaped like a crab and a sprinkler (?) in the shape of a frog climbing on a shell; a watch hangs beside him on the wall.

Recorded at Kensington in 1818 (135); later at Hampton Court.

Probably painted *c.* 1650. The design appears to be based on Van Dyck's portrait of the Earl of Strafford with Sir Philip Mainwaring (Glück, 483), but it is possible that no. 310 is a Dutch and not an English derivation from this source.

311. PORTRAIT OF A GIRL

Holyroodhouse. 48¾×39¼ in., 123,8×99,7 cm.

Three-quarter-length, standing in a landscape and resting her left arm on a lamb.

Recorded in Miss Planta's room at Kew in the reign of George III (Geo. III, *Kew: A Lady with a Lamb. Sir P. Lely*); at Kew in 1870 (*V.R. inv.*), but recorded at Holyrood in 1884 (*ibid.*).

Probably painted *c.* 1650–5; the design is Van Dyckian in feeling, but the treatment of the draperies is slightly reminiscent of Gerard Soest.

312. PORTRAIT OF A WOMAN

Buckingham Palace. 30×24½ in., 76,2×62,2 cm.

Head and shoulders in a carved painted oval.

Recorded at Buckingham Palace in 1876 (*V.R. inv.*, no. 1163). It is impossible to identify no. 312 accurately in earlier sources, but it could have been no. 590 at Kensington in 1818: *Portrait of a Lady Wissing*, measurements given as 30×25; moved to Hampton Court in 1833.

Formerly suggested as a portrait of the Duchess of Portsmouth. Probably painted *c.* 1675–80; in design and type no. 312 is Lelyesque, but the handling is close to a painter such as Simon Verelst.

313. PORTRAIT OF A CHILD

Hampton Court (215). 25¼×21 in., 64,1×53,3 cm.

A boy, seated full-length and almost naked, as St. John the Baptist, embracing the lamb and holding the cane cross.

Recorded at Hampton Court on 18 October 1872 (*V.R. inv.*, which quotes the reference from a label on the back to an inventory of 27 July 1852).

Literature: Law, 1881, 1898 (835).

Apparently painted *c.* 1680–90, probably in England, and in a style slightly reminiscent of John Riley. The sitter is possibly William, Duke of Gloucester. If so, no. 313 would have been painted *c.* 1690 (*cf.*, no. 341), but it does not seem to have been in Queen Anne's possession; it may have been the portrait, described as the Duke of Gloucester and attributed to Lely, recorded at Hampton Court in 1849 in *The Stranger's Guide* (358).

Artists Unknown : Stuart Conversation Pieces

314. AN INTERIOR WITH CHARLES I, HENRIETTA MARIA, THE EARLS OF PEMBROKE AND JEFFERY HUDSON (*Plate* 90)

Kensington Palace. 43½ × 58 in., 110,5 × 147,3 cm.

An interior, of a vaguely Jacobean flavour, with a vista through to a gallery with figures looking out of the window. Through a doorway on the right Charles I and his Queen enter, followed by the 4th Earl of Pembroke and received by his elder brother, the 3rd Earl; behind the 3rd Earl stands the dwarf Jeffery Hudson.

Seen by Walpole in 1763 in the collection of Mr. Cooper (*d.* 1768) at Phillis Court, near Henley (*Visits*, p. 50) : '...a picture extremely valued, which they say Whitlocke had from the collection of King Charles... The palace is said to be Whitehall... I take the figures to be by Van Bassen after Van Dyck, & the building to be by Stenwyck, at least in the Original'; no. 314 may have belonged to Bulstrode Whitelocke (1605–75), whose great-granddaughter married Walpole's Mr. Cooper; probably remained in the possession of the Cooper family until the death in 1864 of the Rev. E. P. Cooper, whose son-in-law, the Rev. F. A. H. FitzGerald, sold it to Sir John Eardley-Wilmot; sold in his sale at Christie's, 9 June 1888 (362A), when it was acquired for the royal collection.

Literature: Collins Baker, *Windsor*, p. 127; Miss M. R. Toynbee, 'A Charles I Conversation Piece', *Burl. Mag.*, vol. LXXXIX (1947), pp. 245–7.

No. 314 is probably the best version of a design of which three other versions are known. (I) A good version is at Tyninghame; stated to be the version recorded by Walpole (*Anecdotes*, vol. I, p. 342) in the possession of Earl Poulett, this was sold by A. M. Grenfell at Christie's, 26 June 1914 (32). (II) A version, definitely inferior and formerly at Tythrop, was last on the art-market at Christie's, 21 June 1957 (84), and now belongs to the Earl of Pembroke. (III) A version formerly in the collection of Lord Chesham, was sold at Sotheby's, 13 February 1946 (7), and was later with William Hallsborough. (IV) A copy, stated to be by Brompton, is at Highclere Castle. The interior has not been satisfactorily identified. The tradition, which goes back to the time of Walpole, that it represents Theobalds cannot be substantiated. The insertion into the background (but not of the ex-Lord Chesham version) of two of Charles I's most famous Titians, the *Entombment* and the *Supper at Emmaus* (both now in the Louvre), cannot be cited as evidence for the interior being Whitehall, as these two pictures were hanging with ten other pictures in the First Privy Lodging Room (*Van der Doort*, pp. 15–16). The interior is probably imaginary, but if an actual house was represented it would be as likely to be a residence of the Earls of Pembroke (possibly Durham House in the Strand) as they are so prominently represented. No. 314 may have been painted indeed, as a record of their service to the

Crown. It is almost certain that the architecture and figures are by different hands. The architecture seems to lack Steenwyck's sharp touch and the figures not to have the painterliness of Van Bassen or Poelenburgh, whose names were associated by Walpole with Lord Poulett's version. The figures are, in any case, copied from existing portraits 'in large'. The figure of the King is based on a design by Mytens, of which a version, dated 1629 and showing the King holding his hat, was on the art-market in 1957–8. The figure of William Herbert, 3rd Earl of Pembroke (see no. 107), is also based on Mytens. A portrait, formerly at Bramshill and sold at Sotheby's, 16 July 1952 (83), showed the Earl against an imaginary architectural background not unlike that in no. 314, though on a much larger scale. The portrait of his brother, and successor as Lord Chamberlain, Philip Herbert, 4th Earl of Pembroke (1584–1650), appears to be based on Van Dyck, ultimately on the full-length at Wilton (Glück, 407). Both Earls carry their white staves of office, the 3rd Earl as Lord Steward, the 4th Earl as Lord Chamberlain. The figure of Jeffery Hudson is based on no. 125. The dogs come from Van Dyck: that near Jeffery Hudson from no. 150; the other from the portrait of Lady Spencer at Althorp (Glück, 484). No. 314 can hardly have been concocted before *c.* 1635. The figures may conceivably be by Jan van Belcamp, though they are clearly more competent and on a larger scale than those in no. 197. Belcamp, like Cornelius Johnson, was employed by Charles I in the making up of small royal portraits from existing sources and not *ad vivum* (see above, p. 90).

315. CHARLES II (?) LEAVING HAMPTON COURT

Buckingham Palace. 6⅝ × 25⅛ in., 16,8 × 63,8 cm.

A coach, in which the passenger seems to be Charles II, attended by horsemen and footmen, leaving Hampton Court Palace.

Formerly in the collection of Arthur Hill, F.S.A., whose book-plate is on the back; acquired by Her Majesty Queen Mary; at Windsor Castle (2997) in 1936.

A later inscription on the back describes the scene as Charles II at Hampton Court and attributes the canvas to Lely with the date 1675. No. 315 was, however, painted *c.* 1660–5 and cannot be by Lely; it is close in quality to Jacob Esselens, who was in England at that time. The background of no. 315 agrees fairly well with the east front of Hampton Court as seen in no. 397.

316. 'THE PINEAPPLE PICTURE': CHARLES II PRESENTED WITH A PINEAPPLE

Windsor Castle (2914). 38 × 45 in., 96,5 × 114,3 cm.

Charles II, wearing the star of the Garter, standing on a terrace while a gentleman, usually identified with John Rose, presents a pineapple to him. In the background is a formal garden and a large modern house.

Formerly in the Breadalbane collection, which passed by descent to the Hon. T. Morgan-Grenville-Gavin; sold at Christie's, 27 March 1925 (48); presented in 1926 to Her Majesty Queen Mary by Lady Mountstephen.

Literature: Sir L. Cust, 'The First Pine-apple grown in England', *Apollo*, vol. III (1926), pp. 73–9.

Apparently a slightly later copy of a design of which the best version, probably the original and painted *c.* 1675, belongs to the Marchioness of Cholmondeley (Arts Council, *British*

Life, 1953 (81);[1] another version belongs to Lord Harlech and a copy, painted by Hewart in 1787, is at Ham House). The original has been attributed to Danckerts: he is unlikely to have painted the figures, but the background has affinities with his style. The house in the background was traditionally identified as Dorney Court in Buckinghamshire, but is perhaps more likely to have been Dorney House, near Oatlands Park, where pine-pits were constructed (correspondence in the Surveyor's Office with Major Benton Fletcher). The scene is traditionally stated to represent the offering by Rose to Charles II of the first pineapple grown in England. It is, however, unlikely that pineapples were grown in England at this date (see M. Hadfield in *Country Life*, vol. CXXV (1959), pp. 1072–3) and the pineapple presented to Charles II had probably been imported to this country. John Rose (1619–77), a distinguished horticulturist, was Chief Gardener to Charles II.

Robert Streeter

1624–80. Decorative and landscape painter; appointed Serjeant-Painter in 1663, he was responsible for routine decorative painting on the King's barges and coaches and in the royal residences, including Windsor, at the time of Verrio's activity there, Greenwich, Hampton Court and Whitehall, where he worked in the new theatre, the Queen's buildings and the Long Gallery. Charles II owned a copy by Streeter after Titian (Charles II, *Whitehall* (507): *Streeter after Titian The Buriall of o^r Savior*, measurements given as 46×63 in.) and, presumably, a picture recorded in James II's collection at Windsor: *By Streeter. Jupiter upon a Rock, a small peice to shew the Winds* (B. M. Harl. MS. 1890, f. 51 v.; Bathoe, *James II* (185). James II owned four landscapes by Streeter (*ibid.* (1093–5, 1146)). None of these works can now be identified in the royal collection.

317. BOSCOBEL HOUSE AND WHITELADIES (*Plate* 119)

Hampton Court (1279). 53½×83¾ in., 135,9×212,7 cm.

On the left are the ruins of the Cistercian Convent (in the garden of which two men are in conversation), attached to a more modern house, of Whiteladies, with various outbuildings and a troop of horse riding away from it. Whiteladies is divided by woods, the Spring Coppice and, in the foreground, Boscobel Wood, from Boscobel House. Boscobel House is surrounded by a garden, in the corner of which stands an arbour on a mound; just outside the garden fence is a rustic seat and a hexagonal table. In the right foreground is the Royal Oak with two figures concealed in it; two more figures are also seen crouched in the undergrowth at the foot of a tree in the foreground. There are remains of a set of contemporary numbers on different episodes in the composition (see below).

Presumably painted for Charles II and hung at Whitehall, where it is recorded in the reign of James II, probably hanging in the Square Table Room: *By Streeter A large Landskip with Boscobell and white Ladies Houses* (B. M., Harl. MS. 1890, f. 47 v.; Bathoe, *James II* (75)); later at Windsor (348).

Literature: Collins Baker, *Hampton Court*, pp. 139–40; 'Robert Streater', *Burl. Mag.*, vol. LXXXIV–V (1944; editorial), p. 4; exh. Worcester, 1951, *Paintings from 1642 to 1651* (46); Waterhouse, *Painting in Britain*, p. 79; H. V. S. and M. Ogden, *English Taste in Landscape in the Seventeenth Century* (Ann Arbor, 1955), pp.

115, 154; Whinney and Millar, p. 265; R. A., *The Age of Charles II*, 1960–1 (29).

Almost certainly commissioned by Charles II, probably *c.* 1670. The King was never tired of talking of his escape and may have desired a permanent visual record of its most dramatic moments. In fact Streeter's composition records two separate stages in the escape and the two houses are in reality just under a mile apart.[1] Late on 3 September 1651, after his crushing defeat at Worcester at the hands of Cromwell, Charles was escorted by Charles Giffard to Whiteladies. He arrived in the early hours of 4 September at the house, in which the Penderel family were living and of which nothing now survives. His adherents galloped away and he was disguised as a woodman; he spent the day with Richard Penderel in Spring Coppice, sheltering from almost continuous rain under the thickest of the trees. That night they made an abortive attempt to cross the Severn, so that the King could escape to Wales, but decided to return to Boscobel. Very early in the morning of Saturday, 6 September, they reached the house, a lonely hunting lodge which survives, though considerably altered. Here the King found Colonel William Careless or Carlos in hiding and later in the morning the King and Carlos were taken into Boscobel Wood, 'to that so much celebrated oak', which is thought long since to have disappeared and in which Carlos had himself earlier taken refuge. In the King's own words 'we ... carried up with us some victuals for the whole day, viz. bread, cheese, small beer, and nothing else, and got up into a great oak, that had been lopt some three or four years before, and being grown out again, very bushy and thick, could not be seen through, and here we staid all the day ... while we were in this tree we see soldiers going up and down, in the thicket of the wood, searching for persons escaped, we seeing them now and then, peeping out of the wood.' The King slept for much of the vigil and passed that night in the house. Part of Sunday, 7 September, he spent reading in the arbour in the garden and as dusk fell he left Boscobel to join Lord Wilmot at Moseley Hall.

Streeter's composition is clearly related to, but almost certainly later than, Hollar's etching (*Fig.* 39) for Thomas Blount's *Boscobel* of 1660. Certain topographical details, and the relation between them, are slightly different in the two compositions, and for no. 317 it is conceivable that Streeter made a visit to the sites he was commemorating. Hollar's plate, moreover, is numbered and explained by a key, and with it the reader can follow many of the above happenings. The numbering in no. 317 is now partly indecipherable, but the following numbers can perhaps be made out:

　1: on Boscobel House
　5: on the smaller outhouse on the left
　6: on the fence round the garden of Boscobel House
　7: on the garden in the monastery ruins
　8: on the Royal Oak

Illegible numbers can be detected on Whiteladies, on one of the outhouses and on the arbour; Streeter's numbering thus seems different from Hollar's and no. 317 was presumably originally equipped with a key. In Hollar's plate can be seen more clearly certain details of the story: the gate leading from the garden to the wood, the stone table in the wood and the King and Richard Penderel hiding in Spring Coppice while the royalist horsemen gallop away.[2] The little figures

1. Photographs of the houses as they appear today are reproduced in H. P. Kingston, *The Wanderings of Charles II* (1933).

2. Hollar's plate describes these horsemen as 'His Ma^tys Troop marching from White-Ladies'; otherwise one might have thought them the troop of enemy horse which appeared on the scene a few hours later, while the King was in Spring Coppice.

1. Walpole's earliest account of the picture occurs in a letter to William Cole, 6 March 1780 (*Correspondence*, ed. W. S. Lewis and A. D. Wallace (1937), p. 200).

in the foreground of no. 317 are probably intended for William and Richard or Joan Penderel 'peaking up and down' while the King was in hiding.

A smaller version of no. 317 (with variations) at Swynnerton probably belonged to the Fitzherbert family, which inherited Whiteladies from the Giffards. No. 317 should also be seen as part of the cult of the Royal Oak which inspired much royalist propaganda during the Interregnum and was manifested in a variety of ways at the Restoration. On his return the King, indeed, contemplated founding an Order of Knights of the Royal Oak, and the Oak figures prominently in Michael Wright's painting for the ceiling of the King's Bedroom at Whitehall (R. A., *The Age of Charles II*, 1960–61 (161)).

Elizabeth, Countess of Carnarvon

1633–78. Daughter of Arthur, 1st Baron Capel, she married in or before 1653 Charles Dormer, 2nd Earl of Carnarvon; she seems to have been an amateur painter and drawer of flowers and in Lely's portrait of her with her sister Mary, later Duchess of Beaufort, she holds a little framed drawing of a flower signed as in no. 318 (Beckett, *Lely*, pl. 36); the Duchess was an enthusiastic gardener and botanist.

318. FLOWERS IN A VASE

Kew (*Hampton Court no.* 1465). Gouache on paper, mounted on panel: $16\frac{1}{8} \times 12\frac{1}{8}$ in., $41 \times 30,8$ cm.

Signed and dated: *E Carnarvon: 1662:*

A rose, iris, tulip and other flowers, with a Brimstone butterfly, in a glass vase.

Possibly a piece (un-numbered) at the end of the inventory of pictures at Kensington in 1818: *Flowers. 'in Body Colors'*. Recorded at Windsor (1384) in 1879 (*V.R. inv.*).

Literature: Whinney and Millar, p. 281.

The drawing gives the impression of having been copied from an earlier, presumably Flemish or Dutch, flower-piece, and not to be an *ad vivum* study. In manner it suggests the botanical drawings executed later by Daniel Frankcom and Everard Kickius for the Countess's sister, the Duchess of Beaufort (W. Blunt, *The Art of Botanical Illustration* (1950), pp. 129–30).

Willem Wissing

1656–87. A native of Amsterdam who studied in The Hague; came to London in 1676, became perhaps Lely's most successful pupil and inherited much of his fashionable practice. His portrait of Mary of Modena, recorded in the collection of James II (B. M., Harl. MS. 1890, f. 82 v.; Bathoe, *James II* (1090): *Wissing. The Queenes Picture att halfe length*) appears no longer to be in the royal collection; and his portrait of *Two of the Ld. Rochesters younger Daughters Door Piece*[1] was in the Prince's Eating Room at Windsor in the time of Queen Anne (Queen Anne, *Windsor* (222)), was recorded in the royal collection until 1819, but is now in the possession of the Duke of Brunswick.

319. CHARLES II (*Plate* 133)

Windsor Castle (3064). $49\frac{1}{2} \times 40$ in., $125,7 \times 101,6$ cm.

Three-quarter-length, standing in armour, wearing the

---

1. The group was engraved by John Smith as *The Lady Henrietta and the Lady Mary Hide*.

ribbon of the Garter, holding a baton in his right hand and with a cavalry engagement in the background.

Recorded at Kensington in the reign of Queen Anne: *Wisson King Charles the 2d ½ length* (Queen Anne, *Kensington*, store (1) and later placed over the chimney in the *Little Wainscotted Room on ye Princes side*); later at St. James's.

Literature: Collins Baker, *Lely*, vol. II, p. 18.

Painted late in the King's life, *c*. 1683, and in the standard martial pattern that Wissing was to use, with little variation, for his other royal sitters, James II, William III (nos. 321 and 322) and Prince George of Denmark. A copy was sold at Christie's, 7 October 1949 (17); a head and shoulders copy is at Drummond Castle.

320. JAMES, DUKE OF CAMBRIDGE

Hampton Court (389). $57\frac{3}{4} \times 35\frac{3}{4}$ in., $146,7 \times 85,7$ cm.

Full-length, walking in a landscape, holding a crook (?) over his shoulder, pointing towards a stag pursued by hounds in the distance, and with a dog running beside him.

Probably painted for Mary II when she was Princess of Orange (see below) and first recorded at Windsor in the reign of Queen Anne, *In ye Garden House in ye Queens drawing Room: Wisson The Duke of Camebridge at length in a hunting Posture ovr ye door* (Queen Anne, *Windsor*, after store, no. 4).

Literature: Law, 1881, 1898 (192 as William, Duke of Gloucester, by Kneller); Collins Baker, *Lely*, vol. I, p. 219, *Hampton Court*, p. 80 (as by Huysmans).

A posthumous portrait, apparently painted by Wissing for Mary II when she was Princess of Orange; her brother the Duke of Cambridge had died (1667) many years before Wissing's arrival in London. The Princess wrote to Lady Bathurst on 14 July (1687?): '... I had orderd Mr. Wissing when he was heer to make me a copy of ye princes picture onely a head ... but ... I have changed my mind as for my mothers and brothers picturs haveing writt for them to the King ...' (B. Bathurst, *Letters of Two Queens* (1924), p. 202). It seems that Wissing had been commissioned to paint the little Duke, presumably on the basis of one of Michael Wright's *ad vivum* portraits (see no. 287) to which no. 320 is closely related, but that the original commission for a small portrait developed into a demand for a full-length in which Wissing made use of Lely's Arcadian portrait of the Duke's uncle (no. 248). The design was engraved by Peter Schenk.

321. WILLIAM III WHEN PRINCE OF ORANGE (*Plate* 137)

Hampton Court (1230). $49 \times 40\frac{3}{8}$ in., $124,5 \times 102,6$ cm.

Signed: *W: Wissing: fecit.*

Three-quarter-length, standing in armour, wearing the ribbon of the Garter, holding a baton in his right hand and resting his left hand on a helmet, with a battle raging round a town in the distance.

It is impossible in the earlier inventories to identify with certainty the portraits by Wissing of William III and his Queen; no. 321 may have been the portrait in store (137) at Kensington in the reign of Queen Anne (*King William the 3d when he was Prince of Orange ½ length*). It was in the Dressing Room at Buckingham House and later in Buckingham Palace (495).

Literature: V. & A., *William & Mary and their Time*, 1950 (47); O. Millar, in *Burl. Mag.*, vol. XCIII (1950), p. 233; A. Staring, 'De Portretten van den Koning-Stadhouder', *Nederlandsch Kunsthistorisch Jaarboek*, vol. III (1950–1), p. 183; Whinney and Millar, p. 178.

Probably the best version of the portrait painted, with that of his wife, for James II in 1685 (see no. 323); a signed version, presumably given by the King to the Earl of Romney, is at Penshurst. The type was engraved by R. Williams before the Prince became King of England.

322. WILLIAM III

Windsor Castle (3065). 49½×40 in., 125,7×101,6 cm.
Signed: *W: Wissing. fecit*, and inscribed later: WILLIAM III. WISSING.

See no. 321. Probably the portrait in store (125) at Kensington, with no 323, in the reign of Queen Anne (*Wissing King William the 3ᵈ when he was Prince of Orenge at ½ length*); later at Kensington (possibly previously at St. James's) and, with its companion, at Windsor and St. James's.

Literature: R. A., *Kings and Queens*, 1953 (204).

A repetition of no. 321.

323. MARY II WHEN PRINCESS OF ORANGE (*Plate* 136)

Windsor Castle (3066). 49½×40⅛ in., 125,7×101,9 cm.
Signed: *W:Wissing | fecit*, and inscribed later: QUEEN MARY . WISSING.

Three-quarter-length, seated in a landscape and holding her veil in her right hand.

See no. 322. Probably the portrait in store (126) at Kensington, with no 322,[1] in the reign of Queen Anne (*Wisson Queen Mary when She was Princes at ½ Length*); perhaps thereafter at St. James's and later, with its companion, at Kensington, Windsor and St. James's.

Literature: R. A., *Kings and Queens*, 1953 (212).

See no. 321. This and its companion were probably the portraits which Wissing, at the command of James II, went to Holland to paint in 1685. On 24 August Constantyn Huyghens wrote to his brother Christiaan from Dieren: 'je ne scay si je vous ay mandé qu'ils ont envoyé un peintre d'Angleterre pour faire ceux de leurs Altesses pour le Roy. C'est un disciple de Lely nommé Wissingh, mais il' n'est pas encore arrivé à la perfection de son maistre. Il a apporté le portrait de la Princesse de Danemarc [? no. 325] de sa façon, mais ce n'est pas grand chose. Celuy qu'il a fait de madame ressemble assez bien' (Christiaan Huyghens, *Oeuvres Complètes*, vol. IX (The Hague, 1901), p. 23). The portrait proved very popular and a number of versions and variants were produced, *e.g.*, in the collection of the Earl of Clarendon, in the Scottish National Portrait Gallery (1385), at Drayton, Redlynch, Cirencester and in the Dutch royal collection. The one at Cirencester is presumably the portrait referred to by the Princess in her letters to Lady Bathurst: '& then the Queen sent over a picture drawer for my picture all wch time I durst not write . . . for fear of makeing my eys red'; and, a few days later, '. . . as for my picture Mr. Wissing is now in England so I cant give you an original but if you will have a copie he may make you one when ever you please do but give him order & I shall take care to pay him when he sends the picturs I expect from him' (B. Bathurst, *Letters of Two Queens* (1924), pp. 193, 194; Earl Bathurst, *Catalogue of the Bathurst Collection of Pictures* (1908), pp. 22–4). The type, which was engraved by R. Williams, and its companion continued to serve as the source for portraits of the Prince and Princess after their accession to the throne (*e.g.*, a pair at Lamport), and the variants on no. 323 merge almost imperceptibly into the portraits painted for Mary II by Wissing's former colleague Jan van der Vaart.

1. The portrait (*yᵉ Princesse of Oringe ½ lenght by Wisson*) over the chimney in the Earl of Oxford's lodgings at St. James's in January 1715 could perhaps have been no. 323 or no. 324 (H.M.C., *Cowper MSS.*, vol. III (1899), p. 112).

324. MARY II WHEN PRINCESS OF ORANGE

Hampton Court (23). 49⅝×40¼ in., 126,1×102,2 cm.
Signed: *W. Wissing | fecit*, and inscribed later: QUEEN MARY . WISSING.

Three-quarter-length seated, in a richly ermined cloak, holding a tress of hair in her right hand and with an elaborate baroque palace in the background.

See no. 321. Possibly the portrait in store (173) at Kensington in the reign of Queen Anne: *Wisson Queen Mary at ½ length*. Soon after placed appropriately with her 'Court Ladyes' (nos. 351–8) in the Eating Room below Stairs at Hampton Court. Later at St. James's and Kensington.

Literature: Law, 1881, 1898 (27).

A variant, perhaps painted slightly later, of no. 323. A version, formerly at Cuerdon Hall, belongs to the Ministry of Works; another is at Dyrham.

325. QUEEN ANNE WHEN PRINCESS OF DEN-MARK (*Plate* 134)

St. James's Palace. 49¼×40¼ in., 125,1×102,2 cm.
Signed: *W. Wissing. | fecit*

Three-quarter-length, seated in a landscape.

Recorded in her collection in store at Kensington (127): *Wisson Queen Ann when She was Princes at ½ Length*. Later, as a portrait of Mary II, at Buckingham House and Buckingham Palace (497).

Probably painted *c.* 1683 and perhaps the portrait ('pas grand chose') taken by Wissing to Holland, presumably as a present for Mary II, in 1685 (see no. 323). Versions, with slight variations, are at Luton Hoo and Cirencester. The latter, which has in the past been wrongly identified with Mary II, may have been the portrait which the Princess, probably just before her marriage, had promised to Lady Bathurst: '. . . I do realy love you very well & will ever do so & as for ye picture you shall have one very soon & pray beleeve what I say for it is realy true' (B. Bathurst, *Letters of Two Queens* (1924), p. 168; Earl Bathurst, *Catalogue of the Bathurst Collection of Pictures* (1908), p. 20). The same head seems to be used in Wissing's full-length of the Princess, probably painted with Jan van der Vaart, in the Scottish National Portrait Gallery (939). The Princess and her husband were steady patrons of Wissing.

326. MRS. LAWSON

Hampton Court (194). 49¼×41 in., 125,1×104,1 cm.
Signed: *W. Wissing fec.*

Three-quarter-length seated, resting her left hand in her lap.

Perhaps painted, with nos. 327 and 328, for Mary II. First recorded at Hampton Court in the reign of Queen Anne over the chimney in the Eating Room below Stairs with nos. 351–8: *Sʳ Peter Lelly Mʳˢ Lawson ½ Length* (Queen Anne, *Hampton Court*, added by Thomas Coke after no. 103); soon after taken, with nos. 327 and 328, to replace three landscapes by Danckerts over the doors in the Queen's Private Eating Room at Windsor (*ibid.*, *Windsor*, replacing nos. 72–4 in that inv.) which was hung with Lely's *Beauties* (nos. 257–66).

Literature: Law, 1881, 1898 (200); Collins Baker, *Lely*, vol. II, pp. 16–17.

Probably painted *c.* 1680–5.

Possibly the lady who was rumoured early in 1681 to be the mistress of Charles II: 'a new mistress is spoken of for the King. Her name is Lawson . . . Methinks she is handsome'.

327. MRS. NOTT (KNOTT)

Hampton Court (181). 49 × 39¾ in., 124,5 × 101 cm.

Signed: *W: Wissing fecit.*

Three-quarter-length seated, holding a book in her lap.

Perhaps painted, with nos. 326 and 328 for Mary II. First recorded in store (135) at Kensington in the reign of Queen Anne: *Wisson Mrs Knott at ½ length,* but soon after sent with nos. 326 and 328 to hang with Lely's *Beauties* in the Queen's Private Eating Room at Windsor (Queen Anne, *Windsor,* replacing nos. 72–4 in that inv.).

Literature: Law, 1881, 1898 (191); Collins Baker, *Lely,* vol. II, p. 16.

Probably painted *c.* 1680–5. A copy is at Hitchin Priory.

Possibly Susan (*d.* 1711), grand-daughter of Sir Thomas Nott, Gentleman Usher of the Privy Chamber to Charles II.

328. AMILIA OF NASSAU, COUNTESS OF OSSORY (*d.* 1688) (*Plate* 130)

Hampton Court (192). 49⅛ × 39 in., 124,8 × 99,1 cm.

Three-quarter-length seated, leaning on an urn on which are carved two putti holding a wreath over a skull.

Perhaps painted, with nos. 326 and 327, for Mary II. First recorded in the reign of Queen Anne in the Prince's Eating Room at Windsor (Queen Anne, *Windsor* (221): *Wissing The Lady Ossery at ½ length Door Piece*); soon after hung (with nos. 326 and 327) with Lely's *Beauties* in the Queen's Private Eating Room (Queen Anne, *Windsor,* replacing nos. 72–4 in that inv.).

Literature: Law, 1881, 1898 (198, as the Duchess of Somerset).

Probably painted *c.* 1683. The air of mourning and the carving on the urn are presumably allusions to the death of her husband in July 1680. In a version (probably not autograph) with variations at Petworth (482) the urn lacks the funeral motive.

Daughter of Lodewyk of Nassau, Heer van Beverweerd, an illegitimate son of Prince Maurice of Nassau; married (1659) Thomas Butler, Earl of Ossory.

John Riley

1646–91. An English portrait painter, overshadowed by his foreign contemporaries; painted Charles II at the end of his reign and, in succession to Verrio, was appointed Principal Painter to William III and Mary II, jointly with Kneller; in his later portraits he sometimes collaborated with Johann Baptist Closterman (1660?–1711), a native of Osnabrück who probably came to London in 1681 and later travelled to Spain and Italy.

329. PRINCE GEORGE OF DENMARK (*Plate* 135)

Windsor Castle (3063). 49¾ × 40¼ in., 126,4 × 102,2 cm.

Three-quarter-length, standing in a breastplate and semi-classical costume, wearing the ribbon of the Garter and holding a baton in his left hand.

Presumably painted for the Prince or Queen Anne and probably the portrait over the chimney in her Bedchamber in the Garden House at Windsor: *Prince George of Denmark at ½ length* (Queen Anne, *Windsor,* after store (5); no artist's name is given); it had been seen in the same position, *c.* 1701–3, by Celia Fiennes (*Journeys,* p. 359); later at Buckingham Palace (499) and St. James's, and attributed in the nineteenth, and possibly also in the eighteenth, century to Kneller.

Literature: Collins Baker, *Lely,* vol. II, pp. 29, 160; R. A., *Kings and Queens,* 1953 (220).

Perhaps the portrait referred to by Princess Anne in a letter to her sister Mary, written from Richmond, 11 April 1687: '. . . I must in the first place tell you that the Prince has sat once for his picture, and if I can get the man to come hither it shall be made an end of out of hand' (*Letters of Queen Anne,* ed. B. Curtis Brown (1935), p. 27). It was a popular portrait and versions are at Cirencester, in the National Portrait Gallery (326), in the collection of the Earl of Jersey, at Gaunø Castle (237) and Rosenborg (9233). The copy at Althorp, and a companion portrait of Princess Anne, are among the portraits by 'Mr. Royelly' recorded in the Duchess of Marlborough's possession before the death of William III. A copy was sold at Christie's, 10 April 1959 (44). The type was engraved by Isaac Beckett.

330. BRIDGET HOLMES (1591–1691) (*Plate* 125)

Windsor Castle (838). 88¾ × 58½ in., 225,4 × 148,6 cm.

Signed: *I.R. PI·t·* [apparently strengthened] and inscribed, probably by the artist: BRIDGET. HOLMES. / ETAS SUÆ: 96. A:D:1686:

Full-length, standing in an elaborate interior, clutching her broom while a Page of the Backstairs peeps at her round a curtain.

Presumably painted for the Crown; first recorded in the reign of Queen Anne at Windsor, at first in store (3) and soon after over the chimney in the Prince's Eating Room: *Riley A whole length of Bridget Holmes* (Queen Anne, *Windsor,* after no. 222).

Literature: R. A., *King's Pictures* (42); Waterhouse, *Painting in Britain,* p. 96; Whinney and Millar, p. 189; exh., *Le XVIIe Siècle Européen,* Rome, 1956–7 (248).

The handle of the carved vase in the background appears to be an addition by Riley to the original design.

A 'Necessary Woman' who was in royal service from the reign of Charles I until her death, at the age of a hundred, in the reign of William and Mary.

John Riley and Johann Baptist Closterman

331. KATHERINE ELLIOT (*d.* 1688) (*Plate* 144)

Kensington Palace. 50 × 40¼ in., 127 × 102,2 cm.; there is a probably contemporary addition of 3½ in. on the left.

Three-quarter-length, seated in a richly stuffed chair and in widow's dress.

Presumably painted for the Crown, for James II or one of his daughters; first recorded in store at Kensington in the reign of Queen Anne: *Mrs Eliet at ½ length* (Queen Anne, *Kensington,* store (136), with note by Thomas Coke when it was moved into the Cistern Room: *Ryley ye Head Closterman ye Drapery. Over ye Chimney*); later at Buckingham House and Hampton Court (58).

Literature: Walpole, *Visits,* p. 78; Law, 1881, 1898 (372); Collins Baker, *Lely,* vol. II, pp. 31–2, 159; B.F.A.C., *British-born Painters . . . ,* 1938 (21); R. A., *King's Pictures* (27); Waterhouse, *Painting in Britain,* pp. 96–7; Whinney and Millar, p. 189.

Probably painted *c.* 1687–8. Apart from the face, the hood tied round the head and possibly the white sleeves may be by Riley, but the remainder of the figure and the background seem to be entirely by Closterman, who may also have made the enlargement. A copy of the head is at Corsham Court (211).

Recorded in 1635 as Nurse to the infant James II when he was Duke of York; she became Dresser and Woman of the Bedchamber to both his Duchesses.

Johann Kerseboom

d. 1708. Portrait painter of German descent, possibly trained in Holland, whose uncle Friedrich, also a portrait painter, died in London in 1693; in his later portraits Johann Kerseboom sometimes collaborated with Wissing's former assistant, Jan van der Vaart (*c.* 1647–1727). In Queen Anne's inventory is recorded in store (54) at Kensington: *Vandervart. Lott and his Daughters*, which does not appear to have survived in the royal collection.

332. ROBERT BOYLE (1627–91) (*Plate* 145)

Kensington Palace. 49⅝ × 40½ in., 126,1 × 102,9 cm.

Three-quarter-length, seated at a table and turning the leaves of a book with his left hand.

First recorded, probably early in the reign of George I, at Kensington: *Ryley* [sic] *Mr Boyle, . . . assis dans un Fauteuil, tenant La Main sur un Livre* (B. M., Stowe MS. 567, f. 17 v.); later at Hampton Court (56).

Literature: Vertue, *Notebooks*, vol. IV, p. 177; Law, 1881, 1898 (843); Collins Baker, *Lely*, vol. II, pp. 50–2; Whinney and Millar, p. 192; R. A., *The Age of Charles II*, 1960–1 (241); R. E. W. Maddison, 'The Portraiture of . . . Robert Boyle', *Annals of Science*, vol. XV (1962), pp. 159–72.

Boyle was apparently persuaded in 1689 by Sir Edmund King to sit for his portrait. Pepys, in a letter of 30 August 1689 to Evelyn, wrote of 'those few whose memorys, when dead, I finde myselfe wishing I could do any thing to perpetuate; among which fills a principall place, the most excellent Mr. Boyle, concerning whom I lately bespoke your favour, and dare now be the bolder in doing it againe, from my haveing heard that he has newly beene prevayl'd with by Dr. King, to have his head taken by one of much lesse name than Kneller's, and a stranger, one Causabon' (*Letters and the Second Diary*, ed. R. G. Howarth (1933), pp. 204–5). On 12 September 1689 Robert Hooke 'Saw Mr Boyles Picture at Van der Vert, Henrietta Street with Sir Edm. King'; on 23 January 1690 he was 'At Mr. Boyles . . . Refused his picture, promisd me one . . .'; and on 15 February 1690 he saw 'At Sir Edm. King: Mr Boyles picture . . .' (see R. T. Gunther, *Early Science in Oxford*, vol. X (1935), pp. 106, 148, 182, 188). No. 332 is probably the original that belonged to King; on the back of the canvas there used to be, before re-lining, a seal with the initials *EK* (*V.R. inv.*, 14 April 1860). There appear to be traces of an old join round the upper part of the figure, including the right hand, as if the portrait had been at first designed on a smaller scale and then inserted into a larger canvas. It appears, nevertheless, to be wholly by Kerseboom. Versions, variants and copies seem to have been in production almost immediately: the good version in the Royal Society was presented by Boyle's executors on 16 November 1692; the version in the National Portrait Gallery (3930) may have been painted by Van der Vaart. Other versions are at Bolton Abbey, in the Boyle School at Yetminster, and at Williamsburg (presented by Lord Burlington in 1732). Reduced versions also exist (*e.g.*, in the National Portrait Gallery (734)). As the standard portrait of Boyle the type was engraved, *e.g.*, by John Smith (1689), Schenk, White and Vertue as well as by Bernard Baron as the frontispiece to Boyle's *Works* (1744).

Son of the 1st Earl of Cork; chemist, natural philosopher, a pioneer in the experimental method of scientific study, and one of the group of scientists established in Oxford during the Commonwealth. After the Restoration he was one of the founders of the Royal Society.

Ann Killigrew

1660–85. Daughter of Henry Killigrew, Chaplain and Almoner to the Duke of York; poetess and amateur painter and Maid of Honour to the Duchess of York.

333. JAMES II

Windsor Castle (511). 41¼ × 34 in., 104,8 × 86,4 cm.

Signed: *Ann Killig . . .* (the signature is obscure)

Full-length standing in a glade at the steps of a terrace, wearing the insignia of the Garter; beside him is a carved stone coat of arms, surmounted by a crown and inscribed J A C O B' I I R E X.

Acquired by George IV and recorded at Carlton House in 1816 (357) in store, as a portrait of George II.

Literature: Sir L. Cust, 'Notes on Pictures in the Royal Collection, no. XXXIV, Anne Killigrew', *Burl. Mag.*, vol. XXVIII (1915), p. 112; Collins Baker, *Windsor*, p. 184.

Presumably painted between the King's accession on 6 February, and the artist's death in June, 1685. Walpole's reference (*Anecdotes*, vol. II, p. 107) to Miss Killigrew's portraits of James II and his Queen was probably deduced from Dryden's *Ode* (1686) to her memory:

> . . . . . with bold Erected Look
> Our Martial King the sight with Reverence strook;
> For, not content t' express his Outward Part,
> Her hand call'd out the Image of his Heart,
> His Warlike Mind, his Soul devoid of Fear,
> His High-designing *Thoughts* were figur'd' there,
> . . . .
> Our Phenix queen was portrai'd too so bright,
> *Beauty* alone cou'd *Beauty* take so right:

Sir Godfrey Kneller

1646?–1723. Native of Lübeck; travelled in Holland, Italy and France and was in England by 1676. In 1677 he painted a portrait of James Vernon, secretary to the Duke of Monmouth, which led to successful sittings from the Duke (1678) and ultimately from Charles II. Thereafter he painted official portraits of successive sovereigns and their consorts; Charles II sent him in 1684 to paint Louis XIV at Versailles; by William III and Mary II he was appointed Principal Painter and Gentleman of the Privy Chamber; he was knighted in 1692 and created a Baronet in 1715. A full-length of Charles II by Kneller, probably in the King's Bedchamber at Whitehall, was among the pictures in James II's collection which had not belonged to Charles II (B. M., Harl. MS. 1890, f. 83 v.; Bathoe, *James II* (1128)); this seems later to have been in St. James's House (Queen Anne, *St. James's* (19); B. M., Stowe MS. 567, f. 74), where it was seen by Vertue (*Notebooks*, vol. I, p. 69) in 1720(?) and Walpole (*Visits*, p. 16) in 1758. It was a seated full-length in Garter robes and Vertue stated that it was signed and dated 1685. It was therefore probably a version of the design of which versions are in the Walker Art Gallery, Liverpool (exh. *Kings and Queens*, 1953 (21), illustrated souvenir, pl. 18) and Powis Castle. Charles II owned a full-length by Kneller of the Duchess of Portsmouth which hung in the King's Great Bedchamber at Windsor (B. M., Harl. MS. 1890, f. 72; Bathoe, *James II* (752); for Defoe's reference to it see below, p. 147). Queen Anne owned, hanging over the chimney in the Prince's Bedchamber at Kensington, *The Queen and Duke of Gloucest^r at ½ length*; Thomas Coke's note in Queen Anne's inventory (*Kensington* (183)) adds: *given to Monsr Pless & carried into Denmark But Mr Hook says it is att Sr Godfrey Knellers to be copyed for Mr Pless*. This was probably the source of the copy in the National Portrait Gallery (325) and is not recorded in later inventories of the royal collection. In Queen Anne's reign, hanging in the Bedchamber of State at St. James's was: *Sr Godfry Kneller Two Daughters of the Duke of Marlborough*, identified by Coke as *Lady Harriot Ryalton* and *Lady Sunderland* (Queen Anne, *St. James's* (14)); this is probably the group at Althorp, signed and dated 1688. For Queen Anne or Prince George Kneller and Dahl painted fourteen naval portraits, which were hung in the Little Gallery at Kensington (Queen Anne, *Kensington* (168–81)); Kneller painted for this set Viscount Torrington, Sir Thomas Dilkes, Sir John Jennings, John Benbow, Sir Stafford Fairborne, Sir John Leake and John Graydon. To these was later added, probably after his death, the portrait of Admiral George Churchill. The set was probably planned as a sequel to Lely's (see nos. 240, 252 and 254). They remained in the royal collection until they were sent by command of George IV from Hampton Court to Greenwich Hospital on 5 February 1824.

334. JAMES II

Windsor Castle (2201). 29½ × 25 in., 74,9 × 63,5 cm. Painted as an oval; the spandrels have been filled in at a later date.

Head and shoulders in armour, wearing the ribbon of the Garter.

Purchased by Sir Richard Holmes in Edinburgh *c.* 1890; attributed earlier to Largillierre.

Literature: Collins Baker, *Windsor*, p. 185.

Probably painted *c.* 1683–5, when the sitter was still Duke of York; the head is very close to the full-length in the National Portrait Gallery (666), painted just before his accession. The type was also used by a French painter in making up the half-length of James II at Sizergh Castle, and, for a companion portrait of Charles II, Kneller's contemporary head of the elder sovereign was used in the same way.

335. WILLIAM III (*Plate* 149)

Windsor Castle (217). 96 × 58 in., 243,8 × 147,3 cm., slightly stretched in lining.

Full-length, standing in robes of state, beside a table on which are the crown and orb.

Painted with its companion (no. 338) for the King and Queen; the portrait of the King was hanging in the Council Chamber at Kensington by 1697 (B. M., Harl. MS. 7025, f. 194), and they were both there in the next reign: *Sr G. Kneller King William in the Robes at length . . . Queen Mary in the Robes at length* (Queen Anne, *Kensington* (113, 114)); they were sent to Windsor on 24 July 1795.

Literature: Collins Baker, *Windsor*, p. 185; A. Staring, 'De Portretten van den Koning-Stadhouder', *Nederlandsch Kunsthistorisch Jaarboek*, vol. III (1950–1), pp. 184–6; Whinney and Millar, pp. 194–5.

The heads in nos. 335 and 338 should probably be associated with the sittings to Kneller at Kensington recorded on 17 and 20 March 1690 by Constantyn Huygens (quoted by Staring, *loc. cit.*); and the finished portraits were perhaps referred to in the order of 16 July 1691 for payment to Kneller of £200 for portraits of the King and two of the Queen (*Cal. Tr. Bks.*, vol. IX (iii), p. 1232). They were almost immediately regarded as the approved official likenesses of William and his Queen, and Kneller evolved the machinery that is still associated with the State Portrait for producing copies for despatch to the King's ministers,

friends, and representatives abroad, to foreign sovereigns and governments and to institutions at home. For a full-size copy he seems normally to have been paid £50. There are records of payment for a number of these copies. On 19 April and 14 August 1693 he received payments of £500 for, on each occasion, ten full-length portraits 'for theire ma^ties service' (*The Athenaeum*, no. 3497, 3 Nov. 1894, pp. 611–12): these could have included the two originals and, conceivably, the *Beauties* (see nos. 351–8) if the actual payment for them had been delayed. By a warrant of 20 May 1694 Kneller was paid for two portraits, presumably of the King and Queen, for the Governor of the Barbados; on 13 May 1697 he was paid for three portraits of the King, for the Earl of Manchester, Ambassador to Venice (presumably the copy still at Kimbolton), for Sir James Rushout, Ambassador to the 'Emperor of the Turks', and for the Earl of Bellomont, Governor of New York and New England; and in June 1699 Kneller was paid for a portrait of the King for Sir William Norris, Ambassador to the Great Mogul (*ibid.*). All these portraits were full-lengths. The Earl of Albemarle received the King's permission to have two copies of the King's, and one of the Queen's, portrait, and a warrant for payment to Kneller for them was issued on 16 January 1700 (H. M. C., *Buccleuch MSS.*, vol. II (ii) (1903), pp. 631, 635); in 1697 Kneller was ordered to fit up a portrait of the King for despatch to Louis XIV (N. Luttrell, *Brief Relation* (1857), vol. IV, p. 309); and in the next reign Kneller sent a petition for the money due to him by virtue of a Lord Chamberlain's warrant for six full-lengths of King William (R. W. Goulding, *Catalogue of the Pictures . . . at Welbeck Abbey . . .* (1936), pp. 455–6). Copies of the state portraits of William and Mary were made for the Guildhall, the Merchant Taylors' Company (painted for them in 1697), the Inner Temple (bought and set up in the Hall in 1694), Chelsea Hospital (where there are two of the King), and the Examination Schools at Oxford. Copies of both portraits are also at Hatfield, Narford, Penshurst, Grimsthorpe, Drayton, Northwick, Shrublands Park, Bramshill (formerly), Hardwick, Temple Newsam, Welbeck (see R. W. Goulding, *op. cit.*, 459, 460); the copies at Drumlanrig were originally in the Council Chamber in Edinburgh and were given afterwards by Queen Anne to the Duke of Queensberry. The King alone is at Blenheim and Bolton Hall. A copy by Highmore is in the Mansion House, York. See also nos. 364 and 366. Copies are recorded in Holland, *e.g.*, at Middachten, Het Loo, and Beverweerd. Reductions are common, at half or three-quarter-length (*e.g.*, of William at Belvoir, Gorhambury, and the Joslyn Art Museum, Omaha) or head and shoulders (*e.g.*, of William in the Scottish National Portrait Gallery (807)); and small copies, such as two of the King by Nicholas Dixon at Welbeck and a pair of both sovereigns at Knebworth, are also found. Derivations, such as the portrait of William acquired from Thomas Murray by the Middle Temple in 1725, are not uncommon (and see A. Staring, *loc. cit.*). The two portraits were further reproduced by engravings by, for example, William Faithorne, John Smith, John Simon, Gerard Valck, John Faber junior and Houbraken (1744). It is probable that Kneller used his portrait of 1690 for the King's head in no. 337. There is possibly a *pentimento* in the right outline of the head in no. 335.

336. WILLIAM III (*Plate* 165)

Windsor Castle (1633). Oil on plaster, 36 × 27 in., 91,4 × 66 cm.

Half-length, wearing the robes of the Garter.

Literature: Collins Baker, *Windsor*, p. 302.

Formerly attributed to Verrio, but he is not known to have worked at Windsor for William III. It is almost certainly a fragment from the wall-painting by Kneller, probably painted *c.* 1695–1700 and apparently from a sitting *ad vivum*, which formed part of the semi-illusionist decoration at the end of St. George's Hall and thus completed the decoration of the room initiated by Charles II. The early descriptions of this part of the decoration are conflicting, but Ashmole stated that 'At the upper End of the Hall is the Picture of King *William* III. seated on a Throne, ten Steps high, five of which only are painted; and above this St. *George* killing the Dragon' (*The Antiquities of Berkshire* (1719), vol. III, pp. 118–9); and Bickham (pp. 160–1) describes the King as 'richly drest, in the Order of the Garter, with his Cap on his Right Hand, and the Crown on his Left. This Painting is look'd upon as one of Sir *Godfrey Kneller's* most accurate Performances. There are five Steps of real Marble going up to the Picture, and a fictitious one of five more on the Canvas, so naturally painted, that they deceive in the most agreeable Manner, the Eye of, almost every Spectator. This was contriv'd by the Painter, to supply the Place of the real Ascent with Marble, a Balustrade and a half Pace, which formerly were actually there, with Room for a Throne, or Chair of State for the Sovereign to sit on, when on publick Days he thought proper to make his appearance in due Form' (see also, *e.g.*, J. Pote, *The History and Antiquities of Windsor Castle, . . .* (1749), p. 424, and R. and J. Dodsley, *London and its Environs Described* (1761), vol. VI, pp. 344–5). On 3 June 1801 Benjamin West asked that John Bacon, who was at work on the equestrian statue of William III in St. James's Square, should have 'a sight of the pictures of King William – in his Majesty drawing room [*i.e.*, no. 335] – and under the Canopy in the Great Hall' (MS. in office of the Surveyor of The Queen's Pictures). By 1807 (see *The Windsor Guide* of that year, p. 54) the painting of William III had 'given way to modern improvement'. This fragment and no. 296 are thought to have been removed by Sir Jeffry Wyatville during his work at the Castle and taken by him to his residence at Winchester Tower.

337. WILLIAM III ON HORSEBACK (*Plate* 146)

Hampton Court (25). 174 × 167 in., 439,4 × 424,2 cm.

Signed and dated: *Godfrey Kneller.Eques | Faciebat: A⁰ 1701*
The King, wearing armour and the collar of the Garter, rides along the shore over the emblems of war, observed by Neptune and greeted by Ceres and Flora with the attributes of Peace and Plenty and accompanied by a boy who carries flowers; in the sky Mercury, putti and a female figure carry palm branches, the King's helmet and a scroll inscribed: PACATVMQVE REGIT PATRIIS VIRTVT[IBVS ORBEM].[1]

Painted for the wall of the Presence Chamber at Hampton Court on which it still hangs: *Sʳ G. Kneller. King William on Horseback with other Figures* (Queen Anne, Hampton Court (1)).

Literature: Buckeridge, p. 397; Bickham, p. 68; Vertue, *Notebooks*, vol. II, pp. 67, 121, vol. IV, p. 74; Walpole, *Anecdotes*, vol. I, p. 307, vol. II, p. 203; Law, 1881, 1898 (29); Collins Baker, *Hampton Court*, p. 85; A. Staring, 'De Portretten van den Koning-Stadhouder', *Nederlandsch Kunsthistorisch Jaarboek*, vol. III (1950–1), p. 186; Whinney and Millar, p. 196.

Probably commissioned by the King in 1700. On 2 April 1700 Sir John Stanley wrote to the Duke of Shrewsbury, then Lord Chamberlain, of his official activities on the Duke's behalf at Hampton Court: 'I have sent a warrant . . . for the King's picture on horseback, by his order' (H. M. C., *Buccleuch*

MSS., vol. II (ii), (1903), p. 645). Traditionally 'Great Nassau to Kneller's hand decreed To fix him graceful on the bounding Steed' (Pope, *Imitations of Horace*, ed. J. Butt (1939), p. 227) to celebrate the King's return from the negotiations that led to the Peace of Ryswick; the treaty had been signed on 20 September 1697, the King landed at Margate on 14 November and returned in triumph to London on 16 November. There is clearly a reference to William's triumph as a peace-maker and to a treaty by which Louis XIV had officially recognised him as King of Great Britain; the same iconographical terms are employed, for example, in Daniel de Lange's design for one of the many medals struck to commemorate the Peace. Kneller's use of them is reminiscent of Verrio's glorification of Charles II (no. 297).[1] Payment for the picture seems to have been delayed and Queen Anne seems to have disliked it. Her reaction on 19 May 1703 to a petition from Kneller for payment for portraits of herself and of King William was that she would pay for the former but 'does not care for the picture of 350l.' (*Cal. Tr. Bks.*, vol. XVIII, p. 50). Horace Walpole (*op. cit.*, vol. II, p. 203) described no. 337 as 'a tame and poor performance', but said that 'the original sketch of it at Houghton is struck out with a spirit and fire equal to Rubens. The hero and the horse are in the heat of battle. In the large piece it is the king riding in triumph with his usual phlegm'. He also stated (*Ædes Walpolianæ*, 2nd edn. (1752), p. 45) that 'Mrs. *Barry* and another Actress sat for the Two Emblematic Figures, on The Fore-ground, in the great Picture'. The sketch from Houghton was later in the Hermitage. A very fine *modello* by Kneller (*Fig.* 46) was (1949) in the possession of Mr. Ray Murphy and may have been the sketch seen by Vertue in the collection of T. Walker (*Notebooks*, vol. V, p. 43, '. . . a large sketch first done by Sʳ G. Kneller . . . the Model for that Large painting at Hampton Court'). A small copy of the whole composition is at Drumlanrig and a large copy, but without the subsidiary figures, is at Drayton; a copy of the King at half-length from no. 337 is at Houghton. The same 'spirit and fire' that Walpole admired in the sketch can be seen in Kneller's *modello* (probably painted in 1706) of the Triumph of the Duke of Marlborough in the National Portrait Gallery (902), where some of the elements of no. 337 re-appear in a martial context. Much of no. 337 seems to have been painted by Kneller himself; the figure and the horse are wholly, and the rest of the design probably, by him. See no. 384.

338. MARY II (*Plate* 150)

Windsor Castle (216). 88 × 57¾ in., 223,5 × 146,7 cm.; *c.* 6½ in. of original canvas are turned over at the bottom.

Signed and dated on the canvas that is turned over: *Godfrey Kneller fecit 1690*; the last digit is very obscure.

Full-length, standing in robes of state beside a table on which is her crown, resting her right hand on the orb; in the distance is the Banqueting House.

See the companion portrait, no. 335. No. 338 is possibly the *hole lenght of ye laite Queen in a guilt frame* recorded at Kensington in March 1697. John Smith's mezzotint after the portrait of the Queen is inscribed as '. . . ab illa sola Originale (dum regnavit) depicta' (Chaloner Smith, p. 1197). The portrait of the Queen does not seem to have been repeated so constantly as that of the King. A version is at Belvoir and reduced versions also exist, *e.g.*, at Adlington, Berkeley Castle, Thoresby, at Cobham (formerly), and Beloeil.

1. The iconography of no. 337 is strikingly close to the glorification of Charles II by Verrio and Henry Cooke at Chelsea Hospital (1687–9) and is the source of a wall-painting of George I at 11, Bedford Row, London (E. Croft-Murray, *Decorative Painting in England 1537–1837*, vol. I (1962), pp. 246, 260, pls. 114, 122).

1. The inscription is now partly obscure and the reading s made good from Bernard Baron's engraving.

339. QUEEN ANNE

Kensington Palace. Oval, 30 × 25¼ in., 76,2 × 64,1 cm.

Signed: *GKneller* (initials in monogram).

Head and shoulders in profile to the left, wearing a little crown, robes of state and the collar of the Garter.

Formerly in the collection of Earl Howe, sold at Christie's, 2 July 1948 (20); purchased by Her Majesty The Queen for the Royal collection in 1953.

Painted as the model from which the Queen's head was taken for her coinage and medals. The design was engraved by John Simon 'from yᵉ Original Picture by wᶜʰ all the Medals & Coin has been & are now Made'. According to a confused account by Vertue (*Notebooks*, vol. V, pp. 47–8), Kneller, after orders had been given that a medal should be struck to commemorate Queen Anne's accession, painted a 'profil face' and Francis Bird made a model from it which the Queen disliked; Kneller was asked to go to the Mint and try and make such corrections as were required. The Queen's accession (*Fig.* 44) and Coronation medals were in fact made by John Croker; no. 339 is particularly close to the former (*Medallic Illustrations* . . . (1910), pl. CXV, 1–3). A signed version of Kneller's profile is at Patshull, other versions are at Blenheim and Welbeck (not autograph; R. W. Goulding, *Catalogue of the Pictures . . . at Welbeck Abbey . . .* (1936), 372).

340. QUEEN ANNE

Windsor Castle (218). 84¾ × 58 in., 215,3 × 147,3 cm.; but see below.

Full-length, seated in an ermine-lined cloak, wearing the star of the Garter and holding in her right hand the George suspended on a blue ribbon; on the wall behind the crown is a carved trophy.

First recorded in the Queen's Gallery at Kensington in the reign of George II, in the set of royal full-lengths: *Kneller Queen Anne* (Vertue, inv., *Kensington*, f. 22).

Literature: Collins Baker, *Windsor*, p. 186.

A version, possibly executed in Kneller's studio, of a standard portrait of the Queen; the head is probably by Kneller himself. The best version, signed and dated 1705, is at Wrest Park and was probably given by the Queen to the Lord Chamberlain, the Duke of Kent; it shows that no. 340 has been considerably cut at the bottom of the design. A copy with variations in the Delegates' Room in the Clarendon Building, Oxford, was presented by George Clarke. A good version of the head and shoulders is at Petworth (246), where there is also a standing variant (208). A miniature of the head, signed by Laurence Crosse, was sold at Christie's, 9 February 1960 (178). See also no. 369. Engraved by Houbraken (1744) as at Kensington; the type is also very near the head engraved by Vertue. The Queen does not appear to have owned a version of either of the two official state portraits which seem to have been in production in Kneller's studio from late in 1702; the seated type and its derivations come close to no. 340 and may have been derived ultimately from the same sittings. The design of no. 340 was used by Kneller in his portrait, signed and dated 1708, of the 2nd Duchess of Beaufort at Euston.

341. WILLIAM, DUKE OF GLOUCESTER

Windsor Castle (1154). 58 × 40 in., 132,1 × 101,6 cm.; there is an original addition at the top of c. 4½ in. and a later addition of c. 4 in. at the bottom. The canvas seems to have been slightly cut on both sides.

Full-length seated, in loose draperies, wearing a feathered cap and pointing to a dog; a relief in the background incorporates the intertwined initials DG under a royal ducal coronet.

Conceivably in the collection of Queen Anne, perhaps recorded at Kensington in the reign of George III (Geo. III, *Kensington*, f. 32: *Duke of Gloucester – whole length – Kneller*), and definitely there in 1818 (65; and see Faulkner, p. 366); later at St. James's.

Probably painted in 1691. John Smith's engraving shows a little more of the design on both sides. No. 341 seems to be by Kneller himself.

342. WILLIAM, DUKE OF GLOUCESTER (*Plate* 142)

Kensington Palace. Oval, 30 × 25 in., 76,2 × 63,5 cm.

Signed and dated: *GKneller Eques | fecit 1699* (initials in monogram)

Half-length in a breastplate and ermine-lined cloak, with his left hand on his hip.

Queen Anne seems to have owned at least three portraits of her son by Kneller: *The Duke of Gloucester in an Oval 3 qrs*, in the Green Damask Closet in the Gallery at Windsor; and two at St. James's House: *The Duke of Gloucester over the door* in the Bedchamber of State, and *Duke of Gloucester an oval* in the Queen's Bedchamber (Queen Anne, *Windsor* (154), *St. James's* (13, 23); in store at Kensington (174) was *The Duke of Gloucesᵗ in 3 qrˢ Oval in Armour*, but with no artist's name attached to it); no. 342 was probably later at Kensington and was sent to Hampton Court (885) on 15 December 1835.

Literature: Vertue, *Notebooks*, vol. IV, p. 65; Law, 1881, 1898 (830); V. & A., *William & Mary and their Time*, 1950 (25).

A good version is at Thoresby; a copy is at Hampstead Marshall. The type was used by Claret for his portrait of the little Duke (no. 381), and was engraved by Houbraken (1745). A variant by Kneller, also painted in 1699 and showing the Duke in contemporary costume and wearing the star of the Garter, was engraved by John Smith. See also no. 370.

343. GEORGE II WHEN PRINCE OF WALES (*Plate* 147)

St. James's Palace. 94¼ × 58¼ in., 239,4 × 148 cm.

Signed and dated: *GKneller Baronᵉᵗˢ | 1716* (initials in monogram).

Full-length, standing in robes of state and wearing the collar of the Garter, holding his sword in his left hand and with his coronet as Prince of Wales on a stone table beside him.

It is probable that the references to portraits of George II and his Queen by Kneller and Seeman were confused in the earlier sources, and possible that no. 343 and its companion (no. 345) are the portraits that hung in the Queen's Gallery at Kensington or those referred to by Dodsley in the King's Dining Room at Windsor: 'the Picture of his present Majesty, and the late Queen *Caroline*, whole lengths, by *Zeyman*' (J. Pote, *The History and Antiquities of Windsor Castle*, . . . (1749), p. 421; and see nos. 508 and 511); they were both sent, probably to Hampton Court (later inv. no. 783), on 7 August 1832.

Literature: Law, 1881, 1898 (522).

The portrait seems to have been regarded as an official image of the Prince of Wales and derivations of it and its companion continued to appear after his accession. Copies of no. 343 are at Narford, Chelsea Hospital (attributed to Seeman), and in the New Club, Edinburgh, in the County Court Room at Northampton and in the Palace of Westminster. Copies of the pair were sold at Christie's, 19 February 1954 (118). The two portraits were used in a mezzotint by John Simon composed from three separate portraits by Kneller (Chaloner Smith, p. 1092); the portrait of the Prince was engraved by Simon and Smith in 1717, by John Faber junior and by Vertue in 1724 and 1727, and the plates after the Prince's accession are suitably altered.

344. GEORGE II WHEN PRINCE OF WALES

Windsor Castle (2597). 94⅛×58 in., 239,1×147,3 cm.

Signed and dated: *G Kneller . Baron . . . | 1716*, and inscribed later GEORGE PRINCE OF WALES | *afterwards* KING GEORGE II.

Full-length, standing in the robes of the Garter, resting his right hand on a table beside his plumed hat of the Order and his coronet as Prince of Wales.

With no. 362 came from the Old South Sea House; sold at Phillip's, 22 May 1894 (144, 145), and bought by Edward VII when Prince of Wales (P.R.O., L. C. 1/605, II, 96).

Literature: Collins Baker, *Windsor*, p. 188.

The figure is certainly original, but is one of Kneller's standard Garter patterns; he had used the design earlier, for, *e.g.*, the 6th Duke of Somerset (1713; Petworth; repeated with slight variations in 1720) and the 6th Earl of Mar (1714, in the robes of the Thistle; Alloa). The type of no. 344 was engraved at three quarter length by J. Faber junior 'from Sᵗ Godfrey Kneller's Painting in the South Sea House.' The pattern was repeated in Kneller's studio for the 2nd Duke of Bolton (Bolton Hall), and by a follower of Kneller for Sir Robert Walpole (Houghton). No. 344 was probably the source of a full-length at Burghley in robes of state and with the regalia.

345. CAROLINE OF ANSBACH WHEN PRINCESS OF WALES (*Plate* 148)

Buckingham Palace. 94½×55¾ in., 240×141,6 cm.; the canvas has been slightly stretched at the bottom, reduced on the left and turned over on the right.

Signed and dated: *GKneller Bar . . . | 1716* (initials in monogram).

Full-length, standing in robes of state in front of a richly carved chair beside a table on which is her coronet, and holding a tress of hair in her right hand.

See no. 343; placed in the State Dining Room at Buckingham Palace (1841, p. 100 (211), later no. 189).

See no. 343. A copy is at Narford and a respectable version in the Scottish National Portrait Gallery (1058); another is in the Palace of Westminster. See also no. 500. The portrait was engraved by John Smith in 1717, by Vertue in 1724 and 1727 and by John Faber junior in 1727; the last is inscribed as 'Done from the last Picture of Sᵗ Godfrey Kneller, with proper alterations . . .'

346. THE ARCHDUKE CHARLES (1685–1740)

St. James's Palace. 94¼×58 in., 239,4×132,1 cm.; there is an addition at the top of *c.* 5½ in., and at the bottom of *c.* 5 in.

Signed: *G. Kneller.*

Full-length, standing in armour, wearing the collar of the Golden Fleece, with a baton in his right hand and his left resting on a crown; in the background is an English warship with a smaller vessel firing a salute and troops on the shore.

Painted for Queen Anne and placed in the Old Gallery at Windsor: *Sᵗ G. Kneller King Charles the 3ᵈ of Spain at length* (Queen Anne, Windsor (144)); later at Kensington, Hampton Court (771) and Kensington.

Literature: Buckeridge, p. 397; Vertue, *Notebooks*, vol. II, p. 121; Law, 1881, 1898 (490); Collins Baker, *Lely*, vol. II, p. 172.

Painted during the Archduke's visit to England: he arrived at Portsmouth on 27 December 1703, was at Windsor 29–31 December and sailed on 5 January 1704 from Portsmouth for Spain with an English naval escort, to which there is perhaps an allusion in the background. The head was engraved by John Smith. According to Vertue (*loc. cit.*) Kneller painted the Archduke at Portsmouth at the command of Queen Anne and was given by his sitter 'a large diamond Ring from his finger'. Another portrait of the Archduke by Kneller at Petworth (245) is stated to have been cut down from a full length that was signed and dated 1704 (C. H. Collins Baker, *Catalogue of the Petworth Collection of Pictures . . .* (1920), p. 67).

Younger son of the Emperor Leopold I of Austria, who ceded to him his claim to the Spanish Succession; it was to support this claim that Great Britain and her allies fought the War of the Spanish Succession, but although the Archduke was crowned in Madrid as Charles III of Spain in 1706, he was driven from the country in 1713, two years after he had succeeded his elder brother as Emperor Charles VI.

347. PETER THE GREAT, TSAR OF RUSSIA (1672–1725) (*Plate* 127)

Kensington Palace. 95×57¼ in., 241,3×145,4 cm.

Inscribed by Kneller and signed and dated: *Petrus Alexeewitz. Magnus Dominus. | Tzar Et Magnus Dux Moscoviæ | Jussu Britanniæ Majestatis Godefridus Kneller Eques | ad vivum Pinxit, 1698.*[1]

Full-length in armour and a fur-lined cloak, richly embroidered with the Imperial arms, holding a baton in his right hand; beside him are his crown and sceptre and in the background (English?) ships at sea.

Painted for William III and hung by 1700 in the Drawing Room at Kensington (B. M., Harl. MS. 5150: *Godfrey Kneller Czar of Moscovy half* [sic] *length*); later at Windsor and Hampton Court (60).

Literature: London in 1710, trans. (from Z. C. von Uffenbach) and ed. by W. H. Quarrel and Mare (1934), p. 157; Vertue, *Notebooks*, vol. II, p. 121; Walpole, *Anecdotes*, vol. II, p. 207; Waagen (1854), vol. II, p. 356; Law, 1881, 1898 (57); Whinney and Millar, p. 194.

Painted during the Tsar's visit to William III, whom he deeply admired, in 1698. The Tsar arrived in London on 10 or 11 January and left on 21 April. He had stayed in Evelyn's house at Deptford which thus became for a short time 'full of people, and right nasty'. There may be an allusion in the background to the mock sea-fight with which the Tsar was entertained at Portsmouth on 22 March or to the *Royal Transport*, the yacht presented to him by William III and in which he had sailed to England. The shipping was thought in the nineteenth century to have been painted by Van de Velde, but it seems certainly to be by Kneller himself. A good version is at Hatfield, copies are at Sherborne Castle and Noseley, and a copy of the head in the Evelyn collection may have been made for Evelyn as a record of the visit of his terrifying tenant. On 8 July 1698 Kneller was given official permission to make a copy of the portrait for the Earl of Albemarle (*The Athenaeum*, no. 3497, 3 Nov. 1894, p. 612). A small copy was sold at Christie's, 9 February 1960 (151). The head was engraved by John Smith and Pieter van Gunst. A drawing by Kneller (*Fig.* 42) of a man in armour, full-

---

1. Parts of this inscription are now obscure, but the reading can be completed from the version at Hatfield and from the inscription on John Smith's mezzotint (Chaloner Smith, p. 1214). The latter gives 1697 as the date of the portrait.

length and signed *GKneller:F:in London*, may conceivably have been Kneller's first idea for the portrait before he actually had a sitting from the Tsar; in design it agrees more closely with a contemporary variant of no. 347 which was sold at Christie's, 16 October 1959 (163).

Ascended the throne in 1682 as joint Tsar with his elder half-brother Ivan, but assumed power in 1695; by the time of his death he had transformed, often by ruthlessly brutal methods, his semi-barbarous, semi-Asiatic inheritance into an Empire strongly influenced by Western technical achievements and civilization.

348. MICHAEL ALPHONSUS SHEN FU-TSUNG, 'THE CHINESE CONVERT'[1] (d. 1691) (*Plate* 151)

Kensington Palace. $83\frac{1}{2} \times 58$ in., 212,1 × 132 cm.

Signed and dated: *G. Kneller . fecit . Aº 1687.*

Full-length standing in oriental dress, laying his right hand on his breast and pointing to the crucifix which he holds in his left hand.

Painted for James II and placed in the King's Presence Chamber, later the Drawing Room, at Windsor: *Kneller. The Chinese at length* (B. M., Harl. MS. 1890, f. 82 v.; Bathoe, *James II* (1092)); it was placed over the chimney, where it remained at least until the time of Pyne, whose plate (vol. I, p. 155) shows it in the same position; later at Buckingham Palace (487).

Literature: Buckeridge, p. 397; Vertue, *Notebooks*, vol. II, p. 29 ('... by a Ladder. I see very fine'), p. 121; Walpole, *Anecdotes*, vol. II, p. 203; R. A., *King's Pictures* (116); Waterhouse, *Painting in Britain*, p. 99; Whinney and Millar, p. 198; exh., *Le XVIIe Siècle Européen*, Rome, 1956–7 (147); R. A., *The Age of Charles II*, 1960–1 (354).

Painted before James II's visit to the Bodleian Library on 5 September 1687, when he asked Thomas Hyde, Bodley's Librarian, if 'the Chinese', whom the King described as 'a little blinking fellow', had been there and added that 'he had his picture to the life hanging in his roome next to the bed chamber' (*The Life and Times of Anthony Wood...*, collected ... by A. Clark, vol. III (1894), pp. 236–7). According to Walpole (*loc. cit.*) 'Of all his works, Sir Godfrey was most proud of the converted Chinese at Windsor'. There appear to be alterations to the outline of the robe. John Faber junior's mezzotint (1736) may have started the confusion by which the portrait came to be identified with Father Philip Couplet rather than with his convert. Michael, born of Chinese Christian parents, had come to Europe under the auspices of Couplet, who was Procurator of the China Jesuits in Rome; they left Macoa in 1681 and visited Italy, France and England, where Michael helped in cataloguing the Chinese MSS. in the Bodleian. Michael left England in 1688 for Lisbon, where he entered the Society of Jesus, but died near Mozambique in 1691 on his way back to China.

349. GEORGE BYNG, FIRST VISCOUNT TORRINGTON (1663–1733)

Kensington Palace. $30\frac{1}{4} \times 25$ in., 76,8 × 63,5 cm.

Signed: *GK* (in monogram)

Head and shoulders in a painted oval.

Purchased by George IV and recorded at Carlton House in 1816 (346): *A head of a nobleman, with a large wig, and a long neckcloth;* the 1816 label is still on the back; later at Buckingham Palace (815).

A very late work, painted *c.* 1720; the type is close to, but slightly later than, the head of Lord Torrington in a double portrait with his son Pattee, formerly at Woburn and sold at Christie's, 19 January 1951 (116), which was signed by Kneller and dated (1718?).

Joined the Navy in 1678; supported the Prince of Orange and took part in most of the important actions of his time; repulsed the Old Pretender's fleet in 1708 and in 1715 prevented supplies from reaching his supporters; Admiral of the Fleet (1718) and First Lord of the Admiralty (1727). See no. 394.

350. HENRY WISE (1653–1738) (*Plate* 166)

Kew (Hampton Court no. 1228). $29\frac{7}{8} \times 24\frac{7}{8}$ in., 75,9 × 63,2 cm.

Signed: *GK* (in monogram)

Head and shoulders within a painted oval.

Presumably painted for the sitter and recorded in the Dining Room in his house at Brompton Park in November 1718: *Mr Wise's piece by Sr Godfrey Kneller* (the inventory is printed in D. Green, *Gardener to Queen Anne* (1956), p. 216); passed by descent to Sir Wathen Arthur Waller, Bart., sold at Christie's, 12 December 1947 (155), and purchased by His Majesty King George VI for the royal collection.

Literature: D. Green (*op. cit.*), pp. 222–3.

Probably painted *c.* 1715; a copy is stated to be in the Shire Hall at Warwick and another is at Matfen Hall.

The famous gardener who, in partnership with George London, ran the celebrated nursery at Brompton Park. The gardens which they designed, or where they made improvements, included Longleat, Blenheim, Chatsworth, Castle Howard, Melbourne, Wanstead and Canons. Their work was deeply influenced by Le Nôtre. Wise had worked for William III at Kensington and Hampton Court and from the accession of Queen Anne until his retirement in 1727 was in almost sole charge of the royal parks and gardens.

351–8. THE HAMPTON COURT BEAUTIES

The series of full-length portraits, painted for Mary II, probably in emulation of Lely's *Windsor Beauties* (nos. 257–66), was described by Defoe as 'of the principal Ladies attending upon her Majesty, or who were frequently in her Retinue'. The series was perhaps initiated with the portrait of the Duchess of Grafton (no. 351): on 16 January 1690 Kneller wrote to Pepys (*Letters and Second Diary*, ed. R. G. Howarth (1932), p. 213) that 'the duchess of Grafton comes to set for the Queen at 2 of the Clok'. The Wardrobe Accounts for work executed in the year ending at Michaelmas 1691 included payment of £400 to 'Sir Godfrind Kneller Our Principall painter for Eight pictures drawne att Length vizt ...' (P. R. O., L.C. 5/43, f. 34)[1]. They were placed by the Queen in her Water Gallery at Hampton Court, 'the more beautiful Sight, because the Originals were all in Being, and often to be compar'd with their Pictures', and were seen there (*c.* 1696) by Celia Fiennes: '... the Water Gallery ... was decked with China and fine pictures of the Court Ladyes drawn by Nellor' (*Journeys*, p. 59). She saw them again (*c.* 1701–3) after they had been moved to the Eating Room below Stairs or 'the constant dineing-roome where are hung all the pictures of the Ladyes of the Bed Chamber in Queen Maryes time that were drawn by Nellor and were then hung in the Water Gallery before that was pulled down' (*ibid.*, p. 357; Queen Anne,

---

1. I am profoundly grateful to Miss Margaret Toynbee for informing me of the researches of Fr. Francis A. Rouleau, S. J., and others, which have identified the portrait with this individual.

1. I am very grateful to Mr. Sidney Gold for drawing my attention to this reference.

Hampton Court (96–103)). When they were placed in this room they were probably put into their present frames, and the portrait of the Queen by Wissing that was placed over the chimney to preside over them (*e.g.*, Vertue inv., *Hampton Court* (1750), f. 10) was probably no. 324 which is in an identical frame. They seem to have been hung in the First Presence Chamber in the reign of George IV.

In his description of Windsor Defoe mentions a full-length of the Duchess of Portsmouth, 'of which 'twas said, King *Charles II.* should say, 'Twas the finest Painting, of the finest Woman in *Christendom*; but our *English* Ladies of Queen *Mary's* Court, were of another Opinion, and the Gallery of Beauties, . . . which her Majesty placed in the Water Gallery at *Hampton Court*, shews several as good Faces, and as good Painting.' The Countess of Carlisle, sister-in-law of no. 354, 'remembered the event' and told Walpole that Queen Mary's commission to Kneller, on which she decided during one of William III's absences, 'contributed much to make her unpopular . . . the famous Lady Dorchester advised the Queen against it saying, "Madam, if the King were to ask for the portraits of all the wits in his court, would not the rest think he called them fools?"'' (*Anecdotes*, vol. II, pp. 206–7). John Faber junior engraved the series and added to it a frontispiece (which incorporated a portrait of Kneller) and plates of the Duchesses of Manchester and Marlborough and of the Countess of Clarendon (from portraits by Kneller that had never been in the royal collection) and of Queen Mary from no. 338 (Chaloner Smith, pp. 309–12); Vertue saw in Kneller's house at Whitton '12 small Copies in oyl. ye beauties of Hampton Court' (*Notebooks*, vol. II, p. 68). The canvases bear later inscriptions identifying the sitters.

Literature: (for the set) *London in 1710*, trans. (from Z. C. von Uffenbach) and ed. by W. H. Quarrel and M. Mare (1934), p. 156; Buckeridge, p. 397; Defoe, *A Tour thro' . . . Great Britain* (1724–7), ed. G. D. H. Cole (1927), vol. I, pp. 175, 305; Vertue, *Notebooks*, vol. II, p. 121; Walpole, *Anecdotes*, vol. II, pp. 206–7; Waagen (1838), vol. II, pp. 118–9, (1854), vol. II, 355; Law, 1898, pp. 10–11, and *The History of Hampton Court Palace*, vol. III (1891), pp. 29–32; Collins Baker, *Lely*, vol. II, p. 172.

351. ISABELLA BENNET, DUCHESS OF GRAFTON (1667–1723) (*Plate* 155)

Hampton Court (43). 91¾ × 56½ in., 233 × 143,5 cm.; including an original addition of *c.* 5½ in., at the bottom.

Standing beside an elaborately carved fountain into which she dips a shell with her left hand.

Literature: Law, 1881, 1898 (46); Collins Baker, *Hampton Court*, p. 85.

The Duchess was apparently sitting to Kneller on the Queen's behalf very early in 1690 (see above). It is possible that the portrait was the first of the series and encouraged the Queen to commission further portraits of this type; it would then have been enlarged (see above) when the uniform height of the portraits had been settled. A version (probably autograph) of the head is at Ingatestone; a little version (*Fig.* 41), sold at Christie's, 19 June 1953 (33) and now in the possession of the Earl of Euston, is probably a *modello* by Kneller. A three-quarter-length copy is at Bolton Hall. The head is close to a three-quarter-length at Ragley. Engraved by Bernard Lens.

Only child of the Earl of Arlington, she married (1672) Henry Fitzroy, 1st Duke of Grafton (*d.* 1690), and, as her second husband (1698), Sir Thomas Hanmer; she walked at the Coronation of Queen Anne; a woman of great charm and virtue.

352. DIANA DE VERE, DUCHESS OF ST. ALBANS (*d.* 1742) (*Plate* 153)

Hampton Court (22). 92 × 45¼ in., 233,7 × 114,9 cm.

Signed: *G.K. fecit.*

Standing holding an orange which she has plucked from a tree that grows in a richly carved gilt vase.

Literature: Law, 1881, 1898 (26); Collins Baker, *Hampton Court*, p. 84.

There are *pentimenti* in the drawing of the base of the column on the left. A three-quarter-length copy is at Bolton Hall. This canvas and no. 354 are of a narrower shape than the other six portraits and were presumably painted to fill two narrower spaces in the Water Gallery.

Daughter and sole heiress of the 20th and last Earl of Oxford, whose famous line thus 'Concludes with lustre in St. Albans' charms'; she married in 1694 Charles Beauclerk, 1st Duke of St. Albans, and was First Lady of the Bedchamber and Groom of the Stole to Caroline of Ansbach when Princess of Wales.

353. MARY COMPTON, COUNTESS OF DORSET (1669–91) (*Plate* 154)

Hampton Court (47). 91¾ × 56½ in., 233 × 143,5 cm.

Signed: *G.K.*

Leaning against a ledge above a carved relief of Ceres.

Literature: Law, 1881, 1898 (50); Collins Baker, *Hampton Court*, p. 86.

A head and shoulders version, possibly by Kneller himself, is at Drayton.

Daughter of the 3rd Earl of Northampton; in 1685 she married, as his second wife (see no. 259), Charles Sackville, 6th Earl of Dorset; Lady of the Bedchamber to Queen Mary, who was much distressed by her early death from small-pox.

354. MARY BENTINCK, COUNTESS OF ESSEX (*d.* 1726) (*Plate* 152)

Hampton Court (26). 91¾ × 44 in., 233 × 111,8 cm.

Walking on a terrace and pointing with her right hand to a distant ship at sea.

Literature: Law, 1881, 1898 (30); Collins Baker, *Hampton Court*, p. 84.

See no. 352.

Daughter of William III's life-long friend, the 1st Earl of Portland; married in 1692 Algernon Capel, 2nd Earl of Essex (*d.* 1710), Gentleman of the Bedchamber to William III, and, in 1714, Sir Conyers D'Arcy.

355. CAREY FRASER, COUNTESS OF PETERBOROUGH (*d.* 1709) (*Plate* 157)

Hampton Court (29). 91¾ × 56½ in., 233 × 143,5 cm.

Signed: *G. Kneller. fecit.*

Leaning against the base of a statue of Minerva.

Literature: Law, 1881, 1898 (33); Collins Baker, *Hampton Court*, p. 84.

Daughter of Sir Alexander Fraser, Physician to Charles II, she had been a Maid of Honour to Catherine of Braganza; married (*c.* 1678) Charles Mordaunt, Earl of Monmouth and later 3rd Earl of Peterborough.

356. MARGARET CECIL, COUNTESS OF RANELAGH (1672–1728) (*Plate* 156)

Hampton Court (33). 91½ × 56½ in., 232,4 × 143,5 cm.

Signed: *Godfrid: Kneller f.* (the signature is very obscure).

Standing on a terrace and pointing with her right hand to a richly carved vase of flowers.

Literature: 1881, 1898 (37); Collins Baker, *Hampton Court*, p. 84.

The design was used verbatim by Allan Ramsay, presumably through Faber's mezzotint, for his portrait (*c.* 1740) of Mrs. Daniel Cunyngham (*Fig.* 40) in the National Gallery of Scotland (2133); and Henry Fielding, in his attempt to convey to his readers the rare charms of Sophie Western, cited the *Beauties* and said of her that 'She was most like the picture of Lady Ranelagh' (*Tom Jones*, Bk. IV, ch. II).

Daughter of the 3rd Earl of Salisbury; married first (1691) John, 2nd Lord Stowell (*d.* 1692), and (1696), as his second wife, Richard Jones, 1st Earl of Ranelagh.

357. FRANCES WHITMORE, LADY MIDDLE-TON (*c.* 1666–1694) (*Plate* 158)

Hampton Court (51). 92 × 56¼ in., 233,7 × 142,9 cm.

Standing in a landscape as a shepherdess, holding a crook in her right hand and accompanied by a lamb.

Literature: Law, 1881, 1898 (53); Collins Baker, *Hampton Court*, pp. 85–6.

In the payment to Kneller for the portraits of the *Beauties* the sitter is referred to as *The Lady Middleton*; comparison with a portrait by Kneller at Plas Power, and with the sculptured portrait of Lady Middleton in the monument by Robert Wynne at Chirk, confirms that she is Frances, widow of William Whitmore, who married (1686) Sir Richard Middleton, 3rd Bart. of Chirk. A three-quarter-length copy is at Bolton Hall. Another slightly earlier portrait of the same sitter by Kneller was engraved at the time (Chaloner Smith, p. 1663).

358. MARY SCROPE, later MRS. PITT (*Plate* 159)

Hampton Court (37). 91½ × 56½ in., 232,4 × 143,5 cm.

Signed and dated: *G. Kneller fecit. 1691* (the last digit is obscure).

Standing, observed by a lizard and holding her hand under a jet of water from a carved fountain.

Literature: Law, 1881, 1898 (40); Collins Baker, *Hampton Court*, p. 85.

In the payment to Kneller for the portraits of the *Beauties* the sitter is referred to as *Mrs Scroop*, but in the early inventories she is described as *Mrs. Pitt(s)*; on Faber's mezzotint she is called *Mrs. Scroop*. She is presumably therefore Mary Scrope (*b.* 1676), who married, probably *c.* 1695, John Pitt of Stratfield Saye, and was daughter of St. Leger Scrope of Louth. She is stated to have been regarded as the most beautiful lady of the Court. A three-quarter-length copy is at Bolton Hall.

Studio of Sir Godfrey Kneller

359. GEORGE I

Windsor Castle (3036). 31 × 25⅜ in., 78,7 × 64,5 cm.

Head and shoulders in armour, in profile to the right within a painted oval.

Recorded at Buckingham Palace (1154) in 1866 (*V.R. inv.*); in 1947 it was placed in the frame made for no. 371.

Literature: Walker Art Gallery, Liverpool, *Kings and Queens of England*, 1953 (30), illustrated souvenir, pl. 26.

An order of 6 May 1715 for payment to Kneller included, in addition to the money for five full-lengths of the King, twenty pounds 'for the coin' (*Cal. Tr. Bks.*, vol. XXIX (ii), p. 508). The original of the design, presumably painted (*cf.*, no. 339) for the new coinage and medals, may have been the version recorded in the collection of the Duke of Brunswick in 1937. No. 359 appears to have been painted in Kneller's studio. A good version is in the National Portrait Gallery (4223); a copy is at Hatfield; and see no. 371. In 1908 a version belonged to Count Kielmansegge. A miniature copy by Lens was sold at Christie's, 11 February 1936 (34). The design, which was engraved by Jacques Chereau, may have been used by Croker (*Fig.* 43) and Ehrenreich Hannibal for their medals commemorating the King's proclamation and Coronation (*Medallic Illustrations . . .* (1911), pl. CXXXIX). Addison's poem *To Sir Godfrey Kneller, on his picture of the King* clearly refers to his latest portrait in his sequence of royal images:

'This image on the medal placed,
With its bright round of titles graced,
And stampt on British coins, shall live,
To richest ores the value give,
Or, wrought within the curious mould,
Shape and adorn the running gold.'

360. GEORGE I

Windsor Castle (219). 94¼ × 58¼ in., 240 × 132,7 cm.

Full-length, standing in robes of state, wearing the collar of the Garter and resting his hand on the orb which is on a table with the crown and sceptre; in the distance is the east end of Westminster Abbey and St. Stephen's Chapel.

Probably the portrait (*Kneller King George the first*) recorded in the Queen's Gallery at Kensington in the reign of George II, in the set of royal full-lengths (Vertue inv., *Kensington*, f. 22).

Literature: Collins Baker, *Windsor*, p. 186.

A studio copy of the official state portrait of the King. The finest, apparently wholly autograph, version is at Houghton; it was presented to Sir Robert Walpole, hung in his study and was described by Horace Walpole as 'the only Picture for which he ever sat in *England*' (*Ædes Walpolianæ*, 2nd. edn. (1752), p. 49, but see also p. 45). From at least 6 May 1715 Kneller was being paid for repetitions of the state portrait, *e.g.*, for sixteen in 1715, about eleven in 1716, eleven in 1717, and five in 1718 (*Cal. Tr. Bks.*, vol. XXIX (ii), pp. 508, 734, vol. XXX (ii), pp. 450, 600, vol. XXXI (iii), p. 688, vol. XXXI (ii), p. 391, vol. XXXII (ii), p. 347) and two in 1718-19 (*Cal. Tr. Papers*, 1714–19, p. 445). Copies are at Narford, Chelsea Hospital, Milton Park, Chevening, in the Scottish National Portrait Gallery (1059) and in the Christchurch Museum, Ipswich. Variants are at Patshull and Burghley and reduced copies at Longleat, Houghton, West Wycombe, Burton Agnes, Port Eliot, Bishopsthorpe and Bisham Abbey. And see nos. 372–6. In a version formerly belonging to Princess Arthur of Connaught the King wears the crown and carries the regalia. For Kneller's correspondence concerning the version for the Guildhall, see above p. 24. The type was engraved by, for example, John Smith and Vertue in 1715 (the latter inscribing his plate 'a solo Originali'), by John Faber junior and by John Simon in his composite mezzotint (see no. 343). It is not always possible to determine whether the engraved heads are based on no. 360 or on Kneller's other standard portrait of the King (*e.g.*, nos. 361 and 362); both types almost certainly derive from the same sitting.

361. GEORGE I

St. James's Palace. 94 × 58 in., 238,8 × 132,1 cm.

Full-length, seated in Garter robes beside a table on which rests the plumed hat of the Order with the crown, sceptre and orb.

Possibly the portrait recorded at Hampton Court in 1835 (489) and certainly there in 1872 (*V.R. inv.*, no. 782), but probably in the royal collection at an earlier date.

Apparently a good contemporary version, executed in Kneller's studio, of a type that was probably based on the same sitting as the original of no 360 (*q.v.*); this type in Garter robes was engraved by Vertue in 1718. The composition had originally been evolved by Kneller for Charles II in 1685 (see Walker Art Gallery, Liverpool, *Kings and Queens of England*, 1953 (21), illustrated souvenir pl. 18). No. 361 seems to have been repeated almost as often as no. 360: versions are, for example, at Syon House, Drayton, Floors Castle, Melbourne Hall, Breamore, the National Portrait Gallery (544), in the County Court Room at Northampton, at Chatham House and in the possession of the Ministry of Works. And see no. 362.

362. GEORGE I

Windsor Castle (2596). 94⅛ × 58¼ in., 240 × 132,7 cm.

Inscribed later: KING GEORGE I. / *after* SIR G. KNELLER.

See no. 344.

Literature: Collins Baker, *Windsor*, p. 188.

A contemporary version, probably painted in Kneller's studio, of the same design as no. 361.

363. SIR ISAAC NEWTON (1642–1727)

Kensington Palace. 49½ × 40 in., 125,7 × 101,6 cm.

Inscribed: *Isack Newton. Esqʳ / Ætatis 47/1689*

Three-quarter-length, standing beside a table on which is a globe and an open book.

Probably one of the 'Portraits of several Poets, Painters, and Philosophers' (some of which may have been collected by Queen Caroline of Ansbach) recorded in the Queen's Dressing Room at Windsor (Bickham, p. 171); later at St. James's and Hampton Court (957).

Literature: Law, 1881, 1898 (846).

The head is identical with Kneller's half-length, signed and dated 1689, in the possession of the Earl of Portsmouth (R. A., *The Age of Charles II*, 1960–1 (217)) and no. 363 was presumably worked up from that, probably in Kneller's studio.

Philosopher, mathematician and scientist and one of the greatest figures in the history of European thought; M.P. for Cambridge, Warden (1696) and Master (1699) of the Mint, and President of the Royal Society (1703–27).

After Sir Godfrey Kneller

364. WILLIAM III

St. James's Palace. 91¾ × 57¾ in., 288,9 × 146,7 cm.

It is probable that no. 364 and its companion (no. 365), and not the pair at Kensington Palace, are the pair from the collection of Frederick, Prince of Wales, seen by Horace Walpole at Kew in September 1761: 'In the Hall. William & Mary, whole Lengths' (*Visits*, p. 39); probably the pair at Buckingham House in 1819 (771, 773, measurements given as 92 × 57 in.).

A good copy of no. 335.

365. MARY II

St. James's Palace. 92¾ × 58¼ in., 235,6 × 132,7 cm.

See no. 364.

A good copy of no. 338.

366. WILLIAM III

Kensington Palace. 95¾ × 59 in., 243,2 × 149,9 cm.

For this and its companion see no. 364.

A copy, perhaps contemporary, of no. 335.

367. MARY II

Kensington Palace. 95¾ × 59 in., 243,2 × 149,9 cm.

See no. 366.

A copy, perhaps contemporary, of no. 338.

368. QUEEN ANNE

Holyroodhouse. 90½ × 54 in., 229,9 × 137,2 cm.

Full-length standing in robes of state, wearing the crown and the collar of the Garter, holding the sceptre in her right hand and resting her left on the orb on a carved table.

Recorded at Holyrood in 1884 (*V.R. inv.*).

A copy of the state portrait of the Queen, of which the original was probably evolved soon after the Queen's accession. A number of versions and variants exist; that in the Inner Temple is stated to have been painted for them by Kneller in 1703.

369. QUEEN ANNE

St. James's Palace. 94¼ × 58¼ in., 239,4 × 148 cm.

Recorded at St. James's in 1864 (*V.R. inv.*).

A nineteenth-century copy of no. 340.

370. WILLIAM, DUKE OF GLOUCESTER

St. James's Palace. 30⅛ × 25 in., 76,5 × 63,5 cm.; originally an oval, later made out.

Head and shoulders, within a (later) painted oval, in a breastplate and ermine-lined cloak, wearing the ribbon of the Garter.

Probably acquired by George IV; recorded at Carlton House in 1816 (302: the 1816 label is still on the back); later at Hampton Court (946).

Literature: Law, 1881, 1898 (41).

Probably derived from a variant of Kneller's portrait of 1699 (no. 342).

371. GEORGE I

Windsor Castle (341). 31 × 25¾ in., 78,7 × 65,4 cm.

Acquired by George IV: in November 1810 Collins delivered to Carlton House *Three half length Gilt Frames to the following Pictures ... George the First in West Anti Room* (Jutsham, *R/D.*, f. 137); on 20 January 1812, however, John Smith sent in his account for £75. 12s. for *superb Frames ... for the Portraits of George the 1st & second* (W. R. A., Geo. 26901), which are presumably the frames on nos. 359 and 620;[1] at Carlton House in 1816 (19); sent to Windsor on 18 March 1829.

Literature: Collins Baker, *Windsor*, p. 188.

A later copy from the same source as no. 359, lacking the painted oval.

1. In 1947 no. 359 was placed in the frame made for no. 371.

372. GEORGE I

St. James's Palace. 94¼×58¼ in., 239,4×132,7 cm.

Recorded at St. James's in 1863 (*V.R. inv.*), but stated on a label on the back to have been sent to Windsor from Mr. Shepperson on 11 February 1823 or 1825.

A later copy of no. 360.

373. GEORGE I

Holyroodhouse. 95½×59½ in., 242,6×151,1 cm.

Recorded at Holyrood in 1884 (*V.R. inv.*) as a portrait of Prince George of Denmark.

A bad late copy of no. 360; the head has been atrociously repainted in modern times.

374. GEORGE I

Buckingham Palace. 45×40¼ in., 114,3×102,2 cm.

Probably purchased by George IV; recorded at Carlton House in 1816 (306): *A half length of King George II* (sic; the 1816 label was on the back before the canvas was lined (*V.R. inv.*, 4 July 1861)); later at Hampton Court (924) and St. James's.

Literature: Law, 1881, 1898 (806).

An unimportant, but probably contemporary, three-quarter-length copy of no. 360.

375. GEORGE I

Hampton Court (1369). 36×28 in., 91,4×71,1 cm.

Recorded at Buckingham Palace (1136) in 1877 (*V.R. inv.*); later at St. James's Palace.

An inferior three-quarter-length copy of no. 360; it was originally a full-length, but was reduced to its present form in 1906.

376. GEORGE I

Buckingham Palace. 14⅜×11 in., 36,5×27,9 cm.

Head and shoulders in a painted oval.

Recorded at Carlton House in 1816 (312) as a portrait of George II (the 1816 label is on the back); later at Kew.

Literature: Buckingham Palace, 1909, p. 218.

An early derivation from no. 360.

377. JOHN LOCKE (1632-1704)

Kensington Palace. 50×40⅜ in., 127×102,6 cm.

Three-quarter-length, seated at a table, resting his left hand by an ink-well.

Recorded at St. James's in 1819 (1030); later at Hampton Court (947).

Literature: Law, 1881, 1898 (824).

A derivation from the head and shoulders portrait, painted by Kneller in 1704, which became a popular type and of which the original is probably the version in the possession of Dr. B. Samuels in New York.

The famous philosopher whose writings, particularly his *Essays* on *Toleration* and *Human Understanding*, exercised a profound influence on European thought. His bust was among those made for Queen Caroline's Grotto by Rysbrack (1733).

378. JOHN CHURCHILL, FIRST DUKE OF MARLBOROUGH (1650-1722)

Windsor Castle (436). 33½×26¼ in., 85×66,7 cm.

On the back, presumably copied from the back of the original canvas, is inscribed: *Duc de Marlboroch. Kneller, Pinx.*

Head and shoulders, within a painted oval, wearing the ribbon and star of the Garter.

Nos. 378 and 379 were formerly, as by Kneller, on the staircase at White-Knights, the house near Reading which had belonged to the Englefield family, but had been purchased in 1798 by the 5th Duke of Marlborough and contained a number of family portraits (Mrs. Hofland, *A Descriptive Account . . . of White-Knights* (1819), pp. 39-40, 133). Stated to have been purchased, with no. 379, at White-Knights in 1828 (*Carlton Palace* (621, 622)).

Apparently a copy, possibly by Enoch Seeman, based on one of Kneller's later portraits of the Duke, possibly the full-length in Garter robes (c. 1708?) of which there are two versions at Blenheim Palace.

The undefeated general whose four famous victories in the War of the Spanish Succession crippled the power of France and laid the foundations of British greatness in the eighteenth century.

379. SARAH JENNINGS, DUCHESS OF MARL-BOROUGH (1660-1744)

Windsor Castle (439). Oval, 29¾×24¾ in., 75,6×62,9 cm.

Head and shoulders in a loose drapery.

See no. 378.

An unimportant copy of the portrait by Kneller at Althorp which was probably painted *c.* 1691.

Maid of Honour and Lady of the Bedchamber to Queen Anne before her accession, and thereafter Mistress of the Robes and Keeper of the Privy Purse, but lost her great influence over the Queen before the end of her reign.

School of Sir Godfrey Kneller

380. GEORGE II WHEN PRINCE OF WALES

St. James's Palace. 87½×63 in., 222,3×160 cm.; see below.

Full-length seated in a chair richly carved with the Prince of Wales's feathers, in Garter robes with the plumed hat of the Order on a table beside him.

Recorded at Kensington in 1818 (424; Faulkner, p. 391 '. . . after Sir G. Kneller-Shackleton'); later at Hampton Court (718) and Kensington.

Literature: Law, 1881, 1898 (477).

The head is apparently based on Keller's official likeness of 1716 (no. 343), and the pose is a repetition of Kneller's long established royal 'Garter' pattern (see no. 361). The canvas should probably be dated *c.* 1720-5 and the crown on the table was probably added after the King's accession in 1727. The canvas was originally of a most unusual shape, rising to a form of stepped arch above the King's head, and was probably designed to fit into a special architectural framework which may have been echoed in the painted reliefs in the background; those on the right are martial trophies.

William Claret

d. 1706. Portrait painter and copyist, who may have been trained in Lely's studio.

381. WILLIAM, DUKE OF GLOUCESTER

St. James's Palace. 87×49½ in., 221×125,7 cm. The canvas seems to have been cut on all sides.

On the back of the original canvas is an inscription: *Duke of Gloucester | Son of Queen Anne | Claret fecit.*

Full-length standing, wearing the robes of the Garter, with the plumed hat of the Order on a table beside him.

Recorded in the Old Gallery at Windsor in the reign of Queen Anne (Queen Anne, *Windsor* (139): *Clarret. The Duke of Gloster at length in yᵉ Gartʳ Robes after Sʳ G Knellʳ*); later at Kensington, Hampton Court and Buckingham Palace (488).

Literature: Collins Baker, *Lely*, vol. II, p. 74.

Presumably painted for Queen Anne. The head and left arm are taken from no. 342, and it is possible that the whole design is a copy from an original full-length by Kneller of the Duke. The pattern seems to recall no. 335. Two other portraits of the Duke by Claret after Kneller are recorded in Queen Anne's inventory (*Windsor*, in the Queen's Bedchamber in the Garden House, after store (6): *Claret. Duke of Gloucestʳ a head in oval after Sʳ G Knellar*, and *St James's House* (25), in the Queen's Closet in the Bedchamber: *Copy of Mʳ Clark* [sic] *Duke of Gloucester in an oval*). Neither portrait is now in the royal collection, but the former was probably that seen by Celia Fiennes at Windsor (*Journeys*, p. 359).

Edmund Lilly

d. 1716. Portrait painter, possibly of Norfolk origin; painted Queen Anne in 1703 (the signed and dated original is at Blenheim); he also painted still-life and history pieces.

382. WILLIAM, DUKE OF GLOUCESTER

Windsor Castle (2497). 86½ × 50½ in., 219,7 × 128,3 cm.; there is a modern addition at the top of 13 in.

Signed: *E Lilly. pinxit.*

Full-length, standing in a colonnade in the robes of the Garter.

Probably acquired by Queen Victoria for the royal collection; formerly at Buckingham Palace.

Literature: Collins Baker, *Lely*, vol. II, p. 206, *Windsor*, p. 228; Whinney and Millar, p. 192.

Probably painted *c.* 1698; the Duke had been nominated and invested as Knight of the Garter on 6 January, and was installed on 24 July, 1696. A copy was (1958) in the collection of Mr. J. Pearson, Satis House, Datchet.

Michael Dahl

1659?–1743. Swedish portrait painter, born in Stockholm; studied under Ehrenstrahl and, after travelling to Italy, settled in London in 1689; patronised by Queen Anne and the Prince of Denmark, but does not seem to have received a commission from the new dynasty after 1714, possibly because of his association with Tory circles. His refusal to paint the Duke of Cumberland as a baby probably led to his being denied the succession to Kneller as Principal Painter, a post which was given instead to Jervas. For the set of naval portraits painted by Kneller and Dahl for Queen Anne or her consort (see pp. 25, 142), Dahl painted Sir William Whetstone, Sir Clowdisley Shovell, Sir Thomas Hopsonn, Basil Beaumont, Sir George Rooke, and Sir John Munden.

383. PRINCE GEORGE OF DENMARK (*Plate* 143)

Kensington Palace. Oval, 30¼ × 25¾ in., 76,8 × 64,8 cm.

Head and shoulders in armour, wearing the ribbon of the Garter.

Presumably painted for the Prince or Queen Anne and recorded in the Queen's Bedchamber at St. James's House: *Mr Dahle Prince of Denmark an oval* (Queen Anne, *St. James's* (22)); later at Kensington, Frogmore, Windsor, Hampton Court (884) and St. James's.

Literature: Law, 1881, 1898 (845); Collins Baker, *Lely*, vol. II, pp. 96–7, 178; W. Nisser, *Michael Dahl . . .* (Uppsala, 1927), pp. 24, 99–100, cat. p. 20; V. & A., *William & Mary and their Time*, 1950 (7).

Probably painted *c.* 1690 and perhaps Dahl's first royal commission. He used the head, presumably slightly later, in a three-quarter-length portrait formerly in the Earl of Ellesmere's collection, sold at Christie's, 18 October 1946 (106). The head of the original was engraved by Houbraken (1745). In addition to nos. 383 and 384 Queen Anne owned a third portrait of her husband by Dahl: *Dahle Prince George at length in the Garter Robes*, which was hung in the Old Gallery at Windsor (Queen Anne, *Windsor* (130)), but is not recorded in the royal collection later than the reign of George II.

384. PRINCE GEORGE OF DENMARK (*Plate* 167)

Kensington Palace. 118½ × 104 in., 301 × 254 cm.

Signed and dated: M : DAHL. *pinx. 1704*

Riding on horseback along the shore, in military dress with the Garter ribbon over his breastplate; in the background are ships of the fleet, of which the nearest flies the royal standard, the red ensign and the Admiralty flag.

Painted for the Prince or Queen Anne and placed in the Queen's Guard-Chamber at Windsor: *Dahle Over the Chimney Prince George on Horse Back* (Queen Anne, *Windsor* (40)); it can be seen in its original position in Pyne, vol. I, p. 88 (later inv. no. 1275); sent to Buckingham Palace in 1877.

Literature: W. Nisser, *Michael Dahl . . .* (Uppsala, 1927), pp. 111–2, cat. p. 20; Whinney and Millar, p. 200.

Painted with obvious allusions to the Prince's position as 'generalissimo' and Lord High Admiral. The horse, reminiscent of William III's in the slightly earlier portrait by Kneller (no. 337), seems to have been painted by Dahl himself; later in the eighteenth century the marine background came to be attributed to Van de Velde, but it is not impossible that it likewise was painted by Dahl.

385. PORTRAIT OF AN OFFICER

Buckingham Palace. 48⅝ × 37⅛ in., 122,9 × 94,3 cm.

Three-quarter-length, standing in a red coat and breastplate, holding a baton in his right hand and his sword in his left; a cavalry action and a burning town in the distance.

Stated to have been purchased by George III in 1805 for four guineas from Mr. Carter, a boat-builder at Eton (Legge's lists of pictures at Windsor in 1813 and 1816; Pyne, vol. I, pp. 151-2).

Formerly attributed to Kneller (*e.g., V.R. inv.,* 19 January 1876, Buckingham Palace no. 471) and identified from the time of its purchase as a portrait of the Duke of Marlborough. It is, however, certainly by Dahl and painted *c.* 1690-5. The sitter has not been satisfactorily identified; a superficial likeness to Frederick, Duke of Schomberg (1615-90), is barely sufficient evidence for suggesting that no. 385 may represent one of his sons, both of whom were distinguished professional soldiers: Meinhard, Duke of Leinster and 3rd Duke of Schomberg (1641-1719), who came to England in 1689, or Charles, 2nd Duke of Schomberg (1645-93), who came to England with his father in 1688. There are *pentimenti* in the background, where the horizon seems originally to have been lower.

Gerhard Bockman

1686–1773. Portrait painter, copyist and engraver; a pupil of Kneller.

386–94. PORTRAITS OF NAVAL COMMANDERS after KNELLER and DAHL

Nos. 386–94 are copies of ten of the fourteen naval portraits that had been painted for Queen Anne or Prince George of Denmark by Kneller and Dahl and presented to Greenwich by George IV (see pp. 25, 142). The reasons for, and time of, their purchase remain obscure. George IV's disbursements in 1824–5 included £200 for *Portraits of Admirals copied & presented to Greenwich Hospital by His Majesty* (W. R. A., Geo. 26531); this could have referred to other portraits in George IV's gift to the Hospital but, if it referred to nos. 386–94, would indicate that his intention was to present the copies rather than the originals. Eight of the portraits are recorded at Kensington in 1818 (119–21, 128, 134, 136–8; all except the portraits of Beaumont and Benbow appear as by Bockman). They were later at Hampton Court and Kensington; almost all of them bear Hampton Court numbers and identifying inscriptions; all are three-quarter lengths with marine backgrounds.

386. BASIL BEAUMONT (1669–1703)

Buckingham Palace. 50½ × 40¼ in., 128,3 × 102,9 cm.

Literature: Law, 1881, 1898 (17).

A copy of the portrait by Dahl of *c.* 1702–3.

Rear-Admiral, drowned in a wreck on the Goodwin Sands.

387. JOHN BENBOW (1653–1702)

Buckingham Palace. 49¼ × 39½ in., 125,1 × 100,3 cm.

Literature: Law, 1881, 1898 (10).

A copy of the portrait by Kneller, which was probably painted in 1701.

Master of the Fleet in the naval battles in the reign of William III; died of wounds after his heroic action off Santa Marta.

388. GEORGE CHURCHILL (1654–1710)

Buckingham Palace. 50½ × 41 in., 128,3 × 104,1 cm.

Literature: Law, 1881, 1898 (22).

A copy of the portrait by Kneller, which is signed and dated 1704.

Younger brother of the Duke of Marlborough and an extremely incompetent manager of naval affairs during the War of the Spanish Succession. Bogdani's pictures of the birds in his aviary were acquired by Queen Anne (see no. 472).

389. SIR THOMAS DILKES (1667?–1707)

Buckingham Palace. 50 × 40 in., 127 × 101,6 cm.

Literature: Law, 1881, 1898 (6).

A copy of the portrait by Kneller, which was probably painted *c.* 1705–7.

Served under James II; in 1705 defeated the French squadron blockading Gibraltar.

390. SIR STAFFORD FAIRBORNE (d. 1742)

Buckingham Palace. 50¼ × 40¼ in., 127,6 × 102,2 cm.

Literature: Law, 1881, 1898 (21).

A copy of the portrait by Kneller, which was probably painted *c.* 1705.

Served in many of the actions in the reigns of William III and Queen Anne and appointed Admiral of the Fleet in 1708.

391. JOHN GRAYDON (d. 1726)

Buckingham Palace. 50 × 40 in., 127 × 101,6 cm.

Literature: Law, 1881, 1898 (15).

A copy of the portrait by Kneller, which was probably painted *c.* 1703–4.

Held commands in naval actions in the reign of William III and served with Rooke at Cadiz and Vigo.

392. SIR JOHN JENNINGS (1664–1743)

Buckingham Palace. 49¾ × 40 in., 126,4 × 101,6 cm.

Literature: Law, 1881, 1898 (18).

A copy of the portrait by Kneller, which was probably painted in 1705.

Held important commands throughout the reign of Queen Anne, a Lord of the Admiralty (1714–27) and Governor of Greenwich (1720).

393. SIR JOHN LEAKE (1656–1720)

Buckingham Palace. 49½ × 38½ in., 125,7 × 97,8 cm.

Literature: Law, 1881, 1898 (13).

Formerly, through a confusion in the inventories, described as a portrait of Edward Russell, Earl of Orford (1653–1727); in fact a copy of Kneller's portrait of Leake, which was probably painted *c.* 1703–4.

Played a prominent part in the reduction of Gibraltar in 1704; a Lord of the Admiralty (1709).

394. GEORGE BYNG, VISCOUNT TORRINGTON (1663–1733)

Buckingham Palace. 50 × 40¼ in., 127 × 102,2 cm.

Literature: Law, 1881, 1898 (14).

A copy of the portrait by Kneller, which was probably painted *c.* 1708–9.

See no. 349.

Charles D'Agar

1669–1723. Portrait painter of Huguenot birth who came to London with his father in or before 1681; worked for some years with his father in Copenhagen, but in 1691 returned to England, where he seems to have been in a successful practice *c.* 1705–20.

Attributed to Charles D'Agar

395. PORTRAIT OF A MAN

Kensington Palace. 49¾ × 40¼ in., 126,4 × 102,2 cm.

Three-quarter-length, seated, resting his left arm on a ledge.

Probably acquired by George III; recorded in Miss Planta's room at Kew (Geo. III, *Kew*) as a portrait of Sir Christopher Wren; later at Buckingham Palace (1187).

Probably painted *c.* 1705. No. 395 is very close indeed to the documented work of Charles D'Agar.

After Charles D'Agar

396. ROBERT DARCY, THIRD EARL OF HOLDERNESSE (1681–1722)

Kensington Palace. 94 × 58 in., 238,8 × 132 cm.

Full-length standing, in peer's robes, with his left hand on his hip and holding his coronet in his right hand.

Recorded at Windsor *c.* 1818 (vol. of miscellaneous lists, f. 108: *Lord Holderness. Qy Kneller*); later at Hampton Court (831).

Literature: Law, 1881, 1898 (554).

Formerly attributed to Jervas, no. 396 is a full-length version, probably by Enoch Seeman, of a portrait of which a three-quarter-length version (*c.* 1715–20) is in the collection of the Marquess of Lothian; this, in a valuation of the Lothian collection in 1752 (Lothian MSS.), is stated to be by 'Dagarre', is presumably the original of the design and is entirely consistent with D'Agar's documented works.

Lord Lieutenant of the North Riding of Yorkshire, a Privy Councillor and a Lord of the Bedchamber, 1719–22.

Hendrick Danckerts

c. 1630–after 1679. Landscape and topographical painter, born and trained in The Hague. Possibly visited England in 1650; in 1653 travelled to Italy; settled in England after the Restoration, but left at the time of the Popish Plot. In 1675 and 1679 he was paid a total of £108 3s. 6d. for 'several prospect pictures and landskips by the King's command' (*Cal. Tr. Bks.*, vol. IV, p. 769, vol. V, p. 1278). The classical landscapes in the royal collection were painted many years after Danckerts's years in Italy, but he used in them material gathered on the spot (Whinney and Millar, p. 264). From the references in the early inventories it is not possibly to identify the classical landscapes painted by Danckerts for Charles II and James II, or accurately to plot their later courses. In store at Whitehall in the time of Charles II were, as by *Danckurs: A greate Landskip that was formerly in the Queene bed chamber*, measurements given as 84 × 64 in., and *A Landskip of Ruaignes & Water. for ov' a doore*, measurements given as 42 × 55 in. (Charles II, *Whitehall* (636, 638)). James II's inventory included seven landscapes at St. James's (B. M., Harl. MS. 1890, ff. 85 v.–86 v.; Bathoe, *James II* (1196–7, 1211–2; 1224, 1235, 1237)) and three at Windsor and five at Whitehall that had not belonged to Charles II (Harl. MS. 1890, ff. 83, 84; Bathoe (1102–4, 1152, 1155, 1158–60). Danckerts had probably painted for Charles II two views of Plymouth, from the land and from the sea, which were hanging in the reign of James II in the Old Withdrawing Room at Whitehall (B. M., Harl. MS. 1890, f. 48 v.; Bathoe, *James II* (102, 104) but are not recorded in the royal collection after 1714;[1] and a *Landskip of Greenwich with the Prospect to London* and *A Landskip of Windsor Castle* (Harl. MS. 1890, ff. 52, 55; Bathoe (195, 297)), which are no longer in the royal collection.

1. A view of Plymouth, signed and dated 1675 by Danckerts, was in the sale of pictures from Flaxley Abbey, sold by Bruton, Knowles & Co., 29 March–1 April 1960 (1372).

397. HAMPTON COURT PALACE

Hampton Court (1250). 40¼ × 39¼ in., 102,2 × 99,7 cm., *c.* 1 in. is turned over on each side.

A view of the east front of the Tudor palace with the new canal and young trees in the foreground and a sportsman approaching some deer.

Probably painted for Charles II and to be identified with the picture at Whitehall in James II's collection: *By Danckers. The Landskip of Hampton Court with the Canall* (B. M., Harl. MS. 1890, f. 52; Bathoe, *James II* (194)); later at Kensington[1], where it was attributed by Horace Walpole in 1763 to Wyck (notes to Bathoe, *James II*), and St. James's.

Literature: E. Law, *The History of Hampton Court Palace*, vol. II (1888), pp. 217–8; Law, 1907 (910); Collins Baker, *Hampton Court*, pp. 31–2 (confusing provenance with no. 439).

Presumably painted *c.* 1665–7, very soon after Charles II's new canal had been completed and his trees planted. In Evelyn's account of a visit to Hampton Court, under the date 9 June 1662, he described the park as 'formerly a flat, naked piece of Ground, now planted with sweete rows of *lime-trees*, and the Canale for water now neere perfected'. The 'flat, naked piece of Ground' can be seen in Willem Schellinks's view (1662) of the palace (P. H. Hulton, 'Drawings of England in the Seventeenth Century . . .', *Walpole Soc.*, vol. XXXV (1959), no. 29) and in a drawing in the Pepysian Library at Cambridge (*Wren Soc.*, vol. VII (1930), pl. XXII). In no. 397 the east front of the old Tudor Palace is seen almost unaltered with, on the left, the range of buildings towards the river and the cupola of the Great Round Arbour. Early in 1669 Pepys was planning to have a view of Hampton Court among the views he was commissioning from Danckerts, but he later decided to have one of Rome instead.

398. A VIEW OF FALMOUTH HARBOUR

Windsor Castle (1276). 38½ × 85½ in., 100,3 × 217,2 cm., including two additions on the right, the first (*c.* 13½ in.) by Danckerts himself, the second (4 in.) apparently slightly later.

Signed and dated: *HDanckers. F 1674* (initials in monogram).

A view looking from the Cornish mainland (on which is a group of figures) across Carrick Roads to the open sea with Falmouth on the right, Pendennis Castle on Pendennis Point in the middle distance, and a glimpse of St. Mawes Castle on the opposite headland on the left.

Probably painted for Charles II; recorded in the Old Withdrawing Room at Whitehall in the reign of James II: *By Young Danckers. A Landskip the Prospect of Pindennis* (B. M., Harl. MS. 1890, f. 48 v.; Bathoe, *James II* (97)).

Literature: Whinney and Millar, pp. 263–4.

Topographically the 'prospect' seems fairly accurate; it can be compared with Willem Schellinks's two drawings of Falmouth Harbour in 1662 (P. H. Hulton, 'Drawings of England in the Seventeenth Century . . .', *Walpole Soc.*, vol. XXXV (1959), nos. 49–50). Danckerts's enlargement of the canvas was probably made in order to incorporate part of Falmouth.

399. A VIEW OF PORTSMOUTH (*Plate* 139)

Buckingham Palace. 36 × 81½ in., 91,4 × 207 cm.; the painted surface has been turned over at top and bottom and on the right.

1. In 1728–9 it appears to have been at Richmond and to have been cleaned by Stephen Slaughter (B.M., MS. 20101, ff. 56, 57).

Signed and dated: *HDankers F | 1675* (initials in monogram).

A prospect of Portsmouth from the land, probably from the West Dock Fields, with a dry dock in the foreground; a yacht on rollers and another small boat are on the bank.

Presumably painted with no. 400 for Charles II. In James II's inventory three views of Portsmouth by Danckerts are recorded, apparently in the Old Withdrawing Room at Whitehall: no. 399 could be either *A Landskip the Prospect of Portsmouth* or . . . *another Prospect of Portsmouth*, and no. 400 was presumably *A Prospect of Portsmouth from the Sea* (B. M., Harl. MS. 1890, f. 48 v.; Bathoe, *James II* (98, 99, 100), all as by *Danckers*). Nos. 399 and 400 were later at Kensington, Somerset House and Hampton Court (674, 675).

Literature (for the pair): Law, 1907 (649), 1925, pp. 53–4; Whinney and Millar, p. 264; H. V. S. and M. S. Ogden, *English Taste in Landscape in the Seventeenth Century* (Ann Arbor, 1955), pp. 153–4, 159, 162 (fig. 126).

Nos. 399 and 400 were probably, with no. 398, a result of the commission stated to have been given to Danckerts by Charles II 'to paint all the Sea-Ports of *England* and *Wales*, as also all the Royal Palaces, which he perform'd admirably well' (Buckeridge, p. 413). Nos. 399 and 400 may have been painted partly to record the extent of the remodelling and rebuilding of fortifications and the construction of new docks at Portsmouth during the reign of Charles II. It is perhaps significant that in 1675 Charles II saw at Portsmouth a little yacht, one of two built by the King for Louis XIV, drawn up on a cradle placed on four wheels, lifted from the shore and launched.

400. A VIEW OF PORTSMOUTH

Buckingham Palace. 36 × 81⅛ in., 91,4 × 207,3 cm.

A prospect of Portsmouth from the sea, from one of the forts near Gosport at the harbour mouth. On the left is the dock-yard and Rope House and opposite the spectator is the town of Portsmouth with its protective batteries (the Great Platform (?) in the centre) and the parish church and the Domus Dei (?) behind. The vessels include a yacht near the shore, watched by a small crowd who appear to have come through the Point Gate.

See no. 399.

The yacht near the shore may be one of three built by Charles II for Louis XIV (see no. 399).

401. A VIEW OF TANGIER

Hampton Court (1332). 43 × 63 in., 109,2 × 160 cm.

Signed and dated: *HDanckerts. | F. 1669.* (initials in monogram).

A view of Tangier from the south-west with the bay in the distance. The Union flag is flying from the Peterborough Tower in the distance and St. George's flag from the (Pole or Norwood?) Fort in the foreground.

Painted for Charles II and recorded at Whitehall in James II's inventory: *Danckers. A Prospect of Tangier from the land* (B. M., Harl. MS. 1890, f. 48 v.; Bathoe, *James II* (101)); in the reign of Queen Anne it was over the chimney in the Billiard Room at Kensington (Queen Anne, *Kensington* (191)); later at Hampton Court, Windsor (1158) and York House.

Literature: Collins Baker, *Hampton Court*, p. 164; Whinney and Millar, pp. 263–4.

On 2 May 1669 Pepys saw at Whitehall '. . . the picture of Tangier, designed by Charles Herbert [= Harbord], and drawne by Dancre, which my Lord Sandwich admires, as

being the truest picture that ever he saw in his life: and indeed it is very pretty, and I will be at the cost of having one of them.' The Earl of Sandwich's admiration presumably led him to commission the version, also signed and dated 1669, formerly at Hinchingbrooke. The interest in the fortress and naval base at Tangier, England's new possession, was considerable, and Danckerts's views of it seem to have preceded, if only by a few months, the famous survey carried out by Hollar (see Whinney and Millar, pp. 267–8). There is no evidence that Danckerts ever went to Tangier and he probably based his views on drawings made by Sir Charles Harbord, Surveyor-General of Crown Lands. The view is taken from the hill under the Catherine Fort and is close to one of the drawings made by Hollar in 1669 (E. M. G. Routh, *Tangier* (1912), p. 156). The Whitehall Fort and the bowling green are seen on the left. Discrepancies in details between the two compositions are probably due to inaccuracies in Danckerts's source. For Charles II he appears to have painted a companion piece, *A Prospect of Tangier from the Sea, with the Mole* (B. M., Harl. MS. 1890, f. 48 v.; omitted in Bathoe, *James II*), which does not appear in the records of the royal collection after 1714.

402. LANDSCAPE WITH STATUES

Buckingham Palace. 87 × 77¾ in., 221 × 197,5 cm.

A lady and gentleman walking among statues and urns beside an elaborate fountain in the garden of an Italian villa, with a view of an Italian town in the distance.

Perhaps to be identified with: *Dankhurst A Landskip wherein is a Fountaine* in the Queen's Bedchamber at Hampton Court in the reign of Charles II (Charles II, *Hampton Court* (194), measurements given as 96 × 78 in.); probably later at Kensington; recorded at Buckingham Palace (687) in 1876 (*V.R. inv.*).

If the canvas can be identified with the picture in Charles II's inventory, it was probably painted *c.* 1665 and was thus among the first pictures painted by Danckerts for the Crown.

403. AN ITALIAN GARDEN

Buckingham Palace. 85¾ × 100 in., 217,8 × 254 cm.

The gardens of an Italian villa with a ruined classical building and walks lined with urns; the fountain in the foreground is apparently intended for Bernini's Fontana del Tritone in the Piazza Barberini in Rome.

Almost certainly painted for Charles II or James II and probably at Kensington in the reign of Queen Anne; recorded at Buckingham Palace (1059) in 1876 (*V.R. inv.*).

Presumably painted *c.* 1675.

404. A CLASSICAL LANDSCAPE (*Plate* 164)

Hampton Court (790). 62½ × 50¾ in., 158,8 × 128,9 cm.; there is a very early addition at the bottom of *c.* 5½ in., and an addition at the top, perhaps by the artist, of 17¾ in.

The garden of a villa from which is seen a view of St. Peter's.

Presumably painted for Charles II or James II; later at Buckingham House and Kensington.

Literature: Law, 1881, 1898 (525).

Probably painted *c.* 1675.

405. A CLASSICAL LANDSCAPE

Windsor Castle (2708). 64 × 42½ in., 162,6 × 108 cm.; there is an old addition at the top of 11½ in.

Signed and dated: *HDanckers 1674* (initials in monogram).

Shepherds with their flocks by a ruined building in an Italian landscape.

Presumably painted for Charles II or James II; later at Buckingham Palace (618).

406. A CLASSICAL LANDSCAPE

Windsor Castle (1127). 75½×46½ in., 191,8×118,1 cm.

Signed and dated: *HDanckers. 1677* (the initials in monogram and the last two digits obscure).

Shepherds and shepherdesses by a ruined, overgrown temple, near a broad river and against a mountainous Italian background.

Presumably painted for Charles II or James II; probably later at Buckingham House.

Literature: The Stuart Period (Connoisseur, 1957), pl. 40B.

407. A CLASSICAL LANDSCAPE

Windsor Castle (2859). 62×50 in., 157,5×127 cm., including a very early addition of *c.* 4½ in. at the top. In the nineteenth century (*V.R. inv.*) its height had been enlarged to *c.* 85 in.

Signed and dated: *HDanckers/F 1676* (initials in monogram).

A group of Italian peasants washing in the pool of an elaborate fountain in the grounds of a villa.

Presumably painted for Charles II or James II; later at Buckingham Palace (551) and York House.

408. A CLASSICAL LANDSCAPE

Windsor Castle (506). 61½×43 in., 156,2×109,2 cm.

The garden of an Italian villa with figures and statues and steps leading away towards a distant view of St. Peter's.

Presumably painted for Charles II or James II and later at Buckingham House.

Literature: Whinney and Millar, pp. 264–5.

Presumably painted at the same time as Danckerts's other decorative canvases of this shape and type.

409. A CLASSICAL LANDSCAPE

Kensington Palace. 62¼×41 in., 158,1×104,1 cm.

Signed and dated: *HDanckers F. | 1677* (initials in monogram).

Two women talking at the foot of a statue; on the base of the statue is inscribed DIS MANIBVS; there are the statue of a sphinx on the right, a villa in the background and mountains beyond.

Presumably painted for Charles II or James II; later at Hampton Court (732).

Literature: Law, 1881, 1898 (489).

410. A CLASSICAL LANDSCAPE

Windsor Castle (2709). 63¾×42½ in., 162×108 cm.; there are early additions on all sides; the original canvas was *c.* 52¾×37 in.

Signed and dated: *HDanckers. | 1677* (initials in monogram).

A group of figures seated among statues and columns in an Italian landscape.

Presumably painted for Charles II or James II; later at Buckingham Palace (619).

411. A CLASSICAL LANDSCAPE

63½×42½ in., 161,3×108 cm.; there are early additions on the right and at the top and the original canvas was *c.* 46½×35 in.

A small Italian town by a river, in which are bathers and small boats and which is partly spanned by a ruined bridge.

Presumably painted for Charles II or James II; probably later at St. James's (in 1819 the measurements of no. 1034 at St. James's were given as 64×44 in.); later at Hampton Court (752), Pembroke Lodge and Clarence House. Lent to the Central Chancery of the Orders of Knighthood in 1947.

Literature: Law, 1881, 1898 (505).

Probably painted *c.* 1675.

412. THE MYSTIC MARRIAGE OF ST. CATHERINE

Hampton Court (1238). 86½×89 in., 219,7×226 cm.

In a spacious landscape St. Catherine kneels in front of the Virgin and the Infant Christ, who places a ring on her finger while an angel holds a cloak around her.

First recorded in the reign of Queen Anne in the Eating Room at Windsor: *Danker A Madona with the Marriage of St Catherine* (Queen Anne, *Windsor* (27); later inv. no. 1253); recently at York House.

Literature: Walpole, *Anecdotes,* vol. II, p. 109; Collins Baker, *Hampton Court,* p. 93.

Although no subject pictures by Hendrick Danckerts are known, the landscape is almost certainly by him. The figures are, however, very close to the subject-pictures by his younger brother Johann (*c.* 1615–1681/7), who had travelled with him to Italy and was in London in the late 1650's. The figures are also suggestive of Lely, with whom the brothers had probably been in contact at the time when he was still painting 'Historical Compositions': in a letter to Sir Charles Cotterell, 30 June (1650?), Hugh May wrote that he had 'obtained this letter from my freind Mr Lely to one Danckers (who is comeing over from the Hague speedily to him)' (MS. at Rousham).

Jan Loten

1618–1681? Landscape painter, native of Amsterdam, who had settled in London by July 1662.

Attributed to Jan Loten

413. LANDSCAPE WITH A BRIDGE (*Plate* 162)

Windsor Castle (2863). 73×59 in., 185,4×150 cm.

An extensive mountainous landscape with figures near a bridge which spans a rocky gorge.

In James II's inventory of pictures at St. James's was: *Loaton. A Landschape* (B. M., Harl. MS. 1890, f. 86; Bathoe, *James II* (1217)), and in the Billiard Room at Kensington in the reign of Queen Anne was: *Loaton A Landskip with Rocks and a Bridge* (Queen Anne, *Kensington* (193)). These entries are perhaps more likely to refer to no. 413 than to no. 414 (*q.v.*). No. 413 was at Kensington in 1818 (496), with an attribution to Colonia, and was later at Buckingham Palace (1081).

Literature: H. V. S. and M. S. Ogden, *English Taste in Landscape in the Seventeenth Century* (Ann Arbor, 1955), p. 146 (fig. 69 as Van Diest).

Formerly attributed to Danckerts and Van Diest, but probably painted *c.* 1660–70, presumably in London and almost certainly by Loten. The scenery was probably a reminiscence of the Swiss Alps, where Loten is stated to have spent a number of years.

414. LANDSCAPE WITH FIGURES BY A BRIDGE

Hampton Court (210). 65¼×55½ in., 165,7×141 cm.

A wooded landscape with a sportsman talking to a woman on a bridge over a gorge.

See no. 413; recorded at Buckingham House in 1819 (818) as by Loten.

Literature: Waagen (1854), vol. II, p. 360; Law, 1881, 1898 (837); Collins Baker, *Hampton Court*, p. 96.

The sportsman's costume seems to be of *c.* 1660 and, although the buildings in the distance are apparently Dutch rather than English, no. 414 is close in style to Loten.

415. LANDSCAPE WITH AN ESTUARY

Holyroodhouse. 32½×39 in., 82,6×99,1 cm.

An estuary in hilly country with a harbour and a fanciful city in the foreground.

Nos. 415 and 416 can possibly be identified with the two pictures recorded in the reign of James II among pictures at Windsor (in the Princess's Guard-Chamber) that had not belonged to Charles II: *Loaton. Landschapes* (B. M., Harl. MS. 1890, f. 82 v.; Bathoe, *James II* (1096–7)); they are last recorded at Windsor *temp.* George I, and can probably be identified with a pair of landscapes at Kew, as by Loten, in the reign of George III (Geo. III, *Kew*); they were still at Kew in April 1870 (*V.R. inv.*) and were sent to Holyroodhouse in 1882.

The pair was probably painted for James II *c.* 1675.

416. A WOODED LANDSCAPE

Holyroodhouse. 32½×39 in., 82,6×99,1 cm.

A path through a wood, leading to a village and a castle(?).

See no. 415.

Johannes Vorsterman

1643?–1699? Landscape and topographical painter, a pupil of Saftleven in Utrecht; came to England, from France, in the reign of Charles II; accompanied Sir William Soames on his embassy to Constantinople in 1686(?).

417. A VIEW OF WINDSOR CASTLE

Kensington Palace. 31¾×42⅞ in., 80,6×108,9 cm.

A view of the Castle from the west, from a point near the river; the bridge is seen in the distance and a sportsman with gun and dogs in the foreground.

Possibly the picture recorded in James II's collection, in store at Whitehall (B. M., Harl. MS. 1890, f. 54 v.; Bathoe, *James II* (269): *By Vorsterman. A large peice of the Prospect of Windsor Castle*); it is difficult to disentangle the references in the later inventories to nos. 417–20, but no. 417 was probably later at Kensington, possibly at St. James's and certainly at Hampton Court (644).

Literature: Law, 1881, 1898 (657).

Formerly attributed to Jan Peter Verdussen (*V.R. inv.*) and Leendert de Koningh (Law, 1907 (362)), no. 417 is certainly by Vorsterman: it can be compared with his view of Althorp of *c.* 1678 (R. A., *The Age of Charles II*, 1960–1 (179). It was

presumably painted at the same period as nos. 418 and 419 and can perhaps be identified with the picture mentioned by Buckeridge (p. 475), who said of Charles II that he 'was pleas'd with his *Manner* of Painting, especially that Piece he made of *Windsor* Castle, now extant in the *Royal-Collection*'.

418. A VIEW OF WINDSOR CASTLE (*Plate* 138)

Windsor Castle (104). 21×32⅞ in., 53,3×83,5 cm.

A 'prospect' of the Castle from the south (see below) with a falconer and dogs in the foreground.

Probably painted for Charles II; nos. 418 and 419 are presumably the two pictures recorded at Whitehall in the reign of James II, both as: *By Vorsterman. Another Prospect of Windsor Castle* (B. M., Harl. MS. 1890, f. 54 v.; Bathoe, *James II* (270, 271)), and in the Old Gallery at Windsor in the reign of Queen Anne: *Vorsterman A Prospect of Windsor Castle* and *A neither Prospect of Windsor Castle of one size* (Queen Anne, *Windsor* (131, 132)).

Literature (for the pair): Vertue, *Notebooks*, vol. I, p. 78; Waagen (1854), vol. II, p. 434; H. V. S. and M. S. Ogden, *English Taste in Landscape in the Seventeenth Century* (Ann Arbor, 1955), pp. 122, 155, 162, figs. 134–5; Whinney and Millar, p. 270.

Nos. 418 and 419 were probably painted *c.* 1678–80 (see no. 420). Vorsterman seems to have been concerned more with the picturesque appearance of the Castle than with a strictly accurate topographical record. Although he must surely have seen the Castle, he seems gravely to have misunderstood its southern aspect and so distorted the natural angle between the walls of the Lower and Upper Wards that the range of buildings between the Earl Marshal's Tower and the Watch Tower seems to be part of the east, and not of the south, front. The path in the foreground is probably the road that led through Frogmore to Old Windsor, but the rest of the topography should (presumably) be treated with suspicion. See no. 420.

419. A VIEW OF WINDSOR CASTLE

Windsor Castle (105). 21×32¾ in., 53,3×83,2 cm.

A 'prospect' of the Castle from the north, with the river in the foreground.

See no. 418.

The pair had been traditionally dated 1674 (*e.g.*, by Waagen, *op. cit.*). The sun, breaking through the clouds, shines prominently on Charles II's new Star Building and, less brightly, on the other new range of building behind and to the east of it. The rebuilding and redecoration of the Castle had been entrusted by Charles II to Hugh May in 1673 and his new buildings on this front seem to have been finished by *c.* 1676–7. Vorsterman's views were probably, therefore, painted *c.* 1678–80. His treatment of the rest of the Castle, of the foreground, the flow of the river and the position of the bridge seem rather more arbitrary. Later derivations of this pair are at Anglesey Abbey, where there is also a good variant of no. 419; a later copy of no. 419, with variations, is at Audley End.

Jan Griffier

c. 1646–1718. Landscape and topographical painter and etcher, a native of Amsterdam, where he was a pupil of Roeland Roghman; probably came to England early in the reign of Charles II and studied under Loten; specialised in views, which are often treated with a strong element of fantasy, of London and of the palaces and houses in the Thames valley.

420. A VIEW OF WINDSOR CASTLE

Windsor Castle (1916). 21¼×31⅝ in., 55,2×80,3 cm.

Signed and dated: J. GRIFFIER. 1681.

A 'prospect' of the Castle from the south, with horsemen and falconers in the foreground.

Probably acquired by Queen Anne from the collection of Admiral George Churchill: among the paintings of 'fowl' by Bogdani which were bought from his executors (see no. 472) was *A Prospect of Windsor Castle a Copy after Vorsterman by Greffier* (note by Thomas Coke in Queen Anne, *Kensington*). Thereafter it may have been confused with Vorsterman's originals (see nos. 418 and 419), and Walpole in his notes (in his copy of Bathoe, *James II*) of 2 June 1763 mentions at Kensington a 'beautifull View of Windsor by Vosterman. clouds & landscape particularly free. a copy of it is on the small staircase'; later at Buckingham Palace (1087).

Literature: H. V. S. and M. S. Ogden, *English Taste in Landscape in the Seventeenth Century* (Ann Arbor, 1955), pp. 154, 159, fig. 132.

Apparently a copy of no. 418 with slight variations in the foreground, but repeating Vorsterman's odd misunderstanding of the south front of the Castle. A version was recently with Leger's.

Adriaen de Hennin

d. 1710. Landscape painter who was active in The Hague and Amsterdam and came to England *c.* 1675–8.

421. LANDSCAPE WITH FIGURES

Hampton Court (251). 64½×45½ in., 163,8×115,6 cm.; *c.* 1 in. of original canvas is turned over on all four sides.

Signed: *ADHenin* (the initials in monogram, the remainder very obscure).

A mountainous classical landscape with a rocky coast in the distance and a woman and child walking along a path past shepherdesses and their flocks.

Apparently first recorded at Hampton Court in 1842 (Mrs. Jameson (220)).

Literature: Law, 1881, 1898 (268); Collins Baker, *Hampton Court*, p. 165; H. V. S. and M. S. Ogden, *English Taste in Landscape in the Seventeenth Century* (Ann Arbor, 1955), pp. 120, 141.

Probably painted in England *c.* 1680.

Leonard Knyff

1650–1722. Landscape, topographical and sporting artist; born in The Hague and probably a pupil of his father, Wouter Knyff; was in London by 1681; he specialised in extensive bird's-eye prospects of palaces and country seats. Queen Anne owned, in store at Windsor: *Knife. A Prospect of Sheerness and Shiping* (Queen Anne, *Windsor*, store (35), with note by Thomas Coke: *in yᵉ Vicechamberlain's lodgings over yᵉ Chimney*). It is no longer in the royal collection.

422. A VIEW OF WINDSOR CASTLE (*Plate* 140)

Windsor Castle (2890). 60×85¼ in., 152,4×216,5 cm.

Signed: *Leonard Knijff* and inscribed: *The North Prospect / of Windsor Castle By / Mr Knife –*

A 'prospect' of the north front of the Castle with the recently constructed banks and terraces and the newly planted 'Maestricht Garden' between the Castle and the river.

Purchased for the royal collection by His Majesty King George V in 1926.

Literature: H. Honour, 'Leonard Knyff', *Leeds Art Calendar*, vol. 7, no. 23 (1953), pp. 22–3, and *Burl. Mag.*, vol. XCVI (1954), p. 337; D. Green, *Gardener to Queen Anne* (1956), p. 79; Whinney and Millar, p. 269.

Painted early in the reign of Queen Anne: William III's wall, which bore the date 1699, surrounds the area known as the 'Maestricht Garden', and the royal standard is of the late Stuart type. In a letter of 9 January 1703 to Lord Irwin's steward, Knyff wrote, presumably of his drawings: 'I have done a great many of Hampton Courte and Windsor for his Highness which are not yett engraved'. 'His Highness' was probably Prince George of Denmark. No. 422 was painted before the canal, probably planned by William III, was dug (in 1708?) in the open space in the middle of the 'Maestricht Garden'; and it seems to be one of the most painstaking and accurate of the early views of the Castle. It can be compared (W. H. St. John Hope, *Windsor Castle . . .* (1913), vol. I, p. 332) with Knyff's drawing for the *Nouveau Théâtre*, which shows in the same careful way the work carried out by Henry Wise (see no. 350) on the North Terrace.

423. A VIEW OF HAMPTON COURT (*Plate* 176)

Hampton Court (1227). 60¼×85¼ in., 153×216,5 cm.

A bird's-eye view from the east of the palace set in its gardens; on the Thames are barges and a ferry transporting a coach; on the other side of the river is the village of East Molesey, and Hampton can just be seen in the distance.

Stated to have been formerly at Hampton Court in Herefordshire; purchased there by Mr. Humphrey Watts and in 1948 purchased from him for the royal collection by His Majesty King George VI.

Literature: Whinney and Millar, p. 269.

Probably painted in the reign of Queen Anne. When no. 423 was acquired in 1948 no artist's name was attached to it, but a nineteenth-century label on the back gives Leonard Knyff as the painter and it is unquestionably by him. By January 1703 Knyff had probably completed a number of studies of Hampton Court (see no. 422), but no. 423 is not directly connected with his view engraved for him by Kip in their *Nouveau Théâtre de la Grande Bretagne*, vol. 1 (1708), pl. 5 (though it agrees with it closely in detail) and is an independent bird's-eye view comparable to Knyff's large canvases of Clandon and Chatsworth (and see nos. 424–6). It seems to be an extremely accurate rendering of the Palace and its surroundings in the early years of the eighteenth century. The work carried out by Wren for William III and Mary II can be seen in its newly-completed state, *i.e.*, the east and south fronts and a glimpse of Fountain Court; they were finished *c.* 1702. On the south side of the palace the Privy Garden[1] stretches to the river, where it is enclosed by Jean Tijou's screen. Beyond is the Banqueting House built by William III *c.* 1700. On the north side of the Palace lie the Melon Ground, the Wilderness and the Maze; beyond them are the former Tiltyard Gardens, turned by William III into kitchen-gardens and overlooked by the only surviving Tiltyard Tower. In the foreground are the two avenues and the canal radiating from the Great Fountain Garden. Queen Anne's lower Orangery seems to be visible beyond Wren's façade on the south front; but the Lion Gates, of which the piers were set up in Queen Anne's reign near the Maze and opposite the entrance to Chestnut Avenue in Bushy Park, are not yet visible.

1. The lay-out of this garden agrees exactly with that recorded in a plan in the Soane Museum (*Wren Soc.*, vol. IV (1927), pl. II) and in the plate by Kip and Knyff.

424. A VIEW OF ORCHARD PORTMAN

Buckingham Palace. 41¼×51¾ in., 104,8×131,4 cm.

A bird's-eye view of the house, surrounded by its walled garden, orchard, bowling-green, stables and fields, in one of which hay-making is in progress; a coach-and-six is approaching the house.

Recorded at Kensington in 1818 (503) as: *View of the Old Palace at Greenwich* with an attribution to Streeter; later at Hampton Court and Buckingham Palace (1063).

No. 424, probably painted *c.* 1705, is almost certainly by Knyff; it is closely related to his drawing of Orchard Portman, engraved by Kip in their *Nouveau Théâtre de la Grande Bretagne*, vol. I (1708), pl. 76. Orchard Portman, which was near Taunton, is there described as the seat of Henry Portman. Henry Seymour Portman (*d.* 1727), fifth son of Sir Edward Seymour, had inherited the estate from his cousin Sir William Portman (*d.* 1690). The house was demolished in the nineteenth century. All three views of the Portman houses (nos. 424–6) may have come into the royal collection at the same time.

425. A VIEW OF ORCHARD PORTMAN

Kensington Palace. 27¾×43¼ in., 70,5×109,9 cm.

Recorded at Kensington in 1818 (293) as: *View (supposed to be the Old palace) at Greenwich* with an attribution to Danckerts; later at Hampton Court and Windsor (1595).

A version of no. 424 with minor variations in detail: the coach-and-six is omitted. The view point is slightly higher and further from the house than in no. 424.

426. A VIEW OF BRYANSTON HOUSE

Buckingham Palace. 27⅝×40¼ in., 70,2×102,2 cm.

A bird's-eye view of the house, surrounded by its gardens and outbuildings; in the foreground are the river and a waterwheel, and hay-making is in progress in a meadow.

Recorded at Kensington in 1818 (368) as: *View of the Palace at Greenwich;* later at Hampton Court and recorded at Buckingham Palace (1064) in 1876 (*V.R. inv.*).

No. 426, probably painted *c.* 1705, is almost certainly by Knyff and is closely related to his drawing of Bryanston House, engraved by Kip in their *Nouveau Théâtre*, vol. I (1708), where (pl. 77) it immediately follows his plate of Orchard Portman (see nos. 424–5). Bryanston House was the other seat of Henry Portman. Very little is known of the appearance of the house at this period, when no. 426 shows it to have contained a handsome seventeenth-century block adjoining the earlier house, to which is also attached a small earlier seventeenth-century wing. Henry Portman's house had been altered before it was rebuilt by Wyatt (1778), whose work was in turn pulled down before the existing structure was put up.

Adriaen van Diest

1655/6–1704. Portrait and landscape painter, born and trained in The Hague. Settled in England by March 1678 and probably specialised in landscapes for decorative purposes.

427. LANDSCAPE WITH FIGURES

61¼×36⅛ in., 155,6×91,8 cm.

A mountainous landscape with a broad river in which fishermen are plying their nets in the foreground; on the far bank is a ruined castle.

No. 427 may have been the piece recorded in the Great Bedchamber at Kensington in the reign of Queen Anne (Queen Anne, *Kensington* (108): *Vandist. A Landskip over the door going into the drawing Room*); in the Queen's House in 1819 (783); later at Hampton Court (750), Pembroke Lodge and Clarence House. Lent to the Central Chancery of the Orders of Knighthood in 1947.

Literature: Law, 1881, 1898 (503).

Probably painted *c.* 1690.

428. LANDSCAPE WITH FIGURES (*Plate* 160)

Buckingham Palace. 24×45½ in., 61×115,6 cm.

Two fishermen (?) beside a river in a mountainous landscape, with a ruinous castle in the distance.

Horace Walpole noted at Kensington on 2 June 1763 (notes to Bathoe, *James II*): 'In the late K's great room below ... 4 indifferent landscapes over doors, by Van Diest ...', which probably refers to nos. 428–31; Vertue had recorded earlier in the King's Drawing Room at Kensington (Vertue inv., *Kensington*, f. 10) two landscapes over doors by Van Diest; no. 428, with no. 429, was later at Kew and was taken to Buckingham Palace (1181) in 1877.

Probably part of a set of decorative landscapes (see nos. 429–31), painted *c.* 1690 to be used as overdoors. They are very close in type to Van Diest's etched landscapes.

429. LANDSCAPE WITH FIGURES

Buckingham Palace. 24×45½ in., 61×115,6 cm.

Two figures with a dog by the edge of a broad river in a mountainous landscape, with a tower on a rocky promontory in the distance.

See no. 428; no. 429 was taken with no. 428 from Kew to Buckingham Palace (1182) in 1877.

See no. 428.

430. LANDSCAPE WITH FIGURES

24×45 in., 61×114,3 cm.

Signed: *AVDiest* (initials in monogram).

Herdsmen with sheep and cattle beside a river in a mountainous landscape.

See no. 428. No. 430, with no. 431, were probably the pair recorded at St. James's in 1819 (1073, 1077); later at Hampton Court (637) and sent in 1928 on loan to the British Embassy in Paris.

Literature: Law, 1881, 1898 (847).

See no. 428.

431. LANDSCAPE WITH FIGURES

24×45½ in., 61×115,6 cm.

Fishermen with their nets by a lake in a mountainous landscape; in the distance is a town with a large church.

See no. 430; later at Hampton Court (633) and sent in 1928 on loan to the British Embassy in Paris.

Literature: Law, 1881, 1898 (827).

See no. 428.

Attributed to Adriaen van Diest

432. LANDSCAPE WITH FIGURES

41×38 in., 104,1×96,5 cm.

A man and woman near a river in a mountainous landscape; in the distance are figures near laden barges.

Recorded at St. James's in 1819 (1082) as by Griffier; later at Hampton Court (647) as by Van Diest and sent in 1928 on loan to the British Embassy in Paris.

Literature: Law, 1881, 1898 (814).

Probably painted *c.* 1690 to be set into an overmantel or overdoor.

433. LANDSCAPE WITH FIGURES

Buckingham Palace. 51¾×38 in., 131,4×96,5 cm.

A mountainous landscape with a shepherd reclining in the foreground watching two women who are approaching him.

It is impossible to identify no. 433 accurately in the eighteenth century sources; it was recorded at Buckingham Palace (1086) in 1876 (*V.R. inv.*).

Formerly attributed to Danckerts, but probably painted *c.* 1690 and closer in style to Van Diest.

Gerard van Edema

c. 1652–*c.* 1700. Landscape painter, pupil of Allart van Everdingen in Amsterdam; possibly established in England before the death of Charles II; travelled to Surinam and visited Norway and Newfoundland.

434. LANDSCAPE WITH FIGURES

Hampton Court (208). 74×54⅜ in., 188×138,1 cm.; the canvas has been roughly cut at the top and on the left where *c.* 2 in. has been turned over in both instances.

Signed: *G. Edema.*

An inn by a stream under a hill, with figures crossing a bridge.

Recorded, with no. 435, at Kensington in 1818 (392, 486); both were taken to Hampton Court in December 1835.

Presumably painted in England *c.* 1695–1700.

435. LANDSCAPE WITH FIGURES (*Plate* 161)

Hampton Court (212). 73⅞×53⅞ in., 187,6×136,8 cm.

A cottage on a hill overlooking a valley.

See no. 434.

Literature: Law, 1881, 1898 (840).

Presumably painted in England *c.* 1695–1700. The distant landscape seems to have been painted from a point on Richmond Hill and to be a reasonably accurate impression of the Thames valley just above Richmond with Ham House (?) on the left and the tree-covered islands in the middle of the river. It can be compared with, for example, a view from Richmond Hill in the collection of Mrs. Basil Ionides (reproduced in *The Correspondence of Bishop Brian Duppa and Sir Justinian Isham*, ed. Sir G. Isham (1954), p. xxxiii) and in a view from a slightly different point by Jan Siberechts (1677) at Easton Neston.

436. LANDSCAPE WITH FIGURES

Kew (*Hampton Court no.* 751). 71½×39 in., 181,6×99,1 cm.

Signed: *G Edema.*

Two women and a man holding a pike, by a waterfall in a rocky gorge.

Recorded at Kensington in 1818 (654); later at Hampton Court.

Literature: Law, 1881, 1898 (504); Collins Baker, *Hampton Court,* p. 41.

Probably painted in England *c.* 1695–1700.

437. LANDSCAPE WITH FIGURES

Windsor Castle (1514). 58¾×52¾ in., 134×129 cm.

Signed: *G: Edema.*

An estuary, cut in a mountainous landscape, with figures on a path in the foreground and occupied with their nets on the shore in the distance.

Recorded at Kensington in 1818 (485); later at Hampton Court.

Probably painted in England *c.* 1695–1700.

Artists Unknown: Stuart Topographical Paintings

438. A VIEW OF PONTEFRACT CASTLE

Hampton Court (1252). 45½×41¾ in., 115,6×106 cm.; probably cut down on both sides; there is an addition at the top of *c.* 1¾ in.

A view of the Castle from the south-east, with cottages grouped round it and figures in the foreground, including a shepherd piping to his flock.

Recorded at Kensington in 1818 (601: *Landscape with a Castle. Momper*); later at Hampton Court and Windsor (1593).

Literature: A. S. Ellis, 'Picture of Pontefract Castle at Hampton Court Palace', *Thoresby Soc.*, vol. XXIV (1919), pp. 1–5; Law, 1925 (16); Collins Baker, *Hampton Court,* p. 53.

The view of the Castle in no. 438 is taken from Bag Hill. In general it seems to be a fairly accurate rendering of the Castle as it was before its destruction in the Civil Wars, with the principal towers, from the Great Round Tower on the left across to the King's Tower on the right, and the road known as South Gate running along in front of the castle. It can be compared with early draughts of the castle (*The Sieges of Pontefract Castle*, ed. R. Holmes (1887), pp. 413–7). Probably painted *c.* 1625–30, no. 438 does not seem of sufficient quality to support the old attribution to Joos de Momper, though it is probably Flemish. The Castle was besieged on three occasions in the Civil War and was finally demolished by the Parliamentarians in 1649 after it had surrendered to General Lambert. A larger version of no. 438 is at Northwick Park. It is clearly by the same hand, but there are variations in the figures and smaller buildings and the prospect is considerably extended on both sides to include St. Giles's and All Saints' Churches; the perspective of the Castle is slightly different (reproduced in H. V. S. and M. S. Ogden, *English Taste in Landscape in the Seventeenth Century,* (Ann Arbor, 1955), fig. 131). The painting at Northwick probably belonged to Charles I. This was valued at £5 by the Trustees for Sale at Hampton Court in October 1649 (L. R. MS., f. 120: *Pomfrett Castle*), sold to John Embree or Emery on 24 May 1650 (S.P. 29/447, 24, 1), declared by him to the House of Lords Committee on 19 May 1660 (H. of L. MSS.) and placed in the King's Gallery at Hampton Court (Charles II, *Hampton Court* (163), measurements given as 43×74 in. which agree with those of the picture at Northwick Park. It is not recorded in the royal collection after 1714.

439. HAMPTON COURT PALACE

Hampton Court (1249). $31\frac{1}{2} \times 72\frac{1}{4}$ in., $80 \times 183,5$ cm.

A view of the front of the Tudor palace facing the river on which are a ferry taking a coach across the river, lesser craft and a state barge, flying the Union flag and rowed by twelve oarsmen in scarlet livery.

In 1804 (see below) belonged to Sir Joseph Banks (1743–1820) and had been in the possession of Dr. Combe; stated by Sir L. Cust (MS. in office of the Surveyor of The Queen's Pictures) to have been bought at Sir Joseph Banks's sale by Dr. H. W. Diamond of Twickenham House, to have passed to his daughter Theresa and to have been bequeathed to her son, Hugh Clarke, in 1919. Acquired from Mr. Clarke for the royal collection.

Literature: Law, 1925 (IV); Collins Baker, *Hampton Court*, p. 32 (confusing provenance with no. 397).

Formerly attributed to Danckerts (*e.g.*, by Law and Collins Baker, *op. cit.*), but clearly considerably earlier. The costumes appear to be of *c.* 1640; the state barge on the river has the royal arms on the stern and the three figures seated in the stern, beside two trumpeters, may have been intended for Charles I and his two eldest sons. No. 439 probably provides the clearest extant view of the river front of the Tudor palace with the inn on the extreme left and the buildings on the water which, with the Great Round Arbour, were soon to be swept away; it is conceivably by the same hand as a view of Richmond Palace in the Society of Antiquaries. James Basire's engraving of no. 439 was published on 1 December 1804 for the Society of Antiquaries (*Vetusta Monumenta . . .*, vol. II (1789), supplementary to pl. XXVII) and the Society ordered impressions to be made of this engraving from 'a painting late in the possession of Dᴿ Combe and now of . . . Sir Joseph Banks . . . ' (Soc. of Antiquaries, *Council Minutes*, 7 December 1804). Dr. Combe was probably Taylor Combe (1774–1826) or possibly his father, Charles (1743–1817).

440. THE THAMES AT WHITEHALL

Kensington Palace. $16\frac{1}{2} \times 37\frac{1}{2}$ in., $419 \times 95,3$ cm.

The river at Whitehall Palace with the Banqueting House and Great Hall beyond the buildings on the river front; among the craft on the river is, apparently, the 'Folly' pleasure boat.

Probably the picture recorded at Kensington in 1818 (557: *A View on the Thames*, measurements given as $16\frac{1}{2} \times 38$ in.); later at Hampton Court (742).

Literature: Law, 1881, 1898 (497); *London Topographical Society*, publication no. 81 (1948).

Recording the river front of the Palace as it had been *c.* 1640–60, but perhaps painted later in the seventeenth century.

441. THE LORD MAYOR'S WATER-PROCESSION ON THE THAMES (*Plate* 170)

Kensington Palace. $59\frac{3}{4} \times 102\frac{7}{8}$ in., $151,8 \times 261$ cm.

A procession of state barges rowing in a stiff breeze past Whitehall Palace with the Banqueting House and the buildings at Westminster in the distance; the barge of the City of London, with the new Lord Mayor on board, is escorted by the barges of the City Livery Companies, with musicians on board and flying their flags and the royal standard, and by yachts and lesser craft. There is a crowd of spectators and boats around the Privy Stairs and Whitehall Palace Stairs, and among the courtiers on the leads outside the Queen's Withdrawing Room and Privy Chamber is a

figure, wearing a hat and the star of the Garter, who is presumably Charles II.

Formerly at Clopton House, Warwickshire, where it was seen by J. C. M. Bellew (*Shakespeare's Home at New Place . . .* (1863), pp. 159–60) *c.* 1862; sold in the Clopton House sale, 8–12 September 1873 (101) as by 'Storke'; purchased in 1875 by the Lord Chamberlain from Graves, Pall Mall; later at Windsor (1829) and Buckingham Palace.

Literature: L.C.C., *Survey of London*, vol. XIII (1930), p. 69; Whinney and Millar, p. 263.

No. 441 is usually associated, probably correctly, with the procession recorded by Narcissus Luttrell (*A Brief Historical Relation . . .* (1857), vol. I, p. 285) on 29 October 1683 when 'Sir Henry Tulse, being commissionated by his majestie to be lord mayor of London for the year ensueing, was sworn before the barons of the exchequer at Westminster, whither he went by water, accompanied by the late lord mayor, the new recorder, aldermen, and sherriffs, and attended by diverse of the companies in their barges; their majesties and the duke of York being upon the leads at Whitehall when they passed by.' The barges of the following Livery Companies can be identified from the standards flying on their barges: Apothecaries (?), Fishmongers, Goldsmiths, Mercers, Skinners, Vintners and Weavers. Other flags are impossible to identify but the Companies' state barges also probably sport the flag of the Master of the Company. No. 441 provides one of the largest and most detailed records of the appearance of Whitehall Palace before the rebuilding of the Queen's apartments on the river front by Wren in the next reign and before its almost complete destruction in the fire of 1698. It was formerly attributed to Dirk Stoop, but on insufficient evidence. It seems to be the work of a Dutch painter in London and has stylistic affinities with Jacob Knyff or Jacob Esselens, who was a considerable traveller and had been in England some twenty years earlier, but is not known to have been in London at this later date.

442. A VIEW OF GREENWICH

Kensington Palace. $27\frac{5}{8} \times 43\frac{1}{8}$ in., $70,2 \times 109,5$ cm.

A view across the park, in which figures are conversing and walking, over to the Observatory and down to the Queen's House and the new buildings at Greenwich, to the tower of St. Alphege, the river, the Dockyard at Deptford and the distant City.

Recorded at Kensington in 1818 (289) with an attribution to Danckerts; later at Hampton Court (1016).

Literature: Law, 1881, 1898 (918).

Probably painted *c.* 1685 and a version of a very popular design. The Observatory had been built in 1675, and the Charles II block at Greenwich in 1662–9; there is no trace of the later building at Greenwich, which began in 1698, and the distant view of St. Paul's Cathedral shows it without the dome.

443. ST. JAMES'S PALACE

St. James's Palace. $24\frac{1}{2} \times 41$ in., $62,2 \times 104,1$ cm.

A view of the south front of the palace with figures strolling in the garden; on the left is seen the top of the Tudor Gatehouse and on the right, beyond the Mall, is a distant glimpse of the Banqueting House.

Bought by George IV at the sale of the Duke of York's pictures at Christie's, 7 April 1827 (11), and sent in 1829 to the Corridor at Windsor (later inv. no. 347).

Probably painted *c.* 1690. The garden front of the Palace

seems to be very much as it appears in the view published by Kip and Leonard Knyff in *Nouveau Théâtre* (1708) pl. 2, but the central part of the front, between the new building (probably executed for Princess Anne) and a section of the old Tudor palace, had, by the time of Knyff's plate, been modernised and the balcony, clearly visible in no. 443, replaced by an elaborate flight of steps. This modification to the garden front is also seen in a drawing by François Gosselin (see E. Sheppard, *Memorials of St. James's Palace* (1894), vol. I, p. 6, and a drawing in the British Museum (E. Croft-Murray and P. Hulton, *Catalogue of British Drawings*, vol. I (1960), p. 327)). The balcony apparently led from the Drawing Room and is still there in a plan published in 1689 (Sheppard, vol. II, p. 12). Nor is there any trace in no. 443 of the statues and the slightly more extensive planting of trees that are seen in Knyff's plate; an estimate of July 1702, moreover, had provided for the enlargement of the new block on the left into a new Council Chamber and Drawing Room (*Wren Soc.*, vol. VII (1930), p. 210). In style no. 443 is not far from Knyff's painted views (*e.g.*, nos. 422–6). A rather coarser variant of no. 443 was sold at Bonham's, 5 April 1962 (99).

444. A VIEW ON THE THAMES

Kensington Palace. 27¾ × 39⅛ in., 70,5 × 99,4 cm.

A view across the river, on which are a yacht, barges and lesser craft, to the Temple. The stern of one of the barges is decorated with the cipher A R with crowns and the date 1703.

Recorded at Kensington in 1818 (370); later at Hampton Court (1026).

Literature: Law, 1881, 1898 (922).

Presumably painted in 1703, by the same provincial hand as no. 445. See also no. 448.

445. THE TOWER OF LONDON

Kensington Palace. 28 × 40½ in., 71,1 × 102,9 cm.

A view across the river to the Tower, with the royal standard flying from the White Tower. Among the craft on the river is a royal yacht with the cipher A R carved on its stern; the cipher also appears on one of the flags on the turrets of the White Tower.

Recorded at Kensington in 1818 (366); later at Hampton Court (1024).

Literature: Law, 1881, 1898 (920).

Presumably painted at the same period, and certainly by the same hand, as no. 444.

Artists Unknown: Views of Windsor Castle

446. A VIEW OF WINDSOR CASTLE

Windsor Castle (1926). 47 × 53 in., 114,3 × 134,6 cm.

A view of the Castle from the north-west, with barges on the river and figures and cattle on the bank.

Possibly acquired by Queen Victoria; recorded at Windsor in 1879 (*V.R. inv.*).

Probably painted *c.* 1685, no. 446 is an unconventional piece, not related to the standard views popular at this date. The handling of the figures and the landscape is very close to Robert Streeter.

447. A VIEW OF WINDSOR CASTLE

Windsor Castle (3032). 28¾ × 51 in., 73 × 129,5 cm.

A view of the north front of the Castle, with houses and a coach at the foot of the hill by the river, on which are a barge and smaller vessels.

Purchased by His Majesty King George VI in 1946 from Dr. C. Malden, to whom the picture had passed from his father-in-law, Mr. C. Durant of Clewer Court.

A version of a standard view of the Castle, probably painted *c.* 1685. The royal standard on the Round Tower is of the late Stuart form.

448. A VIEW OF WINDSOR CASTLE

Windsor Castle (2811). 27¾ × 40¼ in., 70,5 × 102,2 cm.

The north front of the Castle with the river in the foreground.

Possibly the *View of Windsor Castle*, recorded at Kensington in 1818 (369, measurements given as 30 × 40 in.); later, sometimes with an attribution to Danckerts, at Hampton Court (767), Kensington and St. James's.

Literature: Law, 1881, 1898 (508).

Painted, possibly by the same hand as no. 444 and 445, early in the reign of Queen Anne: the royal standard flying on the Round Tower is of the late Stuart form and one of the barges on the Thames has the cipher A R on the stern. It is a good example of the repetition by provincial painters of a very popular view of the Castle. For the distortions that are common in such repetitions it should be compared with no. 422.

449. A VIEW OF WINDSOR CASTLE

Windsor Castle (2827). Oil on paper: 7⅜ × 24¼ in., 18,7 × 61,6 cm.; mounted on a panel 8⅜ × 25⅛ in.

A view of the Castle from the north with the river in the foreground.

Stated to have been purchased at the Duke of Cambridge's sale, but not apparently in the sale at Christie's, 11 June 1904. Sent from Buckingham Palace to Windsor in May 1916.

Probably painted *c.* 1710. No. 449 may be *au fond* a water-colour drawing, and the sky and trees may have been superimposed at a later date; they are certainly in oil and may have been applied to give no. 449 a more painterly appearance.

450. A VIEW OF WINDSOR CASTLE

Windsor Castle (1915). 36¼ × 48 in., 92 × 121,9 cm.

A 'prospect' of the Castle from the south with huntsmen and falconers on the lane to Datchet Ferry in the foreground.

First recorded, with an attribution to Vorsterman, at Buckingham Palace (915) in 1876 (*V.R. inv.*).

Probably painted *c.* 1715. The view of the Castle seems to be fairly accurate, though rather attenuated (*cf.*, Knyff's drawing for the *Nouveau Théâtre* of 1708, reproduced in W. H. St. John Hope, *Windsor Castle* . . . (1913), vol. I, p. 334). At that date, however, a number of houses, subsidiary buildings and gardens spread up to the south front of the Castle; of these there are shadowy traces in no. 450 of Queen Anne's Garden House and its lesser buildings and surrounding wall. It is conceivable therefore that no. 450 was begun as a strictly topographical survey in the manner of Leonard Knyff (see no. 422), but that it was completed and adapted in a more decorative and painterly style by a painter such as Gerard van Edema.

451. A VIEW OF WINDSOR CASTLE

Windsor Castle (2636). $35\frac{1}{2} \times 76\frac{1}{4}$ in., $90,2 \times 193,7$ cm.

A view of the river with barges and rowing boats, with a group of horsemen and dogs on the bank and the north front of the Castle in the distance.

Sold from the collection of Lady Swansea at Christie's, 23 April 1904 (139; Christie's stencil is on the back); purchased for the royal collection by King Edward VII from J. R. Saunders in 1907.

Probably painted *c.* 1730. At the time of its purchase it was attributed to Peter Tillemans, an ascription which is not impossible; a more fanciful view of the river and Castle, from a slightly more westerly view-point, but certainly by the same hand, was on the art-market in London in 1959. For the distorted treatment of the Castle no. 451 should be compared with no. 422.

452. A VIEW OF WINDSOR CASTLE (*Plate* 169)

Windsor Castle (1144). $39\frac{1}{2} \times 53\frac{1}{4}$ in., $100,3 \times 135,3$ cm.

The north front of the Castle with barges and other craft on the river and groups of figures disporting themselves in the foreground.

Probably the picture presented to George IV by the 4th Earl of Fife in 1829 (*Carleton Palace* (630): *View of Windsor Castle, with figures. Angelis*). Recorded at Windsor in 1879 (*V.R. inv.*)

Probably painted *c.* 1730–40 and formerly attributed to 'Van Aiken'; an inscription on the back, *Low Parlour*, may not refer to a royal residence. In style no. 452 is suggestive of Frans or Josef van Aken. In Lord Fairhaven's collection is a view of Windsor close to no. 452 in arrangement, in the relation between figures and setting, and in the drawing of the Castle, but it does not seem to be by the same hand. There are also in no. 452 reminiscences of Tillemans, and the attribution in 1829 to Pieter Angillis is understandable.

453. A VIEW OF THE LOWER WARD, WINDSOR CASTLE

Windsor Castle (3080). $19\frac{7}{8} \times 24\frac{1}{4}$ in., $50,5 \times 61,6$ cm.

A view from the Round Tower to the Lower Ward: at the bottom are Crane's Buildings, in the centre St. George's Chapel and, on the right, the Guard-room and the seventeenth-century house next to Winchester Tower.

Recorded in the Royal Library before 1926.

Painted by the same hand as no. 454. It is conceivable that the two canvases formed part of a series of such views looking out from the Castle to different points of the compass.

454. A VIEW FROM WINDSOR CASTLE

Windsor Castle (3044). $28 \times 39\frac{5}{8}$ in., $71,1 \times 100,7$ cm.

A view from the Castle to the Long Walk: in the foreground are the greenhouse of the Garden House, the Garden House itself, and, beyond, Burford House; a group of figures are dancing in the Little Park on the left.

Purchased from Mr. E. Croft Murray in 1949.

Painted *c.* 1745, by the same hand as no. 453. No. 454 provides an accurate record of the principal buildings which lay on the south side of the Castle. Garden House had been enlarged and rebuilt by Queen Anne; Burford House had been built for Nell Gwynn and was later the residence of the Dukes of St. Albans.

Artists Unknown : Later Stuart Landscapes

455. LANDSCAPE WITH RUINS

Windsor Castle (1602). $59\frac{3}{4} \times 64$ in., $151,8 \times 162,6$ cm.

A landscape with an elaborate ruined building in the foreground and a peasant walking beside a river in the foreground with a laden ass.

Recorded at Frogmore in the nineteenth century (*V.R. inv.*) with an attribution to Van Diest.

A decorative landscape, probably painted *c.* 1680–1700 and by the same hand as nos. 456 and 457, in a broader, coarsened version of Danckerts's style.

456. LANDSCAPE WITH RUINS

Windsor Castle (2858). $78\frac{3}{4} \times 60\frac{1}{2}$ in., $200 \times 153,7$ cm.

An overgrown ruin in a rocky, Italianate landscape, with a man leading a laden ass in the foreground.

Possibly the *Landscape with Buildings and Figures* recorded at Kensington in 1818 (495) with an attribution to Danckerts, measurements given as 79×60 in.; later at Buckingham Palace (1078).

Probably by the same hand as nos. 455 and 457 and bearing the same close relation to Danckerts's decorative style.

457. LANDSCAPE WITH RUINS

St. James's Palace. $55\frac{1}{2} \times 73\frac{1}{4}$ in., $141 \times 186,1$ cm.

An elaborate ruin in a wooded Italianate landscape with goats on the right and a man and woman conversing in the foreground.

Recorded at Hampton Court in 1870 (*V.R. inv.*, 1124), but probably formerly at Windsor.

Probably by the same hand as nos. 455 and 456. There is a join in the canvas *c.* 35 in. from the left and the canvas may originally have formed two separate compositions.

458. A GARDEN

Windsor Castle (972). $24\frac{1}{4} \times 45$ in., $61,6 \times 114,3$ cm.

A garden with figures walking in the foreground by a fountain and steps leading up to a garden house in the distance.

Probably *A Garden with a Fountain and Figures, ov* *a Chimney* in the Duchess of Marlborough's Bedchamber in the Garden House at Windsor (Queen Anne, *Windsor*, after store (11)); later probably at Kensington.

Painted, almost certainly in England, *c.* 1690–1700, by a specialist in decorative landscape overdoors and overmantels in the manner of Adriaen van Diest or Gerard van Edema.

459. FIGURES IN A LANDSCAPE

Windsor Castle (1615). $15\frac{3}{8} \times 37$ in., $39,1 \times 94$ cm.

A man and woman walking in a wooded landscape towards a ruined temple.

Recorded at Kensington in 1818 (249: *Landscape with Ruins and Figures*).

Probably painted in England *c.* 1695, by a painter very close in style to Adriaen van Diest; it is possible, indeed, that there are traces of a signature that may be that of Van Diest.

460. LANDSCAPE WITH FIGURES

Holyroodhouse. 40½ × 62 in., 102,9 × 157,5 cm.; enlarged at the top and on the left; the original canvas was *c.* 29 × 51½ in.

A mountainous landscape with a river and, in the foreground, a pedlar (?) with a woman, a child and a dog.

Probably the landscape recorded at St. James's in 1819 (1078, measurements given as 40 × 61½ in.) with an attribution to Vorsterman; later, as by Van Diest, at Hampton Court (634) and Windsor (2633).

Literature: Law, 1881, 1898 (432).

Probably painted in England *c.* 1680–1700; no. 460 is suggestive of Van Diest, but the style and date indicate that the earlier attribution to Vorsterman is perhaps more accurate.

461. LANDSCAPE WITH RUINS

Hampton Court (744). 42¾ × 51⅛ in., 70,5 × 129,9 cm.

A landscape with figures among ruins and fragments of antique masonry and statuary; prominent in the foreground is an elaborately carved classical urn.

Recorded at Kensington in 1818 (287: *Ruins and figures*).

Literature: Law, 1881, 1898 (499).

Formerly attributed (*e.g.*, by Law, *loc. cit.*) to Jan Griffier. Although perhaps painted by one of the minor landscape and genre painters working in England at the end of the seventeenth, or early in the eighteenth, century, no. 461 is not so precise in handling, or so strong in its contrasts of light and shade, as Griffier's compositions of this type, *e.g.*, at Sudbury Hall. It is slightly more reminiscent of William Gouw Ferguson. The figures, awestruck in front of the fragments in the foreground, appear to have been superimposed on the finished landscape, perhaps by another hand.

462. FIGURES IN A GARDEN

St. James's Palace. 59½ × 97¾ in., 151,1 × 278,3 cm.

An extensive garden with courtiers strolling near a long water and a cascade between two grottoes; on the right are huntsmen and dogs and in the distance a stag-hunt.

Probably painted *c.* 1710. Two figures wear the ribbon of the Garter; the one in conversation beside the water may be George II as a young man.

Francis Barlow

1626–1704? Animal and sporting painter and a prolific draughtsman who designed a large number of book illustrations.

463. AN EGYPTIAN GOOSE

Kew (Hampton Court no. 681). 36 × 41¾ in., 91,4 × 106 cm. The bird seems to have been painted at first on a canvas *c.* 26 × 31½ in. which Barlow later enlarged.

Signed: *F: Barlow*

Standing beside the edge of a stream on a bank with bullrushes, iris and other plants.

Recorded at Hampton Court in 1868 (*V.R. inv.*).

Literature: Law, 1881, 1898 (455a), *Kew* (1924), p. 16; Pigler, pl. XXIX.

Perhaps painted *c.* 1670–80.

After Francis Barlow

464. THE LAST RACE AT DATCHET

Windsor Castle (2931). 33¼ × 66 in., 84,5 × 167,6 cm.

A horse-race in progress on the course at Datchet Mead with Windsor Castle in the background. The race is watched by groups of spectators and, from a small royal box, by Charles II and a group of courtiers and members of his family; the box is guarded by Yeomen of the Guard and behind the box is the King's coach and a troup of household cavalry. The jockey's weighing scales are in front of the box and from the box hang two cups, presumably racing trophies to be awarded.

Purchased by His Majesty King George V in April 1928.

Literature: R. A., *The Age of Charles II*, 1960–1 (425).

A contemporary copy of the etching by Barlow which is inscribed: *August 24. 1684 | The last Horse Race | Run before* CHARLES *the Second... | By Dorsett Ferry | near Windsor Castle | Drawen | From the Place | and | Design'd | By | Francis Barlow | 1687* (W. Shaw Sparrow, *British Sporting Artists* (1922), pp. 42–4). The plate also bears a tribute in verse to Charles II's love of horse-racing and to Dorsett's (*i.e.*, Datchet's) 'much lov'd plains'. The race-course on the Mead near Datchet Ferry had been much patronised by Charles II, but was probably abandoned when Queen Anne inaugurated the course at Ascot. The race shown in no. 464 was presumably for the Datchet Ferry Plate, always held on 24 August.

G. Wilson

The painter of no. 465 may have been the Wilson who was the first master of Gawen Hamilton and was described by Vertue (*Notebooks*, vol. III, p. 81) as one 'who painted fowles birds of no great reputation, afterwards was Auctioneer.'

465. A GREYHOUND

Kew (Hampton Court no. 1467). 29 × 34 in., 73,7 × 86,4 cm.

Signed: *G: Wilson Pt.*

A bitch, seated on a cushion in a landscape with the end of a building in the distance.

Recorded at Kensington in 1818 (453); thereafter at Hampton Court and Windsor (1014).

Apparently painted *c.* 1690–1700, presumably in England.

Jacques Rousseau

1630–93. Born in Paris, a Huguenot, pupil and brother-in-law of Herman van Swanevelt; travelled to Italy in his youth. As a specialist in architectural fantasies and perspectives he was employed in a number of the French royal houses, including Versailles and Marly; in 1681 he was expelled from the Académie Française, of which he had become a Member in 1662; travelled to Switzerland and Holland and came to London (?in or before 1688) to work with La Fosse and Monnoyer on the decoration of the Duke of Montagu's house in Bloomsbury. Constantijn Huygens the younger recorded that on 24 November 1690 William III advised him to go and see Rousseau's paintings there (*Journalen, Werken, van het Historisch Genootschap*, Utrecht, N. R. vol. XXIII (1876), p. 365).

466. A BUILDING WITH FIGURES

Hampton Court (21) 73½×49½ in.; 186,7×125,7 cm.; the original canvas was *c.* 51¼×36 in., to which was added a very early strip of canvas on the left (*c.* 3½ in.) and later additions on the left and at top and bottom.

Figures in the courtyard of a vast classical palace.

Nos. 466 and 467 were recorded in the time of Queen Anne in the positions in the Presence Chamber at Hampton Court that they still occupy: *Rousseau. Two Landskips with Ruines over the door* (Queen Anne, *Hampton Court* (3, 4)).

Literature: Vertue, *Notebooks*, vol. IV, p. 74; Law, 1881, 1898 (25); Collins Baker, *Hampton Court*, p. 127; Whinney and Millar, pp. 272–3.

The five canvases by Rousseau (nos. 466–70) placed over the doors in the Presence Chamber and Eating Room at Hampton Court cannot have been painted originally for these positions. All were originally of a smaller size; the additions were made in a slightly looser and coarser hand than Rousseau's, presumably between his death in 1693 and the completion (*c.* 1700?) of the spaces into which the enlarged canvases were to be placed. In certain instances Rousseau's original design was modified by the painter responsible for the additions. The canvases are still in their fine original carved frames. Among the Lord Chamberlain's payments for work ended in Michaelmas 1691, was £100 'to Rousseau Painter for three pictures bought by our particular Command and for our service in our Clossett att Whitehall' (P. R. O., L.C. 5/43, f. 34); these could have been among the pictures still in the royal collection.

467. A CLASSICAL LANDSCAPE WITH RUINS

Hampton Court (62). 73×49¼ in., 185,4×125,1 cm.; the original canvas was *c.* 55½×39¾ in.; there are additions on the left and at top and bottom.

Classical ruins with figures by a pool in the foreground and a villa in the distance.

See no. 466.

Literature: Law, 1881, 1898 (67); Collins Baker, *Hampton Court*, p. 127.

See no. 466.

468. RUINS IN A LANDSCAPE

Hampton Court (107). 73¾×49½ in., 187,3×125,7 cm.; the original canvas was *c.* 41×41 in., which was enlarged first at the top by *c.* 12 in. (probably by Rousseau himself to make it *en suite* with the other canvases he had painted for the Crown) and later on the left and at top and bottom.

A classical landscape with a ruined triumphal arch and a fountain.

Nos. 468–70 were recorded in the time of Queen Anne in the positions in the Eating Room at Hampton Court that they still occupy: *Rousseau. Three Pieces over Dores with Landskips and Ruines* (Queen Anne, *Hampton Court* (6,7,8)).

Literature: Law, 1881, 1898 (105); Collins Baker, *Hampton Court*, p. 128.

See no. 466.

469. A BUILDING WITH FIGURES

Hampton Court (63). 73¼×49¼ in., 186,1×125,1 cm.; the original canvas was *c.* 52½×40 in., and there are additions on all four sides.

A semi-ruined classical palace in a landscape with women fetching water from a pool in the foreground.

See no. 468.

Literature: Law, 1881, 1898 (68); Collins Baker, *Hampton Court*, p. 127.

See no. 466.

470. A RUIN IN A LANDSCAPE (*Plate* 163)

Hampton Court (82). 73½×53 in., 186,7×134,6 cm.; the original canvas was *c.* 49×40 in.; there are additions on the right and at the top.

A ruined temple in which is the statue of a river god and a pool from which women are carrying water.

See no. 468.

Literature: Law, 1881, 1898 (81); Collins Baker, *Hampton Court*, p. 128.

See no. 466.

Jean-Baptiste Monnoyer

1636–99. Still-life and flower painter; an important member of the team of painters working under Le Brun at Vaux-le-Vicomte, Versailles and Marly; was brought to England by the 1st Duke of Montagu to work on the decoration of Montagu House. Buckeridge (p. 401), discussing his works in England states: 'the most curious of all, is the *Looking-Glass* at *Kensington*-House, which he Painted for the late Queen *Mary*, . . . her Majesty sitting by him almost all the while'. This was presumably the piece in the Council Chamber in the time of Queen Anne: *Baptist. A Glass painted wth Festoons of flowrs wth boys & grotesk work over ye Chimney* (Queen Anne, *Kensington* (115)); Vertue mentioned it (*Notebooks*, vol. IV, p. 57, vol. V, pp. 22, 25) and stated that it was dated 1691. *Two Pieces of Flowers over the Doors* by *Baptista* are recorded in the Little Bedchamber at Hampton Court in the time of Queen Anne (Queen Anne, *Hampton Court* (18, 19)), but do not seem still to be in the royal collection.

471. FLOWERS IN A VASE (*Plate* 173)

Buckingham Palace. 73½×43¾ in., 186,7×111,1 cm. There are very early, possibly original, additions at the top and on both sides; the original canvas was *c.* 69×33½ in.

A lavish collection of flowers in a gold vase, standing on a ledge in a niche.

Probably painted for the Crown and perhaps the picture recorded in the reign of Queen Anne in the Queen's Green Closet at St. James's House (Queen Anne, *St. James's* (47): *Baptist. A flower Piece over the Chimney*). Probably at St. James's in the reign of George III and recorded at Buckingham House in 1819 (804); later at Hampton Court (800) and Kensington.

Literature: Law, 1881, 1898 (532).

Presumably painted to fit into the decoration of an interior, over a door or fireplace. The enlargements appear to be by Baptiste himself; they coincide exactly with the sides and top of the painted niche and were presumably applied when the canvas had to be adapted to a slightly larger setting than had been at first envisaged.

Jakob Bogdani

d. 1720. Still-life, flower and animal and bird painter, born in Hungary; was settled in London by 1691. Vertue stated (*Notebooks*, vol. I, p. 127) that of the pictures by him in the royal palaces, many were painted for Queen Anne, 'who was pleas'd with his performances. & encourag'd him much'. He had also worked for William III at Hampton Court. In 1694–6 he had been paid £60 'for work . . . done in the Queen's Looking Glasse Closett in the Thames Gallery in 1694' (*Wren Soc.*, vol. IV (1927), p. 28). On 7 August 1697 Charles Hatton went 'to see ye few best plants yet remaining of ye noble collection of plants at Hampton very well painted by one Bugdan, a Hungarian and excellent painter of fruit and flowers' ('Correspondence of the Family of Hatton', ed. E. M. Thompson, *Camden Soc.*, N. S. vol. XXIII, pt. II (1878), p. 228).

472. BIRDS IN A LANDSCAPE

Kew (*Hampton Court no.* 1464). 77½ × 111½ in., 196,9 × 283,2 cm.

Signed: *J. Bogdani*.

An elaborate formal garden with a domed building and fountain; turkeys and other domestic poultry perched on a tree or a stone ledge; ruffs and a lapwing with various ducks, two domestic Chinese geese and a black-headed gull in the foreground by water that trickles from a *jet-d'eau*.

Literature: Pigler, pl. XXXV.

Bought by Queen Anne from George Churchill's executors. All the pictures bought from this source are inserted by Thomas Coke in the inventory of Queen Anne's pictures: no. 472 appears (*A Large Piece of Fowl wth Ruffs and Reeves*) among a group listed as: *These fowl were done by Bogdane and bought of Admiral Churchils Executors*; later at Hampton Court and Windsor (1421).

Admiral George Churchill, younger brother of the 1st Duke of Marlborough, had constructed a famous aviary in The Little Park at Windsor, which he had filled with a very valuable collection of rare birds. The aviary was at Ranger's Lodge which the Admiral had been lent, in or before December 1706, by his sister-in-law, the Duchess of Marlborough, and was near the present Dairy at Frogmore. It also had a famous garden. After his retirement from the Admiralty in October 1708 Churchill devoted most of his time to the aviary; Bogdani's remarkable record of the Admiral's birds (and a few animals) may have been composed between that date and Churchill's death on 8 May 1710. The aviary was bequeathed by him to his two close friends, the 2nd Duke of Ormonde and the Earl of Torrington.

473. BIRDS IN A LANDSCAPE (*Plate* 171)

Kew (*Hampton Court no.* 1476). 78¾ × 105½ in., 189,9 × 268 cm.

A turkey standing on a capital in the centre; doves and pigeons; peafowl on a ledge on the right; ducks, geese and a Guineafowl in the foreground; a building in the distance.

Among the pictures by Bogdani (see no. 472) bought by Queen Anne from George Churchill's executors; placed in the Waiting Room hung with Green Damask at Kensington (Queen Anne, *Kensington: Bogdane. a Large piece of Fowl wth Guinea Hens Turkys & Peacocks bought of Admiral Churchils Executors*); later at Hampton Court and Windsor (1422).

Literature: Pigler, pl. XXXIV.

See no. 472.

474. BIRDS AND DEER IN A LANDSCAPE

Kew (*Hampton Court no.* 1472). 76½ × 110¼ in., 194,3 × 280 cm.

Signed: *J. Bogdani*.

Three macaws perched on a tree in the centre; below them a chital, gazelle and small antelope; also a stork, a Guineafowl, ducks, domestic poultry, geese and a red-legged partridge; and in the distance a large building.

Among the pictures by Bogdani (see no. 472) bought by Queen Anne from George Churchill's executors and placed at Kensington (Queen Anne, *Kensington: . . . by Bogdane . . . A Large Piece of Beasts & fowl wth an India Deer an antelope & a guinea Deer*); later at Hampton Court and Windsor (1423).

Literature: Pigler, pl. XXXVIII.

See no. 472.

475. BIRDS IN A LANDSCAPE (*Plate* 172)

Kew (*Hampton Court no.* 680). 37¾ × 56¼ in., 95,9 × 142,9 cm.

Signed: *J. Bogdani*.

Finches and other small birds perched on a tree, pigeons on a broken column; oyster-catcher, partridges and a quail in the foreground.

Among the pictures by Bogdani (see no. 472) bought by Queen Anne from George Churchill's executors; placed in the Waiting Room hung with Green Damask at Kensington: *Bogdane a Piece of Fowl wth Pidgeons Red legd Partridges and a broken Pillar bought of Mr Churchils Executors* (Queen Anne, *Kensington*); later at Hampton Court.

Literature: Law, 1881, 1898 (455); Pigler, pl. XXXVII; Norwich Castle Museum, *Still-Life, Bird and Flower Paintings*, 1955 (3).

See no. 472.

476. BIRDS AND FRUIT IN A LANDSCAPE

Kew (*Hampton Court no.* 677). 29¾ × 41¼ in., 75,6 × 104,8 cm.

Signed: *J. Bogdani*.

A cockatoo perched on a stone, with other birds, mainly of the passerine and parrot tribes, and peaches, grapes and figs.

Nos. 476 and 477 are definitely not recorded among the pictures bought from George Churchill's executors (see no. 472) and may have been painted for the Crown; no. 476 is first recorded at Kensington, probably in the reign of George I, in B. M. Stowe MS. 567, f. 15 (*Bogdan Un Cacatoo, avec du Fruit et des autres Oyseaux*) on the *Escalier de robe du Roy* at Kensington, which is probably the Pictured Staircase on which hung a large number of pieces by Bogdani in the time of George II (Vertue inv., *Kensington*, f. 23); later at Hampton Court.

Literature: Law, 1881, 1898 (455); Pigler, pl. XLIII.

See no. 477.

477. BIRDS AND FRUIT IN A LANDSCAPE

Kew (*Hampton Court no.* 678). 30 × 41¼ in., 76,2 × 104,8 cm.

A woodcock, two-barred crossbill, parrots and a small passerine; peaches, grapes and a melon in the foreground; in the background an elaborate garden and a domed building in the distance.

See no. 476; recorded on the Painted Staircase at Kensington in the reign of George II (Vertue inv., *Kensington*, f. 23: *Bogdane A picture with a green Parrot & fruit*); later at Hampton Court.

Literature: Law, 1881, 1898 (455); Pigler, pl. XLIII.

Although nos. 476 and 477 are not recorded among the pictures bought by Queen Anne from George Churchill's executors (see no. 472) it is possible that they originally formed part of Bogdani's record of his aviary.

478. BIRDS IN A LANDSCAPE

Kew (*Hampton Court no.* 679). 72 × 63 in., 182,9 × 160 cm.

A capucin monkey and doves in a tree and below a guan and two curassows; a chough, a Guineafowl, stone curlew, ducks and ducklings by water in the foreground.

Almost certainly, with no. 479, among the pictures bought by

Queen Anne from George Churchill's executors (see no. 472): the pictures listed in her inventory (Queen Anne, *Kensington*) as coming from this source included: *A Large Piece of fowl Higher then Broad wth West India Queams of 2 Sorts*; definitely recorded at Kensington, probably in the reign of George I, at Kensington: *Bogdon Plusieurs Oyseaux des Indes et d'Autres Oyseaux, et un singe qui monte sur un Arbre* (B. M. Stowe MS. 567, f. 15); later at Hampton Court.

Literature: Law, 1881, 1898 (455); Pigler, pl. LIV; Whinney and Millar, p. 280.

No. 478 is almost certainly a companion piece to no. 479; the pair was presumably part of Bogdani's record of Admiral Churchill's aviary.

479. BIRDS IN A LANDSCAPE

Kew (Hampton Court no. 683). 70¾ × 62½ in., 179,7 × 158,8 cm. Signed: *J. Bogdani.*

A flamingo with turacos, curassows, a guan, a troupial and a chachalaca in a landscape which seems to be intended for a West Indian or South American setting.

See no. 478; recorded on the Pictured Staircase at Kensington in the time of George II: *Bogdani A large picture with a Fleming & other birds* (Vertue inv., *Kensington*, f. 24); later at Hampton Court.

Literature: Law, 1881, 1898 (462); Pigler, pl. LV.

See no. 478.

480. DUCKS SURPRISED BY A HAWK

Kew (Hampton Court no. 1471). 87½ × 53½ in., 222,3 × 135,9 cm.

Waterfowl standing on a ledge, taking fright at a bird of prey which is pursuing other duck in the air.

Probably among the pictures bought by Queen Anne from George Churchill's executors (see no. 472); no. 480 seems clearly to have been designed to hang at a considerable height and may be the piece placed in the Cistern Room at Kensington: *Bogdan Over ye Door a Piece of Fowl bought of Admiral Churchills Executors* (Queen Anne, *Kensington*); later at Hampton Court and Windsor (1425).

Literature: Pigler, pl. XL.

The steep perspective in which the ledge in the foreground is painted, the duck flying down as if into the room, and the fluttering feather indicate that no. 480 was probably designed to be set into a special position in an interior.

481. BIRDS IN A LANDSCAPE

Kew (Hampton Court no. 682). 39½ × 42 in., 100,3 × 106,7 cm.

A large gull, moorhen, coot, duck and a kingfisher by a stream.

Probably among the pictures bought by Queen Anne from George Churchill's executors (see no. 472), but not certainly identifiable in her inventory unless it is the picture placed in the Waiting Room hung with Green Damask at Kensington: *Bogdane A Piece of Fowl wth Ducks & Olives bought of Mr Cherchills Executors* (Queen Anne, *Kensington*); later at Hampton Court.

Literature: Law, 1881, 1898 (455a); Pigler, pl. XXXIII.

No. 481 was attributed by Law, *op. cit.*, to Barlow, but seems definitely to be by Bogdani and thus, almost certainly, to be part of his record of Admiral Churchill's aviary.

482. BIRDS IN A LANDSCAPE (*Plate* 174)

Hampton Court (229). 84½ × 49 in., 214,6 × 124,5 cm.
Signed: *J. Bogdani*

Domestic fowls and pigeons with a peacock standing on a ledge; turkeys, waterfowl and pheasants; in the background is a garden with a fountain.

Painted, as a series with nos. 483 and 484, for Queen Anne, or conceivably for William III, and recorded in the Queen's inventory in the position at Hampton Court that it still occupies *In the Closet above Stairs: Bugdan A Piece of Fowles over the Chimney* (Queen Anne, *Hampton Court* (20)).

Literature: Law, 1881, 1898 (243); Collins Baker, *Hampton Court,* p. 10; Pigler, pl. L.

Presumably painted with nos. 483 and 484 to form part of the decoration of what is now the King's Closet.

483. FLOWERS IN A VASE (*Plate* 175)

Hampton Court (222). 68 × 33 in., 172,7 × 83,8 cm.

A luxuriant collection of flowers in a richly carved vase, standing on a ledge beside a bullfinch.

Painted, with no. 484, for Queen Anne, or conceivably for William III; the pair are recorded in Queen Anne's inventory in the positions they still occupy *In the Closet above Stairs Bugdan Two Pieces of Flowers over the Doors* (Queen Anne, *Hampton Court* (21, 22)).

Literature: Law, 1881, 1898 (225a); Collins Baker, *Hampton Court,* p. 10; Pigler, pl. XVII.

See no. 482.

484. FLOWERS IN A VASE

Hampton Court (232). 68⅛ × 33 in., 173 × 83,8 cm.

A collection of flowers in a richly carved silver vase, standing on a marble ledge beside a small parrot.

See no. 483.

Literature: Law, 1881, 1898 (246); Collins Baker, *Hampton Court,* p. 10; Pigler, pl. XVIII.

See no. 482.

485. FLOWERS IN A VASE

Hampton Court (202). 40⅛ × 54¾ in., 101,9 × 139 cm.
Signed: *J. Bogdani*

A collection of flowers in a carved gold bowl on a marble ledge.

Painted for Queen Anne, or conceivably for William III, and recorded in her inventory in the position at Hampton Court that it still occupies: *In the great Bed Chamber Bugdane Two Pieces of Flowers over the doors* (Queen Anne, *Hampton Court* (16, 17)).[1]

Literature: Law, 1881, 1898 (208, as by Baptiste); Collins Baker, *Hampton Court,* p. 9; Pigler, pl. XIX.

Presumably painted to form part of the decoration of the King's Bedchamber. Like nos. 483 and 484 it is still in its original carved frame, on the back of which is a working drawing for a section of the pattern.

486. A VASE OF LILIES (*Plate* 226)

Buckingham Palace. 25½ × 19½ in., 64,8 × 49,5 cm.

A carved gilt vase, filled with lilies, standing in a niche between a pair of bearded tits perched on grapes and peaches.

Among the pictures bought by Queen Anne from Admiral Churchill's executors (see no. 472); placed at Kensington in the Waiting Room hung with Green Damask: *Bogdan A Pott wth Jersey Lillys bought of Admiral Churchils Executors* (Queen Anne, *Kensington*); later at St. James's, Kensington, Hampton Court (814) and Kew.

Literature: Law, 1881, 1898 (540); Pigler, pl. XII.

Probably painted for a special position, perhaps over a door, in a cabinet or other small room.

1. The canvas now over the other door in the King's Bedchamber (inv. no. 169) does not appear to be by Bogdani nor, on examination of the canvas, to be the original canvas for that position.

Artist Unknown

487. A CROWNED CRANE

Hampton Court (543). 109¾×32¼ in., 278,8×81,9 cm.; the canvas has, however, been enlarged at top and bottom and the original size was 50×32¼ in.

Standing on a bank by an ivy-covered tree.

Probably painted for Charles II; first recorded in the reign of James II at Windsor, apparently in the Passage between the King's Eating Room and the Queen's Drawing Room (B. M. Harl. MS. 1890, f. 73 v.; Bathoe, *James II* (799): *A peice with the Japan peacocke in itt*).

Literature: Law, 1881, 1898 (496); Collins Baker, *Hampton Court*, p. 10; Pigler, pl. L.

Attributed in the nineteenth century and by Collins Baker, *loc. cit.*, to Bogdani. The appearance of no. 487 in James II's inventory indicates, however, that it was painted before Bogdani's arrival in England; it is, moreover, drier and more restrained in quality than comparable canvases by Bogdani (*e.g.*, no. 482). The canvas is in the type of frame made for the pictures set into positions in the new State Apartments in the time of Charles II and may thus have been heightened, and perhaps cut at the sides, at that time, soon after it was painted, to fill a special place in a passage (see above). The additional canvas is painted in a much coarser style than the original bird and the background of the original canvas was overpainted at the same time and by the same hand.

Alexander van Gaelen

1670–1728. Sporting and battle painter; native of Amsterdam and a pupil of Huchtenburg; went to Germany in 1694 and later (?*c.* 1700) came to London and had considerable success with his battle-pieces.

Attributed to Alexander van Gaelen

488. QUEEN ANNE'S PROCESSION TO THE HOUSES OF PARLIAMENT

Kensington Palace. 19¾×35 in., 50,2×88,9 cm.

There are indecipherable remains of a signature.[1]

The Queen is seen in her state coach, which is approaching the old Horse Guards and is accompanied by an escort of Household Cavalry and by a group of Walking Footmen (or possibly Watermen) and Yeomen of the Guard.

Bought by George IV at the sale of the Duke of York's pictures at Christie's, 7 April 1827 (2, as by Tillemans) (W. R. A., Geo. 26554; *Carlton Palace* (609)); later at Windsor (435) and St. James's.

The attribution is based on the fragmentary signature which could be that of Van Gaelen; moreover, a large canvas in the Art Gallery and Museum, Brighton, probably representing a siege during William III's campaigns in Flanders, is signed *A. V. Gaalen* and appears to be by the same hand. A slightly earlier version of no. 488, on the art-market in London in 1954, showed, among other slight variations, William III in the coach, and appeared to be lighter and freer in touch. The rider nearest to the coach appears in both versions and is thus presumably Gold Stick rather than Prince George of Denmark. In a very feeble version sold at

Christie's, 4 February 1955 (18), and attributed to Alexander van Gaelen, two figures, probably intended for the Queen and Prince George, were seen in the coach. A large canvas at Serlby, probably showing William III's return to London from signing the Treaty of Ryswick in 1697, has affinities with no. 488 and is probably by the same hand.

Peter Tillemans

1684–1734. Topographical, landscape and sporting painter; a native of Antwerp; came to England in June 1708.

489. QUEEN ANNE IN THE HOUSE OF LORDS (*Plate* 206)

Kensington Palace. 55×48⅛ in., 139,7×122,2 cm.

Signed: *P. Tillemans P . . .*

The Queen is seated on the throne in the old House of Lords, which is hung with the famous Armada tapestries; a very tall long-case clock points to about 12.55 p.m.; the Queen is attended by her ladies, Officers of State, Heralds and pages, with the House in session before her: the temporal and spiritual peers seated round the chamber (the two Archbishops near the Throne), the Lord Chief Justice and lesser legal dignitaries on the Woolsack in front of her, and the Clerks at their table. In the foreground are members of the lower House at the bar, among them two of the three officers of the Household who carry white staves.

Bought by George IV at the sale of the Duke of York's pictures at Christie's, 7 April 1827 (4) (W. R. A., Geo. 26554; *Carlton Palace* (606); later at Windsor (516) and St. James's.

Literature: Whinney and Millar, p. 283.

Presumably painted between Tillemans's arrival in London in June 1708, and Queen Anne's death on 1 August 1714; Prince George of Denmark, who died on 28 October 1708, does not seem to be present. For his little image of the Queen, Tillemans may have drawn on Kneller's seated state portrait and it is probable that a number of the figures in the scene are intended for portraits. Tillemans's record of the scene is very close to B. Cole's print of George II in the House of Lords in 1755. It is possible that Tillemans recorded an actual event in the House of Lords, but slight internal evidence (the Queen's not wearing the crown; and the disposition of the Bishops in a way that assists the composition but does not tally with their actual attendance at this period) seems to indicate that he was commissioned to paint, perhaps for a member of the upper House, the participants in the positions they would take up at the official ceremony enacted when the Sovereign was in the House. The figure in the foreground with a white staff could be Thomas C ke, Vice-Chamberlain of the Household and the writer of notes in Queen Anne's inventory. Tillemans's signed view of the House of Commons, virtually a pendant to no. 489, was painted at the same time and is now in the House of Commons.

Peter Monamy

c. 1690–1749. Marine painter; a native of Jersey; deeply influenced by the work of the Van de Veldes.

490. A CALM WITH A ROYAL YACHT FIRING A SALUTE (*Plate* 196)

Buckingham Palace. 40½×50 in., 102,9×127 cm.

Signed: *P. Monamy Pinxt.*

---

1. These were noted in 1878 (*V.R. inv.*), when they seem to have been a little clearer.

A ship-rigged royal yacht firing a salute, surrounded by lesser vessels. The yacht wears the royal standard and one of the state barges, pulling for the shore, also wears the standard.

Recorded at Kensington in 1818 (362) with an attribution to Van de Velde, but recorded by Faulkner (p. 390) as by Monamy and as a representation of the landing of George II on his return from Hanover; later at Hampton Court (226) and Kensington.

Literature: Law, 1881, 1898 (901).

Probably painted in connection with the landing of George II in England from one of his visits to Hanover. A variant (signed and dated 1727), in which the yacht and the two state barges appear very much as in no. 490, was sold at Sotheby's, 1 February 1950 (35); it was described as the arrival of George II in the *Peregrine* at his accession to the throne, but the new King was, in fact, at Richmond when his father died. A copy of part of the composition was sold at Christie's, 14 April 1950 (143). The *Peregrine Galley*, built in 1700 and rebuilt as the *Royal Caroline* in 1733, had brought George I to England in 1714. The presence of the royal standard indicates that the sovereign is present in no. 490.

Joshua Mollineux or Molyneux

*fl.*1718–*c.*1730. Presumably an amateur painter and draughtsman of marine and topographical subjects, and probably a native of Lancashire; recorded in 1722–8 in the service of the 10th Earl of Derby at Knowsley; a view of the south front of Knowsley is still in the house.

491. THE ENGLISH AND DUTCH SQUADRONS AT SPITHEAD IN 1729

Buckingham Palace. 46¼×90 in., 117,5×228,6 cm.

The two fleets off Spithead; the smaller vessels in the foreground include a Manx man-of-war.

Recorded at Buckingham Palace (624) in 1876 (*V.R. inv.*) and there stated to have been bequeathed by the Duchess of Gloucester to Queen Victoria in 1857;[1] later at Kensington.

Literature: 'The Old Blue Coat Hospital', *Hist. Soc. of Lancashire and Cheshire*, vol. 109 (1957), pp. 151–4.

No. 491 is probably a copy of a design of which there were two versions at Knowsley (G. Scharf, *A . . . Catalogue of the Collection of Pictures at Knowsley Hall* (1875), 257, 258). The larger of these two versions appears in an inventory of 1736 as by 'Mollineux' and the design is engraved with the inscription: *Joshua Molineux Fecit apud Knowsley*.[2] The presence of the Manx vessel is clearly significant for an artist working at Knowsley. The version still at Knowsley, and the engraving, bear a full description of the scene as showing the English and Dutch squadrons of men-of-war, under the command of Sir Charles Wager, Vice-Admiral of the Red (on board the *Cornwall* in the middle of the design), Sir George Walton, Admiral of the White (on board the *Princess Emilia* on the left), and Vice-Admiral van Sommelsdyke (on the *Leyden*), 'as they lay Equip'd at SPITHEAD during the Whole Sūmer MDCCXXIX.'

1. It is possible that this statement by Redgrave is an error. No marine subject appears in the list of pictures bequeathed by the Duchess of Gloucester to Queen Victoria in 1857 and only one of the two versions of no. 491 formerly at Knowsley (no. 258 in Scharf's catalogue) can now be located there. It is thus possible that Scharf's no. 257 is identical with our no. 491; it may thus have been given to Queen Victoria by the 15th Earl of Derby.

2. I am very grateful to Mr. Michael Robinson for telling me of this rare engraving, of which an impression is in the collection of Dr. R. C. Anderson, and for his report on the version of no. 491 remaining at Knowsley.

Artists Unknown : Marine Paintings

492. THE BATTLE OF VIGO BAY (*Plate* 141)

Buckingham Palace. 28×40¼ in., 71,1×102,2 cm.

A bird's-eye view from the south of the breaking of the boom by the Dutch and English fleets in Vigo Bay.

Recorded at Kensington in 1818 (149) as: *The Breaking of the Boom at Cales;* later at Hampton Court and Windsor (1002).

No. 492 seems an accurate contemporary record of the moment, on 12 October 1702, when Vice-Admiral Sir Thomas Hopsonn on the *Torbay*, at the head of the allied fleets under the command of Sir George Rooke, broke the boom behind which the Spanish Treasure fleet, with its convoy of French warships, was sheltered in the harbour of Redondela. The *Torbay* can be seen almost through the boom, near the fire-ship which set her ablaze for a short time. On the near shore can be seen the troops marching under the command of the Duke of Ormonde from Teis, where they had been set on shore, to Fort Randa at the southern end of the boom. All the Spanish and French ships were captured or destroyed. Mr. Michael Robinson has suggested that no. 492 may have been painted for the captain of the English ship so prominently shown on the left.

493. AN ENGLISH FIRST-RATE SHIP

Buckingham Palace. 28×40¼ in., 71,1×102,2 cm.

A starboard broadside view of an English three-decker wearing the royal standard.

Recorded at Kensington in 1818 (367: *Portrait of a First Rate Man of War*); later at Hampton Court (1034) and Kensington.

Literature: Law, 1881, 1898 (924).

The royal standard is of the late Stuart form, but the vessel in no. 493 cannot be identified with any of the three-deckers likely to have had the sovereign on board. Nor did any ship have, as has the ship in no. 493, complete gun posts on the poop deck. No. 493 is probably a slightly later derivation of the picture of the *Britannia* by Isaac Sailmaker (1633–1721) signed and dated 168(3?), sold at Christie's, 27 October 1961 (127), and now in the collection of Mr. J. D. Layton.

494. SHIPPING OFF HURST CASTLE

Buckingham Palace. 27¾×40¼ in., 70,5×102,2 cm.

On the left, in a rough sea off Hurst Castle, an English ship close-hauled and, on the right, an English flute-sterned merchant ship.

Recorded at Kensington in 1818 (148: *Sea piece with a Castle in the distance*); later at Hampton Court and Windsor (1017).

The scene could be dated *c.* 1720, but it is possible that no. 494 is a slightly later work, perhaps based on a design by Bakhuizen. The castle and mainland agree closely with a drawing attributed to Peeters in the collection of Sir Bruce Ingram.[1]

495. A CALM WITH A FLAG-SHIP SALUTING

Buckingham Palace. 20¼×33 in., 51,4×83,8 cm.

A calm, with an English three-decker flying the flag of a Vice-Admiral of the Red.

Possibly acquired by William IV; probably recorded at Hampton Court in 1849 (*The Stranger's Guide* (1008): 'a Sea Piece, by

1. Mr. Michael Robinson kindly drew my attention to this drawing.

Monamy'); certainly at Hampton Court (1080) in 1861 (*V.R. inv.*); later at Kensington.

Literature: Law, 1881, 1898 (915), as by Monamy.

The ships are of *c.* 1720 and the composition is very reminiscent of Monamy, but no. 495 appears to be a copy, probably after Monamy, by a painter working late in the eighteenth, or early in the nineteenth century, such as J. C. Schetky, who was marine painter to George IV, William IV and Queen Victoria.

496. AN ACTION BETWEEN ENGLISH AND SPANISH SHIPS

Buckingham Palace. 37 × 49¾ in., 94 × 126,4 cm.

English and Spanish ships engaged off the coast; the English appear to be under the command of a full Admiral of the Blue.

Recorded at Hampton Court (1015) in 1868 (*V.R. inv.*).

Literature: Law, 1881, 1898 (891).

No. 496 cannot be accurately dated or its subject identified. It must represent an action between the English and Spanish fleets in the first quarter of the eighteenth century and may be intended for the Battle of Cape Passaro, 11 August 1718; but there are inaccuracies which make it impossible to establish this. In style it is very close to Peter Monamy, to whom it was formerly attributed, and may have been painted in the 1730's.

497. SHIPS IN A BREEZE

Buckingham Palace. 20¼ × 33¼ in., 51,4 × 84,5 cm.

A Dutch fishing-boat in the foreground with two English men-of-war, that on the left flying the blue, that on the right the red, ensign.

Possibly acquired by William IV. Recorded as by Brooking at Hampton Court in 1849 (*The Stranger's Guide* (1003), later inv. no. 1078); later at Kensington.

Literature: Law, 1881, 1898 (913).

No. 497 was probably painted *c.* 1740. It seems too meticulous in handling to be by Brooking.

Georg Wilhelm Fountaine or Lafontaine

c. 1680-1745. Portrait painter, of Huguenot origin; court painter in the service, from 1698, of Duke Georg Wilhelm of Celle and later of the royal family in Hanover; a portrait of Frederick, Prince of Wales, is engraved by J. Smith (Chaloner Smith, pp. 1167-8) as *Painted at Hanover by Mr. Fountain 1723*;[1] a portrait of the same date of George II is engraved by Simon (*ibid.*, p. 1091) as *Fountain pinx ad Vivam*. In 1730-1 he was paid for the expenses of a move from London to Hanover, where he succeeded Giusti as court painter (information from the Staatsarchiv in Hanover, kindly communicated to me by Dr. Plath).

498. GEORGE I (*Plate* 189)

Buckingham Palace. 50¼ × 40 in., 127,6 × 101,6 cm.

Three-quarter-length standing, holding his hat in his right hand and wearing the ribbon of the Garter, beside a table on which is the crown and sceptre; the Banqueting House is seen in the distance.

1. A painted version of this type is at Bishopsthorpe.

Probably the portrait recorded in the Council Room in the King's private apartments at Windsor in 1813 and 1816 (Legge's lists): *King Geo. I given to the King by Mrs Howe. 4.1-3.3.* (later inv. no. 44).

The design was engraved in 1733 by G. W. Monguibert as by Fountaine and was probably painted at the end of the King's life. Although the design is not unrelated to Kneller's state portrait (no. 360), no. 498 appears to be an *ad vivum* portrait with a more informal air. Mrs. Howe, who gave the portrait to George III, was probably the Hon. Mrs. Caroline Howe; her mother, the 2nd Viscountess Howe, was a daughter of the Countess of Darlington by George I. A version of no. 498, with Windsor Castle in the background, is in the Niedersächsisches Heimatmuseum in Hanover, with companion portraits, possibly also by Fountaine, of George II and Frederick, Prince of Wales. Collins Baker records a portrait stated to have been drawn from the life in 1727 (*Lely*, vol. II, p. 197); this is presumably a full-length, inscribed as 'Drawn from ye Life in ... 1727 by G. Fountaine', which belongs to Lt. Col. F. M. Bailey[1] and is very close to Kneller's state portrait in design.

John Vanderbank

d. 1739. Portrait and history painter, possibly of French origin; in 1736 he painted the full-length of Queen Caroline which is at Goodwood, and in March 1738 his studio was visited by the Prince and Princess of Wales (Vertue, *Notebooks*, vol. III, p. 82).

499. GEORGE I (*Plate* 168)

Windsor Castle (2964). 123½ × 94¼ in., 315 × 239,4 cm.

Signed and dated: *J. Vanderbank. Fecit. | 1726;* inscribed later: *George ye first.*

Riding on horseback with a baton in his right hand and wearing the ribbon and star of the Garter; in the background is an encampment with members of the household cavalry, including a kettle-drummer and a negro trumpeter.

Stated to have been formerly in Lord Bateman's collection at Shobdon Court; presented to Their Majesties King George V and Queen Mary by Lady Edward Spencer-Churchill in 1932.

Literature: Collins Baker, *Windsor*, p. 298.

The portrait appears to have been based on a sitting; the composition is clearly influenced by Van Dyck's equestrian portrait of Charles I, at that time in the collection of the Duke of Marlborough (see no. 144), and is perhaps the earliest imitation of it on this scale.

Charles Jervas

c. 1675-1739. Portrait painter and copyist (especially of the works of Van Dyck) of Irish birth; studied under Kneller and in Italy; on 25 October 1723 was appointed Principal Painter to the King in succession to Kneller. Soon after the accession of George II, Jervas drew the King and his consort for the new (Coronation?) medals by Croker, but he had 'no success in painting their Majesties pictures & from thence he lost much the favour & Interest at Court' (Vertue, *Notebooks*, vol. III, pp. 33, 59, 61-2, 99). In 1738 he went to Italy, allegedly to purchase pictures for the royal family (*ibid.*, pp. 85, 93).

1. I am very grateful to Mr. J. Goodison for telling me of this portrait.

Studio (?) of Charles Jervas

500. CAROLINE OF ANSBACH WITH WILLIAM AUGUSTUS, DUKE OF CUMBERLAND

St. James's Palace. 92 × 65½ in., 233,7 × 166,4 cm.

Double full-length; the Queen stands in robes of state resting her right hand on the shoulder of her son who stands beside her in robes of the Bath, with his coronet in his right hand, in front of a table on which is his mother's crown.

In the collection of George IV: sent to Carlton House on 5 April 1816 (*A Whole Length Portrait of Queen Caroline with Her Son ... by Jervis*) by Seguier 'by desire of Lord Tyrconnel[1] for The Regent's inspection . . . if approved was intended as a present' (Jutsham, *R/D*, f. 365); placed in store (*Carlton House*, 1816 (240); the label is still on the back); later at Hampton Court (770).

Probably painted *c.* 1728 in Jervas's studio and apparently on the basis of separate portraits of the Queen and the Duke. According to Vertue (*Notebooks*, vol. III, p. 17), Jervas was (1728) 'imployd. by the Queen to paint the Picture of Prince William'. Vertue himself engraved the portrait of the Duke of this type. Vertue added that the portrait (of which a version is reproduced in Hon. E. Charteris, *William Augustus, Duke of Cumberland* (1913), p. 22) was a success and 'the Queen sat to him. & the King'. In 1727 the Guildhall had commissioned from Jervas a portrait which proved to be of this type (R. A., *Kings and Queens*, 1953 (226)), but is perhaps of less good quality than no. 500; a version is at Burghley and another was at Woburn (sold Christie's, 19 January 1951 (135)).

After Charles Jervas

501. SAMUEL CLARKE (1675–1729)

Kensington Palace. 50¼ × 40½ in., 127,6 × 102,9 cm.

Three-quarter-length in clerical costume, seated at a table with his left hand on an open book; on the shelves behind, below a bust of Newton, are the works of Bacon, Boyle's *Lectures* (which Clarke preached, 1704–5), and Newton's *Opticks* (1704; probably Clarke's Latin translation of 1706) and *Principia* (1687). Behind Dr. Clarke is inscribed: SAMUEL CLARKE D.D. | *Rector of St IAMES'S Westm. | In every part of Usefull | Knowledge, and Critical | Learning, perhaps without | a Superior; in all united, | certainly w*tʰ*out an Equal: | In his Works, the Best Defen- | der of Religion: In his Prac- | tice, the Greatest Ornament | to It: In his Conversation, | Communicative; and in an | Uncommon manner, In- | structive; In his Preaching & | Writings, Strong, Clear, & | Calm: In his Life, High in the | Esteem of the Great, y*e* Good, | & the Wise; In his Death, | lamented by Every Friend | to Truth, Virtue, & Liberty. | He died MAY 17.1729. in | the 54*tʰ* year of his Age.*

The Earl of Egmont recorded (18–20 January 1730) that 'the Queen . . . has caused the picture of the late Doctor Samuel Clark . . . to be set up in Kensington Palace, with this inscription to his honour, composed by Dr. Hoadly[2] . . .' (H. M. C., *Egmont MSS., Diary of the first Earl of Egmont*, vol. I (1920), pp. 7–8); later at St. James's, Hampton Court, and (attributed to Thomas Gibson) Buckingham Palace (444).

According to Vertue (*Notebooks*, vol. II, p. 74) a copy was painted for Queen Caroline (and another for Mrs. Clayton)

1. This was John Delaval Carpenter, 4th Earl of Tyrconnel (1790–1853).
2. Benjamin Hoadly, Bishop of Winchester.

of the portrait of Dr. Clarke by Jervas that then belonged to Lady Lechmere. No. 501 could well be a copy of a portrait which had been painted by Jervas *c.* 1725.

Metaphysician and disciple of Newton; a Chaplain to Queen Anne and later Rector of St. James's, Piccadilly; he held a philosophical correspondence with Leibniz in which Queen Caroline showed great interest; she had a warm admiration for him and 'seldom a Week pass'd in which SHE did not with pleasure receive some proof of the Greatness of his Genius, and of the Force of his Superior Understanding'. Dr. Clarke's *Works* (1738) were dedicated to her. Among the busts installed by the Queen in the Hermitage in Richmond Park was one of Clarke by Guelfi.

William Aikman

1682–1731. Scots portrait painter, who returned to Edinburgh in 1712 from a period of study in Rome and travel in the Middle East. He moved to London at about the time of Kneller's death in 1723. In 1730 Vertue noted that 'Mr Eckman lately painted at Court several of the Princesses pictures' (*Notebooks*, vol. III, p. 43).

502. JOHN CAMPBELL, SECOND DUKE OF ARGYLL and DUKE OF GREENWICH (1680–1743) (*Plate* 192)

Holyroodhouse. 95 × 59 in., 241,3 × 150 cm.

Full-length, standing by the entrance to a tent, wearing the ribbon of the Garter over a breastplate and military coat and sash; he points with his left hand to a fortress in a barren landscape.

Presumably acquired by Queen Victoria with no. 503. Recorded at Holyrood in 1884 (*V.R. inv.*).

Literature: R. A., *Scottish Art*, 1939 (43).

Vertue said of the Duke that he was Aikman's 'great Patron' (*Notebooks*, vol. III, p. 51). A number of portraits exist of the Duke by Aikman, though they could perhaps be reduced to two basic types. The head of no. 502 is used in a three-quarter-length at Abercairny House and probably in a half-length at The Ross. No. 502 was probably painted *c.* 1709, and may be the original of the type. The upper part of the costume is in an unsatisfactory condition and the Garter ribbon appears to have been painted over another ribbon, going from right to left. No. 502 may have been painted therefore after the Duke received the Thistle (1704) and amended after 22 March 1710, when he received the Garter and would have wished to have the earlier ribbon altered. The background also appears to have been altered. As it stands it may allude to the Duke's period of command in Spain and not to his campaigns under Marlborough or in the Rebellion of 1715, but may originally have been intended to celebrate one of the sieges at which the Duke was prominent: Menin (1706), Ghent (1709) or Tournay (1709).

A distinguished soldier and an active promotor of the Union with Scotland in 1707; commanded under Marlborough at Ramillies, Oudenarde and Malplaquet; went to Spain in 1711 as Ambassador and commander-in-chief; in command of the forces in Scotland that put down the Rebellion of 1715. Groom of the Stole to the Prince of Wales (1714–16), High Steward of the Household (1719) and Master-General of the Ordnance (1725).

503. ARCHIBALD CAMPBELL, EARL OF ILAY and later THIRD DUKE OF ARGYLL (1682–1761)

95½ × 60¼ in., 242,6 × 153 cm.

Full-length, standing in peer's robes by a table, holding an Earl's coronet in his left hand.

In the collection of Queen Victoria by July 1863; lent to the Faculty of Advocates in Edinburgh in 1864.

Literature: J. H. Stevenson, 'Portraits of the Marquis of Argyll . . .', *The Scottish Antiquary*, vol. XI (1897), pp. 97–100.

Probably painted *c.* 1715. The sitter is painted as Earl of Ilay, but the design was engraved by R. Cooper after he had succeeded his brother (no. 502) in the Dukedom, and the coronet was amended accordingly in the print.

One of the most powerful men of his day, a prominent Hanoverian and described as the 'King of Scotland' in the age of Walpole; in his youth he had served under Marlborough; successively Lord High Treasurer (1705) and Lord Justice-General (1710) of Scotland and Keeper of the Great Seal (1733).

William de Nune

c. 1710/15–1750. Scots portrait painter, who signed the Indenture of the Academy of St. Luke in Edinburgh in 1729; his signed and dated portraits range from 1742 to 1749 and his sitters came from the Edinburgh and Dumfries areas.

504. PORTRAIT OF A WOMAN

Kensington Palace. 49½ × 40 in., 125,7 × 101,6 cm.

Signed and dated: *De Nune pinx: | 1742.*

Three-quarter-length, seated, holding in her right hand a miniature of a man.

Bequeathed to King Edward VII by Mrs. Maidstone-Smyth as a portrait of Caroline Matilda, Queen of Denmark.

Literature: Buckingham Palace, 1909, p. 139.

Presumably a portrait of a Scots sitter, painted by De Nune at Edinburgh or Dumfries; the miniature may be a portrait of her husband.

William Kent

1685?–1748. History painter, decorative painter, interior decorator and architect. From 1709 to 1719 he was in Italy, where he bought pictures for the English travellers who were supporting him, studied painting under Benedetto Luti and met his most influential patrons of the future, among them the Earl of Burlington who in 1722 secured for him the commission for the painted decorations at Kensington Palace. From the early 1730's he was increasingly occupied with architecture, but in 1728 he had been appointed inspector of paintings in royal palaces, in which capacity he restored (1733–4) Rubens's ceiling in the Banqueting House. In 1739 he succeeded Jervas as Principal Painter to George II, but never seems to have painted a portrait of the King.

505. THE BATTLE OF AGINCOURT (?)

Kensington Palace. 32¼ × 48¼ in., 81,9 × 122,6 cm.

Signed: *Wᵐ Kent | Pinxᵗ.*

A battle raging in a distinctively classical landscape. In the centre a French royal warrior, wearing the fleur-de-lis on his jupon, is beaten to his knees by Henry V (?).

Probably painted, with nos. 506 and 507, for Queen Caroline (see below); in her Dressing Room at St. James's Walpole saw in 1758 'some pictures of the History of Henry 5th drawn by Kent' (*Visits*, p. 16); with nos. 506 and 507 at Buckingham House in 1819 (814, as *The Battle of Cressy*); no. 505 was later in the Corridor at Windsor, then at Buckingham Palace (919) and later at Windsor (2495).

Literature: R. A., *King's Pictures* (485).

Among disbursements on behalf of Queen Caroline between May 1730 and March 1731 was £166. 6s. paid to William Kent 'For Pictures' (W. R. A., Geo. 53998), which probably included no. 505 and nos. 506 and 507. No. 505 has been described since 1819 as the Battle of Crécy, but Walpole's note in 1758 may indicate that the three pictures were painted as a set illustrating events in the life of Henry V. Moreover, although Kent's inaccuracy in rendering a mediaeval battle is practically complete, he would probably have dressed the Black Prince in dark armour and introduced the Prince of Wales's feathers. His principal English royal figure, moreover, wears the royal arms without the Prince of Wales's label. Close to this principal figure is another apparently royal warrior, and Kent may have been illustrating the moment at Agincourt when Henry V had rushed to the rescue of his brother Humphrey, Duke of Gloucester, who had been struck down by the Duke of Alençon. Alençon was, in turn, forced to yield and was killed. It is perhaps significant that both the Black Prince and Henry V were among the historical royal portrait-busts commissioned by Queen Caroline from Rysbrack (M. I. Webb, *Michael Rysbrack* (1954), pp. 145–6); and it thus seems to have been Queen Caroline who fostered this early interest in mediaeval subjects for artists working in England. Nos. 505–7 are all in magnificent contemporary carved frames; the disbursements on Queen Caroline's behalf (see above) also included £211. 13s. 3d. to William Waters, frame-maker, who may have made them.

506. THE MEETING BETWEEN HENRY V AND THE QUEEN OF FRANCE (*Plate* 193)

Kensington Palace. 30 × 24 in., 76,2 × 61 cm.

Signed: *Wᵐ Kent | pinxᵗ.*

The King, accompanied by his brother(s) and other attendants, greeting the Queen of France, attended by her daughter Catherine and by her ladies and followers.

See no. 505; no. 506 was recorded at Hampton Court (852) in 1862 (*V.R. inv.*).

Literature: Law, 1881, 1898 (784); Nottingham University Art Gallery, *Shakespeare in Art*, 1961 (10).

The scene is presumably intended to represent the meeting that took place on 29 March 1419 between Henry V, the Duke of Burgundy and the French royal ladies; but Kent seems to have been concerned with the actual event and not with its presentation in Shakespeare's *Henry V*, Act V, Sc. II. His treatment of costumes and armour and of the tents which surround the meeting is totally unhistorical, but he has clearly derived the head of the King from one of the two versions of the standard portrait which were then in the royal collection (nos. 6 and 7).

507. THE MARRIAGE OF HENRY V

Kensington Palace. 30 × 24 in., 76,2 × 61 cm.

Signed and dated: *Wᵐ Kent | Pinxᵗ | 1729.*

The King is placing a ring on the finger of his bride; they are surrounded by their attendants and the ceremony is taking place in a spacious Gothic church.

See no. 505; no. 507 was recorded at Hampton Court (857) in 1861 (*V.R. inv.*).

Literature: Law, 1881, 1898 (788); Nottingham University Art Gallery, *Shakespeare in Art*, 1961 (10).

The scene is probably intended to represent the marriage of Henry V and Catherine of Valois, which took place in the Church of St. Jean at Troyes on 2 June 1420. There is, however, an almost completely seventeenth-century or contemporary flavour in the scene and details such as the spectator in profile on the extreme left and the half-naked child holding a hymeneal torch behind the bride are taken from the *Marriage of Marie de Medici* in Rubens's Medici cycle, probably *via* Audran's engraving.

Enoch Seeman

1708?–45. Portrait painter and copyist, working in London but of Dutch extraction; on 26 June 1738 he was paid £37. 16s. for *two Wole-lenghts and two half-lenghts* for the Prince of Wales (D. of Cornwall MSS., vol. VIII, f. 323). It is possible that these were versions of his portraits of George II and Queen Caroline, perhaps the pair (see below) recorded at Buckingham House in 1819.

508. GEORGE II (*Plate* 179)

Windsor Castle (220). 94¼×58¾ in., 239,4×149,2 cm.

Signed: *E. Seeman | pinx* . . .

Full-length, standing in robes of state and wearing the collar of the Garter, his right hand resting on the orb beside the crown and sceptre.

It is impossible to disentangle accurately the references in the earlier inventories to the pairs of royal portraits by Seeman and Kneller (see nos. 343 and 345). No. 508 and its companion piece (no. 511) were possibly the pair placed in the set of royal full-lengths in the Queen's Gallery at Kensington (Vertue inv., *Kensington*, f. 22), described by Walpole (notes in Bathoe, *James II*) as 'execrable both'; this pair was probably sent to Windsor on 24 July 1795.

Literature: Collins Baker, *Windsor*, p. 285.

This and its companion may have been the first versions of Seeman's portrait of George II and his Queen, types probably produced *c.* 1730, soon after the King's accession. See nos. 509 and 510.

509. GEORGE II

St. James's Palace. 94×58 in., 238,8×147,3 cm.

Signed: *E. S. pinx*.

See no. 508. No. 509 and its probable companion (no. 512) were possibly the pair recorded at Buckingham House in 1819 (744, 745) and moved to Hampton Court on 19 August 1833.

A replica of no. 508.

510. GEORGE II

Kensington Palace. 32¾×27½ in., 83,2×69,9 cm.

Head and shoulders in a painted oval.

Recorded at Hampton Court (624) in 1862 (*V.R. inv.*).

A version of no. 508; no. 510 and its companion (no. 513) seem to have been cut down from another pair of full-lengths

as the painted oval on both canvases is a later addition through which the costume can still clearly be seen. They may have been the pair, recorded by Dodsley in the King's Dining Room at Windsor (see no. 343), which may later have been at Hampton Court. A pair of derivations on this scale at Houghton from Seeman's official portraits of the King and Queen are markedly different in the faces.

511. CAROLINE OF ANSBACH (*Plate* 180)

Kensington Palace. 94×57¾ in., 238,8×146,7 cm.

Full-length standing in robes of state, with her crown and sceptre beside her.

Presumably the companion to no. 508; despatched from Windsor on 25 April 1832, probably to Hampton Court (later inv. no. 784).

See no. 508.

512. CAROLINE OF ANSBACH

Buckingham Palace. 94×57¾ in., 238,8×146,7 cm.

Signed (very obscurely): *E See* . . .

Probably originally the companion to no. 509.

A replica of no. 511.

513. CAROLINE OF ANSBACH

Kensington Palace. 33×27¾ in., 83,8×69,9 cm.

Head and shoulders in a painted oval.

See no. 510; recorded at Hampton Court (623) in 1862 (*V.R. inv.*).

A version of no. 511.

Martin Maingaud

Portrait and history painter; was in the service of Max Emanuel, Elector of Bavaria, 1692–1706, and probably (see nos. 514–16) later worked for the English royal family in Hanover.

514. FREDERICK, PRINCE OF WALES, AND PRINCESS AMELIA (?)

Buckingham Palace. 60×47¼ in., 152,4×120 cm.

Full-length, reclining on a bank with a putto flying towards them on the left, possibly in the guise of Zephyrus and Flora; the Prince, who is half naked with wind-swept hair, holds a wreath over his sister's head and a wreath of flowers is suspended between them.

Recorded at Kensington in 1818 (272: *Portraits of Prince Frederick and Princess Amelia when Children. Mongaud*); later at Hampton Court, but recorded at Buckingham Palace (1062) in 1876 (*V.R. inv.*).

Presumably painted *c.* 1720. The identity of the Princess is not completely established. In 1876 she was described as Princess Anne, but the identification in 1818 as Princess Amelia is perhaps more likely. The head of Prince Frederick is close in type to no. 623.

515. PRINCESSES ANNE and AMELIA

Kew (Hampton Court no. 917). 55⅝×43 in., 141,3×109,2 cm.

Signed and dated: *Maingaud | Pᵗ 1718*.

Full-length in a landscape, perhaps loosely symbolising the blessings of Peace and Good Government; the elder, her arm round a lute encircled by a vine, handing a rose to her sister who holds the fasces and wears sandals.

Recorded at Kensington in 1818 (69: *Portraits of two Females in a Landscape Maungaud*); later at Hampton Court and Kensington.

Literature: Law, 1881, 1898 (517).

The sitters are probably Princesses Anne (*b.* 1709) and Amelia (*b.* 1711), who are seen in no. 516 with their sister Caroline (*b.* 1713), but it is conceivable that they are Princesses Amelia and Caroline.

516. PRINCESSES ANNE, AMELIA and CAROLINE

Hampton Court (625). 26½ × 31¼ in., 67,3 × 79,4 cm.

Originally signed and dated on the back: *Maingaud. 1721.* This has been concealed in lining, but was recorded in 1861 (*V. R. inv.*).

Three half-length figures: Princess Caroline, from behind, puts her arm round the back of Princess Amelia on the left and glances up at her; Princess Anne holds at her bosom a rose plucked from a spray over Princess Amelia's shoulder.

Probably the picture seen at Kew by Walpole in September 1761 (*Visits*, p. 38 . . . 'Frederic Prince of Wales; his three eldest Sisters young in one piece'), and recorded there by Sir William Chambers (*Plans, Elevations . . . of Kew* (1763)); recorded at Kensington in 1818 (118); later at Hampton Court and Kensington.

Literature: Law, 1881, 1898 (514).

See no. 515.

Joachim Kayser

fl. 1712–27. Portrait painter in Hanover where he was patronised by the Electoral and royal families. In no. 517 he presumably painted the portrait of the Prince of Wales in collaboration with Johan Anton Klyher (*fl.* 1727–9), a painter at the court of Weimar.

Joachim Kayser and Johan Anton Klyher

517. FREDERICK, PRINCE OF WALES (*Plate* 202)

St. James's Palace. 116½ × 100¼ in., 295,9 × 254,6 cm.; *c.* 5 in. is turned over at the bottom.

Signed and dated: *J: A: de Klijher | & | J: Keijser fec. | 1727.*

Riding on a rearing horse, carrying a baton in his right hand and wearing the ribbon of the Garter over a breastplate.

Perhaps in the Prince's collection; recorded in the Cube Room at Kensington in 1818 (411); later at Hampton Court, Windsor (1274) and Buckingham Palace.

Presumably painted in Hanover.

Joseph Highmore

1692–1780. English painter of subject pictures and portraits, who took up painting after an early training in law and retired in 1762. Although his relations with the royal family seem to have been slight and unofficial (see no. 518), he painted the Duke of Cumberland, and his extant life-size portrait of George II may have been based on a sitting. Two versions of it, in the Walker Art Gallery, Liverpool, and the Mansion House at York, are signed and the latter is stated to have been presented by Lord Rockingham (for whom it may have been painted) to the Rockingham Club in York in 1757.

518. QUEEN CAROLINE OF ANSBACH

Hampton Court (795). Oval, 29¾ × 24¾ in., 75,6 × 62,9 cm.

Signed: *Jos: Highmore | pinx:*

Head and shoulders in profile to the right in a loose ermine-lined robe and wearing a jewelled circlet in her hair.

Probably purchased by George IV; recorded in the West Ante-room at Carlton House in 1816 (6); later at Windsor.

Literature: Law, 1881, 1898 (527); Collins Baker, *Hampton Court*, p. 64.

Highmore's signature has hitherto escaped notice and the portrait has been variously attributed to Enoch Seeman or the German School. Probably painted *c.* 1735, towards the end of the Queen's life. Vertue had written (apparently in 1731; *Notebooks*, vol. III, p. 54) of Highmore, who 'coud not obtain the Honour of the King or Queen setting to him for their pictures did by stealth draw them first on paper at Several Views', and mentioned his concoction of a pair of royal portraits. No. 518 (perhaps with its companion, for which see below) may have been the result of a sitting 'by stealth', but it is almost certainly later and was perhaps done *ad vivum*: Highmore was said to be in the habit of painting 'the faces often at one Sitting'. A portrait of Queen Caroline is among those cited in the obituary notice of Highmore in *The Gentleman's Magazine*, vol. L (1780), p. 179, as evidence of his ability to 'take a likeness by memory as well as by a sitting'. There may conceivably be a connection between no. 518 and Rysbrack's busts (1738) of the Queen in marble and terracotta at Windsor (see M. I. Webb, *Michael Rysbrack* (1954), pp. 150–1, 154–6); the bust of the Queen seems not to have been made from the life. In the inventory of Carlton Palace (6) no. 518 was stated to have been 'Much injured by the Fire in Carlton palace June 8th 1824'; this may be an error, but the companion portrait of George II is stated in all the sources to have been destroyed on that occasion. It can be seen, in Pyne's plate of the West Ante-room (vol. III, *Carlton House*, p. 17), to have been a pendant and to have been in the same fine type of carved frame as still surrounds no. 518. It seems to have been the portrait engraved by John Tinney.

Attributed to Joseph Highmore

519. FREDERICK, PRINCE OF WALES (*Plate* 185)

St. James's Palace. 94 × 58 in., 238,8 × 147,3 cm.

Full-length, advancing in robes of state with the collar of the Garter, his left hand by his sword and his coronet on a ledge above a carved relief of his arms.

Apparently first recorded at Hampton Court in 1842 (Mrs. Jameson (532)) as by Vanloo, but it is difficult to disentangle references in the early nineteenth-century sources to portraits of the Prince with that attribution (*e.g.*, nos. 536 and 540); later at Hampton Court (619), St. James's, Kensington and Marlborough House.

Literature: Law, 1881, 1898 (518).

The attribution to Vanloo has survived until the present day, but in quality and mood the portrait is quite different from Vanloo's official portrait of the Prince. On stylistic grounds it can be attributed with some confidence to Highmore and was probably painted *c.* 1740–50. In the obituary notice of Highmore in *The Gentleman's Magazine*, vol. L (1780), p. 177, it is stated that 'In 1742 he had the honour to paint the late

Prince and Princess of Wales, for the Duke of Saxe-Gotha [presumably on the occasion of his visit to London (see no. 534)]; as he did, some years after, the late Queen of Denmark for that court'. A half-length version is at Celle.

Marcellus Laroon the Younger

1679–1772. Painter of French origin, who travelled as a young man in Italy, France and Holland, was an amateur musician and actor and served in the army in the War of the Spanish Succession and in Scotland in 1715. He was a prolific painter and draughtsman of conversation and fancy pieces.

520. A DINNER PARTY (*Plate* 182)

Kensington Palace. 36 × 33⅞ in., 91,4 × 86 cm.

An elegant company has reached a late stage of a dinner-party and the host, a Knight of the Garter, is pouring out wine at a table on which fruit has been set; the company is attended by servants, a clergyman and a flautist.

Possibly given to George I (see below), but not recorded in the inventories of the royal collection before 1818, when it was at Kensington (505): *An Entertainment containing a Number of Portraits of distinguished persons. M. Laroon*; later at Hampton Court (606).

Literature: Law, 1881, 1898 (812, as by Vanderbank) and *Kensington* (1903), p. 84; R. Edwards, 'The Conversation Pictures of Marcellus Laroon', *Apollo*, vol. XXII (1935), p. 196; R. Raines, 'Marcellus Laroon the Younger – 1', *Connoisseur*, vol. CXL (1957), pp. 241–5, part II, *ibid.*, *Year Book* (1959), pp. 114–5.

The identification of the sitters and the background are, as is usual with Laroon's conversation pieces, obscure. The former identification of the host with Frederick, Prince of Wales (*e.g.*, by Law, *op. cit.*), is clearly impossible, and an earlier suggestion (Faulkner, p. 402) that the scene is a fête in honour of the marriage of the Duke of Wharton is untenable because the Duke did not receive the Garter. The decoration of the interior is however very reminiscent of no. 521 and of *The Levée* at Southill (*Fig.* 51); certain heads or types seem common to all three, and it is possible that the host and hostess, who are very like the principal figures in the other two compositions, are the Duke and Duchess of Montagu. Stylistically the composition seems slightly earlier. The problem is further bedevilled by a drawing (*Fig.* 52) which is closely associated with no. 520. This is signed and dated: *M Laroon* [erasure], / *1719*, but is inscribed in ink, possibly by Laroon and clearly later: *Premiere Pensée* and: *presented to King george 1st* / *a picture I painted in 1725*. If the *Premiere Pensée* really took place in 1719 and the picture was not painted until 1725, there is perhaps additional proof that Laroon did make up such pictures from older material and that, for instance, no. 521 and *The Levée* were based on slightly earlier drawings. If no. 520 should really be dated *c.* 1719–25 there is a much greater probability that the Montagus are represented. But the drawing, with its substantial differences in the background, prove that the backgrounds designed by Laroon cannot safely be regarded as accurate representations of any actual interior.

521. A MUSICAL TEA-PARTY (*Plate* 183)

Kensington Palace. 36 × 28 in., 91,4 × 71,1 cm.

Signed and dated: *Mar. Laroon. F . 1740.*

A company is assembled in a spacious interior in which hangs a large equestrian portrait; a lady is dispensing tea while two musicians perform on the harpsichord and violin: one of the books of music on the floor seems to have Corelli's name upon it.

Presented to the royal collection by Mr. Humphry Ward; recorded at Kensington Palace in 1903 (E. Law, *Kensington Palace* (1903), p. 85), and later at Kew (Law, *Kew Palace* (1924), p. 23).

Literature: R. Edwards, 'The Conversation Pictures of Marcellus Laroon', *Apollo*, vol. XXII (1935), pp. 193–8; R. Raines, 'Marcellus Laroon the Younger – 1', *Connoisseur*, vol. CXL (1957), pp. 241–5, part II, *ibid.*, *Year Book* (1959), p. 116.

The confusions that surround no. 521 are typical of the unresolved problems posed by Laroon's politer conversation pieces. It was formerly described as 'A Royal Assembly in Kew Palace', but this is extremely unlikely. The composition should perhaps be regarded as a pendant to *The Levée* at Southill: the sizes of the two canvases are identical and in the latter the scene revolves round the male counterpart of the hostess in no. 521. A number of Laroon's conversation-pieces have been associated with Montagu House on the strength of a later inscription by Walpole on a drawing in the British Museum. The backgrounds in no. 521 and *The Levée* are closely alike and the interiors are fitted up with canvases very reminiscent of the French painters employed by the 1st Duke of Montagu at Montagu House. The Knight of the Garter in *The Levée* and the hostess in no. 521 resemble, moreover, John, 2nd Duke of Montagu (1690–1749), and his wife (1689–1751), but at an earlier period. The Duke, who held a number of important offices in the Household and was made a Knight of the Garter in 1718, had married Mary, youngest daughter of the Duke of Marlborough, in 1705. It has been suggested that the equestrian portrait in the background of no. 521 is a portrait of the Duchess's father (see O. Millar in *Southill: A Regency House* (1951), p. 47), but it may equally be George II. The background in both pictures, and possibly the two principals, are very close to those in no. 520. It is probable that Laroon concocted his conversation-pieces of this type from material collected over a number of years (the costumes in no. 521 and *The Levée* seem old-fashioned for 1740) and that too much should not be read into the apparently very carefully defined backgrounds and portraits, none of which, incidentally, have so far been convincingly identified.

Philippe Mercier

1689–1760. Painter of portraits and conversation and fancy pieces; of French Huguenot birth, he was probably born in Berlin and studied there under Pesne; also studied in Italy and France; came to England, with a very Frenchified style, *c.* 1725. In 1728–9 Mercier was appointed Painter, Page of the Bedchamber and Librarian to Frederick, Prince of Wales, of whom he may have painted a portrait *c.* 1711. His first important works for the Prince may have been the full-lengths (1728), now in the Town Hall at Hertford, of the Prince and of Princesses Anne, Amelia and Caroline, and they may have brought about his appointment as the Prince's Painter. The Prince's accounts contain payments to Mercier, 1732–5, for pictures, but there is no evidence that they were all from his brush. He is stated later (*c.* 1736?) to have quarrelled with the Prince and left his service: his last payment as Librarian seems to have been in the year ending May 1738 (D. of Cornwall MSS., vols. I–VII). Thereafter he worked mainly in Yorkshire, Scotland and Portugal. Queen Caroline's accounts for 1731–3 include £84 paid to Mercier for a picture (W. R. A., Geo. 54022).

522. 'THE MUSIC PARTY': FREDERICK, PRINCE OF WALES, WITH HIS THREE ELDEST SISTERS (*Plate* 184)

Windsor Castle (437). 31¼ × 22¾ in., 79,4 × 57,8 cm.

The Prince, wearing the ribbon and star of the Garter, is assiduously playing the violoncello while Anne, Princess Royal, is seated at the harpsichord, Princess Caroline plucks the mandora and Princess Amelia listens with a copy of Milton in her lap.

Possibly painted for the Prince or for another member of his family; recorded in store in the 'Pall Mall Apartm^{ts}' in 1767: ... *a picture of His Late Royal Highness Prince of Wales, & 3 Sisters in a Concerto* ... (D. of Cornwall MSS., vol. LIV (1)); at Kensington in 1818 (281: ... *Prince Frederick playing on the Violincello ... Nollekins*), but removed to the Corridor at Windsor in April 1829.

Literature: Collins Baker, *Windsor*, p. 236; R. Edwards, 'Mercier's Music Party', *Burl. Mag.*, vol. XC (1948), pp. 308–12, 359.

Probably painted in 1733. A variant in the National Portrait Gallery (1556) is signed and dated 1733 and shows (*Fig.* 53) the group in a landscape with the Dutch House at Kew in the background. No. 522 is certainly by Mercier himself and may be the first (as it is the better preserved) version of a design which is reminiscent of the central group in a drawing by Mercier in the British Museum (see R. Edwards, *op. cit.*, *Fig.* 4). The appearance of harmony in the group is deceptive as the Prince was at this time on notoriously bad terms with his sisters and, incidentally, divided from his eldest sister in the musical controversies of the day. He had begun to learn the 'cello in 1733 and was passionately devoted to it; during the summer of 1734 he was continuously to be seen at Kensington 'with his violoncello between his legs, singing French and Italian songs to his own playing for an hour or two together, while his audience was composed of all the underling servants and rabble of the Palace'. In no. 522 the Prince appears to be playing a solo accompanied by his eldest sister. The setting of the concert in no. 522 is the Banqueting House at Hampton Court, with a view of the Palace through the window[1]. The gilt mirrors are still at Hampton Court and are probably among those made for the Prince by Benjamin Goodison in 1733, and the picture appears to be one of the set of allegorical figures painted for the Crown (?) by Giovanni Antonio Pellegrini and still at Hampton Court (440). Drawings by Thomas Worlidge after the heads of the Prince and the Princess Royal, with variations, are in the Royal Library (A. P. Oppé, *English Drawings ... at Windsor Castle* (1950), 694–5).

523. PORTRAIT OF A CHILD

Buckingham Palace. 35¾×27½ in., 90,8×69,9 cm.

Full-length, seated naked in a landscape, resting his right hand on the head of a lamb.

Recorded at Buckingham Palace (1061) in 1876 (*V.R. inv.*).

The identity and authorship of no. 523 seem to have been lost. Presumably on the basis of its resemblance to (and possibly its derivation from) no. 246 it was described as a portrait by Lely of Princess Isabella; this was later amended to her brother James, Duke of Cambridge (see no. 287). No. 523 is, however, unquestionably by Mercier, and is thus possibly one of the children of Frederick, Prince of Wales. In 1876 (*V. R. inv.*) it was reduced to its present, and probably original, size from c. 38½×42½ in.; an addition on the right had included a dog. It may be a portrait of Henry Frederick, Duke of Cumberland. At Kensington in 1818 no. 492 was *Portrait of the Duke of Cumberland when a Child*: the measurements were given as 40×38¾ in., but it is possible that they were given in the wrong order. This picture was taken to Hampton Court on 22 December 1835. No. 523,

[1] Identified by Mr. Croft-Murray in 1962.

on the basis of comparison with portraits of Prince Henry Frederick by Knapton (no. 574) and Liotard (no. 585), could be a portrait of the Prince, painted c. 1747–8. In pose, indeed, no. 523 is connected with the figure of the Prince in no. 574.

Attributed to Philippe Mercier

524. COMEDIANS BY A FOUNTAIN (*Plate* 194)

Windsor Castle (1130). 28×36¼ in., 71,1×92,1 cm.

A group of figures, perhaps from the Italian Comedy, sitting by a stream beneath a garden pavilion and beside an elaborately sculptured fountain.

Apparently first recorded at Kensington in 1818 (452; *Figures at a Fountain after Watteau*); later at Hampton Court.

The canvas is almost certainly by Mercier and was probably painted in England c. 1735.

After Philippe Mercier

525. FREDERICK, PRINCE OF WALES

Kew (Hampton Court no. 893). 30×25¼ in., 76,2×64,1 cm.

Half-length in a richly embroidered coat, wearing the ribbon and star of the Garter.

Probably acquired by George IV; recorded at Carlton House in 1816 (349: *A head of a young nobleman, with a star and blue ribbon;* the 1816 label was recorded (*V.R. inv.*) on the back in 1860). Later at Hampton Court and Kensington and formerly attributed to Vanderbank and Vanloo.

Literature: Law, 1881, 1898 (826).

Apparently a contemporary copy of the portrait engraved by J. Simon as by: *P. Mercier serenissimi Walliæ Principis Pictor & Biblithecarius Pinx An° 1734;* this is a reworked state of his engraving after Mercier of 1730. The original is perhaps the version in the possession of Lord Brownlow, stated to have been given by the sitter to Lord Tyrconnel (Walker Art Gallery, Liverpool, *Kings and Queens of England*, 1953 (33)), one of Mercier's earliest English patrons. A variant, signed and dated (1735?), is at Pollok House. A small copy is in the Scottish National Portrait Gallery (964).

Jacopo Amigoni

1682–1752. Decorative and portrait painter, born in Naples, worked in Venice and at the Bavarian court and in England, 1730–39, where he painted portraits and decorative schemes. Thereafter was in Venice until he was summoned to the court of Ferdinand VI of Spain in Madrid, where he died. He painted portraits of the Duke of Cumberland, Queen Caroline and her daughters and is stated by Vertue (*Notebooks*, vol. III, p. 93) to have finished for the Duke of Dorset a group of the Queen with three of her daughters which had been left unfinished by Kneller at his death.

526 FREDERICK, PRINCE OF WALES (*Plate* 198)

Buckingham Palace. 50½×41⅞ in., 128,3×106,4 cm.

Three-quarter-length, seated at a table wearing a breastplate and the Garter ribbon, holding in his right hand a book inscribed *Pope's Homer* and pointing with his left to two flying putti: one wears a wreath and holds a lyre, the other holds the snake of Wisdom and they are probably intended to represent the Arts and Sciences.

Apparently painted for George Bubb Dodington, later Lord Melcombe (see below); probably acquired by George IV; recorded at Carlton House in 1816 (319: *A half length of a nobleman, with two genii, one holding a lyre. Amiconi*); later at Windsor (48).

Literature: R. A., *English Taste in the Eighteenth Century*, 1955–6 (65); J. Woodward, 'Amigoni as Portrait Painter in England', *Burl. Mag.*, vol. XCIX (1957), pp. 21–3.

On 31 March 1736 Amigoni was paid for three portraits of the Prince that he had painted in 1735: for two full-lengths, for the Prince's mistress Anne Vane (now at Raby Castle) and the Duke of Dorset (now at Easton Neston), and for a smaller portrait *for Sgr Doddington*, for which he received £42 (D. of Cornwall MSS., vol. VI (i), f. 315). The head in no. 526 seems unquestionably *ad vivum* and thus to have served for the much more elaborate portrait at Raby (*Fig.* 48); the Duke of Dorset's portrait was of a different design. The Prince was an admirer of Pope, whose translation of the *Iliad* had appeared in 1715–20 and of the *Odyssey* in 1725–6, and in 1735 he paid Scheemakers for some small marble busts for the poet.

527. ANNE, PRINCESS ROYAL AND PRINCESS OF ORANGE (*Plate* 186)

Windsor Castle (3058). 88¾×59¾ in., 225,4×151,8 cm.

Full-length standing, wearing an ermine-lined robe, resting her left hand on a table beside her coronet; behind her fly two putti carrying hymeneal torches, a sprig of orange blossom and a wreath of roses.

Painted, probably in 1734 and at the Queen's charge, for Philip Yorke, 1st Earl of Hardwicke (see below); formerly at Wimpole and sold by the 9th Earl of Hardwicke (bt. Leggatt's); later with Major J. C. G. Dance; purchased from Leggatt's by Her Majesty the Queen for the royal collection in 1954.

Literature: J. Woodward, 'Amigoni as Portrait Painter in England', *Burl. Mag.*, vol. XCIX (1957), pp. 22–3.

The Declared Accounts of the Treasurer of the Chamber for 1735 include a payment to Amigoni for two portraits of the Queen and *a picture of Her Royal Highness the Princess of Orange for Lord Hardwick* (P. R. O., A.O.I. 415, vol. 169). The attributes held by the two putti, and their fusing of the flames of their torches, are clear allusions to the Princess's marriage, on 14 March 1734, to William IV, Prince of Orange. Amigoni also painted at this period a three-quarter-length portrait of the Princess Royal and companion portraits of her sisters Amelia and Caroline; the last is at Ickworth. A copy of no. 527, probably given to the Duke of Kent, is at Wrest Park.

528. BOYS PLAYING WITH A LAMB

Hampton Court (629). 44¼×49¼ in., 112,4×125,1 cm.

Three naked boys putting a wreath round the neck of a lamb while a putto plays on a pipe.

Recorded at St. James's in 1819 (1065) without an attribution; later at Hampton Court, Kensington, St. James's and Marlborough House.

Literature: Law, 1881, 1898 (488).

Nos. 528 and 529 may have been painted (*c.* 1735) for Frederick, Prince of Wales, during Amigoni's residence in London, possibly as part of the decoration of an interior.

529. BOYS PLAYING WITH A GOAT

Hampton Court (711). 44⅛×45¾ in., 112,1×116,2 cm.

Four naked boys playing with a goat and a cornucopia.

Recorded at Kensington in 1818 (75) as by Amigoni; later at Hampton Court, Kensington, St. James's and Marlborough House.

Literature: Law, 1881, 1898 (471).

See no. 528.

John Ellis or Ellys

1701–57. Portrait and genre painter, a pupil of Thornhill; copied pictures in the royal collection and was connected with Vanderbank's tapestry manufacture. He advised Sir Robert Walpole over the formation of his collection and in 1739, as a mark of Walpole's favour, was appointed Master Keeper of the Lions in the Tower. In 1737, presumably in succession to Mercier, he is recorded (*Magnae Britanniae Notitia*, p. 251) as Principal Painter to the Prince, a post he probably held until the Prince's death. On 10 September 1733 he had been paid £160. 9s. 3d. for miscellaneous tasks, presumably at Kew, for the Prince (D. of Cornwall MSS., vol. III, f. 247). His bill for work done for the Prince, 1733–8 (see no. 530), includes lining, stretching and enlarging a Van Dyck to fit over the chimney of the Great Room at Kew; two life-size pastoral figures at each end of the Gallery at Kew; a tea-table and two stands enamelled and painted with pastoral figures, fruit and flowers; a head of George I; a shepherd and shepherdess over the chimney in the Gallery at Kew; he was also involved in the design of tapestry for the Gallery at Kew. His work there is mentioned by Sir William Chambers (*Plans, Elevations . . . at Kew* (1763), p. 2).

Attributed to John Ellys or Ellis

530. FREDERICK, PRINCE OF WALES. *Identity uncertain.*

Windsor Castle (2954). 24¾×18 in., 62,9×45,7 cm.

Signed (obscurely): *J. E P*

Full-length, standing in a landscape and wearing a breast-plate and the ribbon of the Garter.

Sold in the Carrington Heirlooms at Christie's, 9 May 1930 (19), as a portrait of a gentleman by Devis and bought by Her Majesty Queen Mary.

Literature: Collins Baker, *Windsor*, p. 241 (as by Morier and of George III).

It is tempting to associate no. 530 with a payment (1 October 1744) to *Mr John Ellis, Limner* for work done for the Prince of Wales from 1733 to 1738 which included *a small whole length of his Royall Highness in Her Royall Highness Cabinet at Durdans* (D. of Cornwall MSS., vol. XIII, f. 109). The features of the sitter, however, are not entirely convincing as those of the Prince and it is possible that no. 530 is a portrait of William Augustus, Duke of Cumberland.

Charles Philips

1708–47. Painter of portraits and conversation pieces; Vertue stated (*Notebooks*, vol. III, p. 54) that 'in painting small figures portraits & conversations [he] has met with great encouragement amongst People of fashion – even some of ye Royal Family.'

531. FREDERICK, PRINCE OF WALES

Windsor Castle (3072). 94¾×59¼ in., 240,7×150,5 cm.

Full-length, standing in Garter robes with his left hand on his sword, beside a table on which rests the plumed hat of the Order.

Sold with its companion (no. 532) at Christie's, 4 December 1931 (25), and purchased for the royal collection by Her Majesty Queen Mary.

Presumably painted with no. 532 in 1737. Philips may have repeated the design of no. 531 for the full-length of the Prince which he painted in 1739, for which he was paid £25. 4s. on 29 June 1743, and which was despatched at the Prince's order to Lady Irwin (D. of Cornwall MSS., vol. XII, f. 556). The portraits were clearly popular designs: a pair on a smaller scale, stated to be signed and dated 1736, were sold at Christie's, 25 February 1924 (130), and a signed pair at three-quarter-length was sold at Sotheby's, 31 January 1924 (96, 97).

532. AUGUSTA, PRINCESS OF WALES

Windsor Castle (3073). 94¾×59 in., 240,7×150 cm.

Signed and dated: *CPhilips* (initials in monogram). *1737*.

Full-length, standing in robes of state (?) and wearing her coronet, in front of a chair elaborately carved and decorated with the Prince of Wales's feathers.

See no. 531.

See no. 531; no. 532 is very much coarser in quality than the companion piece. The design was engraved, at three-quarter-length, by John Faber the younger as *Chas Philips ad Vivum pinxt 1737*. The female portrait in the three-quarter-length pair sold at Sotheby's on 31 January 1924 is now in the National Portrait Gallery (2093). It shows slight variations from no. 532. The head in no. 532 is very close to the elaborate full-length at Warwick Castle, signed and dated 1737, in which the Princess nurses her eldest daughter Augusta, born 31 October 1737.

533. FREDERICK, PRINCE OF WALES, WITH THE KNIGHTS OF THE ROUND TABLE
(Plate 207)

Kew (Hampton Court no. 1373). 50⅜×40¼ in., 128×102,2 cm.

Signed and dated: *CPhilips. pinxit 1732*.

The club is meeting in a room at Kew House decorated with motives illustrating the chase; over the fireplace, in a frame decorated with the Prince of Wales's feathers, is Philippe Mercier's portrait of Anne, Princess Royal, in the hunting livery, and in the corner are a wine-cooler and empty bottles. The Prince is seated at a round table with eighteen companions drinking wine or punch. They all wear boots and spurs with the hunting livery (see no. 555): dark blue coats with gold lace, scarlet cuffs and scarlet waistcoats trimmed with gold. The gentleman on the Prince's right wears an off-white waistcoat. Apart from the Prince, two other members appear to be Knights of the Garter; the member handing him a glass, while the queue of his wig is being pulled by the member on his right, appears to be wearing the ribbon of the Thistle; and three members wear the ribbon of the Bath. In the foreground a member seems to have upset his chair and glass; the word *Interruption* is inscribed below him and while one member grips him by the arm another holds before him a paper inscribed *Orders and Constitution*.

Probably acquired by George IV; recorded at Carlton House in 1816 (283: *The late Prince of Wales, with the members of 'La Table*

Ronde'. Wootton: remains of the 1816 label are on the back); moved to the Corridor at Windsor (369) on 6 August 1828.

Literature: Windsor (1922), p. 128.

On 7 September 1732 order was given for payment on behalf of the Prince of £113. 8s. *to Mr Charles Philipps for a Picture and Gold Frame for our Use* (D. of Cornwall MSS., vol. II), which possibly refers to no. 533. The portrait in the background was seen by Walpole at Kew in September 1761: 'In the long blue room, Anne Princess Royal in the hunting livery, view of Windsor behind her, by Mercier' (*Visits*, p. 38); the portrait is only known through Simon's mezzotint (Chaloner Smith, p. 1066). No. 533 thus provides a very valuable illustration of the appearance of one of the new interiors designed and decorated for the Prince of Wales by William Kent at Kew House just before this picture was painted.

The identity of the members of the 'Round Table' has not been established. The Knight of the Bath on the Prince's left, holding a glass, is almost certainly the 3rd Earl of Cholmondeley (see no. 555). The Knight of the Garter on the Prince's right may be Charles Lennox, 2nd Duke of Richmond (1701–50), created K.G. in 1726, Lord of the Bedchamber to George I and II (1726–35) and Master of the Horse, 1735–50.

534. JOHANN ADOLF, DUKE OF SAXE-GOTHA (1721–99)

Buckingham Palace. 50⅜×40 in., 128×101,6 cm.

Signed and dated: *CPhilips pinxt 1742* (initials in monogram). On the back there is an early inscription identifying the sitter.

Three-quarter-length, standing in armour, resting his right hand on a helmet and his left on his sword.

Possibly acquired by Queen Victoria.

Presumably painted when the Duke was in England. A second portrait of the Duke by Philips, probably painted on the same occasion, is only known from Thomas Burford's engraving (Chaloner Smith, p. 130).

Youngest son of Frederick II, Duke of Saxe-Gotha, and brother of Augusta, Princess of Wales. See no. 519.

Attributed to Charles Philips

535. THE 'HENRY THE FIFTH' CLUB OR 'THE GANG'

Kew (Hampton Court no. 1459). 28½×35¾ in., 72,4×90,8 cm.

The club is meeting in a room with a bust of Henry V over the fireplace.[1] The names of the sitters are listed in Jutsham's note of receipt (see below). Dilkes stands by a table at which are seated (from the left): Sir Hugh Smithson, Mr. Howe, Bellingham Boyle (?) in front of the table, Lord Middleton on the other side of the table and Lord Inchiquin resting his right hand on an embroidered purse or bag (?); Frederick, Prince of Wales, looks into the room on the right. All the figures wear a little gold badge suspended on a ribbon, except Boyle (?) who holds a badge in his hand. Lord Inchiquin wears the ribbon and star of the Bath.

Perhaps presented to George IV by General Dilkes, who was presumably the son of the Dilkes in the painting: on 21 May 1813 there

1. The bust is reminiscent of the type designed by Rysbrack, of which the original terracotta was formerly in the royal collection.

was received at Carlton House from General Dilkes *A Painting . . . Consisting of Seven Portraits – as follows Viz Frederick Prince of Wales Established a Club – Called the Gang or Harry The Fifth's Club – the members of which were Call'd Fallstaffs Points – Bardolph &c* (Jutsham, *R/D.*, f. 255); recorded in store at Carlton House in 1816 (293: . . . *the members of Henry V's club. Wootton;* the 1816 label is still on the back; moved to the New Gallery at Windsor on 24 July 1828.

Literature: Windsor (1922), p. 128.

Probably painted *c.* 1730–5, perhaps for Dilkes. The canvas is rubbed and, perhaps as a result, the texture seems slightly softer and less tight than is usual with Philips. The attribution to him should be accepted with reserve, and the quality is perhaps closer to Gawen Hamilton (1698–1737).

Sir Hugh Smithson (1714/15–86), 4th Bart. and later Earl (1750) and Duke of Northumberland, was Lord of the Bedchamber to George II and III, 1753–63; Bellingham Boyle (*d.* 1771) was one of the Commissioners of Revenue; Francis Willoughby, 2nd Baron Middleton (1692–1758), was M.P. for Nottingham and later for Tamworth; William O'Brien, 4th Earl of Inchiquin (*d.* 1777), was created K.B. in 1725 and was Gentleman of the Bedchamber to the Prince of Wales, 1744–51; General Michael Obrian Dilkes (*d.* 1775) was Colonel of the 50th Regiment of Foot and Governor of the Royal Hospital near Dublin.

Jean-Baptiste Vanloo

1684–1745. Born in Aix of a family of French painters of Flemish origin, and worked in Provence, Piedmont, Rome and Paris. He arrived in London in December 1737 with a considerable reputation as a court artist and portrait painter, and was an immediate success; by his 'puffing he monopolised', in the words of Hogarth, 'all the people of fashion in the kingdom', and within a few months he had painted Frederick, Prince of Wales, the Princess of Wales and Princess Amelia. He left London in October 1742, apparently owing to ill-health and the death of his son Charles.

536. FREDERICK, PRINCE OF WALES (*Plate* 187)

Buckingham Palace. 94½ × 61½ in., 240 × 156,2 cm.; *c.* 1½ in. are turned over on the left.

Signed and dated: *J. B. Vanloo. pinxit | 1742.*

Full-length, standing in robes of state beside a table on which is his coronet, and wearing the collar and star of the Garter.

On 28 July 1809 (£52. 10s. was paid on behalf of the Prince of Wales to R. Oliver (of 1 Marylebone High Street) for *Two whole Lengths of . . . The Late Prince and Princess of Wales – Gilt Frames – by Vanloo 1742*, which had been received at Carlton House on 17 June (W. R. A., Geo. 26873; Jutsham, *R/D*, f. 97); on 29 July they were *sent to Windsor to His Majesty* (*ibid.*, f. 38), and they were apparently still there in November 1826 when two frames were sent down for a pair of full-length portraits of the Prince and his wife . . . *at Windsor Castle. To be placed in the State Apartments in Store – by His Majesty's Command* (Jutsham, *D*, f. 86). The portraits were apparently sent to Hampton Court in 1832, but were later placed in the series of royal family portraits in the State Dining Room at Buckingham Palace (*Buckingham Palace*, 1841, p. 99; later inv. nos. 192, and, for no. 537, 196).

Vertue records (*Notebooks*, vol. III, p. 110) Vanloo's departure from London on 16 October 1742: 'this last year having not begun any new works only imployd his time to finish those begun. particularly the Prince of Wales & princess done for Poultney, Earl of Bath – at whole, in their robes. finely drest'. The portraits for William Pulteney, Earl

of Bath (1684–1764), may have been painted at the Prince's expense: on 5 October 1742 Vanloo was paid sixty guineas each for *Two Portraitures of His Royal Highness and One of Her Royal Highness whole Lengths* and £21 as *a Bounty from His Royal Highness towards the Expences of his Voyage on his leaving England* (D. of Cornwall MSS., vol. XII, f. 511). The second portrait of the Prince may have been no. 540; and nos. 536 and 537 are perhaps the pair painted for Lord Bath, whose ultimate heiress died in 1808. On 29 April 1736 Lord Bath had moved the congratulatory address in the House of Commons on the Prince's marriage and he was one of the Prince's supporters. The portraits were engraved by Bernard Baron, that of the Prince in 1753. For Baron's drawings see no. 537. Copies of the pair are at Goodwood and, of the heads and shoulders, at Cliveden. See also nos. 540 and 541.

537. AUGUSTA, PRINCESS OF WALES (*Plate* 188)

Buckingham Palace. 94½ × 62 in., 240 × 157,5 cm.

Signed and dated: *J. B. Vanloo. Pinxit | .1742.*

Full-length standing in a richly laced dress under robes of state, holding a sprig of roses in her right hand, beside a table on which is her coronet and gloves. She has on her corsage the magnificent jewels that she is wearing in no. 538.

See the companion portrait, no. 536. There is a *pentimento* in the fold of ermine on the floor, which originally spread slightly further across the floor. Bernard Baron's engraving of no. 537 is dated 1756; his drawings for the engravings of both portraits are probably the drawings in the Royal Library (A. P. Oppé, *English Drawings . . . at Windsor Castle* (1950), 38, 39), which are stated to have been presented, probably to Princess Augusta, by the engraver in 1756 and to have been drawn from the originals in the possession of the Earl of Bath.

538. AUGUSTA, PRINCESS OF WALES, WITH MEMBERS OF HER FAMILY AND HOUSEHOLD (*Plate* 191)

St. James's Palace. 87¾ × 79 in., 220,3 × 200,7 cm.

Signed and dated: *J. B. Vanloo . . . 173[9?].*

The Princess, seated in an ermine-lined robe, holds Princess Augusta by her knee; behind her on a table is seated Prince George, whose hat is held by Mrs. Herbert and who is supported by Lady Archibald Hamilton, who also carries the infant Prince Edward; Lord Boston stands on the right, wearing his key of office as the Princess's Vice-Chamberlain.

Probably painted for the Princess; seen by Walpole in her Dressing Room at Kew in September 1761: 'Another large piece of the Princess & her younger children, her Chamberlain . . .' (*Visits*, p. 39); taken in 1860 to Buckingham Palace (554).

Stated in the inventory of George III's pictures at Kew House to have been painted in 1739. Prince Edward had been born on 14 March of that year. No. 538 was perhaps the first picture painted by Vanloo for the Princess and her husband, who in March 1738 had paid a visit to his studio and 'staid there to see him paint with great satisfaction' (Vertue, *Notebooks*, vol. III, p. 82).

Sir William Irby (1707–75), later (1761) created Lord Boston, had been Page of Honour to George I and George II and Equerry to the Prince of Wales; he was Vice-Chamberlain (1736–51) and Lord Chamberlain (1751–72) to the Princess. Mrs. Herbert was probably the Hon. Arabella Herbert (*d.* 1755), daughter of Francis Herbert, sister to the 1st Earl of Powis and Woman of the Bedchamber to the

Princess; she was appointed (1738) Governess to Princess Augusta and had the care of the royal children. Lady Archibald Hamilton (d. 1752; see also nos. 549 and 550) was Jane, daughter of the 6th Earl of Abercorn, and married Lord Archibald Hamilton, son of the 3rd Duke of Hamilton; she was appointed (1736) Keeper of the Privy Purse, Lady of the Bedchamber and Mistress of the Robes to the Princess.

Attributed to Jean-Baptiste Vanloo

539. PRINCESS AMELIA

Buckingham Palace. 50×40 in., 127×99,1 cm.; the canvas has been made out at the top at a later date to fit its present frame.

Inscribed later: PRINCESS AMELIA.

Three-quarter-length, standing in a richly jewelled dress under a royal robe of state, wearing a delicate jewelled ornament in her hair and pointing with her left hand to her coronet.

Probably the picture presented to George IV by the Rev. Frederick William Blomberg in 1809: on 4 July 1809 Jutsham (*R/D*, f. 99) received at Carlton House from *Revᵈ Bloomburg . . . Portrait of Her Royal Highnes The Princess Amelia – not any Frame*); recorded in store at Carlton House in 1816 (317: *A half length of the Princess Amelia, aunt to his Majesty*; the 1816 label is still on the back); later at Buckingham Palace (642).

Literature: Buckingham Palace, 1909, p. 7.

Formerly attributed to Hudson, whose name is given as the painter in an early inscription on the back identifying the sitter. It does not seem, however, to be by Hudson, but is very close in quality to Vanloo. Vertue, moreover (*Notebooks*, vol. III, p. 84), recorded in 1738 Vanloo's early success in London and mentioned Princess Amelia among his first royal patrons. No. 539 could well be the portrait painted of the Princess, apparently in the first six months of 1738. A version belongs to the Trustees of the Earl of Chichester.

After Jean-Baptiste Vanloo

540. FREDERICK, PRINCE OF WALES

Marlborough House. 94½×57½ in., 240×146,1 cm.

Probably acquired by George IV; recorded in store at Carlton House in 1816 (236), attributed to Ramsay; the 1816 label on the back was noted by Redgrave in 1872 (*V.R. inv.*); later at Windsor (1520).

Literature: Collins Baker, *Windsor*, p. 296.

A contemporary copy of no. 536. It is possible that it is the second portrait of the Prince for which Vanloo was paid on 5 October 1742 (see no. 536) and which would presumably have been executed in his studio.

541. FREDERICK, PRINCE OF WALES

Windsor Castle (276). 36⅛×28⅜ in., 91,8×72,1 cm.; the canvas has been enlarged all round and was originally *c.* 29¼×24 in.

Recorded at Windsor in 1878 (*V.R. inv.*).

A copy of the head and shoulders from the design of which no. 536 is the original. It is possible that no. 541 was cut down from a copy of the whole composition.

542. ROBERT WALPOLE, FIRST EARL OF ORFORD (1676–1745)

Kensington Palace. 55¾×44¾ in., 141,6×113,7 cm.

Three-quarter-length seated, wearing the robes, and holding the Great Seal, as First Lord of the Treasury and Chancellor of the Exchequer, and wearing the insignia of the Garter.

Presented to the royal collection at Hampton Court (620) by W. E. Fanquier (*The Stranger's Guide* (1849), p. 46); later at St. James's.

Literature: Law, 1881, 1898 (357).

A contemporary copy of a standard portrait of Walpole; a version is in the Shire Hall at Warwick and another (head and shoulders) was at Christie's, 12 July 1940 (823). A standing variant, engraved by Faber with the date 1741, was probably based on the same sitting: versions are at Lambeth Palace, the National Portrait Gallery (70) and formerly in the Hanbury-Williams collection. According to Dézallier d'Argenville (*Abrégé de la Vie des plus fameux Peintres . . .* (Paris, 1762), vol. IV, p. 394), Vanloo's portrait of 'M. de Walpool' contributed greatly to the artist's success in London. There are indications in Vertue's *Notebooks* (vol. III, pp. 84, 97, 109) that Vanloo produced at least two portrait types of Walpole.

The great Whig leader, prominent in the counsels of the party from the early years of the reign of Queen Anne, Prime Minister and Chancellor of the Exchequer in the reigns of George I and II, a friend of Queen Caroline and a lavish builder and collector of pictures.

Thomas Frye

1710–62. Portrait painter, engraver and miniaturist; born in Ireland, he came to London in the 1750's. His career as a portrait painter was interrupted in 1744, when he undertook the formation and management of the Bow porcelain factory.

543. FREDERICK, PRINCE OF WALES (*Plate* 181)

Windsor Castle (3046). 44×49¾ in., 111,8×126,4 cm.

Half-length, wearing the ribbon and star of the Garter and looking over a balcony between two columns; the Prince of Wales's feathers appear on the wall behind.

Formerly in the collection of Mark Fawdry, Haining Castle, Selkirkshire, and sold at Sotheby's, 13 February 1946 (36; as by Allan Ramsay), when it was bought by His Majesty King George VI for the royal collection.

The head appears to be identical with that in the full-length portrait of the Prince, painted for the Guild of Saddlers and in their Hall until its destruction in 1940. The Prince and his wife had visited the Hall on 29 October 1736 and on 18 November the Prince stated that he would 'permit them to have his picture' (J. W. Sherwell, *The History of the Guild of Saddlers*, 3rd edn. (1956), revised by K. S. Laurie, pp. 93–4); Frye's own mezzotint of the portrait is inscribed *. . . painted & scrap't by Thoˢ Frye 1741.* No. 543 seems to have been painted *ad vivum*; the column on the right may have been an afterthought as there are traces of the concealed parts of the Prince's left arm.

John Wootton

1686?–1764. Painter of landscapes and of military and sporting pieces. Vertue records a visit by Queen Caroline in the summer of 1732 to Wootton's studio in Cavendish Square, where she saw the large equestrian portrait of George II (now at Blickling) on which Wootton was working with Jervas and 'some horses belonging to the Prince & Ld Malpas lately painted by Mr Wotton' (*Notebooks*, vol. III, p. 62); it may have been through Lord Malpas, later 3rd Earl of Cholmondeley (see no. 555), that Frederick, Prince of Wales, began to employ Wootton. The Prince and his wife were reported in March 1738 to have visited Wootton's studio (*ibid.*, p. 82). Wootton was paid £26. 5*s.* on 1 December 1748 *For Pictures clean'd, lin'd, and mended, att Leicester House for his Royall Highness the Prince of Wales by John Wootton* (D. of Cornwall MSS., vol. XVII, f. 538). Among pictures by Wootton in his sale, 12, 13 March 1761, were: 1st day (lot 9) *Two Views of* Windsor Castle *and a Stag Hunting;* (lot 62) *His late Majesty on Horseback;* (lot 70) *A Land Storm, and a View of* Windsor; 2nd day (lot 44) *The Duke of* Cumberland *on Horseback, and another;* and (lot 59) *A small whole Length of his late Majesty.*

544. WILLIAM AUGUSTUS, DUKE OF CUMBERLAND

Windsor Castle (3081). 18¾ × 16¾ in., 47,6 × 425,5 cm.

The Duke, on horseback, wearing the ribbon and star of the Garter with the frock uniform of the 1st Guards, accompanied by two officers of the same regiment (?).

Purchased by Her Majesty The Queen from Agnew's in 1959; formerly attributed to Reynolds.

A sketch, probably painted *c.* 1745 (see no. 554) and possibly connected with the Dettingen or Culloden campaigns.

545. THE DEATH OF THE STAG (*Plate* 203)

Windsor Castle (367). 77¼ × 78¾ in., 197,5 × 200 cm.

Signed and dated: J. WOOTTON. / *Fecit 1737*

The stag has been brought to bay by the hounds in a pond in the Great Park, near the present Royal Lodge, surrounded by huntsmen in royal livery; in the distance is a view of Windsor Castle. The Prince of Wales stands in the hunting livery, wearing the ribbon and star of the Garter and apparently ordering John Spencer to destroy the hunted animal. Spencer wears a blue-green coat with gold lace and pale blue lining, possibly his uniform as Ranger of the Great Park; the same coat is worn by Colonel Bloodworth on horseback behind the Prince. Behind Spencer are four figures in the hunting livery: Lord Baltimore, the Duke of Marlborough, the Earl of Jersey and the Marquess (?) of Powis; two more riders in the livery are riding up in the background.

Seen, with no. 546, at Kew in September 1761 by Horace Walpole: 'Two large pictures of Prince Frederick & his Court, by Wootton' (*Visits*, p. 38); and recorded by Sir William Chambers (*Plans, Elevations, ... at Kew ...* (1763)) in the Gallery there: ' ... on each side of [the chimney] is a very fine picture by the celebrated Mr. Wootton; the one representing a Stag at Bay, and the other a Return from the chace: the scene of both is Windsor Forest, and the persons represented are the late prince of Wales, the late duke of Marlborough, Mr. Spencer, the duke of Chandois, the marquis of Powis, lord Jersey, lord Boston, lord Baltimore, the colonels Lumly, Schutz and Madden, Mr. Scot, Mr. Bloodworth and several attendants'. The pair was taken to Windsor in August 1828.

Literature: Collins Baker, *Windsor*, p. 322.

Nos. 545 and 546 are presumably referred to in a payment by the Prince to Wootton on 31 March 1738 of £212 *For two Pictures painted for his Royall highnes the Prince of Wales* [£210] and *For lineing the backs of the Pictures with Primed Canvis and puting em up at Kew* (D. of Cornwall MSS., vol. VII, f. 166). There are a number of minor *pentimenti* in the placing of

hounds, horses and riders in the design and indications in the water of at least two hounds which were later omitted. The seven principal heads seem to be of a quality conspicuously better than Wootton's usual portraits. The identities of the sitters in the two compositions can probably not be completely established; the identifications above, and in the description of no. 546, are those found in slightly later notes at the end of Geo III/*Kew*, and in a first draft thereof. Both canvases are in (original?) fine carved frames with the Prince's feathers incorporated into the decoration at the top. They may be the frames for which John Boson was paid £24. 5*s.* on 23 February 1739: *for ... The Prince of Wales att Kew ... 2 Large Rich Frames, for Pictures of Mr Wootons painting, all the Mouldings Carved, Festoons Plumes of Feathers, & other Ornamts ...* (D. of Cornwall MSS., vol. XIX, f. 167). Wootton's preliminary drawing for no. 545 is in the Royal Library.

For Lord Baltimore see no. 555 and for Spencer see no. 547; Spencer's cousin, the Earl of Sunderland, was a considerable patron of Wootton, who was engaged in 1734 on the series of enormous canvases that still decorate the hall at Althorp. Colonel Thomas Bloodworth or Bludworth was Equerry, Keeper of the Privy Purse and Groom of the Bedchamber to the Prince and seems to have acted as his Master of the Horse. Charles Spencer, 3rd Duke of Marlborough (1706-58), was a soldier, a Lord of the Bedchamber and Lord Steward of the Household (1749-55); William Villiers, 3rd Earl of Jersey (*d.* 1769) was Lord of the Bedchamber to the Prince (1733-8). William Herbert, 3rd Marquess of Powis (*c.* 1698-1748) seems to have held no royal post, but his successor, Henry Herbert, 1st Earl of Powis of the second creation (*c.* 1703-1772) was Treasurer to the Prince (1737-8) and later Comptroller of the Household to George III; it is probably he who appears in no. 545.

546. THE RETURN FROM THE CHASE (*Plate* 204)

Windsor Castle (373). 77½ × 76 in., 196,9 × 193 cm.

Signed and dated: J. WOOTTON. / *Fecit. 1737*

In the background is the east front and terrace of Windsor Castle, figures and deer in the park, a group of royal huntsmen and a rider in the hunting livery. The Prince of Wales, in red with the ribbon and star of the Garter, is in the centre of the composition. On the left, standing by his horse, is John Spencer, and behind him is Colonel Bloodworth, hat in hand; both wear the blue-green livery (see no. 545). Behind the Prince is the Duke of Marlborough in military (?) dress; Colonel Schutz, wearing the livery, approaches the Prince on foot; the Duke of Chandos is in profile to the right of the Prince; and Lord Boston, apparently in the blue-green livery, is seen behind his horse.

See no. 545.

Literature: Collins Baker, *Windsor*, p. 320.

See no. 545. There are the usual alterations in painting the horses and riders in the foreground. For the problem of the identities of the sitters see no. 545. Three of the Prince's companions appear in no. 545 and for Lord Boston see no. 538. Colonel John Schutz was Groom of the Bedchamber (1728-42), Master of the Robes (1729-51) and Keeper of the Privy Purse to the Prince; Henry Brydges, 2nd Duke of Chandos (1708-71) was First Lord of the Bedchamber (1728-35), Groom of the Stole (1742-51) and possibly Master of the Horse to the Prince. Sir William Chambers's description of nos. 545 and 546 also mentions Colonel John Lumley (*d.* 1738), sixth son of the 1st Earl of Scarbrough, a Colonel of the Company of Grenadiers in the Coldstream

Guards and Groom of the Bedchamber to the Prince from 1728; Colonel Martin Madan (1701–56), Equerry and Groom of the Bedchamber (from 1749) to the Prince; and William Scott, Page of Honour (1731–8) and Equerry to the Prince. It is possible that these are the three figures who appear (two in no. 545, one in no. 546) in the middle distance in these pieces.

547. THE SHOOTING PARTY; FREDERICK, PRINCE OF WALES, WITH JOHN SPENCER (1708–46) AND CHARLES DOUGLAS, THIRD DUKE OF QUEENSBERRY (1698–1778) (*Plate* 195)

Windsor Castle (365). 35 × 29⅛ in., 88,9 × 74 cm.

Signed and dated: *JW* / *1740*

The Prince is seated, wearing the hunting livery and the ribbon and star of the Garter, with dead game before him and two grooms in royal livery as loaders; John Spencer stands in the livery, holding a partridge, while the Duke of Queensberry points to the distance.

Presumably painted for the Prince. On 1 February 1746 Paul Petit was paid £21 for *a Rich picture frame Carved with birds Richly Ornamented neatley repair'd and Gilt in Burnished Gold to a picture of His Royal Highness painted by M*r *Wootton*, which Petit had finished by 6 October 1742 (D. of Cornwall MSS., vol. XV, f. 329); this was probably the magnificent frame still on the picture. On the other hand R. Cosway was paid £21 in 1784 by the Prince of Wales for *a Picture of The late Prince of Wales with his Hunt* (W. R. A., Geo. 26792), and no. 547 was in store at Carlton House in 1816 (283; the 1816 label is still on the back); removed to the New Gallery, Windsor, on 6 August 1828, having been sent for a short time to the King's Lodge on 27 September 1823 (Jutsham, *D*, f. 48).

Literature: Collins Baker, *Windsor*, p. 320.

There are signs of alterations round the head of the Duke of Queensberry, who may first have been painted wearing a hat and with his head a little to the left of its present position. A version at Drumlanrig shows Windsor Castle in the background and is probably lot 97 on the second day of Wootton's sale, 12, 13 March 1761: 'The late Prince of *Wales*, the Duke of *Queensberry*, and the late *John Spencer*, Esq; shooting near *Windsor*'; lot. 81 on the first day of the sale may have been relevant: 'An upright View of *Windsor Castle*, with Figures and dead Game, a Sketch'.

John Spencer, father of the 1st Earl Spencer, was the favourite grandson of Sarah, Duchess of Marlborough, and in 1744 succeeded her as Ranger of Windsor Great Park; his early death was due to an incurable addiction to brandy, small beer and tobacco. The Duke of Queensberry was the patron of John Gay and had quarrelled with George II in 1728; he was a Gentleman of the Bedchamber to the Prince of Wales (1733–51) and (1758–78) Captain-General of the Royal Company of Archers.

548. A VIEW OF PARK PLACE

Windsor Castle (2988). 35¼ × 60¼ in., 90,2 × 153 cm.

A distant view of Park Place, apparently in the evening light, on the hills above the river at Henley-on-Thames; among the craft on the river is a gaily decorated pleasure barge which is being hauled upstream by eight men in livery.

On a visit to Buckingham House Walpole saw 'three Views of Park place done for Lady Archibald Hamilton when it was hers, or after She sold it to the late Prince, who is walking with the Princess & her in one of them' (*Visits*, p. 79); the three canvases were at Kensington in 1818 (301, 303, 304), were taken to the Corridor at Windsor in April 1829 and were later at Buckingham Palace.

Literature (for the set): Collins Baker, *Windsor*, pp. 322–3; Whinney and Millar, p. 276.

Probably painted, with nos. 549 and 550, *c*. 1742–3. In 1719 Lord Archibald Hamilton had bought the Park Place estate, and he built the house seen in no. 548, of which nothing now survives. Frederick, Prince of Wales, appears to have acquired the estate *c*. 1738 and to have used the house during his estrangement from his father. After his death the estate was purchased by Henry Seymour Conway. Horace Walpole described it as 'one of the most charming places in England'; 'Pan & the Sylvan Deities seem to have made it their favourite residence, & Father Thames enobles it by his fair stream.' The decorated barge on the 'fair stream' is probably the vessel in which the Prince and Princess 'greatly diverted themselves'. Wootton's three 'prospects' seem to be remarkably accurate topographically.

549. A VIEW OF HENLEY-ON-THAMES (*Plate* 197)

Windsor Castle (2990). 39¾ × 61½ in., 101 × 156,2 cm.

Henley and the river are seen in the distance; in the foreground, in the grounds of Park Place, are grooms and falconers in royal livery, a group of horsemen round the Prince of Wales (who wears the ribbon of the Garter), and four of his children, accompanied probably by their mother or by Lady Archibald Hamilton, in a chariot decorated with the royal arms and the Prince of Wales's feathers.

See no. 548.

Probably painted, with nos. 548 and 550, *c*. 1742–3; it is impossible accurately to identify the little royal children, but they are perhaps the Prince's four eldest children, Princess Augusta (*b*. 1737), Prince George (*b*. 1738), Prince Edward (*b*. 1739) and Princess Elizabeth (*b*. 1740).

550. A DISTANT VIEW OF HENLEY-ON-THAMES

Windsor Castle (2989). 39¾ × 60¼ in., 101 × 153 cm.

Henley is seen in the distance from the high ground near Park Place; in the foreground are farm labourers, grooms in royal livery, and the royal party which includes the Prince of Wales walking, probably with the Princess of Wales and Lady Archibald Hamilton, and four of his children playing with dogs.

See no. 548.

Probably painted, with nos. 548 and 549, *c*. 1742–3. The four children, whose activity in the foreground caused a number of *pentimenti*, are presumably the same as in no. 549. It was probably of no. 550 that Walpole was speaking when, having mentioned Lady Archibald Hamilton, he noted the Prince of Wales 'walking with the Princess & her' (see no. 548). Lady Archibald Hamilton was maliciously and probably wrongly said to have been the Prince's mistress before his marriage (see no. 538).

551. THE SIEGE OF LILLE

St. James's Palace. 121¾ × 193 in., 311,2 × 490,3 cm.

Signed and dated: J. WOOTTON *Fecit* / *1742*

An extensive landscape with the city of Lille in the distance under heavy bombardment from the Allied artillery. In the foreground are a dead horse, pioneers, and soldiers attending and carrying off wounded officers; a detachment of pioneers is marching away to the siege-trenches. On the left is the Duke of Marlborough, on horseback and wearing the ribbon and star of the Garter, in a group of staff-officers; the mounted figure on the left of this group, wearing the ribbon and star of the Order of the White Eagle, is probably Frederick Augustus I, Elector of Saxony, who was present at the siege. An officer behind, wearing the ribbon and star of the Thistle, may be intended for George Hamilton, Earl of Orkney (1666–1737).

Nos. 551 and 552 were probably painted to hang on the Great Staircase at Leicester House, where they were seen by Vertue in July 1750: 'two sides large paintings. Seiges painted by Mr. John Wotton' (*Notebooks*, vol. I, p. 11); they were later at Kensington and were moved to St. James's on 22 July 1822.

Nos. 551 and 552 were commissioned by Frederick, Prince of Wales. In November 1739 Vertue noted 'Some large paintings doing for his royal highness by Mr Wooton being Sieges in Flanders by the Duke of Marlbro P-Eugene &c.' (*Notebooks*, vol. III, p. 97). On 19 December 1741 Robert Price wrote to the Earl of Haddington that Wootton 'is at present doing the Siege of Tournay which appears to me to be an undertaking much beyond his capacity' (G. E. Kendall, 'Notes on the Life of John Wootton', *Walpole Soc.*, vol. XXI (1933), p. 30). On 27 April and 31 December 1743 Wootton was paid £300 and £330 respectively *For Painting two Capital Pictures of the Sieges of Tournay & Lisle* (D. of Cornwall MSS., vol. XII, f. 554, vol. XIII, f. 397, where Wootton's account is dated November 1742, presumably the date when he completed the canvases). Late in 1744 or early in 1745 £5. 16s. was paid for *Scaffolding used at Leisster House by Mr Wootten's Orders* (*ibid.*, vol. XV, f. 264); and on 20 April 1743 Paul Petit submitted a bill for £112. 12s. (settled on 1 August 1746) for *Gild. two Large picture frames In Burnished Gold in the best Manner to ye picturs of the Siege of Lisle and Tournuy . . . put up at Leicester House* (*ibid.*, f. 375).

The siege of Lille, the most important of Louis XIV's fortresses, Vauban's engineering masterpiece, manned by 16,000 men under Marshal Boufflers, was the greatest operation so far undertaken by Marlborough. The city was invested on 13 August 1708. Prince Eugene conducted the siege operations under cover of Marlborough's forces. After very heavy casualties in 'this murderous siege' the town surrendered on 22 October and the citadel finally capitulated on 9 December. Wootton's records of Marlborough's campaigns were composed more than thirty years after the event. He seems to have been at some pains to create an accurate impression of the persons and uniforms of that earlier period, but the general officers are suggestive of Wootton's own time and the uniforms throughout seem later than those of 1708–9. Prominence seems to be given in the figures in the foreground of nos. 551 and 552 to the (1st?) Foot Guards. In no. 551 at least four heads in the group of officers (the Elector of Saxony, an officer one away from Marlborough's right shoulder, Marlborough himself and a standing artillery(?) officer with a pike) are noticeably better in quality than the heads painted by Wootton himself. The last, in particular, is good enough to be by Hogarth, but his name could only be put forward with extreme diffidence. There are, as in no. 552, signs of alterations around these portrait heads. At Wootton's sale on 12, 13 March 1761 were sold (1st day, lot 49) '*Two Sketches of the Battles of* Lisle *and* Tournay', which were presumably studies for nos. 551 and 552, and (lot 78) '*Three Sketches of the Battles of* the Wood [*i.e.*, Malplaquet], Blenheim *and* Audenarde'.

552. THE SIEGE OF TOURNAY

St. James's Palace. 121 × 192½ in., 304,8 × 490,2 cm.

Signed and dated: J. WOOTTON. *Fecit* / 1742.

An extensive landscape with the city of Tournay: Tournay Cathedral is prominent and two white flags are hanging

from the walls. In the distance are numerous detachments of troops, a camp, artillery and a coach which may contain a deputation to discuss the terms of surrender. In the foreground are soldiers, including pioneers, some of them near a sutler's booth, two Franciscan(?) friars and the Duke of Marlborough on horseback, wearing the star of the Garter and pointing with his baton to the distant city. Beside him is a mounted general officer, perhaps intended for William, 1st Earl Cadogan (1675–1726); and in front of him stand two officers: one, also pointing to the city, may be an officer of artillery; the other, who wears the ribbon and star of the Garter, is conceivably the 1st Earl of Albemarle (1669–1718) who was present at the siege.

See no. 551.

Tournay, after Lille the strongest fortress of the age, was invested by the Allies on 27 June 1709. The siege was distinguished by an unprecedented underground activity in mines and counter-mines. On 28 July, de Sourville, the French commander in Tournay, hung out the white flags which announced the surrender of the town, but the citadel did not fall until 3 September. As in no. 551 at least four portrait heads are of conspicuously better quality than the remainder: Marlborough himself, his mounted companion, and the two standing officers. There are obvious alterations around these portrait-heads.

553. THE HAMPTON COURT CHESTNUT ARABIAN

Windsor Castle (2965). 40 × 48½ in., 101,6 × 123,2 cm.

Signed and dated: J. WOOTTON / *Fecit. 1726*, and inscribed later: *An Arabian / belonging to / his Majesty / K.G. ye 1st*

The Arabian held by an Arab groom with a landscape behind in which an Arab rider approaches on horseback.

Sold at Christie's, 24 February 1933 (148; the Christie's stencil is on the back); purchased by Her Majesty Queen Mary for Windsor Castle.

The subject is probably George I's chestnut Arabian 'Horn' (1720–40). In a signed variant on the art-market in 1958 the Arabian was seen against a more richly wooded landscape and in front of a partly ruinous classical building on which was carved the royal cipher under a crown. No. 553 may have been lot 95 in the second day of the sale of Wootton's pictures, 13 March 1761: 'The *Hampton Court Arabian*, belonging to King *George* I.' The horse and the groom occur, with very slight variations, in Wootton's portrait at Goodwood of 'Squirrel'.

John Wootton and Thomas Hudson

554. WILLIAM AUGUSTUS, DUKE OF CUMBERLAND, AT THE BATTLE OF DETTINGEN (*Plate 201*)

Windsor Castle (2865). 64¾ × 52½ in., 164,5 × 133,4 cm.

Signed and dated: J. *Wootton* / *Fecit* /1744 and inscribed by him: *The Battle of Dettingen / Won by his Majesty / June ^{16}_{27} 1743*.

The Duke, on horseback, wearing the ribbon and star of the Garter and the frock uniform of the 1st Guards, points with his sword to the battle raging in the distance; behind him is drawn up a body of infantry led by a company of (1st?) Foot Guards with two colours.

Painted for Frederick, Prince of Wales, and hung in Leicester House; later at Kensington, Buckingham House, Windsor, and Buckingham Palace (491).

In 1745 Vertue visited Wootton 'who has lately painted Duk William on horse back for the Prince of Wales – which peice is much commended' (*Notebooks*, vol. III, p. 130). The piece was engraved by John Faber junior as 'Done from the Original at Leicester House. Painted by M͏ʳ John Wootton, and M͏ʳ Thomas Hudson' (Chaloner Smith, pp. 336-7). Only the head, cravat and part of the shoulders of the Duke appear to have been painted by Hudson, and that part of the design was also engraved by Faber (and others) as after Hudson; a derivation of the portrait was engraved by Bockman (1746). A variant by Wootton of the whole composition, in the collection of the Duke of Argyll, is alleged to show the Duke at the Battle of Laffelt (1747), accompanied by Lord Henry Campbell and Sir John Ligonier. There is a *pentimento* in the hind legs of Cumberland's horse in no. 554 which were both at first painted planted on the ground. A small copy was on the art-market in London in 1960.

The Duke of Cumberland, with the rank of Major-General, served with distinction at the victory of Dettingen under his father's command and was wounded: 'he behaved', wrote James Wolfe, 'as bravely as a man could do . . . The soldiers were in high delight to have him so near to them.' The troops behind him in no. 554 are probably the 1st Guards, to which he had been transferred from the Coldstream Guards in 1742.

John Wootton and William Hogarth

555. FREDERICK, PRINCE OF WALES, IN THE HUNTING FIELD (*Plate* 205)

Windsor Castle (370). 84¼ × 108½ in., 214 × 276 cm.

Signed and dated: J. WOOTTON. / *Fecit 1734*

A hunting party in an extensive landscape with the Thames in the distance. The Prince (wearing the ribbon and star of the Garter) and his five companions are in the hunting livery: blue coats with scarlet linings and gold facings, red waistcoats and buff breeches. Lord Cholmondeley in the centre wears the star and ribbon of the Bath (he had been invested in 1725); the six huntsmen are in royal livery (scarlet with blue cuffs) and one holds a horse on whose saddle-cloth the Prince's feathers are embroidered.

First recorded in the Great Hall at Kew (Sir W. Chambers, *Plans, Elevations, Sections, . . . at Kew . . .* (1763)); in the Great Drawing Room at Kensington in the reign of George III (*The late Pr: of Wales returned from Hunting – Wootton*; Geo. III, *Kensington*, f. 18; *Kensington*, 1818 (311)); moved to the Corridor at Windsor on 3 September 1828.

Literature: Collins Baker, *Windsor*, p. 321; R. W. Symonds, 'Hogarth a Ghost for Wootton', *Burl. Mag.*, vol. LXXXI (1942), pp. 176-9; O. Millar, 'John Wootton, William Hogarth and Frederick, Prince of Wales', *Burl. Mag.*, vol. CIII (1961), pp. 383-4.

On 31 August 1734 payment of £246. 15*s*. was made on behalf of Frederick, Prince of Wales, to William Walmesley whose bill had been drawn up on 15 August *for the Hunting Piece for the Earl of Cholmondeley*. £157. 10*s*. was paid *To M͏ʳ Wootton for the Landskape & Figures*; and £31. 10*s*. *To M͏ʳ Hogarth for Painting Six Faces in the Picture at 5 Guineas Each Face*. The remaining £57. 15*s*. was paid to Dufour for the frame (D. of Cornwall MSS., vol. IV, f. 216). Payment for the canvas may have been made through the 3rd Earl of Cholmondeley (1703-70), Master of the Robes, 1726-7, and, from 1728-35, Master of the Horse to the Prince of Wales. It is described by Sir William Chambers (*op. cit.*) as 'a very good hunting piece by Mr. Wootton, wherein are represented his Royal Highness Frederic Prince of Wales, lord Baltimore

lord Cholmondeley, lord Boston, colonel Pelham, and several of his Royal Highness's attendants'. The heads of the Prince and his five companions are of noticeably better quality than the heads of the huntsmen and are entirely consistent with Hogarth's work of the mid-1730's: the likeness between the head of Lord Cholmondeley and the portrait of him in Hogarth's *Cholmondeley Family* of 1732 at Houghton (R. B. Beckett, *Hogarth* (1949), pl. 55) is so close as to suggest that they were done from the same sitting. The head of the Prince is very close to a sketch on a canvas containing four heads, sold at Christie's, 2 June 1961 (58), bt. Agnew's, which may have been Hogarth's *ad vivum* study. For Wootton's collaboration with Hogarth and other portrait painters see O. Millar, *loc. cit.* There are *pentimenti* in the drawing of the horses and the whips; there seems, understandably, to be some confusion around the six heads and they are very slightly too large for their bodies. Wootton's preparatory drawing (*Fig.* 47) for the composition is in the Royal Library (A. P. Oppé, *English Drawings . . . at Windsor Castle* (1950), no. 691); it follows no. 555 fairly closely, but two of the Prince's companions are inscribed as Captain Bloodworth and Mr. Cornwallis. The former is the figure believed to be Lord Boston, the latter the figure who in no. 555 is definitely Lord Cholmondeley. It could perhaps be pointed out that the form of hunting livery worn by the Prince and his companions, with its red cuffs and facings, foreshadows the 'Windsor Uniform' evolved by George III.

Sir William Chambers only mentions five of the principal sitters. The figure on the extreme left may be the one omitted by him. The Prince and Lord Cholmondeley are clearly identifiable. Lord Boston (see no. 538) is probably the bareheaded figure standing near the Prince's horse. The two other figures in the foreground are thus perhaps (on the extreme right) Col. James Pelham (*d.* 1761), Principal Secretary to the Prince (1728-37) and (bare-headed in profile on the left) Charles Calvert, 5th Baron Baltimore (1699-1751), Gentleman of the Bedchamber (1731-47) to the Prince and Cofferer of his Household (1747-51), described by George II as '*entre nous*, . . . a little mad'.

Thomas Hudson

1701-79. Portrait painter, probably a pupil of Jonathan Richardson; for a short time (1740-3) the young Reynolds was his pupil. His most important royal portraits are those of Frederick, Prince of Wales, and his wife, painted in 1750 and now at Cliveden.

556. GEORGE FREDERICK HANDEL (1685-1759) (*Plate* 199)

Windsor Castle (2987). 30¼ × 35 in., 76,8 × 88,9 cm.

Full-length, seated at a table at the head of a large staircase.

Recorded at Buckingham Palace in 1876 (*V.R. inv.*).

Literature: E. M. Davies, *The Life and Work of Thomas Hudson*, unpublished M.A. Thesis, presented to the University of London, 1938, p. 363 (112).

Apparently a preparatory sketch, unfinished in part and with numerous *pentimenti*, for the portrait, signed and dated 1756, which Hudson painted for the composer's friend Charles Jennens (the Gopsall portrait, *Fig.* 49) and which was deposited by Earl Howe on long loan to the National Portrait Gallery (3970). Handel had been painted by Hudson on at least two earlier occasions, in 1743 and 1748, and in April 1750 had offered to present to the Foundling Hospital a portrait for which Handel had agreed to sit (O. E. Deutsch, *Handel*

(1955), p. 687). The head in no. 556 seems not to be *ad vivum*, but to have been based by Hudson on a portrait of the same type as no. 558; but the remainder of the design probably represents Hudson's first attempt at producing an elaborate affair from his own more modest portrait. In the final composition there are considerable alterations in the background, in the shapes of the chair and table and in the disposition of the books. The column, in no. 556 painted over the composer's hand which clasps a stick, was ultimately left out of the design.

Handel had been encouraged by Queen Anne on his first visits to London; before her death he had been appointed Kapellmeister to the Elector of Hanover and after the accession of George I was generously patronised and supported by the new dynasty; he was Music-Master to George II's daughters and much of his work was composed for royal occasions. In 1734 George II and Queen Caroline were described as 'both Handelists, . . . freezing constantly at his empty Haymarket Opera, whilst the Prince . . . went as constantly to that of Lincoln's Inn Fields . . . An anti-Handelist was looked upon as an anti-courtier.' The Prince of Wales nevertheless owned a *portrait of Mr Hendle painted by Mr Goupy*, for which Paul Petit made a frame in 1742 (D. of Cornwall MSS., vol. XV, f 329).

After Thomas Hudson

557. GEORGE, FIRST BARON ANSON (1697–1762)

Buckingham Palace. 56¼ × 44¼ in., 142,9 × 112,4 cm.

Three-quarter-length, standing in peer's robes, resting his left hand on a ledge.

Recorded at Hampton Court in 1842 (Mrs. Jameson, p. 431, later inv. no. 19); later at Kensington.

Literature: Law, 1881, 1898 (5).

A copy, probably after the original by Hudson in the collection of the Earl of Lichfield at Shugborough; the original was presumably painted *c.* 1747. No. 557 was stated in the nineteenth century to be a copy by Bockman; this is not impossible, but it does not seem to belong to his series of copies of naval portraits (nos. 386–94).

The distinguished naval commander who circumnavigated the world in 1744 and defeated the French off Finisterre in 1747; First Lord of the Admiralty, 1751–6 and 1757–62.

558. GEORGE FREDERICK HANDEL

Kensington Palace. Oval, 31 × 28½ in., 78,7 × 72,4 cm.

Recorded in 1813 (Legge's inventory), as an original portrait of Handel by Hudson, in front of the organ in St. George's Hall, where it can be seen in C. Wild's plate in Pyne, vol. I, p. 176; later at Buckingham Palace (407).

Literature: Law, *Kensington* (1903), p. 83.

Apparently a contemporary copy derived from the head and shoulders type which Hudson had used in no. 556.

William Hogarth

1697–1764. Painter of subject-pictures, portraits, conversation, satirical and narrative pieces; in 1757 he was appointed Serjeant-Painter to the King, but his relations with the Crown seem always to have been unsatisfactory.

559. THE FAMILY OF GEORGE II (*Plate* 209)

Buckingham Palace. 25⅛ × 30⅛ in., 63,8 × 77,5 cm.

The royal family is seen out of doors, near a circular garden temple. George II and his Queen are seated in richly carved chairs; the King wears the ribbon of the Garter and so does William, Duke of Cumberland, standing on the left of the composition. In the foreground Princesses Mary and Louisa are playing with a spaniel; and on the right, Frederick, Prince of Wales, wearing the ribbon and star of the Garter, stands with his three eldest sisters, Princesses Anne, Amelia and Caroline, beside an elaborately carved table.

Probably the picture in the collection of Samuel Ireland from 1782 to 1801, and sold in his sale, 7 May 1801 (434): *George the First and his Family*, bt. Vernon; with Leggatt's, 1912; later in the collection of Mrs. Whitelaw Reid, U.S.A., until it was sold, American Art Association, New York, 14–18 May 1935 (1161); later in the collection of Mrs. V. L. Bonham, Connecticut; purchased by Her Majesty The Queen for the royal collection from Agnew's in 1955.

Literature: J. Nichols, *Biographical Anecdotes of William Hogarth . . .*, 3rd edn. (1785), p. 115; S. Ireland, *Graphic Illustrations of Hogarth* (1799), vol. II, pp. 137–9 (eng. by Ryder); J. Nichols and G. Steevens, *The Genuine Works of William Hogarth . . .*, vol. III (1817), p. 206; *Anecdotes of William Hogarth, written by himself . . .* (1833), p. 372; R. B. Beckett, *Hogarth* (1949), pp. 10, 45; Tate Gallery, *William Hogarth*, 1951 (21); R. A., *English Taste in the Eighteenth Century*, 1955–56 (106).

At the time of the preparations for the marriage of Anne, Princess Royal, to William, Prince of Orange, in November 1733, Hogarth applied, through 'some Lady about the Queen', for permission to paint, and publish a print of, the ceremony; permission was granted and then withdrawn, apparently owing to interventions from, or on behalf of, William Kent. Vertue, who is the source for this episode (*Notebooks*, vol. III, p. 68), added that Hogarth complained heavily of such treatment and of another such episode: 'he had some time ago begun a picture of all the Royal family in one peice by order the Sketch being made. & the P. William the Duke had sat to him for one. this also has been stopt. so that he can't proceed.' No. 559 seems to be Hogarth's first *modello* for a royal conversation piece. The design is worked out in detail, and there are no signs of alterations; but, with the possible exception of the Duke of Cumberland, the individual heads do not, at this stage, seem to have been based on sittings. In a smaller variant of this *modello* in the National Gallery of Ireland (*Fig.* 50) Hogarth set the figures, with slight variations in detail, in a spacious interior; in this version of the design the head of the Prince of Wales seems clearly to be a portrait *ad vivum*. No. 559 should perhaps be regarded, therefore, as Hogarth's first proposal for his royal piece, perhaps after he had received the order to produce such a piece but before he had been granted sittings. He may then have been told to take the group indoors, gone a little further with the details of the composition, and been granted one important sitting, before the project was abandoned. But no. 559 is of the scale of Hogarth's earliest 'conversations', whereas the indoor variant is much smaller. The project probably dates from *c.* 1731–2. The Duke of Cumberland had been created a Knight of the Garter in 1730; in no. 559 the figure of the Duke is very close to the single portrait in the collection of Lord Glenconner (R. B. Beckett, *op. cit.*, pl. 38) which is perhaps the portrait painted from the sitting mentioned by Vertue, and to the figure of the Duke in the audience in Hogarth's *Conquest of Mexico* (probably 1731–2) in which the Duke's youngest sisters also appear (*ibid.*, pl. 53).

560. DAVID GARRICK (1717–79) WITH HIS WIFE EVA-MARIA VEIGEL, 'LA VIOLETTE' or 'VIOLETTI' (1725–1822). (Plate 211)

Windsor Castle (775). 52¼×41 in., 132,7×104,1 cm.

Signed: [*W*] *Hogarth*.

Garrick, seated at a writing-table, resting his head on his right hand, while his wife leans across his chair to pluck his pen from his hand; before him lies the draft of *The Prologue to Taste*. Behind him are books, including a copy of Shakespeare; on her arm his wife wears a miniature portrait.

Presumably painted for Garrick, but apparently still in Hogarth's studio, not paid for and apparently unfinished, at his death; given by his widow to Mrs. Garrick; remained in Mrs. Garrick's possession until her death; sold in her sale, Christie's, 23 June 1823 (64); bought for £75. 11*s.* by E. H. Locker, who sold it to George IV,[1] probably not long before 26 May 1826, when it was sent to Seguier to be cleaned (Jutsham, *D*, f. 79: *. . . Recently purchased from Colnaghi*): recorded in the Corridor at Windsor in 1829 (*Carlton Palace* (610)).

Literature: J. Nichols, *Biographical Anecdotes of William Hogarth. . .*, 3rd edn. (1785), pp. 12–13; J. Nichols and G. Steevens, *The Genuine Works of William Hogarth . . .*, vol. I (1808), pp. 21, 212; *Anecdotes of William Hogarth, written by himself . . .* (1833), p. 384; A. Dobson, *William Hogarth* (1907), pp. 94, 205; Collins Baker, *Windsor*, p. 156; R. A., *British Art*, 1934 (154), Commemorative Catalogue (1935), p. 22; Chicago and Tate Gallery, *Masterpieces of English Painting*, 1946–7 (6); R. B. Beckett, *Hogarth* (1949), p. 43; Tate Gallery, *William Hogarth*, 1951 (68); City of Manchester Art Gallery, *William Hogarth*, 1954 (37); C. Oman, *David Garrick* (1958), pp. 154–5; O. Millar, 'Garrick and his Wife' by William Hogarth, *Burl. Mag.*, vol. CIV (1962), pp. 347–8.

On 21 April 1757 John Hoadly wrote to Joseph Warton that 'Hogarth has got again into Portraits; and has his hands full of business, and at an high price. He has almost finished a most noble one of our sprightly friend David Garrick and his Wife: they are a fine contrast. David is sitting at a table, smilingly thoughtful over an epilogue . . . his head supported by his writing-hand; and Madam is archly enough stealing away his pen unseen behind. It is not so much fancy as to be affected or ridiculous and yet enough to raise it from the formal inanity of a mere Portrait' (quoted by J. Nichols and G. Steevens, *op. cit.*, p. 212). Garrick had written and delivered a Prologue to Samuel Foote's comedy *Taste*, first produced on 11 January 1752. If Garrick had not paid for the picture by the time of Hogarth's death that would perhaps confirm the tradition that Garrick was dissatisfied with the likeness or that he and Hogarth had quarrelled during the progress of the picture and that Hogarth had angrily destroyed his first painting of Garrick's eyes (J. Nichols and G. Steevens, *op. cit.*). If that was so the eyes certainly seem to have been made good by Hogarth, though there are still apparently traces of some kind of erasure in the left eye. There are also alterations to the fingers of Garrick's right hand and the position of the pen. Nichols states, moreover (*loc. cit.*) that the picture 'confers no honour on the painter or the persons represented. He has certainly missed the character of our late *Roscius's* countenance while undisturbed by passion . . . It is by no means astonishing, that the elegant symmetry of Mrs. *Garrick's* form should have evaded the efforts of one to whose ideas *la basse nature* was more familiar than the grace inseperable from those who have been educated in higher life . . .' The condition of the canvas as a whole also suggests that Hogarth found it difficult, for whatever reason, to complete it. X-ray reveals that an original background, showing a bookcase and a suggestion of an interior, was overpainted at a very early date, possibly when Mrs. Garrick received the picture; and that, perhaps at the same time, *pentimenti*, *e.g.* round Mrs. Garrick's head and right arm and hand, were tidied up (see O. Millar, *loc. cit.*). It is possible, therefore, that the background was never finished by Hogarth and was completed after his death in a much less elaborate fashion than he had originally planned. The source for the design is generally stated by Nichols (*op. cit.*, p. 12 and see F. Antal, *Hogarth and his Place in European art* (1962), p. 70, pl. 129 b) to be Vanloo's picture of Colley Cibber and his daughter; a further prototype is perhaps a picture by Mercier (*Fig.* 54) sold at Christie's, 20 July 1956 (120).

David Garrick, one of the greatest figures in the history of the English stage, and the most popular actor of his time until his retirement in 1776, was for many years a friend of Hogarth, had sat to him in the part of Richard III, bought the *Election* series and wrote the epitaph over 'Hogarth's honour'd dust' in Chiswick churchyard. His wife arrived in England early in 1746 and married Garrick in 1749; the marriage was extremely happy. In 1777 Garrick was summoned to give a special reading at Windsor which included, for the delight of the royal children, imitations of bird-noises.

561 THE POPPLE AND ASHLEY FAMILIES (Plate 210)

Buckingham Palace. 24¾×29½ in., 62,9×74,9 cm.

Signed and dated: *W*ᵐ *Hogarth: pinx*ᵗ *1730*: this is written in very small script and an accurate reading is very difficult, but the date, which has been variously given in the past as 1731 and 1734, seemed, when the canvas was cleaned in 1956, definitely to be 1730. There is also an indecipherable inscription cut into the overgrown ledge on the right of the composition.

Three men, two women and a little girl near the edge of a lake and observed by an owl; one of the women seated in the foreground holds in her lap a hat, filled with fish caught by the standing gentleman who holds his fishing rod. On the other side of the composition are a younger man walking with a dog and a slightly older man reclining on a bank and pointing to an open book.

Descended to Marianne Popple, the child in the foreground, who married Vincent Matthias; lent in 1817 to the British Institution by her son T. J. Mathias; passed to T. J. Mathias's niece, Marianne Skerrett, who died (aged 94) in July 1887 and bequeathed the picture to Queen Victoria; hung at Osborne, later at Windsor (2466).

Literature: J. Nichols and G. Steevens, *The Genuine Works of William Hogarth . . .*, vol. III (1817), p. 174; *Anecdotes of William Hogarth, written by himself . . .* (1833), p. 373; R. A., *King's Pictures* (81); M. Brockwell, 'A Portrait Group by Hogarth . . .', *Connoisseur*, vol. CXIX (1947), pp. 126–8; R. B. Beckett, *Hogarth* (1949), pp. 9, 24, 39; Tate Gallery, *William Hogarth*, 1951 (26); City of Manchester Art Gallery, *William Hogarth*, 1954 (7).

The identities of the sitters have not been satisfactorily established.[1] When the picture was bequeathed to Queen

---

1. Frederick Locker-Lampson (*My Confidences* (1896), p. 74) remembered the picture in his father's apartments at Greenwich Hospital: ' . . . so life-like that as little children we were afraid of it; so much so that my mother persuaded my father to sell it to George IV . . .'

1. Brockwell (*loc. cit.*) gravely confused the issue by assuming that no. 561 contained portraits of three members of the family who had been dead for a number of years; his identification of the seated man as Maurice Ashley-Cooper can be proved wrong by comparison with established portraits of him. Brockwell's arguments were based on the almost certainly false assumption that no. 561 could be equated with a portrait by Hogarth of William Popple (1666–1722) and one of his sons, recorded in the possession of Sophia Popple at the time of her death in 1778. In the archives of the Surveyor of The Queen's Pictures are letters from Mr. Beckett and Mr. H. C. Wilkinson which contain valuable suggestions about the identities.

Victoria Miss Skerrett described it as representing some members of the Popple and Ashley families and added that Hogarth had painted it out of friendship. She stated that the child in the foreground was her grandmother, Marianne Popple. The adult figures all seem to belong to the same generation, and presumably include some of the children of William Popple (1666–1722). Marianne's father, Alured Popple (1698–1744), and her mother Mary (1704–1773) are presumably represented. The seated figure on the right bears a strong resemblance to the portrait of Alured Popple at Government House, Bermuda. The standing figure could be his younger brother, William (1701–64) or possibly the third brother, Henry (d. 1743). The other seated female figure could perhaps be one of his sisters, but both she and the man with the fishing rod may be two of his relations of the Ashley-Cooper family: Alured Popple's aunt, Katherine (d. 1721), had married Maurice Ashley-Cooper (d. 1726), brother of the 3rd Earl of Shaftesbury. There are traces of alterations throughout the design. Many of the figures give the impression, particularly in the right half of the design, of having been painted on the canvas before their surroundings and of having been adjusted by Hogarth at an intermediate stage. The feet of the two figures on the right show *pentimenti* and there are traces of alterations down the right shoulder and arm of the man with a stick. The left hand of the seated woman on the extreme left was at first painted in her lap, and was at a later stage placed on her companion's shoulder; the edge of her dress on the ground has also been altered. The upper part of the overgrown bank on the right is very indeterminate and it is not certain how much of it was intended by Hogarth to remain in the final design. There is a barely perceptible change of scale between the figures in the two halves of the composition, and the two figures on the right may have been added after the group on the left had been fully evolved. The owl is probably inserted in honour of the Popple family, who used this bird as their crest.

Alured Popple was appointed (1730) Secretary to the Board of Trade and Plantations and in 1737 became Governor of Bermuda. A man of studious tastes, he was an extremely capable administrator and was succeeded in the Governorship in 1745 by his brother William, a minor dramatist and versifier, but no less able and industrious than his brother.

Attributed to William Hogarth

562. FREDERICK, PRINCE OF WALES (*Plate* 177)
Windsor Castle (2926). 30 × 20 in., 76,2 × 50,8 cm.

Full-length standing in Garter robes, resting his right hand on an elaborately carved chair, beside a table on which rests the plumed hat of the Order, and beneath a curtain lifted up by two putti; behind the Prince is a statue of Minerva.

Purchased with the companion picture (no. 563) by Her Majesty Queen Mary in 1929 and presented by her to the royal collection; later at Kew (Hampton Court no. 1383).

Literature (for the pair): Collins Baker, *Windsor*, p. 255; O. Millar, 'John Wootton, William Hogarth and Frederick, Prince of Wales', *Burl. Mag.*, vol. CIII (1961), pp. 383–4.

Formerly attributed, with no. 563, to Philips. The design is more elaborately rococo than Philips's official portraits of the Prince and his wife (nos. 531 and 532) and the portraits show a liveliness of movement and freshness of touch of which Philips would seem incapable, even on this scale (*cf.*, no. 533). In drawing and handling the pair are very close to Hogarth, though there is no evidence that he ever received

so formal a sitting from the Prince of Wales. The pair was presumably painted soon after the Prince's marriage on 27 April 1736. The elaborate accessories would not be incompatible with Hogarth's portraits and conversation pieces at this date or slightly earlier; the putti swinging on a golden cord beneath a rich curtain are reminiscent of a passage in the *Cholmondeley Family* of 1732 (R. B. Beckett, *Hogarth* (1949), pl. 55). Both portraits give the impression of being reductions from very elaborate state portraits of the size of life; but are likewise perhaps not incompatible with Hogarth's reaction to the grand manner at this stage of his career.

563. AUGUSTA, PRINCESS OF WALES (*Plate* 178)
Windsor Castle (2927). 30 × 20 in., 76,2 × 50,8 cm.

Full-length, standing in robes of state before a richly carved chair and underneath a canopy; at her feet are a small black spaniel and two putti with fruit, flowers and the Princess's coronet.

See no. 562; later at Kew (Hampton Court no. 1384).

Formerly attributed, with the companion piece, to Philips. The pose of the figure is certainly close to Philips's official portrait of the Princess (*e.g.*, no. 532) and the putto with her coronet reappears in the clouds in the large portrait of her (1737) by Philips at Warwick Castle (see no. 532). But the quality of no. 563 seems, like no. 562, to be quite distinct from Philips and suggestive, especially in the face, of Hogarth. Moreover, under the canopy is a male head (with indications of a cravat) which is unfinished and has been painted out. It shows that the canvas was originally used for a horizontal conversation piece of the type and scale of Hogarth's earliest conversations (*e.g.*, nos. 559 and 561); and the unfinished head seems to be very close in style to Hogarth.[1] In using the canvas for a second time he would probably have slightly reduced its width.

After William Hogarth

564. A MIDNIGHT MODERN CONVERSATION
Buckingham Palace. 22½ × 36½ in., 57,2 × 92,7 cm.

A party of revellers round a table on which are a bowl of punch, bottles and glasses; a long-case clock in the background stands at 4 o'clock.

From the collection of King Edward VII; formerly at Marlborough House and recorded at Buckingham Palace in 1909 (p. 249).

One of many derivations from the original, painted c. 1732, which is in the Beaverbrook Gallery, Fredericton, New Brunswick, and was engraved by Hogarth himself in 1733 (R. B. Beckett, *Hogarth* (1949), p. 70). There are considerable simplifications and modifications in detail in no. 564, which seems to be contemporary.

Joseph Goupy

c. 1680?–c. 1768. Pastellist, etcher, scene-painter and painter in watercolours; of French origin, but probably born in England; studied abroad. Practised as a copyist, painted snuff-boxes for George I, made small copies of Raphael's *Cartoons* and carried out work on Mantegna's *Triumph of Caesar*. For many years he worked for John Hedges, Trea-

1. The list of pictures that remained unfinished in Hogarth's studio on 1 January 1731 is printed in J. Nichols and G. Steevens, *The Genuine Works of William Hogarth*, ... vol. I (1808), pp. 45-6.

surer to the Prince of Wales. Between at least 1735 and 1753 he was closely associated with the Prince in the formation and maintenance of his collections, and painted many pastels for him (D. of Cornwall MSS., vols. V, VI, VIII, IX, XI, XII, XIII, XIV, XV, XVI, XVII, XIX, XXXV, XLI; W. R. A., Geo. 55240); in 1748 travelled to Paris in an abortive attempt to buy pictures for the Prince; in 1743 he was stated by Vertue (*Notebooks*, vol. III, p. 116) to be teaching the Princess of Wales to draw.

565. BELISARIUS

St. James's Palace. Pastel: 22¼×28 in., 56,5×71,1 cm.

A group of figures giving alms to the aged blind Belisarius, before whom lie his helmet, shield and staff.

Probably painted for Frederick, Prince of Wales (see below); recorded at Kew in 1870 (*V.R. inv.*).

A copy on a small scale of the large picture now at Chatsworth, but then in the Earl of Burlington's collection at Chiswick and attributed to Van Dyck (R. & J. Dodsley, *London and its Environs Described* (1761), vol. II, p. 121). Among the works done for the Prince of Wales by Goupy, seen by Vertue in 1749 at Leicester House, was: 'the Belisarius from Ld Burlingtons picture' (*Notebooks*, vol. III, p. 152). An account from Paul Petit for work done for Frederick, Prince of Wales, between September 1747 and February 1749, includes under 14 September 1747 seven shillings and sixpence *For carring the picture of Belcirio to Mr Goupy making a Inside Slip and gilding and pasting papr upon the Inside Edge of the Glass to prevent the Dust from the picture and putting Ditto in Her Royal Highness's Dressing roome. pr Mr Goupy's Order* (D. of Cornwall MSS., vol. XVII, f. 530). It is possible, therefore, that Petit carved the superb frame, decorated with the Prince of Wales's feathers, in which no. 565 is set. Goupy also made copies of the *Belisarius* for the Earl of Oxford and John Hedges (C. R. Grundy, 'Documents relating to an Action brought against Joseph Goupy in 1738', *Walpole Soc.*, vol. IX (1921), pp. 77–87); another belonged to Handel and was sold (lot 43) at the sale of his pictures, 27–8 February 1760.

Thomas Butler

fl. 1750–5. Bookseller and stationer in Pall Mall who turned to the production of sporting prints and paintings; his signature appears on pictures dated 1750 and 1755 in the same form as in no. 566. He employed a team of assistants who specialised in painting horses and other sporting subjects. An inventory of the Duke of Hamilton's pictures in 1759 (Hamilton MSS.) includes a set of eight portraits of horses by Butler 'set in Gilded frames and Glassed and contain the History of their several Pedigrees and prizes gained by them'.

566. THE GODOLPHIN ARABIAN

Windsor Castle (2307). 30⅛×25 in., 76,5×63,5 cm.

Signed: *Thos Butler | Pall-Mall London*

The Arabian stands in a stable yard within a framework on which is inscribed: *The Godolphin Arabian, | ESTEEM'D | one of the best | Foreign Horses | ever brought | into England; | Appearing so | both from the | Country he came | from, and from | the Performance | of his Posterity. | They being Excelt | both as Racers | and Stallions | and Hitting | with most other | Pedigrees and | mending the | Imperfections | of their Shape. | He was the Sire | among others of | ye following Cattle. | Lath, Cade, Amelia, | Blank, Bajazet, | Babram,*

Regulus, | Dormouse, Slugg, | Whitenose, Dismal. | And of the Bay Colt | that won ye Twelve | Hundred Guins | at Newmarket | Apr. 1757. And | ye Grandsire of ye | best Horses of ye | present Time. as | Dutchess, Black Vic- | torious, Martin, Ruby, | Bywell Tom, Match- | em, and Young Babraham. | And is allowed to have refresh'd the English Blood more than | any Foreign Horse ever yet Imported. he Died | at Hogmagog Decr 25. 1753. Aged 32.

Possibly in the collection of William Augustus, Duke of Cumberland, but not recorded until November 1868 at Stud Lodge (*V.R. inv.*, no. 1149); taken to Cumberland Lodge in January 1896.

Literature: W. T. Whitley, *Artists and their Friends in England 1700–1799* (1928), vol. I, pp. 78–9.

A copy of the standard likeness of the famous horse. The source of no. 566 was probably the version now at Houghton, which is probably by Morier. It bears the same long inscription, but omits the name of Thomas Butler and adds: *The Original Picture taken at the Hills by D: Murrier. Painter. to H:R:H. the Duke Cumberland.* The design may have been developed from the version in the Duke of Leeds's collection, sold at Sotheby's, 14 June 1961 (15), in which there is no surrounding inscription. This version may have been painted for the 2nd Earl of Godolphin when he owned the Arabian. Another version is stated to be in America (see Lady Wentworth, *The Authentic Arabian Horse* (1945), pp. 59–61). The celebrated Arabian sire was born in 1724 and imported from France c. 1730 by Edward Coke; by Coke he was left to Roger Williams, keeper of the St. James's Coffee House; and he was given by Williams to Godolphin who kept him at Babraham, where the likeness of him was presumably taken. 'Whoever has seen this horse must remember that his shoulders were deeper and lay further into his back than any horse yet seen . . .'

John Shackleton

d. 1767. Portrait painter, appointed Principal Painter to George II, in place of Kent, on 7 March 1749; he was confirmed in office by George III, but much of his official practice was taken over by Allan Ramsay. Between 1750 and 1757 he was paid for a number of official portraits of the King for despatch to ambassadors, envoys and governors abroad (L.C.5,23 (123, 124), 24 (24, 177, 245, 296)).

567. GEORGE II

Buckingham Palace. 93½×56¼ in., 237,5×142,9 cm.

Full-length, standing in robes of state, wearing the collar of the Garter and holding the sceptre on a table beside the crown and orb.

Almost certainly the portrait of George II, . . . *whole Length. Robed . . . the Artist Name unknown . . .*, purchased by George IV from Colnaghi in June 1820 (Jutsham, *Receipts*, f. 103, PP., f. 63; W. R. A., Geo. 26475) and recorded at Carlton House in 1816 (*Addn.* no. 573); later at Hampton Court and set up at Buckingham Palace (1841, p. 199, later inv. no. 190) in the State Dining Room (then attributed to Ramsay).

Literature: J. R. Fawcett Thompson and F. Gordon Roe, 'More Paintings at the British Museum', *Connoisseur*, vol. CXLVII (1961), pp. 189–90.

A version, of little quality and presumably produced in Shackleton's studio, of his official portrait of the King which exists in a number of versions and variants. Signed and dated versions are at Wentworth Woodhouse (1750) and the Scottish National Portrait Gallery (221; 1755), and others are at Newby, the Foundling Hospital (1758), the Fishmongers Hall (presented in 1765), the British Museum (painted for the Trustees and finished in 1762), the Town Hall at Huntingdon, the Ministry of Works (painted for the 1st Lord Amherst), and formerly at Hinchingbrooke (sold Sotheby's, 4 December 1957 (89)). A curious version was engraved at St. Petersburg in 1749 by Johann Stenglin. See also no. 568.

568. GEORGE II

Buckingham Palace. 50½ × 40½ in., 128,3 × 102,9 cm.

Three-quarter-length, standing in robes of state, wearing the collar of the Garter and holding the sceptre in his right hand.

Recorded in the inventory of pictures at Hampton Court in 1835 (490: *George the 2nd in his Robes, half length. Ramsay*) and stated to have been bought by William IV from the executors of Sir George Pownall; later at Windsor (41).

A version, probably painted in Shackleton's studio, from the same source as no. 567. It is presumably the portrait painted for Thomas Pownall, Governor of Massachusetts Bay, for which Shackleton was paid £55. 15s. 6d. on 6 July 1757 (L.C.5, 24 (362)).

Robert Edge Pine

c. 1730–1788. History and portrait painter; worked at Bath in the 1770's and in 1784 emigrated to Philadelphia.

After Robert Edge Pine

569. GEORGE II

Kensington Palace. 50½ × 40½ in., 128,3 × 102,9 cm.

Full-length, standing at the head of the King's Staircase at Kensington Palace, holding the hilt of his sword in his left hand and wearing the Garter and the ribbon of the Order. A grenadier of the 2nd Foot Guards and a Yeoman of the Guard are seen lower on the staircase.

Presented to George IV by Mr. Vaughan and received at Carlton House on 28 May 1816 (Jutsham, *R/D*, f. 365 . . . *Small Whole Length . . . George The 2d . . . by Pine* . . .); sent to Cumberland Lodge on 1 October 1823 (*Carlton House*, 1816 (380)); later at Windsor (510), and Buckingham Palace.

A contemporary reduced copy, possibly by Pine himself, of the life-size portrait at Audley End which was engraved in 1766 by William Dickinson as painted in 1759. When Lord Howard de Walden secured the original from Pine in 1784, the artist described the portrait as 'my Original Portrait of our late good old King . . . universally allowed to be the most like of any in being' (J. Woodward, 'Four Royal Portraits at the Walker Art Gallery', *Liverpool Libraries, Museums . . . Bulletin*, vol. 4 (nos. 1 and 2, October 1954), p. 8). On 5 June 1801 Lord Braybrooke, who had hoped to be able to present the original to George III, wrote that he had discovered it to be an heirloom in his family, but that he would do all in his power to enable the King to procure painted or engraved copies from it as it was so important a portrait. Lord Howard had told him that 'Upon [his] expressing a wish to some Friend to have a Portrait of King George ye 2d, and his fears that there were no original portraits of Him except those which were painted early in his life; It was suggested that this Picture by Pine existed . . . Lord Howard applied to the Painter who informed him that he had taken the likeness, unseen by the King, as he was

speaking to one of his attendants at the top of the great Staircase at Kensington Palace . . .' (W. R. A., Geo. 10229; and see R. J. B. Walker, *Catalogue of the Pictures . . .* [at Audley End] (1954), p. 18; R. A., *British Portraits*, 1956–7 (516)). Other small versions and copies exist. See nos. 570 and 571.

570. GEORGE II

St. James's Palace. 82½ × 53½ in., 210 × 135,9 cm.; *c.* 4½ in. are turned over on the right, *c.* 8½ in. on the top and *c.* 2½ in. at the bottom.

Recorded at Hampton Court in 1835 (later inv. no. 598) and probably formerly at Windsor; later at Kensington.

A very bad copy from the same source as no. 569.

571. GEORGE II

St. James's Palace. 56 × 39 in., 142,2 × 99,1 cm.; 4¾ in. is turned over on the left and 2¾ in. on the right.

Recorded at Windsor Castle in 1832 (label on back); later at Buckingham Palace (546).

A very bad copy from the same source as no. 569.

Barthelemy du Pan

1712–63. Swiss portrait-painter who came to England in 1743. In October 1745 he submitted a bill for £80 for *two pictures of His Royal Highness at £40. each*, which he was paid on 4 January 1746; he was paid on 31 January 1747 £25 for another (D. of Cornwall MSS., vol. XV, f. 384, vol. XVI, f. 276). It is probable that a pair of portraits of the Prince and his wife in the collection of Sir Cecil Stafford-King-Harman (R. A., *Kings and Queens*, 1953 (235, 237), illustrated souvenir pls. 62–3) are by Du Pan.

572. THE CHILDREN OF FREDERICK, PRINCE OF WALES (*Plate* 213)

Windsor Castle (2977). 96½ × 145 in., 245,1 × 368,3 cm.

Signed and dated: D V P A N. *pxt*/*1746*

The six eldest children of the Prince and Princess of Wales in the gardens of Park Place (see nos. 548–50). On the right Prince George, in the uniform of the Royal Company of Archers (a richly laced red tartan jacket and breeches and an elaborate laced feathered cap in which is a badge with St. Andrew's cross), has just successfully loosed an arrow at the popinjay; behind him Prince Edward, in military uniform, is loading his flintlock. In the middle Prince William, in 'coats', hands a wreath towards his older brothers and beside him Princess Augusta holds the infant Prince Henry; on the left Princess Elizabeth drives an elaborately decorated dog-cart under a feathered canopy.

Painted for the Prince of Wales (see below) and seen by Horace Walpole in his widow's Dressing Room at Kew in September 1761 (*Visits*, p. 39); later at Kensington, Hampton Court, Buckingham Palace (622), Kensington and St. James's.

Literature: Collins Baker, *Windsor*, p. 71; R. A., *King's Pictures* (114); Waterhouse, *Painting in Britain*, p. 143.

On 31 January 1747 Du Pan was paid £100 *For the original picture of his Royal Highness's Children*, set on his account under the date June 1746, and £150 *For two Copys of that same picture at £75 each*, set under December (D. of Cornwall MSS., vol. XVI, f. 276). Prince Henry had been born on 27 October 1745. Walpole observed (*loc. cit.*): 'It is very remarkable that Prince George has St. Andrew's Cross in his cap ', and it is perhaps even more unexpected that he should be wearing, in a portrait painted two months after the battle of Culloden, a jacket of a red tartan very close to the present so-called Royal Stewart tartan. His dress is however, an accurate rendering of the uniform of the Royal Company of Archers, which had been laid down in 1713 and included a coat of Stuart tartan and a blue bonnet with a coque of white and green ribbons. Prince George's dress is almost identical with the costume shown in a portrait (c. 1740), possibly of James, 5th Earl of Wemyss, Captain-General of the Royal Company, 1743–56 (Ian Hay, *The Royal Company of Archers* (1951), pp. 80, 87–9, 171, 269). The children were formerly thought (e.g., by Faulkner, pp. 390–1) to be playing in the gardens at Kew, but the site was identified as the grounds of Park Place (P. Noble, *Park Place* (1905), pp. 14–15). There are slight *pentimenti* in the composition, e.g., in Prince George's right hand and Prince William's foot. The design was engraved by John Faber junior and, in two parts, by T. Ryley.

George Knapton

1698–1778. Portrait painter; studied under Richardson and, until 1732, in Italy. He had a reputation as an expert on pictures: he drew up an inventory of the Spencer collection in 1746; in 1750 he went with Vertue on the Prince of Wales's survey of the royal collection, recommended to the Prince as 'the most skillfull judge or Connoiesseur in pictures' (Vertue, *Notebooks*, vol. III, p. 154); and in May 1765 he succeeded Stephen Slaughter as Surveyor and Keeper of the King's pictures.

573. THE FAMILY OF FREDERICK, PRINCE OF WALES (*Plate* 212)

Marlborough House. 138 × 181½ in., 350,6 × 462,3 cm.

Signed and dated: *GKnapton* (initials in monogram) / *fe^t 1751.* This is repeated in the modern inscriptions identifying the sitters.

Augusta, Princess of Wales, wearing a black veil to indicate her recent widowhood (the Prince had died on 20 March 1751), is seated in a chair of state under a canopy, in front of a panel on which are worked the Prince of Wales's arms, and nurses the infant Princess Caroline Matilda. In the background hangs a portrait of the deceased Prince in robes of state with a view of Kew Palace in the distance; and on the right of the Princess is a statue of Britannia holding a spear and an olive branch, resting her left foot on a sphere; below this figure is a complex relief symbolic of the Constitution and the Hanoverian Succession and containing a lion crouched over documents inscribed ACT OF SETTLEMENT and MAGNA CHARTA. In the foreground are a portfolio, surveying instruments, and architects' drawing materials on an elevation inscribed *Survey of Kew House & Part of the Gardens.* On the left of the group are George, Prince of Wales, seated near his brother Edward, Duke of York (in military uniform), and examining with him a PLAN *of the* TOWN *and* FORTIFICATION^s *of* PORTSMOUTH; both boys wear the insignia of the Garter. In the foreground Prince Henry Frederick holds a model of a royal yacht to which Prince William Henry, wearing naval uniform, affixes the royal standard; Prince Frederick William, wearing 'coats', plays with two dogs. Princess Augusta stands by her mother's chair and Princess Louisa listens to Princess Elizabeth Caroline performing on a lute. In the corner is a toy drum and a pug pulling at a toy(?).

Presumably painted for the Princess of Wales; recorded in the Presence Chamber at Kensington (*A Catalogue of the Pictures, &c. . . . Kensington Palace* (1778), p. 3); sent to Windsor on 1 January 1805; later at Hampton Court (609) and sent to Marlborough House in 1901.

Literature: Law, 1881, 1898 (361), and p. 311; Waterhouse, *Painting in Britain,* p. 139.

Princess Caroline Matilda was born on 11 July 1751 and Knapton's elaborate tribute to the varied tastes and interests of the family of the late Prince of Wales and to the sanctity of the Hanoverian Succession and the British Constitution was presumably painted towards the end of that year. On 14 September 1752 Ellen Godolphin wrote that she had recently seen the picture, 'and really a fine sight it was.' On 26 September she wrote a full description of it in a further letter in which she stated: 'the Drapery is not finished; the Pictures are all good; the likeness of all the young I cant say anything of, but her Royal Highness I can see no resemblance of, but in all the children I can trace Father and Mother' (letters in Lord Harlech's MSS., printed in Hon. Mrs. Bulkeley-Owen, *History of Selattyn Parish* (n.d.), pp. 113–4). The portrait of the Prince of Wales in the background does not seem to have been based on an existing portrait and may have been invented by Knapton. The design as a whole is clearly inspired by Van Dyck's group of the Pembroke family at Wilton and by such derivations of it as groups of the Marlborough family at Blenheim by Closterman and Hudson. The child's tricorne on the steps appears to have been painted over a baby's feathered cap.

574. THE CHILDREN OF FREDERICK, PRINCE OF WALES: PRINCESS ELIZABETH with PRINCE WILLIAM HENRY and PRINCE HENRY FREDERICK (*Plate* 214)

Windsor Castle (2545). Pastel on paper: 34½ × 31½ in., 87,6 × 80 cm.

Signed and dated: *GKnapton* (initials in monogram) / *fecit 1748.*

Princess Elizabeth, a bunch of corn in her hair, holds a cornucopia; Prince Henry, naked and wearing a wreath of flowers, is partly supported by Prince William, who has grapes and vine leaves round his head.

Painted for the children's parents and recorded at Leicester House in 1748 (see below); with no. 577 recorded in store at Carlton House in 1816 (367: *Portraits of three of the royal children. Crayons*); later at Kew and Buckingham Palace (521).

Literature: Windsor (1922), p. 125.

On 15 June 1748 Knapton delivered *A large Picture in Crayons contaning 3 figures Viz: their Royl Higss Lady Elizabeth, Princ William, & Princ Henry, representing the Spring, Summer, & Winter, drawn according to his Royal Highess the Prince of Wales his directions, & Commands;* for this he was paid £52.10s. on 3 November 1748 (D. of Cornwall MSS., vol. XVII, f. 536).

575. PRINCE HENRY FREDERICK

Buckingham Palace. Pastel on paper, mounted on canvas: 13⅛ × 11 in., 33,3 × 27,9 cm.

Head and shoulders in a white frock.

Probably, with no. 576, among the *Sixteen crayon portraits of the royal family* at Carlton House in 1816 (514); recorded at Buckingham House in 1876 (*V.R. inv.,* no. 740).

Formerly described as a portrait of Princess Louisa Ann, no. 575 is extremely close to the portrait of Prince Henry in no. 574. It was presumably painted in the same year.

576. PRINCESS LOUISA ANN (?)

Buckingham Palace. Pastel on paper, mounted on canvas: $13\frac{7}{8} \times 11\frac{1}{2}$ in., 35,2 × 29,2 cm.

Head and shoulders, wearing a lace cap.

See no. 575; recorded at Buckingham Palace in 1876 (*V.R. inv.*, no. 741).

Formerly described as a portrait of Princess Caroline Matilda. If no. 576 was drawn at the same time as no. 575, *i.e.*, in 1748, it is more likely to represent her older sister.

Manner of George Knapton

577. THE CHILDREN OF FREDERICK, PRINCE OF WALES: PRINCESS AUGUSTA with PRINCE EDWARD and PRINCE GEORGE

Windsor Castle (2544). Pastel on paper: $34\frac{7}{8} \times 30\frac{1}{2}$ in., 88,6 × 77,5 cm.; there are apparently additions on the left of *c.* $1\frac{3}{4}$ in. and, on the right, of *c.* 2 in.

The Princess between her two brothers: Prince Edward, as a putto, crowning her with a wreath of flowers, Prince George, as Cupid, embracing her.

Probably painted for the children's parents; recorded with no. 574 in store at Carlton House in 1816 (366: *Portraits of three of the royal children. Crayons*; the 1816 label is still on the back); later at Kew and Buckingham Palace (522).

Literature: Windsor (1922), p. 125.

Formerly attributed to Knapton, no. 577 is close to him in style, but slightly feebler in quality, less bright in tone and less richly impasted than no. 574. If, as seems probable, the children are correctly identified, no. 577 would be slightly earlier than no. 574, probably *c.* 1742.

Jean-Etienne Liotard

1702–89. Native of Geneva. Portrait painter who specialised in pastels and in miniatures on enamel and ivory; worked in Paris, Italy, Constantinople and Vienna. He was in London from 1753 or 1754 to 1755. He was later established in Geneva, but made journeys to London and Vienna. The set of portraits painted for the Princess of Wales is comparable to his series of portraits of the Habsburg and Bourbon families. The Princess's disbursements included, in 1755, payments to two men *to fetch a Large Picter from Mr Leotarld . . . to Send it to Kew* . . . (D. of Cornwall MSS., vol. XXXVII (1)); this picture was probably not one of Liotard's royal portraits.

578. AUGUSTA, PRINCESS OF WALES (*Plate* 217)

Windsor Castle (1040). Pastel on paper: $25\frac{1}{2} \times 20\frac{1}{4}$ in., 64,8 × 51,4 cm.

Head and shoulders in a pale blue gown trimmed with ermine.

Recorded with no. 579 by Horace Walpole at Buckingham House: 'The late Prince & Princess of Wales by Liotard; hers extremely like, but the body very flat' (*Visits*, p. 79); slightly later in the Queen's Private Drawing Room at St. James's and taken thence to Windsor *c.* 1804–5.

Literature: for the series, N. S. Trivas, 'Liotard's Portraits of Frederick Lewis, Prince of Wales, and his Family', *Burl. Mag.* vol. LXVIII (1936), pp. 117–8; R. A., *King's Pictures* (73–5); Waterhouse, *Painting in Britain*, p. 244.

Liotard was at work on the series of portraits of Augusta, Princess of Wales, and her family early in 1754. On 14 February 1754 George Bubb Dodington waited upon the Princess, 'who was sitting to Leotardi for her picture. Lady Augusta only was with her' (*Diary*, ed. H. Penruddocke Wyndham (1784), p. 261). On 15 August 1755 Liotard signed the receipt for payment of an account submitted to the Princess: *Memoire pour S.A. Royalle Madame la Princesse de Galles des portraits que lui a remis Mr Liotard*

4 portraits en pastel avec leurs bordures & glaces	*Guinees 108*
3 portraits en miniature	*60*
pour une grande bordure avec glace ⅌ *le portrait du* Pce *defunt*	*$5\frac{1}{2}$*

(W. R. A., Geo. 55448)

The portraits appear still to be in their original frames. In the nineteenth century nos. 578 and 579 were attributed to Knapton (*V.R. inv.*).

579. FREDERICK, PRINCE OF WALES (*Plate* 218)

Windsor Castle (1039). Pastel on paper: $26\frac{3}{4} \times 21\frac{3}{4}$ in., 67,9 × 55,2 cm.

Head and shoulders, wearing a richly embroidered coat, with the ribbon and star of the Garter, and an ermine-lined cloak.

See no. 578.

No. 579 is clearly a posthumous portrait painted by Liotard (see no. 578) to complete the set of portraits of the Princess of Wales and her family. It is probably based on a portrait of the Prince of *c.* 1740–5. See no. 628.

580. PRINCESS AUGUSTA (*Plate* 219)

Windsor Castle (2471). Pastel on vellum: $15\frac{1}{2} \times 12$ in., 39,4 × 30,5 cm.

Head and shoulders looking to the right.

Probably drawn in 1754 (see no. 578). There are probable references to Liotard's nine companion portraits of the children of the Princess of Wales in their mother's disbursements: in 1755 two men were paid fifteen shillings and sixpence for *taking Doune 9: picters of the Royall Family at Pallmall* and in October 1756 six shillings *for takeing Doune, and hanging up Pickters of the Royall Family, in the Green Dressing Roome* at Leicester House (D. of Cornwall MSS., vols. XXXVII (1), XXXVIII (i)). The portraits of the children were later at Carlton House (*Carlton House*, 1816 (514): *Sixteen crayon portraits of the royal family*; this group presumably included all nine portraits and the 1816 label is still on all of them except no. 586); in the inventory of Carlton House in 1819 (450) the Liotards are separately listed: *Nine Portraits of the Royal Family. Liotard. Paper. Crayons.* The set was later at Buckingham Palace (524–7, 529, 530–2, 751).

581. GEORGE, PRINCE OF WALES, later GEORGE III (*Plate* 215)

Windsor Castle (2470). Pastel on vellum: $16 \times 11\frac{3}{4}$ in., 40,6 × 29,8 cm.

Head and shoulders in a white coat laced with silver, wearing the ribbon of the Garter.

See no. 580.

A version is in the collection of the Duke of Brunswick and a version in miniature, signed and dated 1754, is in the collection of The Queen of the Netherlands. No. 581 seems to have been used by Reynolds for his three-quarter-length of the Prince at Windsor (2531) of 1759. It is ironical that for his portrait of the Prince Reynolds seems not to have had a sitting, but to have been compelled to copy the portrait by an artist of whom he strongly disapproved. A weaker pastel of Prince George at Wykeham Abbey appears to be related to Liotard, whose pastel of the 3rd Viscount Downe, a Lord of the Bedchamber to the Prince, is in the same collection.

582. EDWARD AUGUSTUS, DUKE OF YORK (*Plate* 216)

Windsor Castle (2473). Pastel on vellum: $15\frac{7}{8} \times 12\frac{1}{4}$ in., 40,3 × 31,1 cm.

Head and shoulders in a blue coat wearing the ribbon and star of the Garter.

See no. 580.

A version is in the collection of the Duke of Brunswick. See no. 589.

583. PRINCESS ELIZABETH CAROLINE (*Plate* 220)

Windsor Castle (2472). Pastel on vellum: $15\frac{1}{2} \times 11\frac{7}{8}$ in., 39,4 × 30,2 cm.

Head and shoulders, looking to the left, with a sprig of blue flowers in her hair.

See no. 580.

See no. 590.

584. WILLIAM HENRY, DUKE OF GLOU-CESTER (*Plate* 221)

Windsor Castle (2477). Pastel on vellum: $15\frac{7}{8} \times 12\frac{1}{4}$ in., 40,3 × 31,1 cm.

Head and shoulders in a pale blue-green coat over a red waistcoat.

See no. 580.

585. HENRY FREDERICK, DUKE OF CUMBERLAND (*Plate* 222)

Windsor Castle (2476). Pastel on vellum: $15\frac{3}{4} \times 12$ in., 40 × 30,5 cm.

Head and shoulders in a blue coat, seated at a card-table on which he has built a card-house.

See no. 580.

No. 585 was engraved and published according to Liotard's directions.

586. PRINCESS LOUISA ANN (*Plate* 223)

Windsor Castle (2469). Pastel on vellum: $15\frac{3}{4} \times 12$ in., 40 × 30,5 cm.

Head and shoulders in a lace cap, seated in a chair.

See no. 580.

Engraved by R. Houston.

587. PRINCE FREDERICK WILLIAM (*Plate* 224)

Windsor Castle (2468). Pastel on vellum: 16×12 in., 40,6 × 30,5 cm.

Head and shoulders in a red coat laced with silver.

See no. 580.

588. PRINCESS CAROLINE MATILDA (*Plate* 225)

Windsor Castle (2474). Pastel on vellum: $16 \times 12\frac{1}{4}$ in., 40,6 × 31,1 cm.

Head and shoulders in a lace cap.

See no. 580.

After Jean-Etienne Liotard

589. EDWARD AUGUSTUS, DUKE OF YORK

Kew (*Hampton Court no. 1460*). $25\frac{1}{4} \times 21$ in., 64,1 × 53,3 cm.

Sold at Sotheby's, 9 July 1947 (55), as a portrait of Frederick, Prince of Wales, and later purchased by His Majesty King George VI and Her Majesty Queen Elizabeth.

A derivation in oil from no. 582.

590. PRINCESS ELIZABETH CAROLINE

Windsor Castle (1031). Pastel: $15\frac{1}{4} \times 12\frac{1}{4}$ in., 38,1 × 30,5 cm.

Recorded at Windsor in 1878 (*V.R. inv.*).

A copy, with slight variations, of no. 583.

David Morier

1705?–1770. Swiss military and sporting painter, who came to England from Berne in 1743. His name is normally associated with standard types of military and equestrian subjects and his *œuvre* has not been adequately disentangled; his documented pictures are of higher quality than the paintings that usually go by his name and he seems to have inspired a large number of imitators. Royal payments to him are recorded between 1764 and 1767, for 'small Pictures' and 'Pictures of Horses' (W. R. A., Geo. 17117, 17127, 17131, 17145, 17181).

591. GEORGE II (*Plate* 200)

Windsor Castle (3027). $113\frac{1}{2} \times 94\frac{1}{2}$ in., 288,3 × 240 cm.

Riding in a scarlet coat over a breastplate, wearing the ribbon and star of the Garter and holding a baton in his right hand. In the background is a battle with French troops drawn up in the distance and, nearer at hand, a group of officers on horseback, the artillery in action and British troops advancing.

Probably presented by the sitter to Charles, 2nd Marquess of Rockingham, Lord of the Bedchamber to George II, 1751–62; Sir Henry Ellis stated that it was given by Lord Fitzwilliam (presumably the 2nd Earl, nephew and heir of Lord Rockingham) to George IV, who had admired it, in exchange for a portrait of George IV when Prince of Wales (MS. *Memoranda of Original Royal Portraits* (1822 and later) in office of the Surveyor of The Queen's Pictures, f. 21v.); placed on the staircase at Carlton House (*Carlton House*, 1816 (64)); replaced by Reynolds's copy of Guido Reni's *St. Michael* and recorded in the King's Closet at St. James's in 1832 (*Carlton Palace* (64)).

The portrait, probably painted *c.* 1745, was engraved by Simon Ravenet, when it was in the possession of Lord Rockingham, as by David Morier, and it was probably the source of the many repetitions and variations on a much smaller scale (*e.g.*, nos. 592 and 593 and in the possession of Sir Danvers Osborn). The background is presumably intended to commemorate the victory at Dettingen in 1743 (see no. 554) at which the King led his troops into battle. There is a *pentimento* in the King's sword, which was at first painted outside the coat. It has been stated that Stubbs's famous *Whistlejacket* still at Wentworth Woodhouse, was intended by Lord Rockingham to become an equestrian portrait of George III and a companion piece to no. 591 (W. Shaw Sparrow, *British Sporting Artists* (1922), p. 120).

Attributed to David Morier

592. GEORGE II

Buckingham Palace. 50 ×40 in., 127 ×101,6 cm.

Riding in military uniform; in the background is a battle in which French and British troops are engaged, with artillery in action on the left.

Probably among the pictures (which included a portrait of George II) offered to George IV by Benjamin Louis Vulliamy, as from his father's property, in a letter of 28 February 1812 (*The Letters of George IV*, ed. A. Aspinall (1938), vol. 1, p. 30); the portrait of George II *in a Gilt Frame on Horseback by Morea* was received at Carlton House from Vulliamy on 9 November 1812 and sent to Simpson two days later to be cleaned . . . *on a Dark Gray Horse* (Jutsham, *R/D.*, ff. 122, 231, measurements given as 50 ×40 in.). Recorded in store at Carlton House in 1816 (267; the 1816 label was recorded on the back in 1876 (*V.R. inv.*)); sent to the King's Lodge on 27 September 1823; later at Buckingham Palace (492).

Literature: Buckingham Palace, 1909, p. 138.

A reduced, apparently contemporary, derivation from no. 591, with slight variations in the figure, uniform, harness and background; the King's horse is grey, whereas in no. 591 it is brown. It is unlikely that no. 592 is by Morier himself. A version is at Wykeham Abbey.

593. GEORGE II

Windsor Castle (446). 50 ×40 in., 127 ×101,6 cm.

Riding in profile to the left in uniform with a baton in his right hand.

Purchased with no. 595 by George IV from Phillips and recorded at Carlton House in 1816 (265) in store (Jutsham, *R/D.*, f. 305, under 18 May 1814 as having been 'some months in the House under consideration but not determined on till this day'; the 1816 label, and another recording the purchase from Phillips in 1814, are on the back).

A reduced and probably contemporary derivation from no. 591, with variations, primarily in the background, the colour of the horse (grey) and the position of the king's head. It is possible that the head has been altered from the usual position in this type. No. 593 does not seem to be by Morier, but to be softer and looser in handling. The painting of the horse is reminiscent of Seymour.

594. GEORGE II

Windsor Castle (1351). 20 ×16 in., 50,8 ×40,6 cm.

Seated on a white horse, holding a baton in his right hand and wearing the ribbon and star of the Garter on a scarlet coat over a breastplate; a cavalry engagement rages in the background.

Probably the *Small Painting. Portrait of George The Second. on a Cream Colour Horse* received on 22 July 1811 at Carlton House from Mr. Troup from General Hammond (Jutsham, *R/D*, f. 171); a 'handsome Gilt Frame' for it was received from Smith on 21 January 1812 (*ibid.*, f. 183) and it was recorded in the Armoury at Carlton House in 1816 (460).

No. 594 is of no quality, but is of a different type (*c.* 1755–60?) from the standard portraits of the King associated with Morier.

595. FREDERICK, PRINCE OF WALES

Windsor Castle (444). 49⅜ ×40 in., 125,4 ×101,6 cm.

Riding to the left in a landscape, on a rearing grey horse with elaborate red and gold harness, wearing the ribbon and star of the Garter over a blue coat and holding a baton in his right hand.

Purchased with no. 593 by George IV from Phillips and recorded at Carlton House in 1816 (266) in store (Jutsham, *R/D*, f. 305; the 1816 label is still on the back).

Probably painted *c.* 1750, possibly by the same hand as no. 593; there is the same reminiscence of Seymour in the painting of the horse. A version is at Wykeham Abbey.

596. FREDERICK, PRINCE OF WALES

Windsor Castle (1415). 49⅛ ×39¾ in., 124,8 ×101 cm.

Riding to the left on a brown horse, with a baton in his right hand, wearing the ribbon and star of the Garter; in the background are a review and a group of general officers that includes the Marquess of Granby.

Bought by George IV for ten guineas from Mr. Cutter on 14 April 1818 (W. R. A., Geo. 27015; Jutsham, *PP*, f. 41) and recorded at Carlton House (*Carlton House*, 1816, additional (540); the 1816 label is on the back); sent to Cumberland Lodge on 1 October 1823 (Jutsham, *D*, f. 45).

The type of head is close to and probably dependent on no. 595, but no. 596 is by an inferior hand, possibly closer to Morier, and the design is apparently dependent on no. 591.

Artists Unknown : Military Paintings

597. GEORGE II AT A REVIEW

Windsor Castle (405). 48 ×141¼ in., 121,9 ×358,8 cm.

The King on horseback with general officers on an eminence overlooking a plain on which cavalry and infantry are drawn up; those nearest the royal party are probably the (1st?) Foot Guards. The officer beside the King, wearing the ribbon of the Garter, is probably the Duke of Cumberland.

Vertue recorded in 1750 at Hampton Court, in a Waiting Room next to the Bedchamber, *Two large pieces representing a Review of his Majesty's Forces at Hanover* (Vertue inv., *Hampton Court*, f. 6); these may have included no. 597, which was in Buckingham House in 1819 (862: *George the 2nd with Duke of Cumberland and Officers at a Review*).[1]

Probably painted *c.* 1745–50. The site and occasion of the review have not been identified. Formerly attributed to Wootton, no. 597 seems to be by a specialist in military pieces, perhaps working for George II or the Duke of Cumberland, close in style, for example, to the painter(s) of nos. 599 and 600.

598. THE BATTLE OF CULLODEN

Kensington Palace. 48½ ×80⅝ in., 123,2 ×204,8 cm.

An extensive view across 'that plain muir' from the high ground near Culloden Parks: on the left is the King's army, under the command of the Duke of Cumberland, drawn up in position; on the right the rebels advancing upon them.

Perhaps the picture recorded at Cumberland Lodge in the Guide to *Windsor, and its Environs* (1768, 1774, pp. 87–8): 'In the bedchamber . . . the battle of Culloden'. At Buckingham House in 1819 (863); later at Windsor and Buckingham Palace.

Literature: Buckingham Palace, 1909, p. 130.

The battle was fought on 16 April 1746, 'a dark, misty, rainy day', when the King's army routed the forces led by Prince Charles Edward. No. 598 seems to be a very accurate

1. It should also be noted that on 26 April 1812 Lord Yarmouth settled a debt for pictures bought by the Prince Regent, including £73 10s. to Cutty for a *Review picture* (W. R. A., Geo. IV, 26925)

statement of the dispositions of the two armies and of the moment when, in face of the King's army and galled by the preliminary cannonade, the Prince's Highlanders advanced in a disorganised fashion. Those on the centre and right broke through the first rank of Cumberland's infantry, but (in the foreground of no. 598) the left, composed mainly of the Macdonalds, disgruntled at being deprived of their hereditary place of honour on the right wing and led by the Duke of Perth (perhaps the figure on horseback urging his troops to the attack), approached half-heartedly the cavalry opposite them. This, on the left of no. 598, consisted of the Duke of Kingston's regiment of Light Horse and one squadron of Lord Cobham's Dragoons. No. 598 was probably painted for the Duke of Cumberland as a record of his victory. It is conceivable that it was painted by Thomas Sandby. He was in the Duke's service, accompanied him on his Scottish campaign and made drawings for him in the Highlands; these include a plan of the battle of Culloden, drawn at Inverness within a few days of the battle, and a 'Sketch of the Field of Battle' which is very close indeed to no. 598 and represents a very slightly earlier moment in the action (A. P. Oppé, *The Drawings of Paul and Thomas Sandby . . . at Windsor Castle* (1947), pp. 4, 45–6).

599. AN INCIDENT IN THE REBELLION OF 1745

Windsor Castle (1285). 23¾ × 39⅛ in., 60,3 × 99,4 cm.

A hand-to-hand combat between a party of Highland warriors and an officer, sergeant and privates of a Grenadier Company of the 4th or King's Own (Barrel's) Regiment, with a Battalion Company officer and drummer of the regiment behind.

One of a set of four battle-pieces recorded in General Taylor's[1] room at Buckingham House in 1819 (865–8).

Usually attributed to Morier and stated to have been painted for the Duke of Cumberland. No. 599 and the three other canvases in the set are clearly by the same hand, which is close in style to nos. 597 and 600, and they all illustrate actions on the same scale between troops of different nationalities. The series was thus possibly painted to illustrate various European uniforms and encounters and no. 599 may not record an actual episode in the rebellion or in the battle of Culloden. At the battle (see no. 598) the 4th Regiment of Foot was on the left wing of the Duke of Cumberland's front line, opposite the Stewarts, Camerons and the Athol brigade. The Highlanders in the centre and right of their line 'attacking sword in hand, broke through Barrel's and Monro's in the first line, and pushed on to the second', but were there destroyed by Sempill's regiment (*The Forty-Five*, ed. C. S. Terry (1922), p. 140). The English and Highland troops are apparently recorded in no. 599 with great accuracy as to their uniforms and accoutrements (see C. C. P. Lawson, *A History of the Uniforms of the British Army*, vol. II (1941), pp. 35–8, 61). No. 599 is a particularly valuable record of Highland dress and weapons. None of the tartans can be identified with those in use today and the clansmen wear jackets, plaids and trews of different setts. It has been stated (C. C. P. Lawson, *op. cit.*; J. Prebble, *Culloden* (1961), pp. 238–9) that the Highlanders in no. 599 were drawn from prisoners captured at Culloden.

600. AN ENCAMPMENT

Windsor Castle (2962). 53½ × 67¼ in., 135,9 × 170,8 cm.

An encampment with artillery in the foreground and middle distance and a distant view of London (?).

1. This was presumably Lt.-Genl. Sir Herbert Taylor (1775–1839).

First recorded in General Taylor's room at Buckingham House in 1819 (864; *An Encampment with Portraits of several Officers*); later at Windsor and Buckingham Palace (493).

It has been suggested (H. G. Farmer, *History of the Royal Artillery Band* (1954), p. 3) that the scene represented is the camp at Byfleet in July–October 1756. The six greys on the left are stated to be drawing the Great Kettledrums of the Ordnance, played by Cotterel Barret as Kettledrummer who is escorted by two trumpeters; they all wear the King's livery. An artillery piper and drummer are seated on the left and the principal mounted figure in the group in the centre is perhaps Captain William Phillips (1731 ?–81), then A.D.C. to Sir John Ligonier (Lt.-General of Ordnance) and later Major-General of the Royal Artillery. In the nineteenth century the canvas was attributed to Wootton, but it is far too undistinguished in quality for him and seems much closer to Morier.

Samuel Scott

1702 ?–1772. Marine and topographical painter. As a topographical painter he was probably influenced by Canaletto's work in England, 1746–55. Scott's name has come to be associated with views of London and the river which reveal the influence of Canaletto but are usually far inferior to pictures certainly by Scott. The group of such views in the royal collection contains a number of the most popular of these standard views and illustrates the problems they pose (see Hilda F. Finberg, 'Canaletto in England', *Walpole Soc.*, vol. IX (1921), p. 51). Almost all are by different hands and none of the hands comes near to Scott in quality. None of the pictures seem to be original *ad vivum* views and a number are associated with engravings. Nor is there evidence to associate any of them with William James, who was exhibiting in London, 1761–71, and whose name is often applied, invariably without evidence, to such pieces, which were being produced in quantity, probably long after Scott himself had ceased to paint. The pictures were acquired at different times during the nineteenth century and therefore do not form part of an integrated series.

Manner or School of Samuel Scott

601. ST. JAMES'S PALACE

Buckingham Palace. 30 × 50 in., 76,2 × 127 cm.

A view of the Tudor Gatehouse and the north-east corner of the palace, with the Queen's Chapel and Marlborough House beyond and Pall Mall leading to St. Martin-in-the-Fields in the distance.

Purchased by His Majesty King George VI.

Probably painted *c.* 1745; a companion piece to no. 603, and a good version of a favourite design, of which variants exist; it is very close to the view engraved by T. Bowles, published in 1754. See also no. 602.

602. ST. JAMES'S PALACE

St. James's Palace. 25¼ × 40¼ in., 64,1 × 102,2 cm.

Purchased for the royal collection by Queen Victoria in 1891 (P.R.O., L. C. 1/552 II, 97).

A variant of no. 601, but of less good quality. A version belongs to the Lady Lever Art Gallery.

603. THE HORSE GUARDS

Buckingham Palace. 30 × 50¼ in., 76,2 × 127,6 cm.

A view of the new Horse Guards and the Admiralty, with the canal in St. James's Park on the left and a number of figures: some are watching a procession, which has turned into the Horse Guards from the Mall and is probably a royal procession to a State Opening of Parliament.

Purchased by His Majesty King George VI.

Probably painted *c.* 1755 and by the same hand as the companion piece, no. 601. Versions are recorded on the art-market in London (*e.g.,* Sotheby's, 20 December 1945 (115), and Christie's, 23 June 1950 (54)). No. 603 may have been painted from T. Bowles's engraving which is inscribed as *Canaletti delin,* presumably records a design by Canaletto, and is very close indeed to no. 603. No. 603 is less closely connected with Canaletto's painting of the Old Horse Guards in the collection of the Earl of Malmesbury (W. G. Constable, *Canaletto* (1962), no. 415).

604. THE HORSE GUARDS

Kensington Palace. 25¼ × 44⅜ in., 64,1 × 112,7 cm.

A view of the Horse Guards from the east end of the Mall in St. James's Park, with a detachment of Foot Guards drawn up on parade.

Recorded at Hampton Court in 1849 (*The Stranger's Guide* (1022), later inv. no. 1022) with an attribution to William James.

Literature: Law, 1881, 1898 (919).

Probably painted *c.* 1755; no. 604 is in a particularly fine carved frame. Versions are recorded on the art-market in London and in the collection of Bertram Currie.

605. THE THAMES AT LAMBETH

Kensington Palace. 30¼ × 50⅛ in., 76,8 × 127,3 cm.

A view of the river, looking across from Millbank Terrace to Lambeth Palace and Lambeth Church with Westminster Bridge and St. Paul's in the distance; on the stern of a barge in the foreground is inscribed: *AC 1740,* probably intended to be read as a signature by Canaletto.

Purchased for the royal collection by Queen Victoria in 1892.

A version of a view painted *c.* 1745. The view is very close to that engraved by Maurer in that year. No. 605 is probably by the same hand as no. 610.

606. THE THAMES AT WESTMINSTER

St. James's Palace. 24 × 44⅛ in., 61 × 112,1 cm.

A view of the river looking towards Westminster Bridge with the Abbey in the distance and, on the right, York Water Gate and the York Buildings Water Tower.

Recorded at Hampton Court in 1849 (*The Stranger's Guide* (1025), later inv., no. 1032) with an attribution to William James; later at Kensington.

Literature: Law, 1881, 1898 (925).

An unimportant version of a view of *c.* 1750. Other versions are in the Tate Gallery (1328), at Gosford House and in the collection of the Earl of Malmesbury; see also no. 607. A variant is in the Ferens Art Gallery, Hull. The design is close to that engraved by Boydell and is probably connected with Canaletto's painting in the collection of Lady Janet Douglas-Pennant (see W. G. Constable, *Canaletto* (1962), no. 427).

607. THE THAMES AT WESTMINSTER

Kensington Palace. 24⅛ × 39½ in., 61,3 × 100,3 cm.

Probably purchased for the royal collection by Queen Victoria in 1892 (P.R.O., L. C. 1/570, 83); recorded at St. James's in 1894 with an attribution to Scott.

A variant of no. 606, probably by the same hand as no. 609. A version is at Mentmore; others were in the Bourke sale at Christie's, 20 November 1925 (25), and in the collection of Lord Boyne.

608. THE THAMES AT SOMERSET HOUSE

Kensington Palace. 23½ × 43¾ in., 60 × 111,1 cm.

A view of the river bank from Somerset House down to St. Paul's Cathedral.

Recorded at Hampton Court in 1849 (*The Stranger's Guide* (1023), later inv. no. 1023) with an attribution to William James.

Literature: Law, 1881, 1898 (921).

A version of a view painted *c.* 1750; another version was in the Bourke sale at Christie's, 20 November 1925 (24), and another is in the collection of the Earl of Malmesbury. See no. 609.

609. THE THAMES AT SOMERSET HOUSE

Kensington Palace. 24 × 39⅝ in., 61 × 100,1 cm.

On the stern of a barge on the river is inscribed the probably false signature: *S. Scott.*

Probably purchased for the royal collection by Queen Victoria in 1892 (P.R.O., L. C. 1/570, 83); recorded at Kensington in 1907 (Law, *Kensington* (1907), p. 24).

A variant of no. 608, painted by a different hand, probably the hand responsible for no. 607.

610. THE THAMES AT THE SAVOY

Kensington Palace. 30¼ × 50¼ in., 76,8 × 127,6 cm.

A view across the river, on which are state barges rowing towards Somerset House, to the Savoy with Cuper's Gardens on the near bank; on the stern of one of the boats is inscribed PR.

Purchased for the royal collection by Queen Victoria in 1892 (P.R.O., *ibid.*).

A version of a view painted *c.* 1750 (see nos. 611 and 612), probably by the same hand as no. 605. A version was in the Bourke sale at Christie's, 20 November 1925 (24); another is at Parham Park.

611. THE THAMES AT THE SAVOY

St. James's Palace. 23½ × 43¾ in., 60 × 111,1 cm.

Recorded at Hampton Court in 1849 (*The Stranger's Guide* (1024), later inv. no. 1031) with an attribution to William James.

Literature: Law, 1881, 1898 (923).

A variant of the same view as no. 610, but by a different hand; a variant is in the Ferens Art Gallery, Hull.

612. THE THAMES AT THE SAVOY

Kensington Palace. 24 × 44⅛ in., 61 × 112,1 cm.

Bought by George IV from Colnaghi on 3 April 1819 as by Scott (W. R. A., Geo. 26465; Jutsham, *Receipts,* f. 62; *Carlton House,* 1816, additional (556); the 1816 label is still on the back); later at Hampton Court (1045) with an attribution to William James.

Literature: Law, 1881, 1898 (885).

A variant of the same view as no. 610, by a different and probably inferior hand.

613. THE THAMES AND THE FLEET CANAL

Kensington Palace. 23½ × 43¾ in., 60 × 111,1 cm.

A view of the river from the Timber Wharf of the Carpenters

Company down to Bridewell Foot Bridge across the Fleet Canal to the City Wharf and Dock, Blackfriars Stairs and the large house, formerly occupied by Dr. Salmon, but by this time converted into a warehouse; on the extreme right is Mr. Howell's Timber Wharf, destroyed by fire in 1756.

Recorded at Hampton Court in 1849 (*The Stranger's Guide* (1020), later inv. no. 1043) with an attribution to William James.

Literature: Law, 1881, 1898 (883).

A version of a view painted *c.* 1750. A good version, attributed to Scott, belongs to the Corporation of the City of London, and another is in the Victoria and Albert Museum.

614. THE THAMES AT LONDON BRIDGE

Kensington Palace. 23½ × 43⅝ in., 59,7 × 110,8 cm.

A view across the river to Fishmongers' Hall, with the Monument rising behind it, and London Bridge.

Recorded at Hampton Court in 1849 (*The Stranger's Guide* (1021), later inv. no. 1044) with an attribution to William James.

Literature: Law, 1881, 1898 (884).

A version of a view painted *c.* 1750; another version was in the Bourke sale at Christie's, 20 November 1925 (25).

615. THE THAMES AT GREENWICH

Kensington Palace. 24⅛ × 40 in., 61,3 × 101,6 cm.

A view down the river towards Greenwich Hospital and, on the right, the church of St. Alphege; beyond are the park and the Observatory.

Stated (*V.R. inv.*) to have been purchased in 1846 by the Commissioner of Woods and Forests for Hampton Court, where it was recorded in 1849 (*The Stranger's Guide* (1027), later inv. no. 1079) with an attribution to William James.

Literature: Law, 1881, 1898 (914).

Probably painted *c.* 1750; a variant was on the art-market in London in 1921; another is in the Athenaeum Club.

Artists Unknown: Early Georgian Topographical Paintings

616. A ROYAL HUNTING PARTY AT GÖHRDE IN 1725

Windsor Castle (1311). 53¾ × 67¼ in., 136,5 × 170,8 cm.

Inscribed: *Göhrde. A./1725.*

George I with members of his family and suite, and Frederick William I of Prussia with a smaller suite, hunting the stag in the forest at Göhrde. The house with its stables and outbuildings is seen on the right, surrounded by horses, grooms, huntsmen and footguards. The hunt is accompanied by huntsmen in royal livery blowing horns.

The principal figures are numbered on the canvas and identified by a contemporary key inscribed at the bottom of the picture: *1. Georg der 1te. 2. Friederich Printz. 3. Ernst Aug: Duc de Jorck. 4. Fried: König v: Preusen. 5. Mülord Townsend Stats Secret: 6. Müladÿ Townsend. 7. Hardenberg Marschall. 8. Fabrice Cammerherr. 9. Ilten Geheimt: Krieges Rath. 10. Ilten General=Adjutant. 11. Ned Finsch 12. Mülord Albemarle. 13. Beaulieu Ober=Jägermeister. 14. Graff von der Bückeburg. 15. Crumkau Preuss:General. 16. Grote Cammerherr. 17. Palant Osnabrükis: Oberstalmeister. 18. Hardenberg Hoff=Juncker. 19. Oenhausen Forsmeister. 20. Pontpietin Obrister. 21.*

Oenhausen Cammer Juncker. 22. Wangenheim Cammer Juncker. 23. Mehemet und [24] Mustapha Cammer Dieners. 25. Piqueurs. 26. Ulrich.

Presumably painted in Hanover: received at Carlton House from Hanover on 24 May 1819: *... Landscape & Hounds... Each Figure described by its Number . . . was brought to Carlton House by the Hanoverian Messenger, some time since − but not unpacked till now* (Jutsham, *Receipts*, f. 78; *Carlton House*, 1816, additional (559); the 1816 label is still on the back).

Probably painted to record a hunt during George I's visit to Hanover in the second half of 1725. He left England soon after Parliament had risen for the summer recess; in Hanover he signed the Treaty of Hanover on 3 September between Great Britain, France and Prussia; and he returned to England on 3 January 1726. He had presumably been accompanied by Charles, 2nd Viscount Townshend (1675–1738), Secretary of State for the North, 1714–16, 1721–30, and by Lady Townshend (1686–1726), a sister of Sir Robert Walpole; by William Keppel, 2nd Earl of Albemarle (1702–54), Lord of the Bedchamber to George II, 1722–51, and Groom of the Stole, 1751–4; and by Edward Finch, a Groom of the Bedchamber and Master of the Robes to George II. The King's two Turkish attendants, Mahomet (*d.* 1726) and Mustapha, had been captured by the Imperialist forces in Hungary. No. 616 provides a valuable topographical record of the forest of Göhrde in Hanover, west of the Elbe and famous for its trees and game. The estate had come to George I on the death of his father-in-law, the Duke of Celle. The hunting-box had been built in the forest in 1689 and enlarged and altered by Giacomo Quirini. It was a favourite hunting-seat of the Hanoverian family. In 1709 the Electress Sophia wrote of it: 'there are no lively pleasures here except for hunting men . . . the stables are at least as beautiful as the Orangery at Herrenhausen, but they do not smell so good.'

617. ST. JAMES'S PARK AND THE MALL (*Plate 208*)

Buckingham Palace. 41 × 54½ in., 104,1 × 138,4 cm.

The east end of the Mall with Westminster Abbey and the canal in the distance, and a glimpse of Horse Guards Parade. The scene is crowded with figures from many walks of life: milkmaids with their cows selling milk, clergymen, sailors, soldiers (including those in Highland and Hanoverian regiments), orientals and people of fashion. The stout figure of a man, seen from behind on the left, wearing a hat and the ribbon of the Garter, is probably George II. Near the centre of the composition is Frederick, Prince of Wales, with a group of companions who include a gentleman wearing the ribbon and star of the Garter;[1] among the figures following the Prince is a gentleman wearing the insignia of the Bath.

In the collection of George IV; in 1808 Edward Wyatt submitted his account (W. R. A., Geo. 26860) for £45 for a frame for *Painting of View in St James's Park*, and the frame (which survives) was delivered to Carlton House on 23 November 1809 (Jutsham, *R/D*, f. 101); recorded in store at Carlton House in 1816 (215: ... *called Hogarth*); later at Windsor (427) and St. James's.

Literature: R. A., *King's Pictures* (501); Arts Council, *British Life*, 1953 (22).

Probably painted *c.* 1745. The early attribution to Hogarth, under which no. 617 was lent by the Prince Regent to the British Institution in 1814, was called in question at the time

---

1. This figure is perhaps the 1st Duke of Newcastle (1693–1768).

by Galt, who suggested that it might have been painted by Geminiani (J. Nichols and G. Steevens, *The Genuine Works of William Hogarth...*, vol. III (1817), pp. 166, 349). It was later attributed to Samuel Wale (*Anecdotes of William Hogarth, written by himself...* (1833), pp. 366–7) and more recently, but on insufficient grounds, by Col. M. H. Grant, to Anthony Highmore (letter of 28 October 1946 in archives of the Surveyor of The Queen's Pictures). Wale's documented works are far less ambitious and competent than no. 617, which may not be by an English hand; it is apparently influenced, particularly in the figures and groups, by Henri Gravelot.

The scene in no. 617 well illustrates an account in 1725 of the 'magnificent place for the game of pall-mall, which extends the entire length of the park, and is bordered on either side by a long avenue of trees... no longer used for the game, but is a promenade... Society comes to walk here on fine, warm days, from seven to ten in the evening, and in winter from one to three o'clock... the park is so crowded at times that you cannot help touching your neighbour. Some people come to see, some to be seen, and others to seek their fortunes; for many priestesses of Venus are abroad... all on the look-out for adventures...' (*A Foreign View of England in the Reigns of George I & George II*, ed. Mme. van Muyden (1902), pp. 47–8).

618. A PROCESSION IN THE STRAND

Kensington Palace. 30¾ × 48½ in., 78,1 × 123,2 cm.

A procession, in which the carriages are followed by trumpeters and cavalry and preceded by riders and walking figures, passing down the Strand, watched by a crowd of spectators on foot, in coaches and in carts; in the background is the gateway to Old Somerset House and the houses and shops on either side.

In the collection of George IV and recorded at Carlton House in 1816 (223: *A view, supposed to be that of the Old Horse-Guards, with the King going to the house*; the 1816 label is still on the back); later at Windsor (1184) and Buckingham Palace.

Literature: Arts Council, *British Life*, 1953 (57).

Probably painted *c.* 1745. No. 618 has been described as a Lord Mayor's procession, but there is no internal evidence to support this. It may represent the procession of a distinguished foreign visitor to Somerset House, such as the Prince of Orange in 1743. The two figures walking before the riders in the procession appear to be wearing the dress of the King's Harbingers.[1]

Artists Unknown: Early Eighteenth-Century Portraits

619. GEORGE I

Buckingham Palace. Oval, canvas mounted on panel: 14½ × 11⅞ in., 36,8 × 30,2 cm.

Head and shoulders in a breastplate, wearing the ribbon of the Garter and a red cloak lined with ermine.

Recorded at Buckingham Palace in 1876 (*V.R. inv.*, no. 1092).

Literature: *Buckingham Palace*, 1909, p. 217.

Apparently *c.* 1720 in type, and not directly related to the standard portraits by Kneller. It is conceivable that no. 619 is the *Head of his Majesty King George the first in the Octagon Room at Carlton house* included in the work done by John Ellys

1. I am very grateful to Mr. J. L. Howgego for his comments on this picture.

for Frederick, Prince of Wales, between 1733 and 1738; he was paid £115 for all the work on 5 October 1744 (D. of Cornwall MSS., vol. XIII, f. 109). On 3 February 1749 Paul Petit set down, in his account of work done for the Prince, eighteen guineas for *two Picture frames carved and Gilt in Burnish'd Gold to the Late King George and his Mother put up at Carlton House* (*ibid.*, vol. XVII, f. 531v.).

620. GEORGE II (*Plate* 190)

Windsor Castle (339). 30 × 25¼ in., 76,2 × 64,1 cm.

Half-length in armour, wearing an ermine-lined cloak and the ribbon of the Garter and holding a baton in his left hand.

Acquired by George IV; in November 1810 Collins delivered to Carlton House *Three half Length Gilt Frames to the following Pictures... George the Second in West Anti Room* (Jutsham, *R/D*, f. 137); on 20 January 1812, however, John Smith sent in his account for the *superb Frames* in which nos. 359 and 620 still appear to be framed; *Carlton House*, 1816 (20); sent to Windsor on 18 March 1829.

Literature: Collins Baker, *Windsor*, p. 188.

Painted, apparently *ad vivum*, *c.* 1740–50, and perhaps in Hanover. The design was the source of Reynolds's portrait of George II at Bishopsthorpe, generally dated 1756 (E. K. Waterhouse, *Reynolds* (1941), p. 41), which was therefore presumably not painted from life. A portrait connected with no. 620 was sold at Christie's, 9 February 1960 (27a).

621. GEORGE II

Buckingham Palace. 99¾ × 57½ in., 253,4 × 146,1 cm.

Full-length standing in robes of state; the regalia are on a table beside him and beyond is the interior of a large Gothic church or cathedral.

Recorded at Buckingham Palace (1082) in 1876 (*V.R. inv.*).

Perhaps ultimately derived from no. 343, but of very bad quality and probably painted in the nineteenth century. A version is at Rokeby Hall.

622. CAROLINE OF ANSBACH

Buckingham Palace. 29⅞ × 24 in., 75,9 × 61 cm.

Head and shoulders in a painted oval, in a green dress, richly laced with gold, and an ermine-lined cloak.

Probably the portrait recorded at St. James's in 1819 (1071; without attribution); at Buckingham Palace in 1866 (*V.R. inv.*, no. 1166).

Possibly painted *c.* 1730. The type is not dissimilar to that developed by Seeman (nos. 511–13).

623. FREDERICK, PRINCE OF WALES

Buckingham Palace. 68½ × 38½ in., 224,8 × 97,8 cm.

Full-length standing, wearing the ribbon of the Garter and pointing with his right hand to a helmet resting on an elaborately carved table; behind is a relief of martial trophies.

Recorded at Kensington in 1818 (493); later at Hampton Court (789) and Kensington.

Literature: Law, 1881, 1898 (795; with a tentative attribution to Seeman and identifying the sitter as William Augustus, Duke of Cumberland).

Presumably painted *c.* 1718–20. In style no. 623 is very close to Maingaud (see nos. 514–6) and may be by him; moreover the type is very close to the head of the Prince in a group at Wilton in which he appears with his sisters and which, on the basis of nos. 514–16, is almost certainly by Maingaud.

624. FREDERICK, PRINCE OF WALES

Hampton Court (926). 55 × 42¾ in., 139,7 × 108,6 cm.

Three-quarter-length, standing in armour, wearing the ribbon of the Garter and an ermine-lined cloak and resting his left hand on his helmet.

Recorded at Kensington in 1818 (361) as a *Portrait of a Prince of Brunswick in Armour*.

Literature: Law, 1881, 1898 (775); Collins Baker, *Hampton Court*, p. 63 (in both references as a portrait of George II).

No. 624 seems without question to be a portrait of Frederick, Prince of Wales. The face bears a close resemblance to no. 623 and was probably painted a few years later. The head in no. 624 is close to that engraved by Smith as after the portrait painted by Fountaine in Hanover in 1723.

625. FREDERICK, PRINCE OF WALES

Windsor Castle (2994). 30¼ × 25 in., 76,8 × 63,5 cm.

Inscribed later: *Frederic Prince of Wales*.

Head and shoulders in a painted oval wearing the ribbon and star of the Garter.

Recorded in the collection of George IV at Carlton House in 1816 (350: *A head of a nobleman in a red coat, with a star, and blue ribbon*; the 1816 label is still on the back); later at Buckingham Palace (1164).

Literature: Buckingham Palace, 1909, p. 145.

Probably painted *c.* 1730–5; formerly attributed to Mercier. A version is at Exton.

626. FREDERICK, PRINCE OF WALES

Buckingham Palace. 30¼ × 23 in., 76,8 × 58,4 cm.

Head and shoulders, in a painted oval, wearing a cuirass and drapery of a loosely classical style.

In the collection of George IV at Carlton House in 1816. The 1816 label is still on the back of the stretcher, but the number on it is 345 which, in the inventory of 1816, is: *A head of a lady, in red drapery*. Although the measurements of no. 345 are given as 30 × 25 in., it is probable that the label was attached to our no. 626 in error or that the wrong number was written on it. No. 626 may be identical with *Carlton House*, 1816, no. 359 (*A head of the late Prince of Wales*, measurements given as 29 × 24 in.), or with no. 341 (*A head of a young nobleman, in armour, with a red mantle*, measurements given as 30 × 25 in.). Later at Buckingham Palace (1124).

Literature: Buckingham Palace, 1909, p. 114.

Probably painted *c.* 1735 and formerly tentatively attributed to Knapton.

627. FREDERICK, PRINCE OF WALES

Buckingham Palace. 49⅞ × 39⅞ in., 126,7 × 101,3 cm.

Three-quarter-length standing, a stick in his left hand and wearing the ribbon and star of the Garter, with Windsor Castle in the distance.

Probably acquired by George IV; recorded at Carlton House in 1816 (322: *The late Prince of Wales, with Windsor Castle in the background*); later at Windsor (54).

Probably painted *c.* 1745; formerly, and perhaps correctly, attributed to Knapton (*e.g.*, in *V.R. inv.*, 20 November 1869).

628. FREDERICK, PRINCE OF WALES

Buckingham Palace. 30¼ × 25 in., 76,8 × 63,5 cm.

Inscribed, or possibly signed, on the back: *Luders fecit*.

Head and shoulders in a richly laced coat, wearing the ribbon and star of the Garter and an ermine-lined cloak.

Probably acquired by George IV; recorded at Carlton House in 1816 (347) as *A head of his Majesty* (*i.e.* George III), *when young* (the 1816 label is still on the back); later at Buckingham Palace (1156).

The identification of no. 628 with George III in the Carlton House inventories of 1816 and 1819 must be a mistake. No. 628 is closely dependent on, or otherwise related to, no. 579. If the inscription of the back of the canvas is the signature of David Lüders (*c.* 1710–1759) no. 628 could have been painted at the same time as Lüders's portrait of George III, engraved by MacArdell as painted in 1751 (later altered to 1754), and was perhaps based on Liotard (no. 579) or derived from the same source. Also closely related to nos. 579 and 628 is a portrait of the Prince attributed to Reynolds and stated to have been painted for Sir George Lee. This was sold from Hartwell House by Sotheby's, 26 April 1938 (58), was later at Bramshill and reappeared at Sotheby's, 16 July 1952 (89) and 19 December 1956 (42). Another version belongs to Mr. John Richardson and another, by a different hand, is in the Belgian royal collection. The relations between Reynolds and Liotard may therefore be the same in this context as in no. 581.

629. WILLIAM AUGUSTUS, DUKE OF CUMBERLAND. *Identity Uncertain.*

Windsor Castle (1404). 30 × 25 in., 76,2 × 63,5 cm.

Riding to the left in uniform, wearing the ribbon and star of the Garter and holding a baton in his right hand; in the background appears to be the rout of a body of Highlanders.

Recorded at Windsor in 1873; formerly at Frogmore (*V.R. inv.*).

Probably painted *c.* 1745–50; the sitter, until recently thought to be George II, may be the Duke of Cumberland and the action in the background may allude to the rebellion of 1745. A version, said to be signed by Dorothe Mercier, was sold by Knight, Frank & Rutley, 29 May 1957 (20).

630. PRINCESS AMELIA

Buckingham Palace. Oval, 22⅜ × 18⅝ in., 56,8 × 47,3 cm.

Head and shoulders with an ermine robe over her shoulders.

First recorded at Buckingham Palace (825) in 1876 (*V.R. inv.*).

Literature: Buckingham Palace, 1909, p. 163.

Probably painted *c.* 1740; formerly incorrectly attributed to Hudson.

631. PRINCESS AMELIA

Buckingham Palace. 25 × 30 in., 63,5 × 76,2 cm.

On horseback in a park, in a blue habit and with a groom in attendance. In the background is an avenue leading to a distant town.

On the back is a label inscribed: *with | the humble duty | of Col Anstruther Thomson*. It is probable that no. 631 was presented to King Edward VII by Col. John Anstruther-Thomson (*d.* 1904). At Buckingham Palace in 1909 (p. 260) as by Morier.

Probably painted *c.* 1755 to show the Princess as Ranger of Richmond Park, an office she held 1751–61. The background could be taken to represent Richmond Park with a distant view of Kingston (?). The style is influenced by James Seymour and suggestive of Spencer or Butler.

632. WILLIAM HENRY, DUKE OF GLOUCESTER

Buckingham Palace. Pastel on paper: 23 × 18 in., 58,4 × 45,7 cm.

Head and shoulders in a blue coat and waistcoat decorated with gold lace.

Conceivably among the *Sixteen crayon portraits of the royal family* at Carlton House in 1816 (514). Recorded at Buckingham Palace in 1876 (*V.R. inv.*, no. 748).

Probably drawn *c.* 1755–8. Formerly attributed to Knapton. See no. 633.

633. WILLIAM HENRY, DUKE OF GLOU-CESTER

Buckingham Palace. 17½ × 14⅛ in., 44,5 × 35,9 cm.

Head and shoulders.

A label on the back records its removal from Windsor on 25 April 1832; at Buckingham Palace in 1876 (*V.R. inv.*, no. 717).

Apparently derived from no. 632; formerly attributed to Knapton.

634–9. A SET OF EARLY EIGHTEENTH-CENTURY ROYAL PORTRAITS

Nos. 634–9 are part of a series of Hanoverian portraits, probably painted in the first half of the eighteenth century, based on existing portraits and all, with the exception of no. 639, by the same hand. They were all recorded at Windsor in 1870–8 (*V.R. inv.*).

634. PRINCESS SOPHIA, ELECTRESS OF HANOVER

Windsor Castle (479). Oval, 16 × 13¼ in., 40,6 × 33,7 cm.

Head and shoulders in a black hood and an ermine-lined cloak.

Probably based on a standard portrait of the Electress, of which there is a version at Herrenhausen.

635. GEORGE I

Windsor Castle (481). Oval, 15½ × 12¾ in., 39,4 × 32,4 cm.

Head and shoulders in robes of state.

A derivation from the state portrait (see no. 360); in no. 635, however, the King appears a good deal more aged and it may have been based on J. Faber junior's engraving (Chaloner Smith, p. 357) after D. Stevens's portrait, which in turn seems closely based on Kneller's prototype.

636. ERNEST AUGUSTUS, DUKE OF YORK

Windsor Castle (480). Oval, 16 × 12¾ in., 40,6 × 32,4 cm.

Head and shoulders in armour, wearing the ribbon of the Garter.

Probably based on the engraving by Simon (1718), which is inscribed as *Done from an Originall Picture lately brought from Hanover* (Chaloner Smith, p. 1127).

637. GEORGE II

Windsor Castle (483). Oval, 15½ × 12¾ in., 39,4 × 32,4 cm.

Head and shoulders in armour, wearing the ribbon of the Garter.

No. 637 is fairly close in type to no. 620.

638. CAROLINE OF ANSBACH

Windsor Castle (484). Oval, 15½ × 12¾ in., 39,4 × 32,4 cm.

Head and shoulders in robes of state.

Derived ultimately from no. 345, possibly through one of the engravings of it.

639. AUGUSTA, PRINCESS OF WALES

Windsor Castle (485). Oval, 15½ × 13 in., 39,4 × 33 cm.

Head and shoulders, wearing a lace head-dress and a mantle lined with ermine.

Based, with variations in costume, on no. 578.

640. GEORGE HOOPER, BISHOP OF BATH AND WELLS (1640–1727)

Windsor Castle (1596). 48½ × 37¼ in., 123,2 × 94,6 cm.

Three-quarter-length, seated in a high-backed chair and wearing bishop's robes.

Recorded at Windsor in 1871 (*V.R. inv.*).

The bishop was formerly unidentified, but other portraits of George Hooper tend to confirm the present identification. No. 640 was probably painted *c.* 1700–10, possibly by J. Scheffer, who is only recorded as the painter of Thomas Ken, a close friend of Hooper.

Chaplain to Bishop Morley at Winchester and then to Archbishop Sheldon; went to The Hague with Princess Mary in 1677 as Almoner; Chaplin to Charles II (1680), Dean of Canterbury (1691) and Bishop of St. Asaph (1702); from 1703 until his death he was Bishop of Bath and Wells.

641. CONRAD ERNEST KOPPERMAN (1709–45)

Kensington Palace. 59¼ × 45½ in., 125,1 × 115,6 cm.

Full-length, standing in a fur cap and a red coat over a very richly gilded and embroidered waistcoat.

Inscribed later: *Conrad Ernest | Copperman – | Born at Linden | Near Hanover | Was Page of the | Backstairs to her | R^l Highness the | Princess of Wales | Dyed aged 35 | Years Nine – | Months was but | Three Feet Five | Inches High –*

Formerly in the collection of Lord Boston; purchased by Her Majesty The Queen from Mr. H. Scott in 1953.

Probably painted *c.* 1740; at the time of its purchase in 1953 no. 641 was attributed to Highmore, but the handling seems nearer to Jonathan Richardson. No. 641 may have been painted for Sir William Irby, later Lord Boston (see no. 538).

Kopperman, a dwarf, was appointed Page of the Backstairs to Augusta, Princess of Wales, in September 1736; he was the last dwarf in court service in England.

642. WILLIAM WOLLASTON (1660–1724)

Kensington Palace. 49⅞ × 40 in., 126,7 × 101,6 cm.

Three-quarter-length, seated in clerical costume at a table, with a pen in his right hand and with his left hand holding open, at page 62, a copy of his *Religion of Nature Delineated*.

Probably one of the 'Portraits of several Poets, Painters, and Philosophers' (some of which may have been collected by Queen Caroline of Ansbach) recorded in the Queen's Dressing Room at Windsor (Bickham, p. 171); at St. James's in 1819 (1031) and later at Buckingham Palace (445).

Probably a posthumous portrait. Wollaston's *Religion of Nature Delineated* was published in the year of his death, although it had been privately printed in 1722. The head appears to be a copy of an *ad vivum* portrait (possibly by Dahl) and to have been worked up (probably *c.* 1730–35 and conceivably by Charles Jervas) into a commemorative 'library' portrait. The portrait was at one time attributed to Dahl (*e.g.*, W. Nisser, *Michael Dahl . . .* (Uppsala, 1927), catalogue p. 49). A version of the head was formerly at Ettington.

Moral philosopher, who took Orders in 1681; his *Religion of Nature Delineated* presented a version of a theory of morality of which Samuel Clarke was the leading contemporary exponent. A bust of Wollaston was among those made by Rysbrack for Queen Caroline's Grotto.

643. PORTRAIT OF A MAN

Hampton Court (835). 29¾ × 24⅞ in., 75,6 × 63,2 cm.

Head and shoulders in a blue wrap, within a painted oval.

Apparently recorded at Kensington in 1818 (588: *Portrait of a Man in a Blue Dress*).

Literature: Law, 1881, 1898 (557), suggesting that the sitter is Edmund Waller; Collins Baker, *Hampton Court*, p. 122, as a portrait of Sir Christopher Wren by a member of Riley's school.

Painted in England, probably *c.* 1715, by a very inferior hand perhaps remotely influenced by John Riley; Collins Baker's identification seems to have been due to a confusion with earlier references to no. 395.

644. PORTRAIT OF A MAN

Kensington Palace. 30 × 25 in., 76,2 × 63,5 cm.

Head and shoulders in a painted oval.

Probably acquired by George IV; recorded at Carlton House in 1816 (333) in store: *A head of a nobleman, in a large wig.* Later at Buckingham Palace (1158).

Formerly attributed to Kneller and identified as Dr. Samuel Garth (1661–1719). The portrait was probably painted *c.* 1715 and is very close in style to Thomas Gibson (1680?–1751).

645. PORTRAIT OF A MAN

Buckingham Palace. 36 × 27⅞ in., 91,4 × 70,8 cm.

Half-length in a blue coat, richly laced, pointing with his right hand.

Probably acquired by George IV; recorded in store at Carlton House in 1816 (299: *A head of a nobleman*; the 1816 label is still on the back); later at Buckingham Palace (791).

Literature: Buckingham Palace, 1909, p. 143.

Probably painted *c.* 1740. The sitter has been identified (*V.R. inv.*), possibly correctly, as Sir William Irby, later Lord Boston (see no. 538); it is conceivable, in that case, that no. 645 had belonged to Augusta, Princess of Wales. Formerly wrongly ascribed to Hudson, no. 645 is perhaps closer to a painter such as J. A. Eckhardt. It has a particularly fine contemporary carved frame.

646. PORTRAIT OF A WOMAN: 'FAIR ROSAMOND'

Hampton Court (937). 30 × 25 in., 76,2 × 63,5 cm.

Head and shoulders, nearly in profile to the left, in imaginary historical costume of a vaguely Tudor flavour.

Possibly the picture placed in 1734 in the Queen's Dressing Room at Kensington (Geo. II, *Kensington: in 1734 . . . Fair Rosamond, taken from Princess Mary's Harpsichord Room . . .*); certainly at Kensington in 1818 (314: *Portrait of Rosamond Clifford . . .*).

Literature: Law, 1881, 1898 (804); Collins Baker, *Hampton Court*, p. 169.

Probably painted *c.* 1720, and an inferior version of a type of which a number of versions are recorded. The sitter is sometimes identified as Lady Jane Grey, but no. 646 has always been associated with Rosamond Clifford (*d.* 1176?), mistress of Henry II.

647. PORTRAIT OF A WOMAN

Buckingham Palace. 36 × 28½ in., 91,4 × 72,4 cm.

Half-length in a painted oval in Turkish (?) costume, wearing a turban decorated with pearls and feathers and her hair hanging in long plaits embellished with roses.

Possibly the *Portrait of a Lady* recorded at St. James's in 1819 (1023, measurements given as 36 × 28 in.); at Buckingham Palace in 1876 (*V.R. inv.*, no. 1125).

The sitter was tentatively identified by Sir Lionel Cust (note in *V.R. inv.*) as Lady Mary Wortley Montagu (1689–1762). The portrait is not incompatible with the portraits of her and, if it does represent her, was probably painted in 1717–18, during her husband's embassy to Turkey. Lady Mary was painted a number of times in Oriental dress.

648. PORTRAIT OF A WOMAN

Hampton Court (945). 30 × 25 in., 76,2 × 63,5 cm.

Head and shoulders with a blue mantle over her head.

Recorded at Kensington in 1818 (468: *Portrait of a Lady in a Blue Mantle. Richardson*).

Literature: Law, 1881, 1898 (426), Collins Baker, *Hampton Court*, p. 167.

Probably painted in England, *c.* 1730; the attribution to Richardson cannot, however, be retained.

Artist Unknown : Sporting Piece

649. 'FLYING CHILDERS'

Buckingham Palace. 27½ × 36¼ in., 70 × 92 cm.

Inscribed: *The Childers*

The horse is ridden by a jockey wearing a blue coat.

Formerly in the possession of Edward VII at Marlborough House; recorded at Buckingham Palace in 1909 with an attribution to Wootton. On the stretcher is a label inscribed *F. de R* and it is possible that no. 649 had been given to King Edward VII by Baron Ferdinand de Rothschild (1839–98).

Painted (*c.* 1735–40?) in a style which is influenced by James Seymour and suggestive of Spencer or Butler (see no. 566). The 'Childers' (1715–41) was bred by Mr. Childers and owned by the Duke of Devonshire. He was 'generally supposed to be the fleetest horse that was ever trained, in this or any other country'.

COMPARATIVE ILLUSTRATIONS

1. Artist Unknown: *Edward VI*. Petworth House.

2. Holbein: *Lady Guildford*. City Art Museum, St. Louis, Mo.

3. Eworth (?): *The Family of Henry VIII*. Sudeley Castle.

4. Cockson: *Robert Devereaux, 2nd Earl of Essex.*

5. Daret: *Henrietta Maria.*

6. Anthonisz.: *The Siege of Thérouanne.*

7. John Hoskins: *James I*. Royal Library,
Windsor Castle.

8. Peter Oliver: *Charles I*. Royal Library,
Windsor Castle.

9. Isaac Oliver: *Henry, Prince of Wales*. Royal Library,
Windsor Castle.

10. Pickering: *Greenwich Armour*. Windsor Castle.

11. Artist Unknown: *Henry, Prince of Wales*. Parham Park.

12. After Mytens: *Charles I and Henrietta Maria*. Welbeck Abbey.

13. Van Dyck: *Charles I*. National Gallery, London.

14. Van Dyck: *Charles I and Henrietta Maria*. Archbishop's Palace, Kremsier.

15. Van Doort(?): *Charles I*. Present whereabouts unknown.

16. Van Dyck: *Charles I*. Buckingham Palace.

17. Van Dyck: *The three eldest Children of Charles I*. Galleria Sabauda, Turin.

18. Van Dyck: *Lord Francis Villiers*. British Museum

19. Van Dyck: *Charles I with M. de St. Antoine*. British Museum.

20. Van Dyck: *Charles I on horseback*. British Museum.

21. Van Dyck: *Study for a Horse*. British Museum.

22. Van Dyck: *Study for the Leg of a Horse*. British Museum.

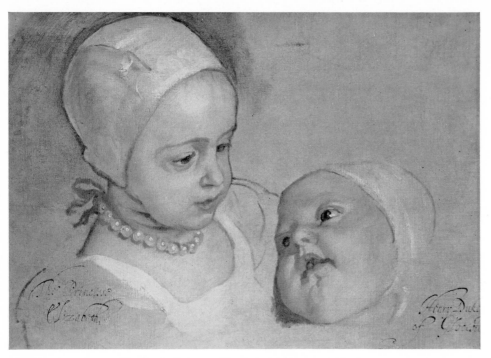

23. Van Dyck: *Princesses Elizabeth and Anne*. Lord Chesham.

24. Van Dyck: *Henrietta Maria*.
Staatliche Schlösser,
Potsdam-Sanssouci.

25. Van Dyck: *James II, when Duke of York*. Christ Church,
Oxford.

26. Van Dyck: *Charles II, when Prince of Wales*. Royal Library,
Windsor Castle.

27. T. Adye (?): *Charles I.* Windsor Castle.

28. Van Dyck: *The Virgin and Child.* Mrs. Charles Volz.

29. Van Dyck: *Henrietta Maria.* Formerly with T. Agnew & Sons, London.

30. After Van Dyck: *Henrietta Maria.* Merton College, Oxford.

31. Van Dyck: *St. Martin dividing his Cloak*. St. Martin's Church, Zaventem, Belgium.

32. P. Lombart: *Oliver Cromwell*.

33. Van Dyck: *Christ healing the Paralytic*. Albertina, Vienna.

34. Huysmans: *Catherine of Braganza*.
Dr. M. B. de Sousa, Azeitao, Portugal.

35. Van Dyck: *Venetia, Lady Digby*. Mrs. Gibbs.

36. Peter Oliver: *The Family of Sir Kenelm Digby*. Nationalmuseum, Stockholm.

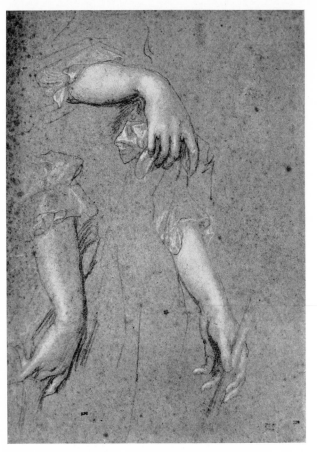

37. Lely: *Study of hands*. Ashmolean Museum, Oxford.

38. Browne after Lely: *Princess Isabella*.

39. Hollar: *Boscobel House and Whiteladies*.

40. Ramsay: *Mrs. Daniel Cunyngham*. National Gallery of Scotland, Edinburgh.

42. Kneller: *A Man in armour*. Formerly with P. & D. Colnaghi & Co., London.

43, 44. Croker: *George I.*, *Queen Anne*. British Museum.

41. Kneller: *Isabella, Duchess of Grafton*. Earl of Euston.

45. Wright: *James, Duke of Cambridge*. Earl Bathurst, Cirencester Park.

46. Kneller: *William III on horseback*. Formerly in the collection of the late Mr. Ray Murphy.

47. Wootton: *Hunting Scene*. Royal Library, Windsor Castle.

48. Amigoni: *Frederick, Prince of Wales*.
Lord Barnard, Raby Castle.

49. Hudson: *Handel*. Earl Howe.

50. Hogarth: *The Family of George II*. National Gallery of Ireland, Dublin.

51. Laroon: *The Levée*. Major S. Whitbread, Southill Park.

52. Laroon: *A Dinner-Party*. Mr. F. Matthiesen.

53. Mercier: *The Music Party*. National Portrait Gallery, London.

54. Mercier: *The Letter-Writer*. Sold at Christie's, 20 July 1956 (120).

INDEX OF PORTRAITS
AND
INDEX OF ARTISTS

INDEX OF PORTRAITS

References in italic type are to the pages of the Introduction. References in roman type are to items in the Catalogue: in heavy type they refer to undoubted portraits of a sitter; in ordinary type they are to items in which earlier, rejected, tentative or suggested identifications are mentioned or discussed.

INDEX OF ARTISTS

References in italic type are to the pages of the Introduction. References in roman type are to items in the Catalogue: in heavy type they refer to paintings directly associated with a given painter; in ordinary type they refer to entries in which older and rejected attributions are mentioned or tentative attributions put forward, or to entries in which the name of an artist or craftsman otherwise occurs.